SPACE SCIENCE TEXT SERIES
A. J. Dessler and F. C. Michel, Editors

William M. Kaula
AN INTRODUCTION TO PLANETARY PHYSICS

AN INTRODUCTION TO
PLANETARY PHYSICS

AN INTRODUCTION TO PLANETARY PHYSICS
The Terrestrial Planets

WILLIAM M. KAULA
Professor of Geophysics
University of California
Los Angeles

John Wiley & Sons, Inc.
New York   London   Sydney   Toronto

To Louis B. Slichter

PREFACE

This book is suitable for an introductory course in planetary physics. The subject matter is essentially the part of planetary physics that is dominated by solid matter containing as important constituents the common heavy elements: iron, silicon, magnesium, and others. By this definition the parts of the solar system with which we are concerned are the terrestrial planets: Mercury, Venus, Earth, Mars, plus the asteroids, meteorites, and so on. However, we can never draw sharp boundaries on a matter of this sort. For example, when we discuss the orbital dynamics that are the consequence of the gravitational interaction between matter, the principal way such cold solid matter can interact at a distance, we will also discuss the dynamics of lighter or more gaseous parts of the solar system, such as the major planets, the comets, and the sun.

Because these colder, more solid parts are less observable than the gaseous parts, and because the theory of the physics of the solid state is less well developed, this part of planetary physics is necessarily very much dependent on, and perhaps even dominated by, the study of the most accessible planet: the earth.

The book's contents can be divided roughly into five parts. The first part is planetary interiors, with emphasis on those aspects of the earth's interior that are conducive to our understanding of the planet as a whole and of how planets in general behave. This part comprises Chapter 1, on data pertaining to the earth's interior; Chapter 2, on the mechanical and thermal aspects of planetary structure, of more general application; and Chapter 3, on the electromagnetism of a planetary interior, an aspect in which the earth appears to be peculiarly active. The second part concerns the dynamics of the solar system: Chapter 4, on the earth-moon system, most accessible to observation as well as of parochial interest; and Chapter 5, on the planetary system. The emphasis is on long-term evolution, in connection with which we are particularly interested in any interactions between bodies which lead to an unidirectional energy change. The third part focuses on other types of observations of planets: Chapter 6 on observations of the planetary surfaces, mostly by passive means of the various parts of the electromagnetic spectrum—radio emission, infrared, etc.—and photographic observations, but also by active means (radar); and Chapter 7 on the interpretation of the observations of the moon and Mars, the two bodies on which enough detail has been acquired to construct some geological theory. The fourth part discusses meteorites and their chemistry, the study of the only solid pieces of the solar system that come to us from outside the earth; this subject has undergone a very rich development in the past few years. The final part attempts to assemble the evidences and hypotheses toward an understanding of the origin and evolution of the planets.

A book that covers so much material is necessarily to some extent descriptive. We will attempt to limit this description to those facts that are more important in shaping our analysis and understanding of the planets, and to aspects of each subject which are conducive to practice in applying fundamental physics to the problems of planetary structure and evolution. To this same end, a list of problems has been added to each chapter.

The principal omissions of this book are descriptions of experimental or observational techniques and of historical developments. To compensate to some extent for these omissions, as well as to supplement the developments presented, an extensive bibliography has been included. This bibliography is by no means complete. For the sake of brevity, in many cases, significant papers have been omitted in favor of more recent works, since the former are referenced in the latter. In order to avoid disturbing the numbering, I have assembled the bibliography in five alphabetic segments: 1–454, 455–515, 516–539, 540–545, 546–586.

A good understanding of any subject area requires reading the more detailed papers in the journals. The leading publication in planetary physics is the *Journal of Geophysical Research*; original papers also appear frequently in *Icarus*, the *Astronomical Journal*, *Geochimica et Cosmochimica Acta*, *Science*, the *Philosophical Transactions* and the *Proceedings of the Royal Society of London*, the *Geophysical Journal* and the *Monthly Notices of the Royal Astronomical Society*, the *Astrophysical Journal*, and *Nature*. Helpful reviews appear in *Science, Reviews of Geophysics, Space Science Reviews, Physics and Chemistry of the Earth*, and *Scientific American*.

The book most comparable with this text in subject matter is *The Solar System*, edited by G. P. Kuiper and B. M. Middlehurst, particularly volumes 2–4: *The Earth as a Planet* (somewhat obsolete); *Planets and Satellites* [232]; and *The Moon, Meteorites, and Comets*. There is a fair amount of overlap with *Introduction to Space Science* [174], edited by W. N. Hess; *Solar System Astrophysics* [43], by J. C. Brandt and P. W. Hodge; *The Earth* [199], by H. Jeffreys; and *The Planets* [405], by H. C. Urey.

Additional important references are handbooks which provide numerical data. The three used most in this book are the *Handbook of Physical Constants*

[74], edited by S. P. Clark, Jr., for geophysical and geochemical data; *Astrophysical Quantities* [4], by C. W. Allen, for astronomical data; and Landolt-Börnstein: *Numerical Data and Functional Relationships* [484], Group VI, Volume 1, for both types.

Considerable numerical data are given in this book. Since the organization of the book is to introduce data in the first context, a list of tables and figures follows the table of contents to facilitate use of the book as a reference.

Although some of the insufficiencies in explanation of planetary phenomena in this book are a consequence of the author's imperfect understanding, in most cases they reflect the current state of comprehension of the physics of the earth and the planets. It is hoped therefore that the book will help direct some students toward interesting and challenging problems.

Acknowledgments

I am indebted to several colleagues for reviewing, correcting, and commenting on various parts of the book: Dan P. McKenzie, Leon Knopoff, Willem V. R. Malkus, Stanton J. Peale, Bruce C. Murray, John A. O'Keefe, John T. Wasson, and Lawrence H. Aller. And I am especially grateful to Mrs. Joan Kaufman for preparing the entire manuscript; without her encouragement I would not have undertaken the task.

Acknowledgment is made to the following publishers for permission to use previously published illustrations either directly or as a basis for line drawings made in a uniform style for this book: American Association for the Advancement of Science (Figures 1.17–1.19, 3.8, 6.12, 6.18, 7.25); American Geophysical Union (Figures 1.15, 1.21, 3.1, 3.2, 6.4–6.6, 6.17, 7.1–7.3, 7.7, 7.8, 8.13); American Institute of Physics (Figures 1.11, 1.12, 1.16, 3.3, 6.9, 9.1); Annual Reviews, Inc. (Figure 5.12); University of Chicago Press (Figures 5.1, 6.7, 8.6, 8.7); W. H. Freeman & Co. (Figure 6.10); Geological Society of America (Figure 1.24); Herman & Cie (Figure 7.26); Johns Hopkins University Press (Figures 6.11, 6.14); Massachusetts Institute of Technology Press (Figure 2.12); Methuen & Co., Ltd. (Figure 5.9); National Bureau of Standards (Figure 6.15); New York Academy of Science (Figures 7.5, 7.6); Pergamon Press, Inc. (Figures 1.10, 9.7); D. Reidel Publishing Co. (Figures 8.10–8.12); Seismological Society of America (Figures 2.13, 2.14); Julius Springer-Verlag (Figure 1.5); John Wiley & Sons (Figures 1.2, 1.6, 1.7, 3.6, 3.7).

William M. Kaula

Los Angeles, California
June 1968

CONTENTS

PRINCIPAL TABLES AND FIGURES

Chapter 1

DATA PERTAINING TO THE EARTH'S INTERIOR

The main parts of the earth are given in Table 1.1. The distinction of the atmosphere and hydrosphere from the crust is, of course, that they are fluid. Between the crust and the mantle the main distinction is a sharp discontinuity in density of about 0.5 gm/cm³. The mantle is distinguished from the core by another sharp discontinuity in density of about 4.5 gm/cm³. In addition, the mantle-core boundary is a transition from solid back to the liquid state again. Table 1.1 should make it manifest that a theory of the planet earth essentially will be a theory of the mantle and the core, since together they constitute 99.6 percent of the total mass of the earth. They are as yet inaccessible to direct observation, however, and hence deductions concerning the mantle and the core inevitably are shaped by the intervening thin crust. The crust in itself is an interesting and vital subject of scientific study, whose interest of course is enhanced by its close relationship to mankind. It appears, however, to be the result of a complicated history that is peculiar to the earth. Hence discussion of the crust will concern what it tells us about the mantle, which is the part of the earth we could expect to have features more in common with the terrestrial planets in general.

TABLE 1.1: MAIN PARTS OF THE EARTH

	Mean Radii		Mean Density (gm/cm³)	Mass (metric tons)	Portion of Total Mass
	Inner (km)	Outer (km)			
Atmosphere	6371	—	—	5.2×10^{15}	0.000001
Hydrosphere	6369	6371	1.0	1.2×10^{18}	0.0002
Crust	6352	6369	2.8	2.4×10^{19}	0.004
Mantle	3473	6352	4.5	4.11×10^{21}	0.672
Outer core	1251	3473	10.9	1.83×10^{21}	0.306
Inner core	0	1251	12.3	1.1×10^{20}	0.018

The structure of the earth as set forth in Table 1.1 was deduced mainly by seismic techniques (with the help of some geodetic boundary conditions), as described in Section 2.2. It seems more appropriate, however, to first take up some subjects which are more descriptive and experimental in nature, and which essentially provide the context that has shaped our theories about the earth.

1.1 Geochemistry and Petrology

The first question we could ask about any object of study is "What is it made of?" Both geochemistry and petrology deal with the chemistry of the substance of the earth. Geochemistry is more global in its concern; the geochemist typically is interested in the distribution of the chemical elements in the earth and such questions as the loss of chemicals by the earth relative to other bodies. Petrology concerns the physics and chemistry of the rocks— the relationships among the minerals that form rocks, the manner in which rocks are formed by melting and recrystallization, and so on. We are interested in these subjects for two principal reasons: (1) to estimate the overall chemical content of the solar system, both in the past and in the present as an important indicator of the origin and evolution of the solar system; and (2) to determine the constituents of the mantle in order to estimate its physical properties.

Rocks and the Geochemical Cycle

The material which is the subject of these studies is a consequence of a rather complicated geochemical cycle which has formed the earth's crust [265]. The main parts of this cycle are shown in Figure 1.1. The bulk of the crust (about 94 percent of it) consists of rocks which apparently are the

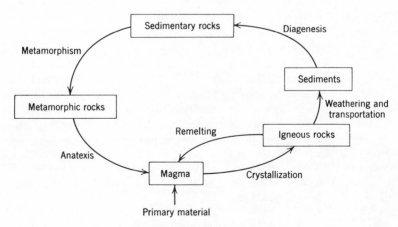

Figure 1.1: The geochemical cycle.

result of crystallization from a molten material. Such rocks are called *igneous* rocks. Molten rocks within the earth, not exposed to the atmosphere, are referred to as *magmas*. A magma that comes out of the earth and is exposed to the atmosphere is a *lava*. The logical starting point therefore for Figure 1.1 is at the bottom with a molten magma which solidifies to form an igneous rock. This igneous rock at the next stage is subject to erosion by the weather and carried away by streams and deposited as sediments. Such sediments constitute about 6 percent of the mass of the crust. These *sedimentary* rocks may be overlaid by other rocks and carried down so that they are raised to a temperature at which they are again melted, in which case they would become igneous rocks again. They may be subjected to such severe pressure and temperature without melting that their form is drastically changed; they are in fact metamorphosed, and hence are known as *metamorphic* rocks, which are estimated to constitute less than 1 percent of the mass of the crust. The cycle can be completed by further melting metamorphic rocks, of course, and, as indicated by Figure 1.1, there are all sorts of possible short cuts across the diagram, inside the main ideal cycle shown in the solid lines. Indeed, it is still a matter of debate whether some common igneous rocks such as the granites come directly from a melt or whether the degree of differentiation they show must necessarily indicate the intervention of a sedimentary process. In any case it seems clear that if we are interested in the crust mainly as a key to the mantle, then the processes important in the geochemical cycle are the formation of magmas and the crystallization of magmas to form igneous rocks. The estimates of the proportions attributed to different materials in the crust—94 percent igneous, 6 percent sedimentary—come first from estimates of the thickness of sedimentary beds in geology, and second from seismological estimates of the depth of the Mohorovicic discontinuity, usually referred to as the *Moho*, which is the boundary between the crust and the mantle. Of these two figures, the thickness of the sedimentary beds is the more uncertain; an auxiliary estimate thereof can be obtained from the salt content of the sea (see problem 1.1). This calculation, based on a single element, sodium, has since been extended to a general geochemical balance calculation involving sixty-five elements in seven types of location [479].

The most important process for deducing the composition of the mantle from materials found in the crust is *fractionation*, whereby in the cooling of a magma, different components crystallize out at different times, and hence at different locations. A consequence of this process of fractionation is a strong vertical segregation of materials in the earth. By *materials* is meant both the elements and, at a more complex stage, the chemical compounds, known as *minerals*, into which the elements are combined. The study of the fractionation process is complex, both theoretically and experimentally. The more important minerals are all quite complicated crystal structures, too complicated to be the subject of any precise theory; furthermore, impurities play an important role. The relationships between different phases of the mineral systems are difficult to observe experimentally because of the very slow rates of reaction and the inability to attain the pressures and temperatures at which some important processes will take place. Consequently a large part of the subject is necessarily descriptive in nature [265, 402].

Minerals

The principal type of chemical compound with which we are concerned is the mineral. Occasionally the mineral has a quite irregular structure, without any grainy character, which is essentially that of a glass. Such structures are usually the consequence of very rapid cooling and often are associated with the material produced by a volcano. The normal form of minerals is that of a conglomeration of ionic and covalent crystals in the form of grains. Within the grain the crystal structure is defined rather clearly and between grains there is an irregularity of structure. The size of the grains is determined by such factors as the proportion of impurities and the rate of cooling. An ionic crystal is one in which the bonding between the atoms composing it is an electrostatic interaction of oppositely charged ions. This ionization is obtained by the transfer of electrons of one type to atoms of a second type; these ions then arrange themselves so that the coulomb attractions of ions of opposite sign are stronger than the coulomb repulsion between ions of the same sign. Probably the simplest example of an ionic crystal is sodium chloride; however, the ones that are important in mineralogy are a good deal more complex. In covalent crystals, the electrons are shared rather than transferred; a simple example is the diamond. Ionic and covalent crystals are distinguished from metallic crystals by the absence of electrons free to move about in the structure. All of these types of bonding are distinguished from molecular bonding in that there is a detachment of electrons from atoms which results in a much stronger tie than if there is merely a weak electrostatic interaction between irregularities of the fields of neighboring atoms. The binding energies involved are 200 kcal/mole for the ionic and covalent bonding, as distinguished from 50 kcal/mole for metallic bonding and 5 kcal/mole for molecular bonding. (See, e.g. Table 9.7.)

Mineralogy is complicated somewhat by the considerable variety of the chemistry of various minerals. This variety arises because the ions that have the same charge and a similar radius can replace each other very easily in a crystal structure. Consequently the distinction between one mineral and another is rather arbitrary; it depends on the difference in percentage content of two metals such as, say, iron and magnesium, which can replace each other easily. Hence there exist series of minerals of different names, in which the distinction between one and the next is arbitrary to a good extent. Also there are different names for minerals which have exactly the same chemical content, but which differ in their *phase*: the arrangement of the atoms in the crystal structure; or even perhaps in their *fabric:* the nature of the grain structure, the size of the grains, and so on.

The one thing, however, that is basic to mineralogy is the silicate tetrahedron—the arrangement characterized by the symbols SiO_4—in which a single silicate atom is bound to four oxygen atoms arranged in the form of a tetrahedron (see Figure 1.2). There are several geometrical arrangements for this tetrahedron. That shown in Figure 1.2 is that for β-quartz, the low-pressure, high-temperature form of silica. It can be characterized as a cube with the oxygen atoms occupying opposite corners and the silicon atom at the center.

Since silicon has a valence of $+4$ while oxygen has a valence of -2, this arrangement leaves a valence count of $(4 \times 2) - 4 = 4$ to be taken up by some other atoms. The distinction between different minerals is essentially in the manner in which these other bonds are occupied, and probably the most fundamental property by which we can classify minerals is the ratio of oxygen to metallic atoms in the mineral. Four ratios are common: $2:1$, $8:5$, $3:2$, and $4:3$.

The highest oxygen-metal ratio is $2:1$, belonging to the simplest of the common minerals: *silica*, which has the formula SiO_2. Silica comprises several different minerals, the distinction between which is based on the arrangement of the atoms in the crystal lattice. The most familiar of these is *quartz;* others are *tridymite, cristobalite, coesite,* and *stishovite.* The latter ones in this list are rare; they are important, however, as indicators of the conditions of formation of the material. For example, they have been taken to be conclusive evidence that certain craters were caused by meteorites rather than by volcanoes, because coesite requires a pressure of 38 kb to form and stishovite requires a pressure of 130 kb (1 kb is 10^6 dynes/cm² or 987 atmospheres).

Decreasing the oxygen-metal ratio to $8:5$, we come to a series of minerals called *feldspars* which are very important in the crust. The general formula for a feldspar can be characterized as $M_2AlSi_2O_8$, where M_2 symbolizes two metal atoms, one of which may be potassium, K; sodium, Na; or calcium, Ca; and the other may be aluminum, Al, or silicon, Si. The principal series of minerals in which these metals replace each other can best be diagrammed by a triangle as shown on Figure 1.3. *Plagioclase* with an albite content of 70 to 90 percent is often referred to as *oligoclase.*

Next, the oxygen-metal ratio of $3:2$ characterizes *pyroxene.* The general formula for pyroxene is $M_2Si_2O_6$. The metals that may fill the two M positions are commonly calcium, Ca; magnesium, Mg; or iron, Fe; less

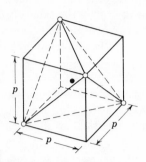

Figure 1.2: The silicate tetrahedron (regular tetrahedron inscribed in cube).

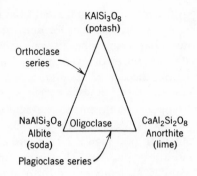

Figure 1.3: The feldspar series.

commonly potassium, K; aluminum, Al; titanium, Ti; or sodium, Na. The principal series of pyroxenes are best diagrammed by a square as shown in Figure 1.4. The most common end members of this square are diopside and enstatite. The arrangement of the silicate tetrahedrons in pyroxene is essentially in long strings, as shown in Figure 1.5. This structure tends to give a certain degree of anisotropy to physical properties of pyroxenes. The skewed arrangement in Figure 1.5 is a *clinopyroxene*; a rectilinear arrangement, called *orthopyroxene*, is more common in the enstatite-ferrosilite series.

Also characterized by an oxygen-metal ratio of 3:2 is a relatively rare mineral which we mention because of its possible importance in the mantle: *garnet*, $M_3Al_2Si_3O_{12}$, in which the M is usually calcium, Ca; or magnesium, Mg.

At an oxygen-metal ratio of 4:3 we have the series of minerals known as *olivine*, which have the general formula M_2SiO_4. The two metal spaces may be occupied by either magnesium or iron. The series of olivines are characterized by a single sequence from Mg_2SiO_4, known as *forsterite*, which is the most common, to Fe_2SiO_4, *fayalite*, the least common. At the 4:3 ratio the amount of oxygen is so decreased that each oxygen atom is bound to only one silicon atom, so that the silicon tetrahedrons are all separated, each tetrahedron being linked only to the metallic atoms. The normal arrangement

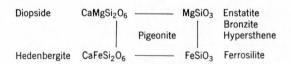

Figure 1.4: The pyroxene series.

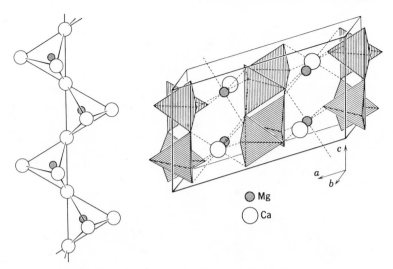

⊙ Mg
◯ Ca

Figure 1.5: The structure of diopside, a pyroxene. The Ca, Mg atoms fall between $(SiO_3)_\infty$ chains in the b as well as the a direction. From Landolt-Börnstein [484, vol. 1, part 4, p. 76].

of the oxygen atoms is in hexagonal densest spherical packing in which each oxygen atom is equidistant to six other oxygen atoms, as shown in Figure 1.6. Another arrangement which has been attained in the laboratory for some olivines is *spinel*, in which the oxygens are in densest possible spherical packing with both octahedral and tetrahedral spherical links to the metallic atoms as shown in Figure 1.7.

The foregoing briefly described five series of minerals are those that are both fairly common and of importance with reference to the composition of the mantle. Other series of silicates are *amphibole* $(M_{9-10}Si_6O_{22}(OH)_2)$, *mica* $(M_{4-5}Si_3O_{10}(OH)_2)$, and *feldspathoid* (like feldspar: less Si, more Na, K). The most important nonsilicates are metal oxides such as those of iron and titanium [90, 402].

Rocks

Rocks are combinations of minerals. They are classified first according to their mineral content and second according to their fabric: the nature of the grain structure, which is very dependent on the conditions of formation. There are two principal categories of fabric: first, the *volcanic*, characterized by a very fine grain structure or lack of a grain structure and often rather porous, including many voids; and second, the *plutonic*, characterized by a coarse grain structure, and generally of very low porosity. As the names imply, the volcanic fabric is associated with rocks that have cooled quickly, often

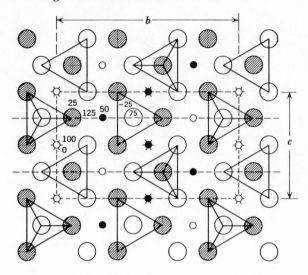

Figure 1.6: The structure of olivine. Olivine structure parallel to (100) plane. Si atoms are at the centers of the tetrahedra and are not shown. Small open circles, $\bigcirc$, are Mg atoms at $x = 0$; small solid circles, $\bullet$, are Mg atoms at $x = \frac{1}{2}$; and $\not\Leftrightarrow$ is the center of symmetry. The a axis is normal to the plane of the paper. From Deer *et al.* [90, p. 2].

in association with volcanic outthrows or lava flows, whereas the plutonic fabric is associated with rocks that have cooled slowly in intrusions that

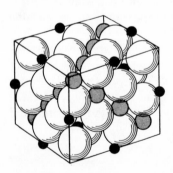

Figure 1.7: Perspective view of the structure of spinel. Large spheres represent oxygen, small black spheres represent fourfold coordination positions, and cross-hatched spheres sixfold positions. From Deer *et al.* [90, p. 425].

remain buried within the earth. Table 1.2 is an arrangement of the principal rocks in accordance to fabric and density, with the density increasing in descending order. The first column gives the principal mineral contents of the rocks on each line. Note that the increase in density is associated with a decrease in oxygen-metal ratio, which is not surprising in view of the lower atomic mass and higher ionic radius of oxygen compared to the metals. The main series in Table 1.2 is the plutonic rocks, granite, diorite, gabbro, peridotite, and dunite. The other rocks, pegmatite and eclogite, appearing above and below this main series, are not commonly found. Pegmatite is important, however, because it usually contains uranium and thorium as well as other elements that have

unusual ion radii such that they do not readily substitute for other elements in common mineral structures. In a crystallizing magma these elements

TABLE 1.2: IGNEOUS ROCKS

Principal Mineral Content	Density (gm/cm³)	Plutonic Rock	Volcanic Rock
Quartz, feldspar		(Pegmatite)	
	2.6		
Quartz, feldspar		Granite	Rhyolite
Feldspar, amphibole		Diorite	Andesite
	2.9		
Feldspar, pyroxene		Gabbro	Diabase, basalt
	3.2		
Pyroxene, olivine		Peridotite	
Olivine		Dunite	
	3.3		
Pyroxene, garnet		(Eclogite)	
	3.5		

apparently get left out until the very end, and hence work their way to the top of the crust. Eclogite is included in Table 1.2 because it is very dense and obtainable by phase transitions from basalt, and hence a possible material of which the mantle is made; dunite may not be quite dense enough. A rock that does not fall neatly in the classification of Table 1.2 is *serpentenite*. It is mainly a combination of olivine and pyroxene with *water*, the importance of which is that water appreciably lowers the melting temperature.

Another way in which the rocks in Table 1.2 are categorized is according to their chemical nature as a range from acidic for granite or rhyolite to basic for basalt or gabbro to ultrabasic for the rocks below gabbro. Granite and rhyolite sometimes are referred to as *sial* and gabbro and basalt are sometimes referred to as *sima*, the names being based upon the principal metal constituents [37, 402]. The yet more basic rocks, peridotite, dunite, and eclogite, are commonly termed *ultramafic* [586].

The materials that appear to be derived most directly from the mantle, and hence indicating its composition, are the ultramafic rocks and coarsely crystalline nodules of olivine, pyroxene, and garnet found in volcanic extrusions. The composition of the upper mantle is generally estimated to be about two-thirds olivine and one-third pyroxene plus perhaps garnet. This olivine-pyroxene mixture is sometimes called *pyrolite*. Such a rock would have a density of 3.31 gm/cm³ at the earth's surface [75, 542].

Phase Relationships

The formation in nature of rocks such as those in Table 1.2 is still an imperfectly understood process. A magma-crystal mixture is a complicated assemblage and the present level of understanding of such mixtures is derived from laboratory experiments with mixtures of minerals that are much simpler, having fewer components than natural rocks. Hence for natural rocks there are only a few general conclusions that can be applied. The situation in a molten mineral mixture generally is expressed by a phase diagram, an example of which is given in Figure 1.8, which pertains to a mixture of three of the minerals described earlier in this section: forsterite, one of the end members of olivine; anorthite, a feldspar; and diopside, a pyroxene.

The proportion of each of these components in any given melt is expressed by a point in the phase diagram where the amount of each component is proportionate to the distance from the side opposite the vertex with the name of that component. Also associated with each of these points is a melting temperature. If the temperature of the mixture is lowered below the melting point, then one or more of the components of the system will solidify out of the melt and hence the proportionate content will change and the assemblage will move in the diagram. This movement will take place, in a cooling

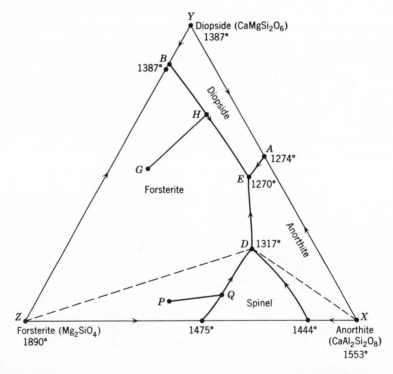

Figure 1.8: Example of a phase diagram of a mineral mixture. From Turner & Verhoogen [402, p. 130].

mixture, in a direction that corresponds to a lower melting temperature in the diagram since matter that is at a higher melting temperature will have solidified out. For all melts except those lying within the triangle XDZ within the diagram, the cooling crystallization will begin with one of the phases of the three members, depending on their location in the diagram. It will move from this point with one component crystallizing until it has hit one of the lines AE, BE, and DE. At this point the mixture will move along this line with two components separating out. Finally at point E all three components will crystallize. An example is shown of a melt that started at point G where the forsterite would start to crystallize at about 1550°C; by the time it had hit point H the temperature would have dropped to about 1330°C, then forsterite and diopside would crystallize until point E when the temperature hit 1270°C. At this point all three components would crystallize. However, it is not always so simple. In the example shown on the diagram, within the triangle XDZ a different behavior would occur—one which to diagram fully would require a third dimension out of the paper. For example, for a liquid starting with a composition at point P, forsterite would crystallize until a point Q was hit. As the temperature dropped below that of Q, we would have forsterite separating simultaneously with a spinel (Figure 1.7), $MgOAl_2O_3$. We would then leave the plane of the diagram and have a four-part composition of the melt: diopside, anorthite, forsterite, silica. This would then move down to point D where there would be no further crystallization of spinel and the mixture would return to the plane of the paper and go on to the same point E with the minimum temperature point of the diagram. Such a minimum temperature is referred to as a *eutectic*. The behavior of the mixture in the triangle XDZ is apparently explicable in terms of an equation in which a combination of anorthite and olivine produces a combination of diopside, enstatite, and spinel. When the process described by the equation takes place from left to right there is a reduction in volume of about 7 percent. Such alternative crystallizations that result in a lower specific volume, or, in other words, higher density, are usually favored more in mixtures of higher temperature or pressure. Hence in real rocks we should expect that denser, more closely packed structures such as the spinel would be associated with crystallization at greater depths where the pressures were higher. Another general rule indicated by Figure 1.8 is that the melting point of a mixture is normally lower than that of the end members of the series. Pure substances melt at temperatures which often are hundreds of degrees higher than the melting point of a mixture of the substances. For example, the minimum on the axis XZ of Figure 1.8 is 1444°C, 100 degrees lower than the melting point of either end member of which the mixture is composed.

Another factor that lowers melting points significantly is the presence of water in the melt. In natural melts the water content may vary from 1 to

8 percent. Lavas are observed to have temperatures ranging from 1100°C to 700°C, all of which are considerably lower than the minimum point of Figure 1.8, which is a mixture of pure minerals. This difference between melting temperatures of natural as compared with artificial magmas is due primarily to water, but other impurities, of course, also have an effect [37, 402].

Fractionation

A real magma very rarely follows as simple a path as that described by Figure 1.8, and it never attains a eutectic point such as *E* where all components solidify at one melting temperature. Consequently, in a real magma there can be expected to be disequilibrium conditions in that earlier crystallizing members will sink through the magma to a place of higher temperature and will react again with the components at that level, and there will be considerable vertical segregation. Another phenomena that can occur is known as incongruent melting, in which a solid changes into a different solid phase and a liquid. The classical discussion of the problem is by Bowen [37], who idealized the fractionation and crystallization of magma by two series of reactions: a continuous reaction series whereby an early form of crystals changed uninterruptedly in composition by reaction with the melt; and a discontinuous reaction series, whereby an early formed phase reacted with the melt giving a new phase with a different crystal structure and a different composition. These series are sketched in Figure 1.9. The discontinuous reaction series is the one of greatest interest to us in attempting to understand the composition of the mantle—it would explain the separation of the crust from the mantle, and would lead us to expect that as we progressed from the surface downward through the crust and toward the mantle there would be a progression from the light high-oxygen content rocks, such as granite, toward the heavier, more basic metallic rocks, such as dunite [37, 402].

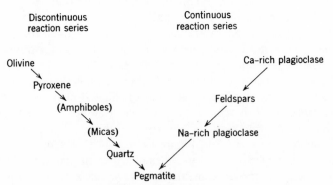

Figure 1.9: Reaction series. From Bowen [37, p. 60].

Geochemical Considerations

The essentially petrological discussion presented so far suggests an explanation for the separation of the major components between the mantle and the crust. We still are concerned, however, about the core-mantle separation for explaining the relative densities of these two parts. We are concerned also about three elements of relatively low abundance—potassium, K; uranium, U; and thorium, Th—because these are the three naturally radioactive elements which in geological time could have generated sufficient heat to melt a portion of the earth. In regard to these questions we turn to more geochemical arguments. The data that we wish to explain are summarized by Table 1.3, taken from Ahrens [2].

In Table 1.3 we have listed oxides rather than pure elements, because they are essentially the minimal building blocks of which minerals are constructed. The outer parts of the earth appear to be thoroughly oxidized on the basis of not only mineralogical analyses but also analyses of volcanic gases, in which the H_2O/H_2 ratio is about 130 and the CO_2/CO ratio about 30. The "total nonvolatile" percentages are averages for chondritic meteorites, which are quite undifferentiated in character and which have a mean density close to that which the material of the earth would have at zero pressure. The "crust" percentages are the means of average compositions of basalt and granite. The petrological explanation pertains to the bulk components which are essentially the first four items in the table: the iron, oxygen, magnesium, and silicon compounds. The behavior for the other elements we should expect to be based on the fact that most of the material in the earth has the structure of an ionic crystal in which the primary property of an atom is its charge and

TABLE 1.3: CHEMICAL ELEMENTS IN THE EARTH

Element	Total Nonvolatiles	Crust
SiO_2	0.380	0.587
MgO	0.238	0.049
FeO	0.124	0.052
Fe	0.118	0.000
FeS	0.057	0.000
Al_2O_3	0.025	0.150
CaO	0.020	0.067
Ni	0.013	0.000
Na_2O	0.010	0.031
K_2O	0.002	0.023
Fe_2O_3	0.000	0.023

the secondary property is the rate at which its field drops off with distance from the atom—a property that customarily is expressed in terms of the ionic radius in angstroms. If the distribution of a minor element is determined by its capability to replace other elements in the crystal lattice, we should expect that the elements that have the same charge and a similar radius to iron or magnesium would be greatly depleted in the crust relative to the mantle, and that elements of a greatly different charge or radius would be appreciably enriched in the crust relative to the mantle. Figure 1.10 gives the results of such an estimate made by Taylor [393]. If the hypothesis is valid, it must apply to these trace elements, and Figure 1.10 indicates that it does. It is thus a demonstration of one of the benefits of the greatly refined chemical techniques (such as neutron-activation analysis [538]) which enable the

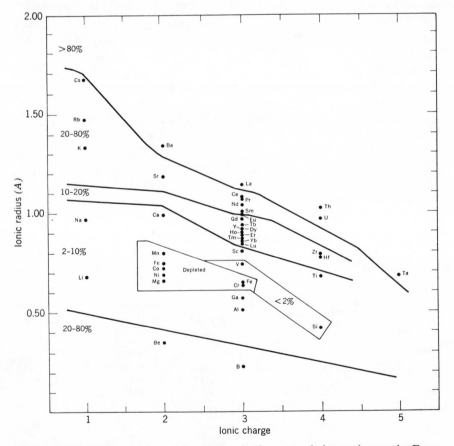

Figure 1.10: Enrichment of oxyphile elements in the crust relative to the mantle. From Taylor [393, p. 1995].

detection of very small quantities of trace elements. Most important, Figure 1.10 indicates a great enrichment of thorium, uranium, and potassium in the crust relative to the mantle. The elements enriched in the crust, as indicated by Figure 1.10, generally are categorized as *oxyphile* or *lithophile*, whereas those that are depleted are characterized as *siderophile*, that is, they have an affinity to iron. Two other categories (not shown on the diagram) in which chemical elements are placed in addition to these are *chalcophile*, having an affinity to sulfur, and *atmophile*, comprising all the gaseous elements. Sulfur and the chalcophile elements, which include copper, zinc, silver, and lead, are also greatly depleted in the crust relative to meteoritic abundances [2, 265, 393]. Elements in the same category have similar chemical properties, as indicated by their grouping in the periodic table, Table 1.4.

Conclusions

Geochemistry and petrology, which we have outlined here, do suggest explanations as to why certain chemical reactions have occurred which in turn explain the distribution of elements in the earth's crust relative to the mantle on the one hand and the meteoritic abundances on the other. They do not explain, however, how the material of the earth moved to a location such that these reactions could take place. To explain such a drastic segregation as appears to be indicated for some elements, and to explain the great density difference between the mantle and the core and the loss of volatile compounds in the earth with regard to the sun, we require a fairly large-scale and drastic overturning of the material in the earth. The fact that remains in doubt is the time scale of such overturning: whether it is relatively short and early in the earth's history, or whether it is a process that has occurred throughout geologic time: an atom moving at 1 cm/yr will go from the center of the earth to the surface of the earth in less than a billion years.

1.2 High Pressure and Temperature Effects

The chemistry of the earth was discussed in Section 1.1 to obtain an idea of its physical properties as expressed by phenomenological parameters which are used in the differential equations expressing mechanical, thermal, electromagnetic, and other relationships in the earth. However, nearly all of these phenomenological parameters vary with temperature and pressure. As summarized in Table 1.5, about the only important parameters that are not significantly temperature and pressure dependent are those related to radioactivity—the decay constant, λ, and the rate of heat generation per cubic centimeter, A.

The simplest way to build a model of a planet is to measure in the laboratory the properties of the likely materials of the earth over the range of temperatures and pressures that exist within the earth. These pressures, calculated

TABLE 1.4: PERIODIC TABLE WITH GEOCHEMICAL CLASSES

H																	He
Li	Be											B	C	N	O	F	Ne
Na	Mg											Al	Si	P	S	Cl	A
K	Ca	Sc	Ti	V	Cr	Mn	Fe	Co	Ni	Cu	Zn	Ga	Ge	As	Se	Br	Kr
Rb	Sr	Y	Zr	Nb	Mo	(Tc)	Ru	Rh	Pd	Ag	Cd	In	Sn	Sb	Te	I	Xe
Cs	Ba	La–Lu	Hf	Ta	W	Re	Os	Ir	Pt	Au	Hg	Tl	Pb	Bi			
			Th	(Pr)	U												

Geochemical classes: ←Lithophile→ · Siderophile · Chalcophile · Atmophile

Based on Mason [265, p. 58].

TABLE 1.5: TEMPERATURE AND PRESSURE-DEPENDENT PROPERTIES OF TERRES-
TRIAL MATERIALS

Symbol	Property	Units	Quantities Related
ρ	Density	gm/cm^3	Mass, volume
k	Bulk modulus	dyne/cm^2	Density, pressure
α	Volume coefficient of thermal expansion	$^\circ$C^{-1}	Density, temperature
μ	Rigidity	dyne/cm^2	Deformation, shear stress
η	Viscosity	dyne-sec/cm^2	Rate of deformation, shear stress
$1/Q$	Dissipation factor	—	Energy dissipated, total energy per cycle
D	Diffusion coefficient	cm^2/sec	Rate of diffusion, concentration gradient
T_M	Melting temperature	$^\circ$C	Solid-liquid transition
ΔH	Latent heat of fusion	cal/gm	Heat, melting
K	Thermal conductivity	cal cm^{-1} sec^{-1} $^\circ$C^{-1}	Heat flow, temperature
C	Specific heat	cal gm^{-1} $^\circ$C^{-1}	Change in temperature, heat
σ	Electrical conductivity	ohm^{-1}	Current, electrical potential
μ	Magnetic permeability	—	Flux density, magnetic field intensity

as described in Section 2.5, rise to more than 3000 kb (3×10^6 atm, or 3×10^{12} dynes/cm^2), and the temperatures probably rise to several thousand degrees Kelvin. Theoretically, by applying a hydraulic force to a limited area, there is no limit to the static pressure that can be attained. For practical laboratory apparatus there is a very severe limit due to the strength of the available containing material at reasonable costs. At present, for low temperatures of, say, 300°C or less, the maximum pressure attainable is 300 kb and the maximum attainable at more elevated temperatures, say 2000°C, is about 150 kb. These pressures correspond to depths in the earth of about 800 and 450 km respectively—about 10 percent of the distance to the center. Furthermore, at these maximum pressures, meaningful measurements of many of the properties listed in Table 1.5 cannot be made—the maximum effective pressure for some measurements may be as low as 30 kb. The pressures within the earth up to the maximum of 3500 kb can be attained by shock techniques for durations on the order of microseconds. Such techniques have, of course, even greater measurement difficulties and also emphasize even more that some of the important properties of the earth, such as phase transitions, or some of the more empirical parameters, such as the viscosity, may be very much time dependent. Familiar examples are the properties of substances such as pitch or "Silly Putty."

Consequently, the approach that must be adopted is to measure as far as possible in the laboratory the properties at high temperature and pressure, and then to extrapolate beyond these measurements with such physical theories as may be available—approximate quantum mechanical or thermo-dynamic or semiempirical. Another device that can be used in conjunction with theoretical treatments is that of scaled experiments—to extrapolate from experimental information about materials different from those in the earth to the earth materials. Finally, for application at the very high pressures that prevail in the core of the earth, we may be able to extrapolate downward from theories applicable to the interiors of stars in which, under the very high pressures, solids become essentially the same in their behavior as electron gases. In this section, we shall discuss briefly the techniques of high-pressure measurements, both static and dynamic, and the results obtained from these measurements with emphasis on phase transitions. We shall also discuss briefly the solid-state theory applicable to the extrapolation from these measurements, but shall leave further discussion of most of the properties given in Table 1.5 to the subsequent sections in which the applications of these properties are developed.

Static High-Pressure Experiments

The simplest way to apply high pressure to a piece of material would be to place the specimen in a narrow tube of fluid, and to pump the fluid up to a high pressure with a piston acting at a lower pressure over a much larger area. In other words, to apply the familiar rule that fluids will transmit force keeping pressure × area constant. The drawback of such a system is that, at pressures of more than 25 kb, even gases will freeze in the lines. Hence in the later stages of a high-pressure device, where such pressures are exceeded, the pressures must be transmitted by solid material in a form such as a tapered piston brought to bear against an anvil. To attain the maximum pressure, the face of the anvil must be made of the hardest possible material, tungsten carbide or diamond, and must be carefully forged and machined. As a consequence, the dimensions available are quite small, about $\frac{1}{2}$ mm across. Such a device, capable of attaining 200 kb pressure at room temperature, was developed as early as 1930 by Bridgman [44]. To attain higher tempera-tures, however, the Bridgman device required that the piston and anvil as well as the specimen be heated; as a consequence, when operated at 1000°C it could not attain more than 20 kb. The next step was the development of small furnaces which could be included with the specimen so that high temperatures could be attained without excessive heating of the pressure-transmitting anvils and pistons. One particularly successful device was essentially an arrangement of four tetrahedral pistons which were brought together. This permitted sufficient access to the sample to introduce a graphite ring which heated upon the passage of electric current. In this manner, pressures of 150 kb at 2000°C have been attained. In addition to the problem of attaining the desired temperatures and pressures, there is, of course, the problem of introducing thermocouples and other devices required to make the measurements, and in general those measurements that must be made on the sample while it is at high temperature and pressure have not been possible except at appreciable reduction from the maximum attainable by the device. There are other phenomena, such as stable phase transitions, about which the desired information can be attained from the sample after removal from the press [38, 39, 309].

Dynamic High-Pressure Experiments

The alternative technique of attaining high pressures for extremely limited periods of time by shock waves entails the explosive propulsion of a piston against the substance being studied. In being rammed against the substance, the piston causes the generation of a shock wave in the substance. This process can be visualized by the analogy of a series of spheres which are coupled to one another, as shown in Figure 1.11. The rate of displacement of the spheres, U, which is called the *mass velocity* of the substance, is the same as the velocity of the piston which is causing the spheres to move. This velocity is always less than the velocity D of the perturbation of the material which is the shock front moving ahead of the compacted mass. From considerations of conservation of matter, energy, and momentum (see problem 1.4), we can write for 0 initial pressure, final pressure P, initial

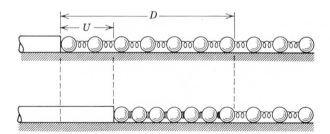

Figure 1.11: One-dimensional model of propagation of a shock wave in an elastic medium. From Al'tshuler [10, p. 53].

specific volume V_0, and final specific volume V:

$$D^2 = V_0{}^2 \frac{P}{V_0 - V} \tag{1.2.1}$$

$$U^2 = P(V_0 - V) \tag{1.2.2}$$

If we plot the lines corresponding to $U = $ constant and $D = $ constant on a pressure versus volume diagram, Figure 1.12, we will have the U hyperbola and the D line intersecting at a particular point which corresponds to the final pressure and volume. If we take the same substance and the same sample, and subject it to different mass velocities U, we will obtain a series of intersections of D lines and U hyperbolas on the graph. This series of intersections will turn out to be a line convex toward the origin which is indicated as P_H in Figure 1.12. The line P_H is known as the *Hugoniot adiabat*.

Now if we could compress the substance so slowly from the initial volume V_0 to the final volume V that it would remain at the same temperature, we would find that our final pressure would be somewhat lower than the pressure P of the shock experiment. Let us call this lower pressure P_c (c denoting cold pressure). The pressure versus volume curve for this cold compression we would also expect to be convex toward the origin for most materials because of the increase under pressure of the bulk modulus of the substance. The area under the curve from the points O and C on the diagram would be the increase in the "cold" internal energy of compression ΔE_c. In the actual shock experiment we would then have an additional area, bounded by lines OAC, which is the thermal energy ΔE_t. The simplest relation between this

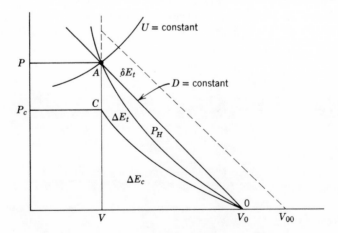

Figure 1.12: *P-V* diagram of shock compression. From Al'tshuler [10, p. 54].

thermal energy ΔE_t and the difference in pressure, $P - P_c$ is:

$$P - P_c = \frac{\gamma}{V} \Delta E_t \qquad (1.2.3)$$

known as the *Mie-Grüneisen equation of state* [10, 333]. The parameter γ is the *Grüneisen ratio*, the theoretical derivation of which we discuss later in connection with the vibrating lattice model of a solid. The parameter γ also may be determined experimentally by using a different sample of the substance which has a greater porosity and hence a greater initial volume, indicated as V_{00} on the diagram. The consequence of this greater initial volume is to displace to the right the $D =$ constant line, and upward the $U =$ constant hyperbola, so that the final volume V is still the same. We then have an increase in E_t which is indicated as δE_t in the diagram. We can use this to obtain the value of γ by elimination from two equations of type (1.2.3). A difficulty in this procedure is uncertainty as to the effect of any phase transitions that may be entailed.

Of the two velocities required, only the shock velocity D is directly measureable; usually the mass velocity U must be inferred from the velocity of some sort of striker or partition. Aside from the Grüneisen ratio determination, the principal difficulty is departure of experimental conditions from those assumed in measuring U due to uneven heating, etc. [10, 89, 333]. Phase transitions inferred from shock experiments and likely to be of importance in the earth are given in Table 1.6.

TABLE 1.6: PRESSURES FOR PHASE TRANSITIONS AT 298°K

Reaction	Range of Results (kb)	Assumed Mean (kb)
SiO_2 (coesite) $\rightarrow$ SiO_2 (stishovite)	89–103	96
Mg_2SiO_4 (forsterite) $\rightarrow$ $2MgO + SiO_2$ (stishovite)	183–216	199
$MgSiO_3$ (enstatite) $\rightarrow$ $MgO + SiO_2$ (stishovite)	166–199	182
Mg_2SiO_4 (forsterite) $\rightarrow$ Mg_2SiO_4 (spinel)	99–120	110
Mg_2SiO_4 (spinel) $\rightarrow$ $2MgO + SiO_2$ (stishovite)	283–359	321
$2MgSiO_3$ (enstatite) $\rightarrow$ Mg_2SiO_4 (forsterite) $+ SiO_2$ (stishovite)	120–200	159
$2MgSiO_3$ (enstatite) $\rightarrow$ Mg_2SiO_4 (spinel) $+ SiO_2$ (stishovite)	114–153	133

From Ahrens & Syono [456].

Phase Transitions in the Earth

The high-pressure techniques, both static and dynamic, have been applied to a wide variety of materials, so it is appropriate to ask a few questions as to which results are most important with respect to the problem of the earth as a planet. Looking at Table 1.3, the abundances for the earth as a whole, it appears that the important experiments would be those applied to compounds of iron, oxygen, silicon, and magnesium. Of these, iron is much more dense than the others; according to Table 1.1, unless there is a spectacular sort of a phase transition in one of the other materials, most of the iron shown in Table 1.3 must be allocated to the core, leaving it as a less important substance in the mantle than magnesium. In the mantle, considering the relative strength of the bonds shown, for example, in Figures 1.5, 1.6, and 1.7, the problem can be further narrowed to different combinations of only a couple of compounds: magnesium oxide, MgO, and silica, SiO_2.

The leading questions we therefore would like to ask are:

1. Solid-Liquid Transitions

(a) What are the melting temperatures of the magnesium-containing pyroxenes, olivines, and spinels at pressures corresponding to those in the mantle: i.e., up to 1400 kb?

(b) What is the melting temperature of iron up to the pressure of the boundary between the inner and outer cores (3200 kb)?

2. Solid-Solid Transitions

(a) What phase transitions are there involving the more common silicates at the temperatures ($100°C$–$500°C$) and pressures (2–15 kb) that might exist at the crust-mantle boundary?

(b) What phase transitions exist involving silica and the magnesium olivines, pyroxenes, and spinels at the pressures prevailing in the mantle (10–1400 kb)?

3. Compression

(a) What is the change in density with pressure of iron, silica (SiO_2), and olivine $(Mg, Fe)SiO_4$ at pressures up to those in the core (2000 or 3000 kb)?

The answers to the first category of questions, melting point, can be obtained only up to the limit of static tests, roughly 60 kb. The results of various experiments are given in Figure 1.13. The curves in Figure 1.13 are essentially straight or slightly concave downward. If we take the melting curves of materials which are much more compressible, such as the alkali earths, lithium, sodium, potassium, rubidium, the downward concavity is

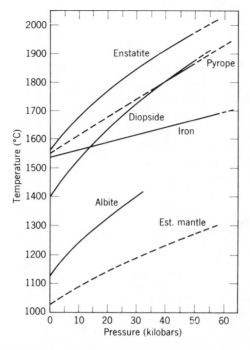

Figure 1.13: Melting temperatures (pyrope is magnesium garnet). From Boyd [38, p. 7].

much more pronounced. This melting curve in the past has usually been approximated by a semiempirical rule known as the *Simon equation* [214, 222]

$$\frac{P}{a} = \left[\frac{T_m(P)}{T_m(0)}\right]^c - 1 \tag{1.2.4}$$

in which a and c are empirical constants determined experimentally for each material. However, if we take the temperature versus pressure diagram and replot it as a melting temperature versus specific volume, the experimental curves become rather straight lines [222]. There is thus a temptation to apply this same linear extrapolation to the materials shown in Figure 1.13 to obtain their melting points at locations much deeper within the earth. To make this extrapolation we require information about the change in density of materials with pressure: we shall take this up when we discuss those experimental results. Another complication in applying the results shown in Figure 1.13 to the actual earth is that we should expect the melting temperatures of a mixture to be depressed below those of any component of the mixture anywhere from 100 to 500°C, the same as it is at zero pressure, as shown by Figure 1.8.

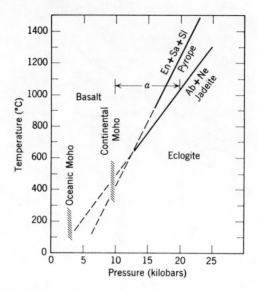

Figure 1.14: Solid transitions involving possible upper-mantle materials (jadeite is sodium-aluminum pyroxene). The interval *a* is the bracket on a transition obtained with natural basalt. From Boyd [38, p. 4].

Transitions at Moho Pressures

The results pertaining to question 2(a) phase transitions at pressures and temperatures in the vicinity of those of the Moho, are well within experimental capability. Figure 1.14 gives some of the pertinent results of the transitions between naturally occurring rocks. The one that is most likely to occur is between basalt (or gabbro) and eclogite, which involves the transformation of a feldspar into a garnet. Also indicated in the figure are the pressures expected to prevail at the Moho beneath the oceans and the continents respectively. The important point is that in order for the Moho to be a phase transition, temperature gradients in the crust would have to have a strong positive correlation with crustal thickness. Such correlation is not indicated by either surface heat flow or upper mantle seismic velocities. Another problem is that of the sharpness of the Moho discontinuity; the transition zone is only about 1 km wide, which would require a rather pure substance to satisfy [10, 150, 189, 494, 576].

Transitions at Mantle Pressures

The various minerals which are compounds of the oxides believed to be the most likely constituents of the mantle, magnesium oxide (MgO) and silica (SiO_2), require higher pressures to undergo phase transitions. The only transitions that have been attained in the laboratory are those of silica of quartz density (density 2.6 gm/cm³) to coesite (2.9 gm/cm³) at 27 kb and 700°C or 39 kb and 1750°C; and to stishovite (density 4.3 gm/cm³) at 130 kb and 1600°C. Both the olivine (Mg_2SiO_4) and pyroxene ($MgSiO_3$) forms of magnesium silicates require pressures higher than those attainable in static experiments to be converted into spinel or spinel plus stishovite forms. Hence some sort of extrapolation is required.

One type of extrapolation is to replace some of the metal elements in these compounds by other metals of equal charge and larger ionic radius. A phase transition should then be made more easily because the transition essentially depends upon attaining a certain ratio of the metal ion radius to the oxygen ion radius, the principal effect of compression being decrease of the oxygen radius. The zero-pressure ion radius of silicon is 0.42 Å; the next +4 metal in size upward from silicon is germanium, of radius 0.48 Å. The zero-pressure radius of magnesium is about 0.68 Å. The next one up of +2 charge is nickel, with about 0.70 Å zero-pressure ionic radius [2, 265].

A series of experiments at 600°C and 0–90 kb was carried out on various mixtures with various ratios of Ni_2GeO_4 to Mg_2SiO_4 by Ringwood and Seabrook [341]. The results of these experiments are shown in Figure 1.15. The extrapolations of the two lines that separate the fields of pure spinel and pure olivine from the mixture have an intersection, which would correspond to a pure forsterite Mg_2SiO_4, at about 140 kb, equal to the pressure at a depth of 400 km in the earth. The density change with this transition would be about 9 percent. More recent experiments on the Mg_2SiO_4-Fe_2SiO_4 system obtain a density change of about 10 percent and estimated pressures of 150 kb at 800°C and 170 kb at 900°C [457, 495].

Experiments with pyroxenes (Mg, Fe, Co) (Si, Ge)O_3 at pressures up to 200 kb and temperatures of 900°C indicate that enstatite, $MgSiO_3$, will probably transform to a denser phase called *ilmenite* at around 230 kb, rather than undergo the transition [496]:

$$2MgSiO_3 \rightarrow \underset{\text{(spinel)}}{Mg_2SiO_4} + \underset{\text{(stishovite)}}{SiO_2}$$

A further transition that is predicted by similar extrapolation is the breakdown of the spinel form of Mg_2SiO_4 into periclase (MgO) plus SiO_2 or $MgSiO_3$ at about 200 kb for the 600°C temperature.

Transitions at Core Pressures

Sufficient information to be useful concerning the compression of materials at high pressures such as prevail in the earth come mainly from the shock experiments. Figure 1.16 is a summary of the results for the likely materials within the earth; the most important uncertainty is the conversion from the

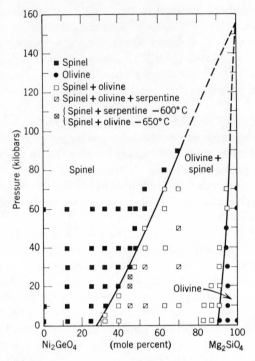

Figure 1.15: Phase transitions obtained in the system Ni_2GeO_4-Mg_2SiO_4 at $600°C$ and 0 to 90 kb. From Ringwood & Seabrook [341, p. 1982].

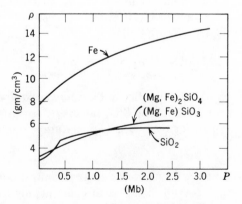

Figure 1.16: Variations of density with pressure obtained from shock compression experiments, with correction from Hugoniot adiabat to $0°K$. From Al'tshuler [10, p. 83].

shock adiabat to the cold compression density. To apply the law that the change in melting point should be directly proportionate to the change in specific volume [222], we obtain from Figure 1.16 the density of iron to be 14.1 gm/cm³ at the boundary between the cores, 3.2 Mb. Applying this law, we get a melting temperature for iron at these depths of about 3700°C (see problem 1.5 at the end of the chapter).

Application of Thermodynamic Theory

To obtain a theoretical explanation of the behavior of solids with temperature, we have two types of theories: *thermodynamics*, which deals with the macroscopic relationships that must prevail in change of energy and temperature and volume and pressure; and *lattice dynamics*, which treats each of the atoms in the crystal lattice as oscillating about an equilibrium point in a manner determined by the interaction of the force fields of neighboring atoms.

Since thermodynamics deals with the energy balance of a system which in turn will provide useful conditions on the more detailed lattice vibration theory, we discuss it first.

The most important concepts of thermodynamics are those of *internal energy* and *entropy* of a system. The internal energy E of a system is defined as a function of the state of the system with the property that for any infinitesimal change in the conditions of the system—temperature, pressure, etc.—the internal energy will increase by an amount that is equal to the heat dq absorbed by the system plus the work dw done on the system:

$$dE = dq + dw, \tag{1.2.5}$$

the first law of thermodynamics. The systems we are talking about in this section are all in mechanical equilibrium: the work done on them is merely that of hydrostatic pressure

$$dw = -P\,dV \tag{1.2.6}$$

Before defining entropy we wish to define *reversibility* and *irreversibility* of processes. A reaction is said to proceed reversibly when the system is balanced so that a small change in the conditions can cause the reaction to proceed in the opposite direction. A reaction is reversible only when it differs infinitesimally from the equilibrium conditions and when the velocity of the reverse reaction is infinitesimally small. For example, when ice melts at 0°C atmosphere pressure, the reaction is reversible since an infinitesimal drop in temperature will cause the water to freeze again. The same reaction proceeding at 10°C is not reversible because the small drop in temperature will not make the water freeze.

Entropy is defined by the properties: (1) in any reversible process the change in entropy in the sytem is measured by the heat received by the system divided by the absolute temperature; and (2) in any spontaneous irreversible process, the change in entropy is greater than this amount. In equations:

$$dS = \frac{dq}{T} \qquad \text{for a reversible process,}$$

$$(1.2.7)$$

$$dS > \frac{dq}{T} \qquad \text{for any spontaneous irreversible process,}$$

the second law of thermodynamics. Substituting equations (1.2.6) and (1.2.7) in (1.2.5) we get

$$dE \leq T\, dS - P\, dV \qquad (1.2.8)$$

Entropy, as formally defined here by the thermodynamic relations, has no physical meaning. To obtain some physical idea of it we must turn to the definition of statistical mechanics, which considers the behavior of large numbers of small particles in a system and derives the macroscopic behavior of the system by applying statistical averaging to the possible states of the small particles in the system. Each macroscopic state is determined by assigning certain velocities and coordinates to all particles of the system. The quantity W is called the probability of the system, and is the same as the number of possible states. The entropy per unit mass is defined as

$$S = k \ln W \qquad (1.2.9)$$

where k is the *Boltzmann constant* ($k = 1.38 \times 10^{-16}$ erg/°C). Hence the increase in entropy S means an increase in the number of possible states W of a system which in turn means an increase in the disorder of the system: more possible varieties of location and motion for the particles in the system, so that entropy is sometimes considered equivalent to disorder.

The principle objective is to predict theoretically the behavior of the material changes in temperature and pressure that we have described previously, such as the various phase transitions, and in the terms of thermodynamics to determine in which direction under given physical conditions the reactions run spontaneously. The possibility for a reaction given the entropy laws of equation (1.2.7) thus depends on certain changes in pressure and volume, or temperature and pressure. The possibility will depend on (1) the change in entropy; (2) the supply or expenditure of heat involved in the change of entropy; and (3) the work that has to be done by or against all the external constraints. The three principal quantities used in studying reactions are first the *Helmholtz free energy F*, defined as

$$F = E - TS \qquad (1.2.10)$$

the *Gibbs free energy G*, defined as

$$G = E + PV - TS \tag{1.2.11}$$

and the *enthalpy H*, defined as

$$H = E + PV \tag{1.2.12}$$

Taking pressure P and temperature T as constant, differentiating (1.2.10), (1.2.11), and (1.2.12) with respect to the other elements, and then substituting equation (1.2.7) and equation (1.2.8), we get for a reversible reaction

$$
\begin{aligned}
dF &= -P\, dV \\
dG &= 0 \\
dH &= T\, dS
\end{aligned}
\tag{1.2.13}
$$

What we have said so far applies only to a system in which the amount of each component is held constant. Now we are interested, of course—in connection with phase transitions, etc.—in systems in which the proportion of each component may change. Let n_i be the number of moles of component i:

$$E \equiv E(S, V, n_i) \tag{1.2.14}$$

since from equation (1.2.8) E is a function of S and V. Differentiate (1.2.14)

$$dE = \left(\frac{\partial E}{\partial V}\right)_{S,n_i} dV + \left(\frac{\partial E}{\partial S}\right)_{V,n_i} dS + \sum_i \left(\frac{\partial E}{\partial n_i}\right)_{S,V,n_j} dn_i \tag{1.2.15}$$

in which the subscripts indicate the quantities held constant while the differentiation is being made and n_j symbolizes all moles except the ith. If we define the *chemical potential μ_i* as

$$\mu_i \equiv \left(\frac{\partial E}{\partial n_i}\right)_{S,V,n_j}$$

Equation (1.2.15) becomes

$$dE = T\, dS - P\, dV + \sum_i \mu_i\, dn_i \tag{1.2.16}$$

Integrating (1.2.16) for constant values of P, T, μ_i, we get

$$E = TS - PV + \sum_i \mu_i n_i \tag{1.2.17}$$

whence from (1.2.11) we get

$$G = \sum_i \mu_i n_i \tag{1.2.18}$$

Let us express the composition of a phase α by the mole of fractions N_i^α of components defined by

$$N_i^\alpha = \frac{n_i^\alpha}{\sum_i n_i} \qquad (1.2.19)$$

Differentiating equations (1.2.11) and (1.2.18) we get two expressions for dG and using (1.2.16) to eliminate dE, we obtain the relationship for a particular phase α

$$-V^\alpha \, dP + S^\alpha \, dT + \sum_i n_i^\alpha \, d\mu_i^\alpha = 0 \qquad (1.2.20)$$

Dividing throughout by $\Sigma_i n_i$, (1.2.20) becomes:

$$-v^\alpha \, dP + s^\alpha \, dT + \sum_i N_i^\alpha \, d\mu_i^\alpha = 0 \qquad (1.2.21)$$

where v^α and s^α are mean molar quantities $V^\alpha/\Sigma_i n_i^\alpha$ and $S^\alpha/\Sigma_i n_i^\alpha$ respectively. Equation (1.2.21) is known as the *Gibbs-Duhem equation*, and shows how the chemical potentials must change for pressure and temperatures dP and dT. Let us consider two phases of one component each, for which (1.2.21) becomes:

$$\begin{aligned} -v^1 \, dP + s^1 \, dT + d\mu_1^1 = 0 \\ -v^2 \, dP + s^2 \, dT + d\mu_1^2 = 0 \end{aligned} \qquad (1.2.22)$$

Now if equilibrium is to be maintained between these two phases for any changes of P or T, (1.2.21) applies and therefore $d\mu_1^1 = d\mu_1^2$. Hence:

$$\frac{dP}{dT} = \frac{s^2 - s^1}{v^2 - v^1} \qquad (1.2.23)$$

Now if Δq is the *heat of transition* of a phase transition—for example, the heat required to cause melting of a substance—then using equation (1.2.7) we can write (1.2.23) as:

$$\frac{dP}{dT} = \frac{\Delta q}{T\Delta v} \qquad (1.2.24)$$

in which we have used Δ's instead of d's because there is no requirement that these be infinitesimal quantities. Equation (1.2.24) is known as the *Clausius-Clapeyron equation*, which may be applied to any two-phase system of one component such as those shown in Figures 1.12 and 1.13, and is also applicable to the phase transitions described by Figures 1.14 and 1.15. Thus if, in a phase transition, we can observe the change in specific volume ΔV—or conversely the change in density—and the change in heat Δq, then we can use the Clausius-Clapeyron equation as a means of getting the slope of the transition line in the phase diagram and hence of extrapolating it to different

TABLE 1.7: THERMOCHEMICAL DATA PERTAINING TO PHASE TRANSITIONS

Mineral		Molar Volume, V (cm³/mole)	Standard Entropy, $S_{298°}$ (cal mole^{-1} °K^{-1})
SiO_2	Quartz	22.69	10.00
SiO_2	Coesite	20.64	9.45
SiO_2	Stishovite	14.02	6.13
MgO	Periclase	11.25	6.44
$MgSiO_3$	Enstatite	31.47	16.19
Mg_2SiO_4	Forsterite	43.79	22.73
Mg_2SiO_4	Spinel	39.86	18.0

From Ahrens & Syono [456].

temperatures and pressures. The thermochemical data necessary to apply
(1.2.7) and (1.2.24) to the phase transitions likely to be of importance in the
mantle are given in Table 1.7. These data apply at a standard temperature of
298°K; the weakness of the calculation is that the pressures necessary to
obtain the transitions at this temperature often must be based on shock
experiments, as given in Table 1.6. See problem 1.6 for examples [265, 317,
331, 402, 466].

Phase transitions involving gaseous states are of interest relative to the
origin of meteorites and planets, as discussed in Chapters 8 and 9.

Diffusion

Besides phase transformations, areas of application of thermodynamics
in the solid earth are preferred crystal orientation and diffusion. Since
preferred crystal orientation entails nonhydrostatic stresses, it is somewhat
more complex [203, 271]. A useful diffusion theory is obtained, however,
using a relatively simple theory [135, 402].

Diffusion theory depends on the chemical potential μ_i, already defined as
proportionate to the concentration of a substance in a particular system.
This potential is like any potential in that the potential gradient gives rise
to a force. If a substance has a concentration gradient in a system of constant
T and P, there exists a force acting on any particle i in the direction x

$$F_{ix} = -\frac{1}{N_A}\frac{\partial \mu_i}{\partial x} \qquad (1.2.25)$$

where N_A is the number of particles per mole. If there is a frictional resistance
that is proportional to the velocity of the particle, then under such a force it

will attain a steady-state velocity at which the two forces—that due to potential gradient and that due to friction—will be equal. This steady-state velocity V_{ix} will have a proportionality B_i to the force F_{ix}. The rate of flow of i, the number S_{ix} of moles flowing per unit time across the unit surface normal to x, will then be

$$S_{ix} = - \frac{c_i B_i}{N_A} \frac{\partial \mu_i}{\partial x} \tag{1.2.26}$$

in which c_i is the number of moles per unit volume. Since it has been assumed that the potential gradient is proportional to the concentration, we get finally

$$S_{ix} = D_i \frac{\partial c_i}{\partial x} \tag{1.2.27}$$

where D_i is the diffusion coefficient—a function of the temperature and pressure of the material in the medium. The diffusion coefficient being proportionate to the potential gradient over the viscosity, we should expect it to be strongly dependent on the temperature. Experimental evidence in fact indicates that the diffusion coefficient has the form

$$D = D_0 \exp\left(-\frac{Q}{kT}\right) \tag{1.2.28}$$

where Q is an activation energy on the order of 3 to 6 electron volts for impurities and vacancies in silicates (1 electron volt $= 1.60 \times 10^{-12}$ erg). This form of temperature dependence in a complicated substance has a variety of explanations [135].

The relevance of diffusion to the mechanical properties of material is discussed in Section 2.3. Its importance—relative to melting and fractionation upon recrystallization—as a means of segregating and transporting material in the earth is a moot point. Manifestly it exists: diffusion is a phenomenon on which depends the process of metamorphosis, defined as changes of rocks which are significant at temperatures below melting. Whether diffusion is as unimportant compared to melting throughout the mantle as it is in the crust is not known.

Measurements of diffusion of silicates were made by Bowen of the mutual diffusion of liquid diopside and plagioclase at a temperature of about $1500°$. The diffusion coefficients depended very much upon the relative concentration, ranging from 1.73×10^{-7} cm/sec to 2.31×10^{-6} cm²/sec, of the end members of the plagioclase series shown in Figure 1.3. For mixtures that started from two pure values at a boundary, the migration per year resulting from these respective diffusion coefficients would be about 4 cm and 60 cm respectively [402].

Application of Lattice-Vibration Theory

To seek a more fundamental explanation of the phase transitions, density changes, etc., we can start with the theory of the crystal lattice in which each atom vibrates like a harmonic oscillator in a potential well of the force field of its neighbors. If we define the kinetic energy of these particles in the usual manner as half of the mass times the square of the velocity of the displacement, and if we define the potential energy as a function of position, then for the oscillations of atoms that exist in a lattice with a regularly recurring pattern it can be shown that the displacement must obey a law of the form:

$$\mathbf{u}_{sl}(t) = e^{i\mathbf{q}\cdot\mathbf{l}}\mathbf{u}_{s0}(t) \tag{1.2.29}$$

in which $\mathbf{u}$ is a displacement from the equilibrium position, the subscript s refers to the position within a cell (a single repetition of a regular pattern of the lattice), and the subscript l refers to the location with respect to an arbitrary chosen origin in the cell. The important feature of equation (1.2.29) is the wave number $\mathbf{q}$, which says that the geometry of the situation requires that the only admissible solutions correspond to a certain discrete set of wave numbers. With each of these wave numbers $\mathbf{q}$ there is associated a frequency v_q. The energy for each of these normal modes must by quantum theory be $\hbar v_q$ ($\hbar$ is $h/2\pi$, where h is *Planck's constant*, 6.625×10^{-27} erg sec). According to the theory of statistical mechanics there will be on the average (see Section 6.2) [331]

$$\bar{n}_q = \frac{1}{e^{\hbar v_q/kT} - 1} \tag{1.2.30}$$

quanta in the qth mode from which we can get the average total internal energy of the system in volume V:

$$E = \sum_q^{3N} \frac{\hbar v_q}{\exp\left(\hbar v_q/kT\right) - 1} + E_0 \tag{1.2.31}$$

where N is the number of unit cells in the volume V of the crystal and E_0 is the internal energy at $0°K$. From (1.2.10)

$$E = F + TS = F - T\left(\frac{\partial F}{\partial T}\right)_V = -T^2\left[\frac{\partial(F/T)}{\partial T}\right]_V \tag{1.2.32}$$

whence

$$F = -T\int\frac{E}{T^2}\,dT = -T\int\sum_q\frac{(\hbar v_q/T^2)\exp\left(-\hbar v_q/kT\right)}{1 - \exp\left(-\hbar v_q/kT\right)}\,dT$$

$$= E_0 + \sum_q kT\log\left[1 - \exp\left(-\hbar v_q/kT\right)\right] \tag{1.2.33}$$

Then, from (1.2.13),

$$P = -\left(\frac{\partial F}{\partial V}\right)_T = P_0 - \frac{1}{V} \sum_q \frac{\hbar \exp\left(-\hbar v_q/kT\right)}{1 - \exp\left(-\hbar v_q/kT\right)} \cdot \frac{d \log v_q}{d \log V} \quad (1.2.34)$$

where P_0 is the pressure at $0°K$. If it is assumed

$$\frac{d \log v_q}{d \log V} = \gamma \quad (1.2.35)$$

the *Grüneisen ratio*, for all q, then (1.2.34) becomes, using (1.2.31),

$$P = P_0 + \frac{\gamma E - E_0}{V} \quad (1.2.36)$$

the same as (1.2.3). The application of the Grüneisen ratio therefore implies that the frequencies v_q are temperature independent and have the same dependence on density [214, 453]. The theory can also be developed assuming the ratio γ to be a function of the wave number q.

Define the *specific heat at constant volume:*

$$C_V = \frac{\partial E}{\partial T} \quad (1.2.37)$$

Then, from (1.2.36),

$$\left(\frac{dP}{dT}\right)_V = \frac{\gamma C_V}{V} \quad (1.2.38)$$

Define the *volume coefficient of thermal expansion:*

$$\alpha = \frac{1}{V}\left(\frac{dV}{dT}\right)_P = \frac{1}{k}\left(\frac{dP}{dT}\right)_V \quad (1.2.39)$$

where k is the bulk modulus, listed in Table 1.5:

$$k = -V \frac{dP}{dV} \quad (1.2.40)$$

Thence

$$\gamma = \frac{Vk\alpha}{C_V} \quad (1.2.41)$$

which expresses the Grüneisen ratio γ in terms of experimentally measurable quantities. The derivation given here obtains that γ is directly proportionate to the specific volume V; an alternative theory obtains a proportionality to $V^{1/2}$ [214, 333, 386].

A theoretical model of melting temperature dependence on pressure requires a specification of the relationship between v_q and $\mathbf{q}$. Substitute (1.2.31) in (1.2.37):

$$C_V = \frac{1}{kT} \sum_q \frac{(hv_q)^2 \exp(hv_q/kT)}{[\exp(hv_q/kT) - 1]^2} \tag{1.2.42}$$

The summation with respect to q is over all polarizations, as well as all different wave vectors $\mathbf{q}$. The wave vectors are distributed with density $V/8\pi^3$ in reciprocal space, when V is the specific volume of a unit cell; hence the summation with respect to wave vectors can be replaced by an integration in reciprocal space:

$$C_V = \frac{1}{kT^2} \frac{1}{8\pi^3} \sum_{\text{pol}} \iiint \frac{(hv_q)^2 e^{hv_q/kT}}{(e^{hv_q/kT} - 1)^2} d^3q \tag{1.2.43}$$

where the factor $8\pi^3$ is the normalization corresponding to the total volume of the $\mathbf{q}$ vector distribution. To integrate (1.2.43) it is the usual procedure to assume a spectrum $f(v)$ such that $f(v)\,dv$ is the fraction of modes with frequency in the range $v \to v + dv$. The simplest model is the *Debye model* in which it is assumed first that all waves travel at the same velocity s:

$$v_q = sq \tag{1.2.44}$$

Second it is assumed that there is an upper limit q_D on the wave number q, such that the minimum wavelength is a bit more than the average diameter of a unit cell; a lattice will be unable to propagate waves in a shorter wavelength. Assuming that the unit cell can be represented as a sphere, then if it is to contain N points, at density $V/8\pi^3$ in $\mathbf{q}$ space,

$$N = \frac{V}{8\pi^3} \tfrac{4}{3}\pi q_D^3 \tag{1.2.45}$$

and

$$\begin{aligned}
f(v)\,dv &= \frac{4\pi q^2\,dq}{(4\pi/3)q_D^3} \\
&= \frac{3v^2}{v_D^3}\,dv
\end{aligned} \tag{1.2.46}$$

For a structure with n atoms per unit cell and hence $3nN$ modes, (1.2.43) becomes

$$\begin{aligned}
C_V &= 3nNk \int \frac{(hv/KT)^2 e^{hv/KT}}{(e^{hv/kT} - 1)^2} f(v)\,dv \\
&= 3Nk \int_0^{v_D} \frac{(hv/kT)^2 e^{hv/kT}}{(e^{hv/kT} - 1)^2} \frac{3v^2}{v_D^3}\,dv \\
&= 9Nk \left(\frac{T}{\Theta}\right)^3 \int_0^{\Theta/T} \frac{z^4 e^z}{(e^z - 1)^2}\,dz
\end{aligned} \tag{1.2.47}$$

in which z is $h\nu/kT$, N is the total number of points in wave number space dependent on the cutoff wave number q_D, and where

$$k\Theta = h\nu_D \qquad (1.2.48)$$

defines the *Debye temperature* Θ. Although the spectrum that corresponds to the Debye model is much smoother and simpler than some spectrums that have been calculated for specific lattices, it does get a fairly good prediction for such properties as the velocity of sound [453].

The melting of the Debye model depends on a parameter called the *scattering vector*. This name arises because the departures from the exact periodicity of the lattice vibrations are observed in the form of scattering of electrons and x-rays. This scattering vector is the measure of the displacement of atoms from their normal position. The potential energy, being as stated dependent upon position, will then be affected by this scattering in a non-linear manner. If the displacements are expressed by an exponential function such as the factor in (1.2.29) and if we develop the exponential as a series in the scattering parameter $\mathbf{K}$, the first-order term in the development will average out to zero, but there will be a nonzero quadratic term. Expressing the energy involved in these displacements by a summation over the wave numbers q of the form

$$W = \tfrac{1}{2} \sum_q |\mathbf{K} \cdot \mathbf{U}_q|^2 \qquad (1.2.49)$$

where the factor $\mathbf{U}$ is the normal displacement by which the scattering displacement $\mathbf{K}$ is multiplied. The potential energy of the simple harmonic oscillation will be half the total energy. The average energy E in a particular mode q is $(\bar{n}_q + \tfrac{1}{2})h\nu_q$, where $\bar{n}_q$ is given by (1.2.30). Then if there is only one atom per unit cell for the amplitude $\mathbf{U}_q$ of the qth mode

$$|\mathbf{U}_q|^2 = \frac{E}{NM\nu_q{}^2}$$
$$= (\bar{n}_q + \tfrac{1}{2})\frac{\hbar}{NM\nu_q} \qquad (1.2.50)$$

where M is the mass of the cell. Applying the assumption of the Debye model and performing integration similar to that of (1.2.47) we get that for high temperatures

$$W \rightarrow \frac{3}{2}\frac{h^2 K^2 T}{Mk\Theta^2} \qquad (1.2.51)$$

Now the mean-square amplitude of the vibration of each atom about its lattice site will be

$$\langle r^2 \rangle = \sum_q |\mathbf{U}_q|^2$$

$$\approx \frac{9\hbar^2 T}{Mk\Theta^2} \tag{1.2.52}$$

using (1.2.49) and (1.2.50). In the vibration lattice model, melting occurs when the mean-square oscillations exceed a certain limit. It seems plausible that this limit will be some ratio to the mean radius r_s of a unit cell, say $x_m r_s$. Substituting $x_m r_s$ on the left of (1.2.52) and solving for T, we get as a solution for the melting temperature [453]

$$T_m \approx \frac{x_m^2}{9h^2} Mk\Theta^2 r_s^2 \tag{1.2.53}$$

known as the *Lindemann melting formula*. x_m appears to be in the range of 0.2–0.25 for most solids. The Lindemann formula works well only for the simplest lattices: that is, frozen inert gases, such as argon. For more complex structures the actual melting temperature is lower than predicted by (1.2.53). The dependence on specific volume is also complicated by the dependence of the Debye temperature Θ on the cutoff wave number q_D, through equation (1.2.48). The basic inadequacy of the Lindemann formula, however, is that it takes into account only the crystal state and neglects the liquid state. More complete theories attempt to find an expression for the energy W, (1.2.49), in the liquid state dependent on some measure of the positional disorder of the atoms in the liquid [119].

In terms of macroscopic parameters, the Lindemann law (1.2.53) becomes

$$T_m \propto \Theta^2 V^{2/3} \tag{1.2.54}$$

However, the Debye temperature Θ is also volume dependent, by (1.2.48), since the vibration frequency ν_D would depend on the lattice spacing. By choosing an appropriate rule for the volume dependence of Θ and utilizing the equation of state for compressibility (2.5.19)—developed after discussing elasticity—the Lindemann formula can be related to the Simon equation (1.2.4) and the Kraut-Kennedy law of linear dependence of T_m on specific volume [134, 222].

We shall return later to the use of both the experimental results and the thermodynamic and lattice theories in constructing a model of the interior of the earth, particularly in Section 2.5. Some of the other temperature- and pressure-dependent parameters listed in Table 1.4 will be taken up in Chapter 2 in connection with their application to the physics of the interior.

Scaled Experiments

Another experimental aspect of geophysics worth mentioning in passing is the use of scaled models to study phenomena in the earth. This has been applied particularly to fluid phenomena in studying circulation systems in meteorology and oceanography. It also has been applied to the solid earth in the study of such phenomena as mountain folding. The main problem in such experimentation is the correct scaling of the phenomena. The representation, for example, of a mountain range that may be several tens of kilometers in dimension by a laboratory model that may be tens of centimeters in dimension requires a similar scaling down of the material parameters, entailing the use of a much weaker material in the laboratory model. And also there is the problem that body forces cannot be scaled down (see problem 1.7) [28].

1.3   Geochronology

It has been known for some sixty years that the decay of a long-lived radioactive element might be used to determine the age of the mineral in which it is found. The extensive application of this principle, however, has been much more recent—it has required the development of accurate mass spectrometers to separate different isotopes of the same element, and of greatly refined chemical techniques that permit the accurate measurement of quantities on the order of 10^{-11} gm. Such accuracy is necessary first to be able to use as many possible different radioactive decay systems as checks against each other, and second to be able to take as a single specimen as large an assemblage of minerals as possible. Both of these desiderata arise from the uncertainty of the event defined by the radioactive dating, the formation of the rock plus its subsequent history: metamorphism, and so on.

Radioactive Decay Systems

Mineral age measurements have been made for the most part by the decay systems given in Table 1.8. The K^{40}-Ca^{40} system has not been used to any great extent. A *decay system* is constituted by a *parent* and a *daughter element*. The parent element is that which loses material through the decay and the daughter element is the product of that decay or of a series of successive decays. To determine the age, it is thus necessary to measure the amount of both the radioactive parent and the radiogenic daughter material. The time T required for the parent to have produced the daughter is given by

$$T = \frac{1}{\lambda} \ln \left(1 + \frac{D}{P} \right) \tag{1.3.1}$$

In (1.3.1), D is the present concentration of radiogenic daughter atoms, P

is the present-day concentration of parent atoms, and λ is the *decay constant* related to the *half-life* $T_{1/2}$ by

$$\lambda = \frac{\ln 2}{T_{1/2}}$$

Equation (1.3.1) may be derived from

$$D = P_0(1 - e^{-T\lambda})$$

$$D = P_0 - P$$

$$P_0 = P \, e^{T\lambda} \tag{1.3.2}$$

$$D = P(e^{T\lambda} - 1)$$

$$T\lambda = \ln\left(1 + \frac{D}{P}\right)$$

where P_0 is the original concentration of the parent atom. In the third column of Table 1.8 the symbol α indicates the loss of an α particle, the equivalent of the nucleus of the helium atom consisting of two protons and two neutrons; the β indicates the loss of a β particle, which is the same as an electron; and the e indicates the capture of an electron. The only branching decay system used in geochronology is that of K^{40}. In this case (see problem 1.10), the lifetime t corresponding to a particular A^{40}/K^{40} ratio is:

$$t = \frac{1}{\lambda_\beta + \lambda_e} \log\left(1 + \frac{\lambda_\beta + \lambda_e}{\lambda_e} \cdot \frac{A^{40}}{K^{40}}\right) \tag{1.3.3}$$

where λ_β is the constant for the $K^{40} \rightarrow Ca^{40}$ decay (4.72×10^{-10} yr^{-1}) and λ_e is the constant for the $K^{40} \rightarrow A^{40}$ decay (5.85×10^{-11} yr^{-1}).

In addition to the decays listed in Table 1.8, there is detectable in natural minerals the decay Re^{187}-Os^{186}, but because of its extremely low energy it is

TABLE 1.8: DECAY SYSTEMS USED IN GEOCHRONOLOGY

Decay System			Decay Constant, λ (yr^{-1})	Half-life, $T_{1/2}$ (10^9 yr)
U^{238}	Pb^{206}	$8\alpha + 6\beta$	$1.54 \times 10^{-10} \times (1 \pm 0.01)$	4.5
U^{235}	Pb^{207}	$7\alpha + 4\beta$	9.72×10^{-10}	0.71
Th^{232}	Pb^{208}	$6\alpha + 4\beta$	$4.99 \times 10^{-11} \times (1 \pm 0.01)$	13.9
Rb^{87}	Sr^{87}	β	$1.39 \times 10^{-11} \times (1 \pm 0.05)$	49.8
K^{40}	Ar^{40}	e	5.85×10^{-11}	11.8
K^{40}	Ca^{40}	β	4.72×10^{-10}	1.47

difficult to measure and hence not useful as a dating device. The dating used in rubidium also has a higher uncertainty than the others, as indicated in the table, due to a large portion of low-energy β particles in its energy spectrum [156, 398].

Application of Radioactive Decay to Mineral Dating

To use these decays summarized in Table 1.8 in dating a mineral or an ensemble of minerals by substituting measured ratios of an element P to an element D in (1.3.1) requires us to answer some questions [398, 434].

1. At what time was the amount of the daughter element D equal to 0? Was it the crystallization of the mineral from a melt, or was it some metamorphism sufficient to have driven out any previous existing amount of the daughter element?

2. Has the subsequent history of the mineral been such that there has been no change or removal of either parent or daughter element by processes such as diffusion which would be enhanced by heightened temperatures approaching metamorphism, or by chemical leaching associated with the passage of water if the mineral was porous, or some other such circumstance?

Uncertainties as to the originating event and the subsequent history of a mineral or a group of minerals has made it virtually mandatory that any lifetime, to be accepted as significant, be obtained from more than one of the decay systems in Table 1.8, and furthermore that agreement be attained between different minerals in the same specimen. A troublesome gradual loss in the history of a mineral is the diffusion of lead. However, if this proportion of loss is the same for all isotopes of lead, then the ratio of the first two decays in Table 1.8 would not be affected by any loss of lead:

$$\frac{Pb^{207}}{Pb^{206}} = \frac{U^{235}(e^{\lambda^{235}T} - 1)}{U^{238}(e^{\lambda^{238}T} - 1)} \qquad (1.3.4)$$

The parent elements in Table 1.8 are all rather rare (except for potassium, K) and they are all peculiar in that they have large ionic radii, more than 1.00 Å. Consequently they do not substitute readily in the crystal lattices of the common minerals and hence they are found in the less common minerals which are associated with the last rock types to crystallize from a melt: the granites and pegmatites (the top two lines of Table 1.2); also with the metamorphized form of granite known as *gneiss*. The minerals used for radioactive dating are given in Table 1.9. The most important are *uraninite*, *zircon*, *biotite*, and *muscovite*. Examples of multiple dating where the multiplicity applies not only to the radioactive element but also to the mineral and the rock are given in Table 1.10, which is taken from Tilton and Hart [398]. Note that the discrepancies in Table 1.10 are larger in many cases than

TABLE 1.9: MINERALS CONTAINING RADIOACTIVE ELEMENTS

Symbol*	Name	Formula	Structure Type	Radioactive Elements
B	Biotite	$KHMg_2Al_2(SiO_4)_3$	Mica	Rb, K
H	Hornblende	$Na_2Mg_3(Al, Fe)_2Si_8O_{22}(OH)_2$	Amphibole	K
L	Lepidolite	$KLi_2Al(Si_4O_{10})(OH)_2$	Mica	Rb, K
M	Muscovite	$KH_2Al_3(SiO_4)_3$	Mica	Rb, K
U	Uraninite	UO_2	Oxide	U, Th
Z	Zircon	$ZrSiO_4$	Silica	U, Th
F	Microcline	$KAlSi_3O_8$	Feldspar	Rb
S	Sanidine	$KAlSi_3O_8$	Feldspar	K

* Used in Table 1.10.

the uncertainties given in Table 1.8. These discrepancies are not due to uncertainties of measurement but rather to uncertainties of the degree of metamorphism that has taken place in the rocks in question. For example, the biotite in Virginia and New York seems to have been more subject to these effects than the zircon. Also the potassium/argon dates in Table 1.10

TABLE 1.10: EXAMPLES OF CONCORDANT RADIOGENIC AGES (UNIT: 10^6 yr)

Location	Rock	Mineral	$\dfrac{U^{238}}{Pb^{206}}$	$\dfrac{U^{235}}{Pb^{207}}$	$\dfrac{Pb^{207}}{Pb^{206}}$	$\dfrac{Th^{232}}{Pb^{207}}$	$\dfrac{Rb^{87}}{Sr^{87}}$	$\dfrac{K^{40}}{Ar^{40}}$
Montana	Pegmatite A	U	2600	2640	2200			
	Pegmatite B	M					2800	2470
	Pegmatite B	F					2700	
Ontario	Gneiss A	Z	2450	2600	2730			
	Gneiss B	B					2630	2520
	Gneiss B	M						2600
Virginia	Gneiss	Z	1070	1100	1150	1100		
		B					880	800
	Pegmatite	H						900
		F					980	
New York	Gneiss	Z	1140	1150	1170	1030		
		B					880	780
	Granite	Z	960	940	1060	850		
		B					930	840

are always lower than the rubidium/strontium dates from the same mineral or the uranium/lead dates from the same rock because of the capability of the gaseous argon to diffuse more readily from the site of the decay.

An example of discordance which evidently is a result of metamorphism is given in Figure 1.17. The figure shows the apparent ages obtained from various minerals in a Precambrian crystalline rock about 1300 million years old in Colorado which was intruded by a large body of granite about 54 million years ago. The difference in apparent age between two different radioactive systems in the same mineral is demonstrated by the discrepancies in the K-Ar and the Rb-Sr in the biotite: the former gives lower ages because the argon gas diffuses more readily from the mineral in the earth under the influence of temperature. Much more marked than the discordance between two radioactive systems in the same mineral is the discordance between different minerals. The erratic behavior of the feldspar in Figure 1.17 appears to be characteristic of feldspar in general. The higher apparent ages of the hornblende also appear to be characteristic of that mineral; it retains the daughter particles much better than other minerals. The curve for the biotite

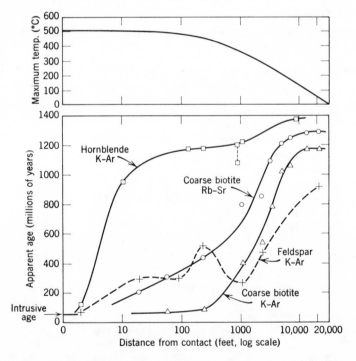

Figure 1.17: Variation of apparent ages of minerals as a function of distance from an intrusive contact. From Tilton & Hart [398, p. 360].

in the instance of the sample shown is also found to depend very much on the grain size. The rate of loss or a rate of diffusion of a daughter product is proportional to D/a^2, where D is the diffusion coefficient (discussed briefly in the previous section), and a is the radius of the crystal grains. Thus a fine-grained specimen will suffer a greater loss than a coarse-grained specimen due to the greater ratio of surface area to volume. The biotite curves in the diagram were accounted for by a model in which the diffusive loss of a daughter product in a particular mineral was proportionate to D/a^2 and the temperature. The temperature at the contact was assumed to be about 500°C and, because of thermal conductivity, to drop off to about 350°C at 1000 ft and less than 250°C at 10,000 ft. An alternative explanation for the curves in Figure 1.17, which was ruled out in this particular instance, is increase of the parent element rather than loss of the daughter element.

A complication that affects the rubidium/strontium method of dating is the fact that Sr^{87} can occur nonradiogenically as well as radiogenically. The technique used to get around this difficulty is to take the ratio of Sr^{87} to Sr^{86} obtained from rocks extremely rich in strontium and weak in rubidium, and then use in the calculations the assumption that the Sr^{87} will be a combination of this ratio to the Sr^{86} plus the radiogenic decay. This ratio has been found in a wide variety of rocks to be approximately 0.700, so that from these considerations we should expect the Sr^{87} content of a radiogenic specimen to be

$$Sr^{87} = 0.700\ Sr^{86} + Rb^{87}(e^{T\lambda} - 1)$$

$$\frac{Sr^{87}}{Sr^{86}} = 0.700 + \frac{Rb^{87}}{Sr^{86}}\ (e^{T\lambda} - 1) \tag{1.3.5}$$

The normal technique then is to plot the Sr^{87}/Sr^{86} ratio against the Rb^{87}/Sr^{86} ratio. For different minerals in a rock of the same age we should expect that the plotted points would fit a straight line with a slope of $\exp(T\lambda) - 1$ and an intercept on the vertical axis of 0.700. If the rock underwent an intensive enough metamorphism that the Sr^{87} was redistributed within the rock, but the rock as a whole did not suffer any loss, then the slope of the line would indicate the time since the metamorphism, but the intercept on the Y-axis would be the Sr^{87}/Sr^{86} at the time of metamorphism—something higher than 0.700. Of course in actuality many systems are much less perfect than the two extremes we have mentioned: first, that of the retention within the mineral of the strontium product; and second, that of the complete mixing of the strontium throughout a rock which remains a closed system. The intermediate imperfections of incomplete mixing and loss of Sr^{87} from the rock occur more frequently.

Metamorphism and diffusion also are the cause of discordances in uranium/lead dating. Except for uraninite, it is unusual for the U^{238}-Pb^{206} and the

U^{235}-Pb^{207} age values to agree within less than 10 percent. This sort of disagreement has occurred both within rocks that have been completely metamorphized and those that have been undisturbed by metamorphism, leading to the suggestion that it has another cause. The half-life of the U^{235}-Pb^{207} decay is very small compared to the half-life of the U^{238}-Pb^{206} decay. Hence if the Pb^{206}/U^{238} ratio is plotted as ordinate against the Pb^{207}/U^{235} ratio as abscissa, the curve will be convex upward, because in younger rocks there has been a relatively large product of Pb^{207} relative to the Pb^{206}. Now if a mineral of age T_1 suffered a loss of lead by metamorphism at time T_2, then the point obtained would be somewhere along the cord from T_1 to T_2, the location being determined by the fraction of the lead that was lost. In this manner the discordant ages for several rocks of different ages and different locations around the world were apparently explained by a metamorphism at approximately 500 million years ago. The simultaneity of metamorphism for minerals of three continents of varying fractions seemed an implausible coincidence. Hence an alternative explanation was explored which assumed that the lead loss occurred by continuous diffusion rather than by a single metamorphism. This diffusion was again proportionate to the ratio D/a^2 and it was assumed that there was no diffusive loss of the parent uranium. The surfaces of the spheres were assumed to have zero lead concentration and, as in Section 1.2, the rate of diffusion was assumed to be proportional to the concentration gradient. The results of this calculation are shown by the diagram on the right in Figure 1.18. Since the calculated curve for the diffusion loss is linear over much of its length, it is apparent that the linear relationships of the points need not imply an episode of lead loss 600 million years ago. Again, as with the other types of discordances, the

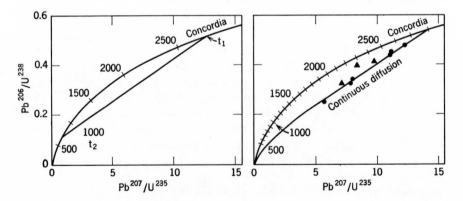

Figure 1.18: Ratios of Pb^{206}/U^{238} and Pb^{207}/U^{235} under the assumptions of (1) perfect concordance, (2) instantaneous loss of lead by metamorphism, and (3) continuous loss of lead by diffusion. From Tilton & Hart [398, p. 363].

explanation of actual discrepancies in dating by uranium/lead decay systems is intermediary between the extreme cases we have described here [398, 434].

The Geologic Time Scale

The application of geochronology has been twofold. The first is to provide a more accurate time scale for the fossil record of geologic history. One reconstruction of this time scale, given in Table 1.11, extends back to the beginning of the Cambrian which is marked by the first identified invertebrates, the *olenellus*. The rocks that are dated by geochronology do not coincide exactly of course with the boundaries between the geologic periods. A large part of the uncertainty in Table 1.11 is due to the uncertainty of interpolation between dated rocks.

The second application of geochronology has been to extend the geological record back to much earlier times than was possible through fossil dating. There have now been found on all continents (except Antarctica) rocks as old as 2.5–2.7 Æ (1 *aeon* (Æ) is 10^9 years), with the oldest rocks being 3.2 Æ in South Africa and 3.5 Æ in Russia. Figure 1.19 is a map which gives the dominant ages of the crystalline rocks for the major regions of North America. Within the areas shown there are many instances of more limited intrusions of younger rocks appearing, but the general picture is that of the figure. It lends considerable support to the idea that the continent was created by accretion of new material around an original nucleus located in the general vicinity of Ontario. The ages found in geochronology also indicate a great variation in activity. A histogram of the distribution with

TABLE 1.11: THE GEOLOGIC TIME SCALE

Era	Period	Beginning of Period $(10^6$ yr)
Cenozoic	Quaternary	1
	Tertiary	65 ± 2
Mesozoic	Cretaceous	135 ± 5
	Jurassic	190 ± 5
	Triassic	225 ± 5
Paleozoic	Permian	270 ± 10
	Carboniferous	340 ± 6
	Devonian	400 ± 10
	Silurian	430 ± 10
	Ordovician	500 ± 15
	Cambrian	600 ± 20

From Faul [464] and Kulp [233].

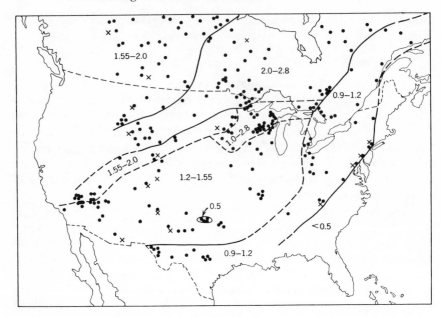

Figure 1.19: Ages, in aeons, of geologic provinces deduced from geochronology. From Tilton & Hart [398, p. 364].

respect to time of radiogenic dates has marked peaks separated by periods of quiescence. The dominant peaks include 0.35 Æ, 1.00 Æ, 1.35 Æ, 1.6 Æ, and 2.6 Æ. Periods of general quiescence were from 0.5 to 0.9 Æ and 2.0 to 2.3 Æ. The entire period from 1.0 to 1.8 Æ is generally high [112, 398].

A recent application of great interest has been the matching of K^{40}-Ar^{40} and Rb^{87}-Sr^{87} ages of locations on opposite coasts of the South Atlantic. Precambrian rocks of ages predominantly in two groups, around 0.55 and 2.0 Æ, from Trinidad (lat. 10°N) to Salvador (lat. 13°S) on the South American coast are very similar in type and ages to rocks from Freetown (lat. 8°N) almost to the Congo River (lat. 5°S) on the African coast [561].

The Age of the Earth

The maximum ages determined for terrestrial rocks of 3.2–3.5 Æ constitute a lower bound on the age of the earth. For an upper bound on the age of the earth we have to consider the amount of radiogenic isotopes relative to nonradiogenic isotopes of the same elements. The most attractive possibility appears to be the uranium/lead system, since we have two isotopes which are of the same element for both the parent and the daughter product. Let us express amounts of these four isotopes as ratios to the amount of the stable nonradiogenic isotope of lead Pb^{204}.

$$\alpha = \frac{Pb^{206}}{Pb^{204}}$$

$$\beta = \frac{Pb^{207}}{Pb^{204}}$$

$$\mu = \frac{U^{238}}{Pb^{204}}$$

$$\nu = \frac{U^{235}}{Pb^{204}}$$

(1.3.6)

Let us suppose we have two rocks 1 and 2 with measured chemical contents $(\alpha_1, \beta_1, \mu_1, \nu_1)$ and $(\alpha_2, \beta_2, \mu_2, \nu_2)$ respectively, and times of crystallization t_1 and t_2 (calculated positively back from the present) determined by the techniques described earlier in this section. Now if we assume:

1. Changes in ratios of isotopes of the same element, α, β, and μ/ν, occur only by radioactive decay.

2. Both rocks 1 and 2 come from the same reservoir which had chemical content $(\alpha_0, \beta_0, \mu_0, \nu_0)$ at time τ.

Then, using equation (1.3.2), we can write four equations for $\alpha_1, \beta_1, \alpha_2, \beta_2$ as a sum of: (a) the content at original time τ; (b) the amount accumulated before crystallization; and (c) the amount accumulated after crystallization:

$$\alpha_1 = \alpha_0 + \mu_0[1 - e^{-(\tau-t_1)\lambda_{238}}] + \mu_1(e^{\lambda_{238}t_1} - 1)$$
$$\beta_1 = \beta_0 + \nu_0[1 - e^{-(\tau-t_1)\lambda_{235}}] + \nu_1(e^{\lambda_{235}t_1} - 1)$$
$$\alpha_2 = \alpha_0 + \mu_0[1 - e^{-(\tau-t_2)\lambda_{238}}] + \mu_2(e^{\lambda_{238}t_2} - 1)$$
$$\beta_2 = \beta_0 + \nu_0[1 - e^{-(\tau-t_2)\lambda_{235}}] + \nu_2(e^{\lambda_{235}t_2} - 1)$$

(1.3.7)

We can also write one equation for the ratio μ/ν as a function of μ_0/ν_0:

$$\frac{\mu}{\nu} = \frac{\mu_0 \exp(-\lambda_{238}\tau)}{\nu_0 \exp(-\lambda_{235}\tau)}$$

(1.3.8)

There are thus five equations for the five unknowns α_0, β_0, μ_0, ν_0, and τ. However, they can be satisfied for any τ greater than both t_1 and t_2, which emphasizes that the effective definition we must adopt for "age of the earth" is chemical separation from other material in the solar system. To apply the aforedescribed procedure, then, one of the rocks must be of extraterrestrial origin: that is, a meteorite. Applying the procedure with rock 1 being the average of many terrestrial rocks and rock 2 being averages of different categories of meteorites has obtained 4.55 Æ for the time τ since the earth and the meteorites had the same isotope ratios. This time is also close to the time t since crystallization for many meteorites obtained by Rb^{87}-Sr^{87} and Pb^{207}/Pb^{206} dating, or the time since gas retention by K^{40}-Ar^{40} dating [425].

1.4   Geology: The Earth's Surface Structure

In this section we take up the principal surface features of the earth as well as some geological terminology and some of the geological deductions as to the behavior of the earth. It is impossible, of course, to summarize such a vast and diverse subject as geology in a brief section. Hence we shall attempt to emphasize only those features that pertain most strongly to the earth's structure on a global scale and its evolution over the aeons.

Structural Geology

Before discussing the geologic activity of the earth's crust we should define some of the terms and discuss the ideas of the subject of *structural geology*; in particular, the division thereof called *geotectonics*. Structural geology is primarily concerned with analyzing the deformation of sedimentary strata; the interdependence of stratigraphical and structural knowledge is greatly emphasized. On a global scale we are not particularly concerned about explaining the record that appears in the sedimentary strata; they have been the most important tool, however, for deducing geological history and, because of the systematic layering of sedimentation, they have furnished some of the most effective clues as to geological processes. Structural geology also has a considerable interaction with petrology in that the physical conditions that determine what sort of folding, upthrust, and other such activity which can take place will also be related to certain temperatures and pressures and will be reflected in the chemical composition and in the fabric of the rocks, as discussed in Section 1.1.

Structural geology is concerned with two main categories of response of strata to forces. These are *faulting* and *folding*. Faulting is the actual breaking of strata and the motion of the rocks on one side of the break with respect to those on the other. Folding is the bending of strata. Since rocks may have varying degrees of plasticity as a consequence of temperature and pressure, there is no sharp line between faulting and folding. Faulting and folding occur as a consequence of the igneous activities—volcanism, upthrusting, etc.—on the one hand, and of the erosion and sedimentation on the other. The various ways in which these four phenomena interact and arrange themselves determine different types of characteristic geological structures: the relative orientation of certain features and their scale.

There are three generally recognized types of faults which differ only in the varying orientation of the three principal stresses in relation to the earth's surface. They are normal (or tension) faults; thrust (or reverse) faults; and transcurrent (or wrench or strike slip) faults. Each of these faults is defined and depicted in Figure 1.20.

The type of fault most commonly found is a *thrust fault,* which is the breaking of strata by horizontal stress, causing the layer on one side to override the layer on the other side of the fault. The *normal faults* are the simplest; they are believed to be due to the tension in the earth's crust where the pulling apart in the crust causes a section to drop. Usually the normal faults tend to be much longer than wide. The simplest type of normal fault is called a *graben* (the German word for trench). Examples are the upper Rhine Valley and the rift zone of East Africa. A large graben is sometimes called a *rift.*

Transcurrent, or *wrench,* faults are more complicated usually, since there is compressive stress involved which results in a good deal of cracking and shearing of rock. An example is the Great Glen of Scotland where the zone of cracking and shearing is $1\frac{1}{2}$ km wide. Also the horizontal displacement on the wrench fault can be considerable: on the Great Glen of Scotland it is a hundred kilometers, and on the Mendocino fault, which has been detected in the Pacific to the west of California, it is several hundred kilometers long. Probably the best known example of an active wrench fault is the San Andreas fault which starts just north of San Francisco and runs through San Francisco and down through California, turning inland just before it reaches Los Angeles.

Unless it continues completely around the world, an ideal transcurrent fault which leaves the surface material unchanged is impossible. For real transcurrent faults of limited length to exist, material evidently must be added to the surface at one end and taken away at the other. A transcurrent fault

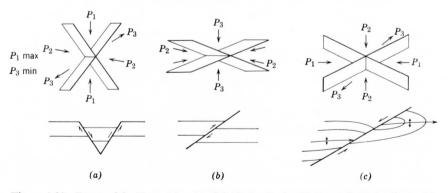

Figure 1.20: Types of faulting: (*a*) normal fault (section); (*b*) thrust fault (section); (*c*) transcurrent fault (plan). From De Sitter [92, p. 95].

along which motion takes place without lengthening the fault—that is, the locations at which material is being added or taken away from the surface remain fixed—has been given the name *transform* fault.

The folds, like faults, are generally much longer in one dimension than in the other; the long axis, called the *strike*, being normally at right angles to the direction of thrust. A fold that is concave upward is called a *syncline*; convex, an *anticline*. Normally folding is quite complex, a typical folded mountain range being an irregular series of overlappings which are planed off, and hence obscured, by the process of erosion removing the tops of the anticlines. Sedimentation also plays a role in compounding the complexity of folding in that the synclines form a natural resting place for sediments. A syncline which has been enlarged and compounded by extensive deposited sediments is called a *geosyncline*.

Igneous features associated with folding and faulting are: the *sill*, a thin horizontal intrusion; the *dike*, a thin vertical intrusion; and the *batholith*, a dome-shaped intrusion. Attempts to classify folding generally are associated with their apparent cause, for example: (1) folding in back of or in front of strata in response to a vertical block movement in the crust; or (2) a quasi-plastic flow possibly accompanied by some metamorphism in response to the intrusion of a magmatic sill or dike; or (3) some type of crumpling as a result of the influence of gravitational forces [27, 92].

Major Geological Features

The major geological features of the earth are shown in Figure 1.21. The oldest geologic features on the earth are the continental shields, shown by the horizontal cross-hatching on the map. The ages of the shields are all more than 0.6 Æ, many of them more than 2.0 Æ in parts, as discussed in Section 1.3. The shields are characterized by rather basic rocks, the diorites and the gabbros in Table 1.2, considerably folded in the remote past but quiescent since the Precambrian. Moving outward from the continental shields toward the oceans, the rocks are successively younger and more acidic. Most of the blank areas are covered by sediments and show no sign of recent geological activity. Nearer to the margins of the continents are areas that are definitely mountainous and characterized by intensive up-thrusting and folding; these are shown by the diagonal cross-hatching on the diagram. The older of these areas, such as the Appalachian area, have ages of about 0.25 Æ. The younger of these areas, such as the Alps, Himalayas, Rockies, and Andes, have ages of only about 70 million years.

If we consider the margin of the continent as the location of rapid decrease in elevation, rather than the water line, then there is an appreciable shallow-water continental margin. On the quiescent margins of continents other than Africa, this shelf is most extensive, in some places having wide marginal seas

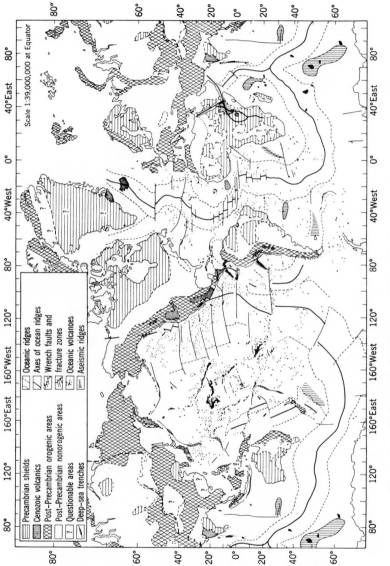

Figure 1.21: Major geological features of the earth. From Lee & Uyeda [240, p. 146].

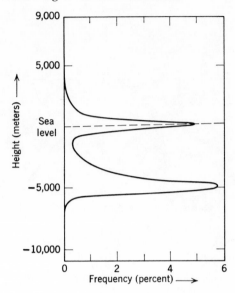

Figure 1.22: Frequency of levels on the earth's surface. From Wilson [442, p. 142].

such as the Gulf of Mexico or the Yellow Sea. On the active margins characterized by more recent activity the shelf is much narrower and it is often
associated with deep trenches, the deepest parts of the ocean.

The ocean proper is characterized by two main regions: (1) the ocean
basins which have broad plains called the *abyssal plains* and occasional rises
such as those associated with the island of Bermuda; and (2) the ocean
ridges, or *rises*, which are complex structures several hundred kilometers
across and running several thousand or even tens of thousands of kilometers
in length, characterized by very uneven topography, high heat flow, and
geological youthfulness. In fact, the entire ocean is geologically young. The
rocks are youngest at the ridges. Moving away from the ridges toward the
continents, the geological age becomes older, but at no place in the entire
oceans of the earth have there been found any rocks which are as old as two
hundred million years. The apparent steady spreading of the ocean floor
away from the ridges has been most strongly evidenced in magnetic anomaly
patterns, described in Section 3.3 [27, 92, 170, 275, 419, 557].

The distinct division of the earth's surface into two main parts—the
continents, including their submerged shelves, and the ocean basins—is
emphasized by the histogram of elevations in Figure 1.22.

Geologic Processes of the Continents

The most evident geological process on the surface of the continents is
that of the *erosion* and *sedimentation*. It is estimated that currently about

3 cm/1000 yr are eroded from the surface of the United States. If this rate of erosion had continued throughout the geological time since the Precambrian, it would have resulted in about fifteen times as much sediments as are believed to exist, unless there has been a great deal of recycling. In more recent time the activity has not been much less: the thickness of sediments found in the last 150 million years is about 1.2 cm/1000 yr.

The other evident current crustal activities are *earthquakes* and *volcanism*, both of which are associated with two principal belts of activity. First, the circum-Pacific belt extends all the way from Antarctica and through the southern end of the Andes, the Rockies, around the northern end of the Pacific, and down through Japan and the East Indies, terminating in the vicinity of New Zealand. The other belt connects with the circum-Pacific belt in southeast Asia and extends across the north of India through Iran and on across the Mediterranean, terminating in the vicinity of Spain. The relative motions associated with earthquakes average at the most a few centimeters per year. At some places this is an accumulation of creep in small jerks, such as along certain sections of the San Andreas fault. In other places there may be abrupt changes of a couple of meters locally, as has occurred in recent years in Chile and Alaska. The geological evidences are that in the last 60×10^6 years there have occurred horizontal displacements as great as 500 km on land and 1400 km at sea.

The general process of crustal deformation—folding, faulting, etc.—is called *orogenesis*. Orogenesis apparently occurs episodically. The normal state of the earth's crust is believed to be quiescent. However, at certain periods and over certain limited areas, as at the present, there is an intensification of orogenic activity for the duration of tens of millions of years. Those that have been identified in the geologic record are described as: (1) the *Alpine*, which had about eleven phases peaking 70 million years ago, located in the same areas, the Alps and the circum-Pacific belt, as the current activity; (2) the *Hercynian*, which peaked about 250 million years ago around the margin of the present continents in Asia Minor, the Baltic area, Brazil, eastern Australia, and along some of the margins of the Canadian shield and, most familiar to Americans, the Appalachian area; (3) the *Caledonian*, which was about 350 million years ago, also around Asia Minor, Canada, and Australia; (4) the *Huronian*, which was 550 million years ago, in Canada. These periods are associated also with the maxima in the geochronological dating. That dating also indicates of course that there were periods of activity alternating with quiescence extending back 2.7 Æ, almost as far as rocks have been dated. The earlier periods of activity are not well described, however, because of the lesser sediments existing at that time, the lack of fossils to date different strata, and the great amount of erosion and overlying of sediments which has taken place since these earlier periods.

The rocks associated with orogeny have become progressively more acidic, as if the chemical separations that are associated with the differentiation of rocks progressed as a consequence of continued working and reworking of much of the same material. In the most recent activity, such as that of the California mountain ranges, the very acidic granites predominate.

A feature that tends to be a forerunner of much mountain-building activity is the geosyncline, an accumulation of sediments which have been severely folded. The thickness of the sediments in many geosynclines indicates that sinking is much more rapid than that solely caused by the sedimentation. Obviously, if only the weight of the sediment caused the crust to sink, then the sediments, being less dense than the underlying rocks, would soon fill up the basin. Consequently, there would be no more loading to cause further sinking. The geologic evidence also corroborates the fact of conservation of matter in that the sinking of an area of the crust associated with a geosyncline also is associated in an adjacent area with a rise that results in mountain building. The two have a common cause, but more complex than a direct cause-and-effect relationship on each other.

As a geosyncline progresses it often has associated with it the formation of magma and the resulting igneous intrusions—batholiths, etc.—causing a complication of folding. Again we have a problem here in that it is not clear how the heat is created and concentrated to generate the magma: whether it is a consequence of mechanical factors, or the concentration of the radioactive materials in the granites associated with magma processes, or the insulating effect of the layers of the sediments of poor thermal conductivity. Often a geosynclinal basin is associated with two mountain ranges, one on each side, and in many places mountain ranges tend to be in pairs, two curving arcs of mountain ranges running parallel for several hundred kilometers; for example, California, with the Sierra Nevada and the coastal range and the intervening central valley. Often associated with the latest states of orogenic activity is the extrusion of lava in large beds on the land such as in the northwest United States and in the southwestern part of India.

Two other types of areas we mention briefly are: (1) *basins*, areas that have sunk and become filled with sediments without undergoing any complex folding or faulting, such as the Los Angeles basin, the Michigan basin, or the Paris basin; and (2) *blocks*, relatively stable regions that have been uplifted, such as the Colorado plateau, which formerly was low lying under 14,000 feet of sediments, and which in recent times has been uplifted directly without any great folding or faulting [27, 92, 112, 157].

The Oceans

The geology of the oceans is distinct from that of the continents, as might be expected from the much thinner crust. Until recently they were regarded as being more quiescent. It is still true that earthquake activities generally are associated with the continents or their margins. The oceans themselves, however, must have considerable extrusive activity, since the entire ocean floor is practically new. In addition, pronounced fractures have been detected by patterns in magnetic anomalies.

The oceanic ridges, or rises, have been the object of the most intensive research in recent years. An oceanic ridge is characterized by a rise above the general level of the ocean floor of about 2000 meters; a width of 1000 km or more; earthquakes concentrated within 100 km of the center; little or no sediments on the crest; a high heat flow; and a rate of outward spreading of 1 to 9 cm/yr from the center indicated by the pattern of magnetic anomalies (see Section 3.3). Oceanic ridges that have a low rate of spreading (less than 2 cm/yr) have sharp relief and a well-defined median valley, as shown in Figure 1.23. Oceanic ridges that have a high rate of spreading (such as the East Pacific Rise) are wider and smoother, and lack the median valley. In some ridges the rate of spread varies from one part to another, implying a rotation [419].

Virtually all ridges are segmented by transform faults, sometimes hundreds of kilometers long. Along these faults are earthquakes whose motions are strike-slip along the fault, consistent in a sense with spreading from the ridges. The earthquakes along the ridges themselves have normal faulting, with axes of maximum tension perpendicular to the strike of the ridge [384].

In a couple of places the ridge system runs into the land. In the northwest Indian Ocean, the ridge system splits at the Gulf of Aden, one branch merging with the rift valleys of East Africa and the other with the Red Sea. It has been suggested that the Red Sea is an incipient mid-oceanic ridge. In the East Pacific, the East Pacific Rise runs up the Gulf of California and intersects the San Andreas fault. The San Andreas fault also appears to intersect the Juan de Fuca Ridge off Washington and British Columbia, and thus may be a transform fault connecting the two ridges [443, 444].

The pattern of magnetic lineaments in some places has been traced a distance equivalent to 2×10^9 yr, or some thousands of kilometers. The notion of sea-floor spreading thus leads to the older idea of continental drift, which also has been indicated by paleomagnetic measurements on land. However, the interaction between ocean and continent is a considerably more

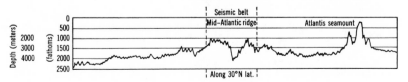

Figure 1.23: Cross section of Mid-Atlantic Ridge along 30°N latitude. Based on Heezen [170, p. 262].

complex matter, both in the sense of the ocean floor pushing into the continent, as will be discussed, and in the sense of a continent being pushed over another ocean—as appears to be the case in western North America [157].

Current spreading of the sea floor has recently been inferred from the direction of motion of earthquakes around most of the oceans. For example, earthquakes up the east side of the Pacific from Mexico to Alaska, across the Aleutians, and down the west side by Japan to the Tonga trench indicate that the entire Pacific floor is moving as one great plate northwesterly from the East Pacific Rise [569, 573, 574].

Difficulties of the sea-floor-spreading hypothesis are: (1) some irregularities in the magnetic anomalies along the ridge and, in places, diminution in intensity of the anomalies (see Section 3.3); and (2) a uniform steady floor of about upper Cretaceous (100–60×10^6 yr ago) age throughout the Atlantic Ocean, overlaid by relatively smooth sediments of 300–500 meters thickness except in the immediate vicinity of the ridge [116, 117].

Over most of the oceans, the rocks are quite basic, being predominantly olivine basalt. For example, in the Pacific, all islands other than coral islands consist of volcanic rocks. Volcanic rocks are not closely associated with the fractional lines of shear zones of the mid-ocean ridges except in the Atlantic.

Islands also form in arcs along the edge of the continental shelf or parallel to it on the border between predominantly SiAl acidic and SiMa basic crusts. Island arcs are normally convex toward the ocean with deep ocean trenches on the convex side and a zone of volcanism on the inner side. The seismic

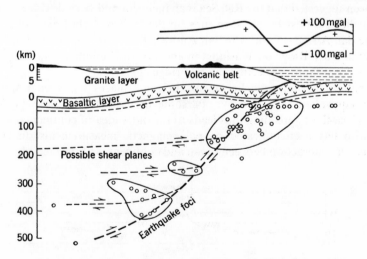

Figure 1.24: Island-arc cross section. From De Sitter [92, p. 371].

activity associated with an island arc is considerable, the foci of the earth-quakes being progressively deeper from the island toward the continent (see Figure 1.24). Island arcs are unique in having deep-focus earthquakes: that is, earthquakes with sources more than 300 km deep. The evident suggestion is that the island arcs are the location of a downbuckling of the sea-floor spread into the mantle, complementary to the upswelling under the ridges [92, 94, 383].

Summary

This section has been largely descriptive; we have attempted to emphasize the main features of the earth's surface in order to provide a context for the more physical measures we shall describe in the subsequent sections, as well as a statement of some of the problems the geophysical measurements might solve. For the moment we can summarize by emphasizing the three main areas of the continents: the shields, the plains, and the mountain-building margins; the transition zone of the continental shelf; and finally, in the oceans, the two dominant areas of the basins and the ocean ridges. In the matter of explanation, the most obvious source of energy is the cycle of erosion and sedimentation. It is also manifest that erosion and sedimentation are secondary phenomena; that there are associated with each other sinkings and upliftings from below the crust which are much more important, since they are necessary to enable the development of such features as geosynclines, mid-ocean ridges, and island arcs. Also not well understood because of the complex mechanics involved is the generation of horizontal forces which appear to be necessary to explain much of the folding on the continents and the sea-floor spreading of the oceans.

PROBLEMS

1.1. For each square centimeter of the earth's surface, there are 278 kg of sea water. The average sodium content of sea water is 1.07 percent; of igneous rocks, 2.83 percent; of sedimentary rocks, 1.00 percent. It is estimated that of the mass of igneous rock weathered away, 97 percent is deposited as sediments. Assuming that all the salt in the sea came from the weathering of igneous rocks, how much igneous rock has been weathered away and how much sedimentary rock has been deposited in geological time?

1.2. In the phase diagram on page 58, to what principal series of minerals would you expect leucite to belong? How should the chemical formulae for leucite and forsterite be rewritten to emphasize that they are combinations of metallic oxides? What would be the approximate percent content and crystallizing temperature of a mixture at point X? What would be the first mineral to crystallize? What would be

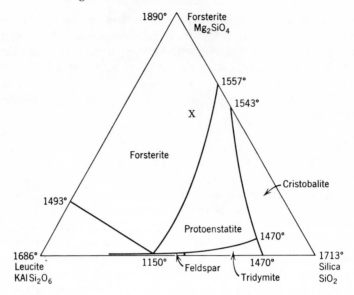

the second mineral to crystallize, and at what temperature? Describe the remaining course as the system cools.

1.3. Would you expect potash ($KAlSi_3O_8$) or soda ($NaAlSi_3O_8$) to have the higher melting temperature? Why?

1.4. For the shock propagation problem described by Figure 1.11, write equations expressing conservation of matter, energy, and momentum in terms of the variables U, D, V_0, V, and P. (Which velocity should be used in writing the kinetic energy? Across which interface should conservation of momentum be considered?) Derive equations (1.2.1) and (1.2.2).

1.5. Given the melting temperatures of iron in Figure 1.13, the densities of iron in Figure 1.16, and the zero-pressure compressibility $(1/V_0)(dV/dP)$ of iron as 5.94×10^{-13} cm²/dyne, calculate the melting temperature T_m at a pressure of 3.2 Mb under the assumption that it is linearly dependent on the specific volume.

1.6. Given the following changes in specific volume ΔV, heat of transition Δq, and equilibrium pressures P at 298°K, predict (assuming constant dT/dP) the temperature for the same phase transitions at 100 kb pressure:

	ΔV (cm³/mole)	Δq (cal/mole)	P (kb)
Quartz $\rightarrow$ stishovite	-8.7	-1100.0	73.0
Enstatite $\rightarrow$ forsterite + stishovite	-2.65	-506.0	97.5

1.7. The shearing strength of rocks is about 10^9 dynes/cm² at low temperatures. If the behavior under stress of a mountain 10 km in dimension is to be imitated in the laboratory by a model 20 cm in dimension, what should be the strength of the material of which the model is made? If it is believed that the rocks in the mountain were deformed at stresses approaching the shear strength at an effective viscosity of 10^{12} dynes-sec/cm^2 over 10^5 yr, what should be the viscosity of the model material in order to carry out the experiment within one day?

1.8. A mineral sample has a Pb^{206}/U^{238} ratio of 0.292 and a Pb^{207}/U^{235} ratio of 5.98. What is the lifetime of the sample deduced from each ratio? If there is evidence of a metamorphism 0.5 Æ ago, what is the lifetime of the sample deduced, assuming that the same proportion of each isotope was lost? What is this proportion? What further information is required to deduce whether the ratios were altered by continuous diffusion?

1.9. A rock sample contains 10 percent mineral A and 20 percent mineral B with rubidium and strontium ratios:

	Sr^{87}/Sr^{86}	Rb^{87}/Sr^{86}
10% A	0.795	5.0
20% B	0.765	2.0

Assuming a metamorphism has occurred with complete mixing but no loss of the Sr^{87}, what are the ages deduced for the original formation and the metamorphism of the rock?

1.10. Derive equation (1.3.3) for the age derived from the potassium-argon ratio K^{40}/A^{40}, taking into account the two decays $K^{40} \rightarrow A^{40}$ and $K^{40} \rightarrow Ca^{40}$ with decay constants λ_e and λ_β respectively.

REFERENCES

The most accessible textbooks on geochemistry are those by *Mason* [265] and *Krauskopf* [482]. The small volume by *Ahrens* [2] is also helpful. The classic on igneous petrology is *Bowen* [37]; the text by *Turner & Verhoogen* [402] has been used the most in this book. *Taylor* [393] discusses the role of ionic radii and other effects in determining trace-element abundances. The calculation of the geochemical balance was done by *Horn & Adams* [479]. Useful handbooks are those by *Deer et al.* [90] on minerals and by *Clark* [74] on experimental data pertaining in general to geology. *Clark & Ringwood* [75] and *Harris et al.* [542] discuss upper-mantle composition, to which the volume edited by *Wyllie* [586] also pertains.

The early work in high-pressure experiments was done largely by *Bridgman* [44]. A useful summary of static-pressure experiments as applied to the earth is by *Boyd* [38]. Dynamic techniques and results are reviewed by *Al'tshuler* [10]; see also *Deal* [89]. An important recent paper on shock measurements of silicates is by *McQueen et al.* [489]. Symposia volumes on high pressure are *Bradley* [39], *Paul & Warschauer* [309], and *Griggs & Handin* [151]. The foundations of the theory of solid behavior at high pressures and temperatures are thermodynamics (e.g., *Reif* [331] or *Pippard* [317]) and solid-state physics (e.g., *Kittel* [213] or *Ziman* [453]). The extension of thermodynamic theory to nonisotropic conditions is done by

Kamb [203] and *McLellan* [271]. A useful text on diffusion is that by *Girifalco* [135]. The olivine-spinel phase equilibria discussed are described in *Ringwood & Seabrook* [341]. More recent work on phase transitions of silicates is reported by *Akimoto & Fujisawa* [457], *Ringwood & Green* [494], and *Ringwood & Major* [495, 496]. Calculations applicable to phase transitions in the mantle are by *Ahrens & Syono* [456], *Anderson* [458], and *O'Connell & Wasserburg* [576]. The Mies-Grüneisen equation of state and related matters are developed in *Rice et al.* [333], *Knopoff* [214], *Alder* [3], and *Takeuchi & Kanamori* [386]. References on melting are *Kraut & Kennedy* [222], *Gilvarry* [134], *Ito & Kennedy* [189], and *Finney & Bernal* [119]. Scaled experiments are reviewed by *Belousov & Gzovsky* [28].

The section on geochronology is based mainly on the review by *Tilton & Hart* [398]. The most detailed recent textbook on the subject is by *Hamilton* [156]. The geologic time scale is from *Kulp* [233]. Other geochronological references are *Kulp* [234], *Wetherill et al.* [434], *Faul* [464], *Wasserburg* [425], and *Goldich et al.* [470]. The age matches across the South Atlantic are by *Hurley et al.* [561].

Texts on structural geology are *Hills* [476], *De Sitter* [92], and *Belousov* [27]. The geological evolution of North America is reviewed by *Engel* [112] and *Hamilton & Meyers* [157]; see also *Taylor* [505] on continental growth. Papers pertaining to the geologic evolution of the oceans are *Vine* [419], *Wilson* [443, 444], *Dietz* [94], *Heezen* [170], *Hess* [173], *Sykes* [383, 384], *Ewing et al.* [116, 117], *Talwani et al.* [387, 388], *Ewing & Ewing* [463], *Le Pichon* [569], *McKenzie & Parker* [573], and *Morgan* [574]. The subject is also discussed in the book by *Menard* [275] and in the symposia volumes edited by *Runcorn* [349] and *Blackett et al.* [35].

Chapter 2

MECHANICAL AND THERMAL ASPECTS OF A PLANETARY INTERIOR

To determine the state of the earth deeper than geological evidence can show and hence to arrive at a more fundamental understanding of the evolution and condition of the earth, we must resort to indirect measurements of the various force fields and energy flows such as the gravity field, the elastic waves set up by disturbances in the solid earth, the flow of heat, and the magnetic field. Also to understand some of the surface evidences we need to understand the fields that cause certain surface effects.

2.1 Gravity and the Figure of a Planet

The simplest of these fields is gravity: the combination of the gravitational attraction that arises from the mass distributed in the planet and the centrifugal acceleration that arises from its rotation. The acceleration of gravity can be determined absolutely by such methods as measuring the time it takes an object to fall a specified distance, or by measuring the period of swing of a pendulum. As with many types of measurements, however, it is much easier to measure very small variations of the total quantity than to measure the absolute value, and for the purposes of explaining geological or geophysical irregularities at the earth's surface we would expect that variations in the gravity field would be of most interest. These variations have been measured over quite extensive areas by pendulums and, in recent decades, by delicate spring balances that measure the change in gravity from place to place by the change in the pull on a constant mass as registered by the change in tension on a spring which is supporting that mass.

Spherical Harmonics

Before discussing the implications of these variations in the gravitational field as to the state of the earth's interior and its history, it is necessary to construct a model of a planet. Most planets are quite nearly spherical, which is the shape we would expect that a mass of fluid not rotating would take under the force of gravitational attraction; the parts of the fluid would try to get as close together as possible, which would be obtained by a spherical

61

form. The effect of rotation would be to cause the equator to bulge out, we would expect, from the effect of centrifugal acceleration. However, the earth's centrifugal force effect is still quite small compared to that of the central effect which tends to make the planet spherical. We would expect that the shape of the boundary involved, the sphere, would have considerable influence on the type of mathematical treatment that is most effective. The functions that are most convenient in the case of the earth are known as spherical harmonics. They apply to the mathematical treatment not only of gravity, but also of seismic waves, heat transfer, and the magnetic field on a global scale. Hence it is worthwhile to go into some detail as to the form and the manner of derivation of spherical harmonics. Scalar spherical harmonics are most conveniently derived as solutions to Newton's law. Newton's law gives the force of attraction between two point bodies of masses m, M: $F = G(mM/r^2)$, where G is the gravitational constant (6.67×10^{-8} cm^3 gm^{-1} sec^{-2}) and r is the intervening distance. The corresponding vector **a** for the acceleration of m with respect to M can be expressed as the gradient of a scalar V: $\mathbf{a} = \nabla V$, $V = GM/r$ where ∇ denotes the gradient. Then

$$\nabla \cdot \nabla V = \nabla^2 V = GM \sum_i \left(-\frac{1}{r^3} + \frac{3x_i^2}{r^5} \right) = 0 \qquad (2.1.1)$$

Equation (2.1.1) is known as the *Laplace equation*; it can be regarded as an alternate form of Newton's law. To derive the spherical harmonics, substitute

$$\left.\begin{array}{c} x \\ y \\ z \end{array}\right\} = r \left\{ \begin{array}{l} \cos \varphi \cos \lambda \\ \cos \varphi \sin \lambda \\ \sin \varphi \end{array} \right.$$

where r, $\dot{\varphi}$, λ are radius, latitude, and longitude respectively. Then

$$r^2 \nabla^2 V = \frac{\partial}{\partial r} \left(r^2 \frac{\partial V}{\partial r} \right) + \frac{1}{\cos \varphi} \frac{\partial}{\partial \varphi} \left(\cos \varphi \frac{\partial V}{\partial \varphi} \right) + \frac{1}{\cos^2 \varphi} \cdot \frac{\partial^2 V}{\partial \lambda^2} = 0 \quad (2.1.2)$$

It would be convenient if the potential V had the form

$$V = R(r)\Phi(\varphi)\Lambda(\lambda) \qquad (2.1.3)$$

The justification for the assumption of (2.1.3) is the post hoc one that it works.

Substitute (2.1.3) in (2.1.2) and divide by $R\Phi\Lambda$:

$$\frac{1}{R} \frac{d}{dr} \left(r^2 \frac{dR}{dr} \right) + \frac{1}{\Phi \cos \varphi} \frac{d}{d\varphi} \left(\cos \varphi \frac{d\Phi}{d\varphi} \right) + \frac{1}{\Lambda \cos^2 \varphi} \cdot \frac{d^2\Lambda}{d\lambda^2} = 0 \quad (2.1.4)$$

The variable r has been isolated in the first term. Hence this term must be a constant. Express this constant as $l(l + 1)$ (which is $\geq -\frac{1}{2}$; the reason for this limitation appears later):

$$r^2 \frac{d^2R}{dr^2} + 2r \frac{dR}{dr} - l(l + 1)R = 0 \tag{2.1.5}$$

R must be a power of r to satisfy (2.1.5):

$$R = r^k = Ar^l + Br^{-l-1} \tag{2.1.6}$$

where A and B are constants of integration. Substitute $l(l + 1)$ for the first term in (2.1.4) and multiply the equation by $\cos^2 \varphi$:

$$l(l + 1) \cos^2 \varphi + \frac{\cos \varphi}{\Phi} \frac{d}{d\varphi}\left(\cos \varphi \frac{d\Phi}{d\varphi}\right) + \frac{1}{\Lambda} \frac{d^2\Lambda}{d\lambda^2} = 0 \tag{2.1.7}$$

Now the λ term is isolated. Express its constant value as $-m^2$, so that

$$\Lambda = \begin{Bmatrix} \sin \\ \cos \end{Bmatrix} m\lambda \tag{2.1.8}$$

Substitute the $-m^2$ for the Λ term and multiply by $\Phi/\cos^2 \varphi$:

$$\frac{1}{\cos \varphi} \frac{d}{d\varphi}\left(\cos \varphi \frac{d\Phi}{d\varphi}\right) + \left\{ l(l + 1) - \frac{m^2}{\cos^2 \varphi} \right\} \Phi = 0 \tag{2.1.9}$$

Or, substituting μ for $\sin \varphi$,

$$\frac{d}{d\mu}\left\{(1 - \mu^2) \frac{d\Phi}{d\mu}\right\} + \left\{ l(l + 1) - \frac{m^2}{1 - \mu^2} \right\} \Phi = 0 \tag{2.1.10}$$

This equation must have originally taken some time to solve; the answer comes if we substitute $(1 - \mu^2)^{m/2} v(\mu)$ for Φ:

$$(1 - \mu^2) \frac{d^2v}{d\mu^2} - 2(m + 1)\mu \frac{dv}{d\mu} + (l - m)(l + m + 1)v = 0 \tag{2.1.11}$$

Then if we assume v to be a power series,

$$v = \sum_{k=0}^{\infty} a_k \mu^k \tag{2.1.12}$$

we get a recurrence relationship for the coefficients:

$$a_{k+2} = \frac{k(k + 2m + 1) - (l - m)(l + m + 1)}{(k + 1)(k + 2)} a_k \tag{2.1.13}$$

Setting the numerator equal to zero yields a maximum for k:

$$k_{\max} = l - m \tag{2.1.14}$$

So we can substitute $l - m - 2t$ for k, to get as the coefficient of $\sin^k \varphi$:

$$T_{lmt} = -\frac{(l - m - 2t + 1)(l - m - 2t + 2)}{2t(2l + 2t + 1)} T_{lm(t-1)}$$

$$= \frac{(-1)^l(2l - 2t)!}{2^l t!(l - t)!(l - m - 2t)!} \tag{2.1.15}$$

using the customary definition of T_{lm0}. And finally for Φ:

$$\Phi = P_{lm}(\sin \varphi) = \cos^m \varphi \sum_{t=0}^{[(l-m)/2]} T_{lmt} \sin^{l-m-2t} \varphi \tag{2.1.16}$$

where $[(l - m)/2]$ is the integer part of $(l - m)/2$, known as a *Legendre function*. The full spherical harmonic expression of a function $V(r, \varphi, \lambda)$ obeying Laplace's equation (2.1.1) or (2.1.2) is then a linear combination of solutions $R\Phi\Lambda$ from (2.1.6, 8, 16):

$$V = \frac{GM}{r} \sum_{l=0}^{\infty} \sum_{m=0}^{l} \left(\frac{R}{r}\right)^l P_{lm}(\sin \varphi)[C_{lm} \cos m\lambda + S_{lm} \sin m\lambda] \tag{2.1.17}$$

in which M is the total mass of the planet, C_{lm} and S_{lm} are constants of integration, and R is the radius of the planet, introduced so that C_{lm}, S_{lm} will be dimensionless. It is customary to take the origin of coordinates as the center of mass, in which case the terms for $l = 1$ disappear. Also using M as the multiplier makes C_{00} equal to 1 (see problem 2.1) [71, 206, 221, 260, 385].

The part of the spherical harmonic dependent on φ, λ, called a *surface spherical harmonic* $Y_{lm}(\varphi, \lambda)$, may be used to represent the variation of any function over a sphere, regardless of whether it is a solution of Laplace's equation. In this respect, spherical harmonics represent a variation on a sphere analogous to the representation of a variation in time by Fourier series. As can be deduced from equations (2.1.8) and (2.1.16), a spherical harmonic has $2m$ zeroes in the 360 degrees around a parallel of latitude, and $l - m$ zeroes in the 180 degrees along a meridian. So we can draw pictures of their variation over a sphere, as shown in Figure 2.1.

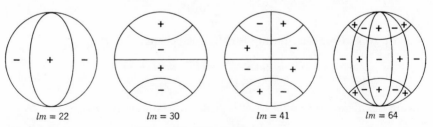

Figure 2.1: Spherical harmonics.

Problems of Planetary Gravity

To study the shape and external gravitational field of a slowly rotating planet ("slowly" meaning the centrifugal acceleration of rotation is small compared to the centripetal acceleration of gravitational attraction), there are three principal problems we wish to solve:

1. The external gravitational field corresponding to a given distribution of mass.

2. The shape of an equipotential surface, bounding all masses, corresponding to a given potential of gravity ("gravity" means gravitation plus rotation).

3. The shape of a rotating fluid of a given concentric density distribution.

From an observed gravitational field and rate of rotation, we can calculate the shape of the bounding equipotential from the solution of problem 2, but we are still left with a range of possible density distributions, according to the solution of problem 1. We therefore must introduce further assumptions pertaining to the density distribution. The simplest assumption is that the planet is a perfect fluid, which in turn requires that equipotential surfaces are surfaces of constant density. The shape of an equipotential still, however, will be affected by the radial density distribution. Hence a solution of problem 3 will furnish a model to compare to the shape obtained from a solution of 2 based on observations that will be a measure of the departure of the planet from a fluid state.

The solutions of these problems will be in spherical harmonics as much as possible to develop facility for their application to other problems.

External Gravitational Field Corresponding to a Given Distribution of Mass

The variations in density of a nearly spherical planet can be expressed by variations over a series of concentric spherical shells. At any point r, φ, λ inside the planet we can express the density ρ as

$$\rho = \rho_0(r) + \sum_{l,m,i} \rho_{lmi}(r) Y_{lmi}(\varphi, \lambda) \tag{2.1.18}$$

where $\rho_0(r)$ is the mean density for radius r, and $Y_{lmi}(\varphi, \lambda)$ is a surface spherical harmonic:

$$Y_{lm1} = P_{lm}(\sin \varphi) \cos m\lambda, \qquad Y_{lm2} = P_{lm}(\sin \varphi) \sin m\lambda$$

In a spherical shell of thickness dr the volume density ρ can be considered as replaced by a surface density σ:

$$\rho(r)\, dr = \sigma(r) = \sigma_0(r) + \sum_{l,m,i} \sigma_{lmi}(r) Y_{lmi}$$

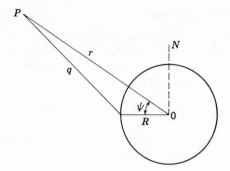

Figure 2.2

If the potential is desired at point P, of coordinates r, φ, λ, the contribution due to the surface density σ will be:

$$T = G \int_{\text{sphere}} \frac{\sigma}{q} dS \qquad (2.1.19)$$

where q is the distance from a point on the sphere to P, and dS is an element of surface area on the sphere. Let the angular coordinates be expressed as distance ψ and azimuth α from the axis OP, as shown in Figure 2.2. Then in (2.1.19) we can make the replacements

$$dS = R^2 \sin \psi \, d\psi \, d\alpha \qquad (2.1.20)$$

$$\sigma = \sum_{l,m,i} \sigma_{lmi} Y_{lmi}(\psi, \alpha) \qquad (2.1.21)$$

where Y_{lmi} are surface spherical harmonics, and

$$\frac{1}{q} = [r^2 + R^2 - 2rR \cos \psi]^{-1/2} = \frac{1}{r} \sum_{n=0}^{\infty} P_n(\cos \psi) \left(\frac{R}{r}\right)^n \qquad (2.1.22)$$

where $P_n(\cos \psi)$ is the Legendre polynomial, $P_{n0}(\cos \psi)$ (see problem 2.2). Then

$$T = \frac{G}{r} R^2 \int_{\text{sphere}} \left[\sum_{l,m} \sigma_{lm} Y_{lm}(\psi, \alpha) \right] \left[\sum_n P_n(\cos \psi) \left(\frac{R}{r}\right)^n \right] \sin \psi \, d\psi \, d\alpha$$

$$= \frac{G}{r} R^2 2\pi \sum_l \frac{2}{2l + 1} \left(\frac{R}{r}\right)^l \sigma_{l0} \qquad (2.1.23)$$

using the orthogonality of the zonal harmonics to other harmonics and the formula for $\int_{-1}^{1} [P_l(x)]^2 \, dx$ (see problem 2.3). Then apply the addition theorem (problem 2.4) to both surface density and potential:

$$P_{l0}(\cos \psi) = P_{l0}(\sin \varphi_T)P_{l0}(\sin \varphi_\sigma)$$

$$+ 2 \sum_m \frac{(l - m)!}{(l + m)!} P_{lm}(\sin \varphi_T)P_{lm}(\sin \varphi_\sigma)$$

$$\times [\cos m\lambda_T \cos m\lambda_\sigma + \sin m\lambda_T \sin m\lambda_\sigma] \quad (2.1.24)$$

where the subscript T denotes the location of potential T and the subscript σ denotes the location of surface density σ. We get:

$$T(r, \varphi, \lambda) = 4\pi GR \sum_{l,m,i} \left(\frac{R}{r}\right)^{l+1} \frac{\sigma_{lmi}}{2l + 1} Y_{lmi}(\varphi, \lambda), \qquad r > R \quad (2.1.25)$$

Replacing (2.1.22) by an expansion for $1/q$ appropriate to $r < R$, we get for a point inside the sphere R:

$$T(r, \varphi, \lambda) = 4\pi GR \sum_{l,m,i} \left(\frac{r}{R}\right)^{l} \frac{\sigma_{lmi}}{2l + 1} Y_{lmi}(\varphi, \lambda), \qquad r < R \quad (2.1.26)$$

Thus for the total gravitational potential external to the body we have, replacing σ by $\rho \, dR$,

$$V = G \int_0^a \frac{\rho(R)}{q} 4\pi R^2 \, dR$$

$$= \frac{GM}{r} + \frac{4\pi G}{r} \sum_{l,m,i} \frac{1}{(2l + 1)r^l} Y_{lmi}(\varphi, \lambda) \int_0^a R^{l+2}\rho_{lmi} \, dR \quad (2.1.27)$$

$$= \frac{GM}{r} \left[1 + \sum_{l,m} \left(\frac{a}{r}\right)^{l} P_{lm}(\varphi, \lambda)\{C_{lm} \cos m\lambda + S_{lm} \sin m\lambda\}\right] \quad (2.1.28)$$

$$\left.\begin{matrix} C_{lm} \\ S_{lm} \end{matrix}\right\} = \frac{4\pi}{Ma^l(2l + 1)} \int_0^a R^{l+2}\rho_{lmi} \, dR \quad (2.1.29)$$

where M is the mass and a is the radius of the planet.

If the center of mass of the planet is taken as the origin of the coordinates, then the $l = 1$ terms in (2.1.27) and (2.1.28) drop out.

The $l = 2$ terms are of interest in relation to the moments of inertia, which are important in connection with the response of the planet to torques. Taking x, y-axes in the equatorial plane and the z-axis as the rotation axis, define

$$A = \frac{1}{2} \left[\int_{\text{vol}} \rho(x^2 + z^2) \, d\tau + \int_{\text{vol}} \rho(y^2 + z^2) \, d\tau\right]$$

$$= \int_{\text{vol}} \rho r^2 [\tfrac{1}{2} \cos^2 \varphi + \sin^2 \varphi] r^2 \cos \varphi \, d\varphi \, d\lambda \, dr \quad (2.1.30)$$

$$C = \int_{\text{vol}} \rho(x^2 + y^2) \, d\tau = \int_{\text{vol}} \rho r^2 \cos^2 \varphi r^2 \cos \varphi \, d\varphi \, d\lambda \, dr$$

Substitute the expression for ρ from equation (2.1.18), $1 - \sin^2 \varphi$ for $\cos^2 \varphi$, and $(\frac{2}{3}P_{20} + \frac{1}{3})$ for $\sin^2 \varphi$, and get

$$A = \int_0^a \left[\frac{8\pi}{3} \rho_0(r) + \frac{4\pi}{15} \rho_{20} \right] r^4 \, dr$$

$$C = \int_0^a \left[\frac{8\pi}{3} \rho_0(r) - \frac{8\pi}{15} \rho_{20} \right] r^4 \, dr$$

$$(2.1.31)$$

Comparing (2.1.29) and (2.1.31),

$$C_{20} = \frac{A - C}{Ma^2} = -J_2 \qquad (2.1.32)$$

a more conventional notation [199].

Shape of the Equipotential Corresponding to a Given Potential

The centrifugal acceleration being $\omega^2 s$ for a rate of rotation ω at distance s from the axis (see Figure 2.3), the acceleration due to rotation can be expressed as the gradient of a potential:

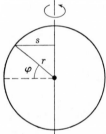

$$U_{\text{rot}} = \tfrac{1}{2}\omega^2 s^2 = \tfrac{1}{2}r^2\omega^2 \cos^2 \varphi = \tfrac{1}{3}\omega^2 r^2 [1 - P_{20}(\sin \varphi)]$$

$$(2.1.33)$$

Hence we can express the shape of the bounding equipotential for a planet with only radial variation of density as:

Figure 2.3

$$r = r_0 \left(1 - \frac{2fP_{20}}{3} \right) + O(f^2) \qquad (2.1.34)$$

In (2.1.34), r_0 is the mean radius and f is the *flattening:*

$$f = \frac{a - b}{a} \qquad (2.1.35)$$

where a is the equatorial radius, and b is the polar radius. Define the total potential U as

$$U = \frac{GM}{r} \left[1 - J_2 \left(\frac{a}{r} \right)^2 P_{20} + O(f^2) \right] + \frac{1}{3} \frac{g_e m}{a} r^2 (1 - P_{20}) \qquad (2.1.36)$$

where g_e is the mean acceleration of gravity at the equator and the dimensionless ratio m is:

$$m = \frac{\omega^2 a}{g_e} \qquad (2.1.37)$$

Substitute $r_0{}''[1 - (2n/3)fP_{20} + O(f^2)]$ for r^n in (2.1.36), and rewrite it separating the zero-order, P_{20}, and higher-order terms:

$$U = U_0 + U_2 + U_4$$

$$= \left[\frac{GM}{r_0} + \frac{1}{3}\frac{g_e m}{a} r_0{}^2\right] - \left[\frac{GM}{r_0}\left\{-\frac{2}{3}f + J_2\left(\frac{a}{r_0}\right)^2\right\} + \frac{g_e m}{3a} r_0{}^2\right]P_{20}$$

$$+ \frac{GM}{r_0} O(f^2) \tag{2.1.38}$$

If the surface is an equipotential, then U_2 must be zero, and hence the coefficient of P_{20} in (2.1.38) must be zero. This gives us one equation for f and r_0; the other equation comes from the requirement that g_e is the negative of the gradient of U at the equator:

$$\frac{GM}{r_0}\left[1 + J_2\left(\frac{a}{r_0}\right)^2\right] + \frac{g_e m}{3a} r_0{}^2 = 0 \tag{2.1.39}$$

$$\frac{GM}{a^2}[1 + \tfrac{3}{2}J_2 + O(f^2)] - g_e m = g_e \tag{2.1.40}$$

Whence

$$r_0 = a\left(1 - \frac{f}{3} - \frac{f^2}{5}\right)$$

$$J_2 = \tfrac{2}{3}f(1 - \tfrac{1}{2}f) - \tfrac{1}{3}m(1 - \tfrac{3}{2}m - \tfrac{2}{7}f) \tag{2.1.41}$$

$$GM = a^2 g_e[1 - f + \tfrac{3}{2}m - \tfrac{15}{14}mf]$$

For the earth, observations obtain that J_2 is 0.00108265, m is 1/288.37, and f is 1/298.25. Other terms C_{lm}, S_{lm} in the exterior potential (2.1.28) are of an order-of-magnitude 10^{-6}; hence to analyze observations the order f^2 terms in (2.1.41) are required. Then, for the variations C_{lm}, S_{lm} in the exterior potential a linear treatment suffices.

Let N denote the *geoid height*, the small displacement of the actual equipotential from the ellipsoid expressed by (2.1.41). Then for the potential:

$$U = \text{const} = V(r + N)$$

$$= V(r) + \frac{\partial V}{\partial r} N \approx V + \frac{\partial U}{\partial r} N$$

$$= V(r) - gN \tag{2.1.42}$$

$$gN = V - U$$

and

$$N = \frac{V - U}{g}$$

$$= \frac{T}{g} \tag{2.1.43}$$

For a reference figure of radius r_e, the measurable quantity is $g(r_e + N)$, but the calculable quantity with which to compare it is $\gamma(r_e)$, the negative of the derivative of U normal to the reference figure. Hence it has become convention to express the variations of the external gravitational field as the "gravity anomaly" Δg:

$$\Delta g = g(r_e + N) - \gamma(r_e),$$

$$= -\left[\frac{\partial V}{\partial n}\right]_{r=r_e+N} + \left[\frac{\partial U}{\partial n}\right]_{r=r_e}$$

$$= -\left[\frac{\partial T}{\partial n} + \left\{\frac{\partial U}{\partial n}\right\}_{r=r_e} + \frac{\partial^2 U}{\partial n^2}N\right] + \left[\frac{\partial U}{\partial n}\right]_{r=r_e}$$

$$= -\frac{\partial T}{\partial n} + \frac{\partial \gamma}{\partial r}N \tag{2.1.44}$$

where $\partial/\partial n$ denotes a normal derivative, negligibly different from $\partial/\partial r$ for a linear approximation. Substituting $-\partial U/\partial r$, or GM/r^2, for γ, we get $-2\gamma/r$ for $\partial\gamma/\partial r$, whence

$$\Delta g = -\frac{\partial T}{\partial n} - \frac{2\gamma}{r}N$$

$$= -\frac{\partial T}{\partial n} - \frac{2T}{r} \tag{2.1.45}$$

Hence if we have a harmonic expression of the disturbing potential T given by the coefficients C_{lm}, S_{lm} of equation (2.1.29), the corresponding coefficients A_{lm}, B_{lm} of the gravity anomaly Δg will be [171, 199]:

$$\left.\begin{matrix} A_{lm} \\ B_{lm} \end{matrix}\right\} = \gamma(l-1)\left\{\begin{matrix} C_{lm} \\ S_{lm} \end{matrix}\right. \tag{2.1.46}$$

Figure of Equilibrium of a Rotating Fluid

In the element of matter of mass $\rho\, dr\, da$, we have a radial force due to gravity $\rho\, dr\, da\, dV/dr$ balanced by the change in surface force $p\, da$ across the element, as shown in Figure 2.4.

$$p\, da - (p + dp)\, da = -\rho\, dr\, da\, \frac{dV}{dr}$$

Dividing through by the elemental volume $dr\, da$, we get:

$$\rho\frac{dV}{dr} - \frac{dp}{dr} = 0 \tag{2.1.47}$$

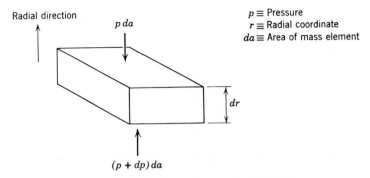

Figure 2.4: Element of matter inside a slowly rotating fluid mass.

Hence surfaces of constant potential V are surfaces of constant density; and if V has a variation due to rotation as in (2.1.33) then any internal surface of mean radius r_1 will have a variation in shape expressible by an equation like (2.1.34):

$$r = r_1[1 + \alpha_2(r_1)P_{20}] \tag{2.1.48}$$

Assuming ρ to vary radially, the potential $V(r_1)$ on the surface of mean radius r_1 will be a combination of: (1) the potential from matter inside the shell r_1; (2) the potential from matter outside the shell r_1; and (3) the rotational potential, from (2.1.33). The potential (1) can be considered as the integral of potentials dV' which are the differentials between successive potentials V_I' in turn the sum of the potential due to a uniform sphere of mass $4\pi\rho(a')a'^3/3$ and a layer of density $\alpha_2(a')\rho(a')P_{20}$; using (2.1.25):

$$V_I' = \tfrac{4}{3}\pi G\rho(a')\left[\frac{a'^3}{r} + \frac{3}{5}\frac{a'^5}{r^2}\alpha_2 P_{20}\right]$$

A similar formula applies for the potentials (2) due to shells external to r_1, using (2.1.26). Then for $V(r_1)$:

$$V = \tfrac{4}{3}\pi G\int_0^{r_1}\rho'\,\frac{\partial}{\partial a'}\left(\frac{a'^3}{r} + \frac{3}{5}\frac{a'^5}{r^3}\alpha_2 P_{20}\right)da'$$

$$+ \tfrac{4}{3}\pi G\int_{r_1}^{r_0}\rho'\,\frac{\partial}{\partial a'}\left(\tfrac{3}{2}a'^2 + \tfrac{3}{5}r^2\alpha_2 P_{20}\right)da' + \tfrac{1}{3}\omega^2 r_1^2(1 - P_{20}) \tag{2.1.49}$$

Let the mean density inside the shell r_1 be ρ_0:

$$\rho_0 = \frac{3}{r_1^3}\int_0^{r_1}\rho'a'^2\,da' \tag{2.1.50}$$

Replace $1/r$ in the first term of (2.1.49) by $(1 - \alpha_2 P_{20})/r_1$ and r^2 and $1/r^3$ by r_1^2 and $1/r_1^3$:

$$\tfrac{4}{3}\pi G \left\{ \frac{1 - \alpha_2 P_{20}}{r_1} \int_0^{r_1} 3\rho' a'^2 \, da' \right.$$

$$\left. + \tfrac{3}{5}P_{20} \left[\frac{1}{r_1^3} \int_0^{r_1} \rho' \, d(a'^5\alpha_2) + r_1^2 \int_{r_1}^a \rho' \, d\alpha_2 \right] \right\} + \tfrac{1}{3}\omega^2 r_1^2 (1 - P_{20})$$

$$= \text{function of } r_1 \quad (2.1.51)$$

The coefficient of P_{20} must vanish on a surface of constant potential:

$$-\frac{\alpha_2}{r_1} \int_0^{r_1} \rho' a'^2 \, da' + \frac{1}{5}\left[\frac{1}{r_1^3} \int_0^{r_1} \rho' \, d(a'^5\alpha_2) + r_1^2 \int_{r_1}^a \rho' \, d\alpha_2 \right] - \frac{3\omega^2 r_1'^2}{4\pi G} = 0$$

$$(2.1.52)$$

Multiply by r_1, differentiate, and drop the 1 subscript on r, since the distinction between r and r_1 is no longer important. Simplifying,

$$-\left(r^2 \frac{d\alpha_2}{dr} + 2r\alpha_2 \right) \int_0^r \rho' a'^2 \, da' + r^4 \int_r^a \rho' \frac{d\alpha_2}{da'} \, da' - \frac{15\omega^2 r^4}{16\pi G} = 0 \quad (2.1.53)$$

Divide by r^4, differentiate again, and use (2.1.50):

$$\rho_0 \left(\frac{d^2\alpha_2}{dr^2} - \frac{6\alpha_2}{r^2} \right) + \frac{6\rho}{r}\left(\frac{d\alpha_2}{dr} + \frac{\alpha_2}{r} \right) = 0 \quad (2.1.54)$$

called *Clairaut's equation*. One hundred and forty-two years after it was written a solution was found by making the substitution

$$\eta = \frac{d \log \alpha_2}{d \log r} = \frac{r}{\alpha_2} \frac{d\alpha_2}{dr} \quad (2.1.55)$$

Substituting in (2.1.54),

$$r \frac{d\eta}{dr} + \eta^2 - \eta - 6 + \frac{6\rho}{\rho_0}(\eta + 1) = 0 \quad (2.1.56)$$

From (2.1.50)

$$\rho r^2 = \frac{1}{3}\frac{d}{dr}(\rho_0 r^3), \qquad \frac{\rho}{\rho_0} = 1 + \frac{1}{3}\frac{r}{\rho_0}\frac{d\rho_0}{dr} \quad (2.1.57)$$

whence

$$r \frac{d\eta}{dr} + \eta^2 + 5\eta + 2 \frac{r}{\rho_0}\frac{d\rho_0}{dr}(1 + \eta) = 0 \quad (2.1.58)$$

To eliminate $d\eta/dr$, use:

$$\frac{d}{dr}(\rho_0 r^5 \sqrt{1 + \eta}) = \rho_0 r^5 \sqrt{1 + \eta} \left[\frac{1}{\rho_0}\frac{d\rho_0}{dr} + \frac{5}{r} + \frac{1}{2(1 + \eta)}\frac{d\eta}{dr} \right] \quad (2.1.59)$$

from which (2.1.58) becomes

$$\frac{d}{dr}(\rho_0 r^5 \sqrt{1+\eta}) = 5\rho_0 r^4 \psi(\eta) \tag{2.1.60}$$

where

$$\psi(\eta) = \frac{1 + \frac{1}{2}\eta - \frac{1}{10}\eta^2}{\sqrt{1+\eta}} \tag{2.1.61}$$

called *Radau's equation*.

The reason for all this manipulation is that for any reasonable variation of density, ψ varies less than 0.0008 from 1. Hence (2.1.60) can be integrated assuming ψ constant. From (2.1.31) at the surface to the first order, on integrating by parts

$$C = \frac{8\pi}{3} \int_0^a \rho(r) r^4 \, dr$$

$$= \frac{8\pi}{9} \int_0^a \left(3r^4 \rho_0 + r^5 \frac{d\rho_0}{dr}\right) dr$$

$$= \frac{8}{9}\pi \left[\rho_0(a)a^5 - 2\int_0^a \rho_0 r^4 \, dr \right] \tag{2.1.62}$$

From (2.1.60–62),

$$\sqrt{1+\eta(a)} = \frac{15}{4}\left(\frac{2}{3} - \frac{C}{Ma^2}\right) \tag{2.1.63}$$

From (2.1.53, 55), using (2.1.34, 36, 41, 50):

$$\eta(a) = \frac{a}{\alpha_2}\left(\frac{d\alpha_2}{dr}\right)_{r=a}$$

$$= -\frac{5\omega^2}{4\eta G \rho_0 \alpha_2} - 2$$

$$= \frac{5m}{2f} - 2 \tag{2.1.64}$$

Hence a fluid planet of mass M, moment of inertia C, radius a, and rotation ω, will have a shape expressed by the flattening [199]

$$f = \frac{5m}{2}\bigg/\left[1 + \left(\frac{5}{2} - \frac{15C}{4Ma^2}\right)^2\right] \tag{2.1.65}$$

As in the relationships (2.1.41), a full treatment requires $O(f^2)$ terms in (2.1.65).

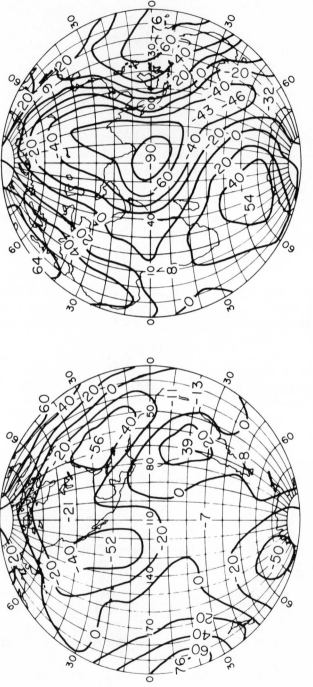

Figure 2.5: Geoid heights, in meters, referred to an ellipsoid of flattening 1/298.25. From Kaula [207, p. 5310].

Parameters of the Earth's Gravity Field

One quantity that cannot be obtained from measurements of gravity at the earth's surface is the earth's moment of inertia, as defined by (2.1.30), which is needed as a control on the radial variation of density. We can obtain the difference of moments $C - A$ from J_2, as given by (2.1.32). To obtain the moment itself, C or A, of a planet requires a measurement of its response to a torque. The only thing that can exert a great enough attraction to exercise a perceptible torque on a planet is another celestial body, as discussed in Section 4.3. The precession of the earth's axis due to the torques exercised by the moon and sun yields a measure of $(C - A)/C$ of 0.0032732. Using this value with the value of J_2 obtains:

$$C = 0.33076 M a^2 \tag{2.1.66}$$

Other important geodetic quantities are

$$a = 6378150 \text{ meters}$$
$$GM = 3.98601 \times 10^{14} \text{ m}^3/\text{sec}^{-2} \tag{2.1.67}$$

The order of magnitude of the irregularities Δg in the gravitational field defined by (2.1.45) is ± 0.035 cm/sec^2 (rms); hence the unit of acceleration commonly used in geodesy is the *milligal*, equal to 0.001 cm/sec^2. The order of magnitude of the geoid height variations N defined by (2.1.43) is ± 33 m (rms).

A representation of the variations in the earth's gravitational field in the form of geoid heights N is given in Figure 2.5. As is evident from the figure the correlation of the broad variations in the gravitational field with the topography is virtually zero. However, shorter wavelength variations, that which would be represented by harmonics of the fifth or higher degree in the potential expression (2.1.17) of Section 2.1, do have some positive correlation. The variations of the gravitational field also are smaller, by a factor of about four, than would exist if the topography were a rigidly supported surface layer on a homogeneous sphere. In other words, the phenomenon of *isostasy*—the compensation of the topographic excesses on the surface by deficiencies at depth and, conversely, deficiencies at the surface by excesses at depth—prevails. Statistical best fits of the depth of this compensation to the regional variations of gravity yield a most probable compensation depth around 35 km—that is, close to the bottom of the crust under the continents. However, for the long wavelength variations that predominate in Figure 2.5 there is a significant residual that indicates irregularities in density in the upper mantle. To discuss these irregularities meaningfully, we must take into account the mechanical properties of the mantle, which in turn depend on its thermal state—the subjects of Sections 2.2–4 [127, 171, 199, 207].

TABLE 2.1: NORMALIZED SPHERICAL HARMONIC
COEFFICIENTS OF THE EARTH'S GRAVITATIONAL
POTENTIAL

Degree l	Order m	$\bar{C}_{lm}$ 10^{-6}	$\bar{S}_{lm}$ 10^{-6}
2	0	−484.17	
2	2	2.42	−1.36
3	0	0.97	
3	1	1.79	0.18
3	2	0.78	−0.75
3	3	0.57	1.42
4	0	0.54	
4	1	−0.56	−0.46
4	2	0.30	0.60
4	3	0.92	−0.19
4	4	−0.06	0.32
5	0	0.04	
5	1	0.00	−0.02
5	2	0.44	−0.28
5	3	−0.31	0.03
5	4	0.02	0.11
5	5	0.10	−0.49
6	0	−0.18	
6	1	−0.10	0.10
6	2	−0.01	−0.28
6	3	0.09	0.04
6	4	−0.19	−0.43
6	5	−0.17	−0.60
6	6	−0.05	−0.26

From Kaula [207].

Table 2.1 is a listing of the leading spherical harmonic coefficients $\bar{C}_{lm}$, $\bar{S}_{lm}$ of the potential corresponding to Figure 2.5. These coefficients differ in magnitude from the C_{lm}, S_{lm} in (2.1.17) because they pertain to functions $\bar{Y}_{lmi}$ which have been *normalized:*

$$\int_{\text{unit sphere}} [\bar{Y}_{lmi}]^2 \, d\sigma = 4\pi \qquad (2.1.68)$$

Normalization is generally applied in data analysis so that significant differences in magnitude of coefficients are more readily perceived. The normalized coefficients of the earth's gravitational field up to about degree

$l = 15$ conform rather closely to the empirical law:

$$\frac{1}{2l+1} \sum_m (\bar{C}_{lm}{}^2 + \bar{S}_{lm}{}^2) \approx \frac{10^{-10}}{l^4} \tag{2.1.69}$$

2.2   Seismic Waves

Any solid with the cohesiveness demonstrated by the material of the earth responds *elastically* to variations in forces on the material that are small enough and of short enough duration. In other words, it suffers a deformation that is proportional to the force, which is the same as saying that if the force is small enough regardless of its nature, the effect of the resulting deformation can be truncated in the first term of a Taylor series. Furthermore, when the force is removed it resumes its original state, so that we can set up a law that the *strain* or measure of deformation is proportional to the *stress*, the force per unit area.

Within the earth, transient forces are exercised by earthquakes which may contain as much as 10^{25} or 10^{26} ergs energy. Such shocks can cause the propagation of forces through the earth sufficient to cause displacements on the order of tenths of a millimeter. These displacements can be measured and their character used to determine something of the properties of the earth through which the shock wave from the earthquake traveled. Hence the circumstance of earthquakes can be used to determine a great deal about the state of the interior of the earth. This indeed is the manner in which earthquakes have been principally used. We have a much better notion of certain properties of the interior of the earth as a whole as a consequence of earthquakes than we do of the mechanism of the earthquakes themselves, which are being used mainly as a source of energy to deform the earth sufficiently to measure its properties of response to these forces. Before discussing the seismic waves in the planet we should review the elements of the theory of elasticity starting with the stresses imposed on an elemental cube of matter.

Theory of Elasticity

The stresses against $(i = j)$ and along $(i \neq j)$ the faces of an elemental cube of dimensions $\delta x_1, \delta x_2, \delta x_3$ can be represented as in Figure 2.6. The stress on the opposing face to a component p_{ij} will be $p_{ij} + dp_{ij}$. Then the net force in the 1 direction on the cube will be:

$$F_1 = dp_{11}\, \delta x_2\, \delta x_3 + dp_{12}\, \delta x_1\, \delta x_3 + dp_{13}\, \delta x_1\, \delta x_2$$

$$F_i = \frac{\partial p_{ij}}{\partial x_j}\, \delta x_j\, \delta x_k\, \delta x_l; \qquad k = j(\mathrm{mod}\ 3) + 1, \quad l = k(\mathrm{mod}\ 3) + 1$$

summing over the repeated subscript.

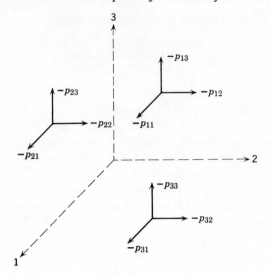

Figure 2.6: Forces on an elemental cube.

Per unit volume, this force will be:

$$F_i = \frac{\partial p_{ij}}{\partial x_j}$$

The equation $F = ma$ applies to the elemental cube; adding the body forces as in (2.1.2),

$$\rho \ddot{x}_i = \frac{\partial p_{ij}}{\partial x_j} + \rho \frac{\partial V}{\partial x_i} \qquad (2.2.1)$$

where ρ is density and V is the gravitational potential.

The strain is defined by:

$$du_i = \frac{\partial u_i}{\partial x_j} dx_j = (e_{ij} - \xi_{ij}) \, dx_j$$

where du_i is the deformation, a displacement from a reference state, and

$$e_{ij} = \frac{1}{2} \left(\frac{\partial u_j}{\partial x_i} + \frac{\partial u_i}{\partial x_j} \right) \qquad (2.2.2)$$

$$\xi_{ij} = \frac{1}{2} \left(\frac{\partial u_j}{\partial x_i} - \frac{\partial u_i}{\partial x_j} \right) \qquad (2.2.3)$$

The quantity ξ_{ij} is one-half the curl of u_i; it expresses purely rotation. Strain, constituting distortion of the material, is expressed entirely by e_{ij}.

The assumption of elasticity is that stress is proportionate to strain. If we assume the material to be isotropic in its properties, we can write:

$$p_{ii} = Ae_{ii} + B(e_{jj} + e_{kk}) + Ce_{jk} + D(e_{ki} + e_{ij})$$
$$p_{jk} = Ee_{ii} + F(e_{jj} + e_{kk}) + Ge_{jk} + H(e_{ki} + e_{ij})$$

$(2.2.4)$

If the coordinate axes are taken as the principal axes—axes of maximum and minimum strain—the off diagonal components $(i \neq j)$ of the stress matrix will be zero. Rotating 90 degrees in turn about each of the coordinate axes and considering the change in representation of the stresses yields:

$$C = D = F = H = 0, \qquad A - B = G$$

The two nonzero parameters remaining are conventionally defined as:

$$\lambda = B = k - \tfrac{2}{3}\mu \tag{2.2.5}$$

and

$$\mu = \tfrac{1}{2}(A - B) = \tfrac{1}{2}G \tag{2.2.6}$$

known as *Lamé's constants. k* is the *bulk modulus*, expressing resistance to compression, and μ is the *rigidity*, expressing resistance to shear. In the earth $\lambda \approx \mu$, hence

$$k \approx \tfrac{5}{3}\mu \tag{2.2.7}$$

The expression of the stress tensor p_{ij} becomes

$$p_{ij} = \lambda e_{kk}\delta_{ij} + 2\mu e_{ij} = \lambda\Delta\delta_{ij} + 2\mu e_{ij} \tag{2.2.8}$$

where δ_{ij} is the *Kronecker delta*:

$$\delta_{ij} = 0, \qquad i \neq j$$
$$\delta_{ii} = 1$$

and Δ is the *dilatation*, $\Sigma_j \, \partial u_j / \partial x_j$, and

$$e_{kk} = \sum_k e_{kk}$$

Then (2.2.1) becomes:

$$\rho\ddot{u}_i = (\lambda + \mu)\frac{\partial\Delta}{\partial x_i} + \mu\,\nabla^2 u_i + \rho\,\frac{\partial V}{\partial x_i} \tag{2.2.9}$$

The energy stored is force times displacement; for elastic deformation,

$$p_{ij}\,de_{ij} = dW$$

whence

$$p_{ij} = \frac{\partial W}{\partial e_{ij}} \tag{2.2.10}$$

Integrating,

$$2W = e_{ij}p_{ij}$$

$$= k\Delta^2 + 2\mu(e_{ij}^2 - \tfrac{1}{3}\Delta^2) \tag{2.2.11}$$

The mechanical propagation of energy through a solid planet has the form of waves in an elastic medium: that is, points in the body undergo a displacement from a reference state expressed by a vector $\mathbf{u}$, (u_1, u_2, u_3) in accordance with the equations of motion [58, 199, 385]:

$$\rho\ddot{u}_i = (\lambda + \mu)\frac{\partial\Delta}{\partial x_i} + \mu\,\nabla^2 u_i + \rho\frac{\partial V}{\partial x_i} \tag{2.2.12}$$

Body Waves

Neglecting the gravitational term $\partial V/\partial x_i$ in (2.2.12), we can obtain solutions to (2.2.12) without further specification of the problem. Taking the divergence (i.e., differentiating with respect to x_i and summing over i) we get:

$$\rho\ddot{\Delta} = (\lambda + 2\mu)\,\nabla^2\Delta \tag{2.2.13}$$

Taking the curl (i.e., the operation $\partial/\partial x_i - \partial/\partial x_j$) we get:

$$\rho\frac{d^2}{dt^2}\,\mathrm{curl}\,(u_i) = \mu\,\nabla^2\,\mathrm{curl}\,(u_i) \tag{2.2.14}$$

Equations (2.2.13) and (2.2.14) are both forms of the wave equation [260]

$$\ddot{y} = c^2\,\nabla^2 y \tag{2.2.15}$$

If it is assumed that the wave is propagating only in the x_1 direction (i.e., a wave front parallel to the x_2x_3 plane), a solution to (2.2.15) is:

$$y = f(x_1 + ct) + g(x_1 - ct) \tag{2.2.16}$$

that is, the wave moves with velocity c. The direction x_1 is arbitrary and we should expect the plane wave to approximate the actual motion in any case where the displacement $\mathbf{u}$ is small compared to the radius of curvature of the wave front. Hence a solution to (2.2.13) will be a pure dilatation Δ moving with velocity

$$\alpha = \left(\frac{\lambda + 2\mu}{\rho}\right)^{1/2} \tag{2.2.17}$$

and a solution to (2.2.14) will be a pure rotation curl u_i moving with velocity

$$\beta = \left(\frac{\mu}{\rho}\right)^{1/2} \tag{2.2.18}$$

Figure 2.7: Example of a seismogram.

Hence a purely compressional wave—called P in seismology—will move with a velocity α greater than the velocity β of a purely rotational wave, called S in seismology. Waves that move in accordance with (2.2.17) and (2.2.18) are called *body waves*. Figure 2.7 is a simplified example of a typical seismogram, showing the onsets of the P and the S waves. The larger amplitude waves later in the seismogram are *surface waves*, which suffer less diminution with distance, as discussed later.

Consider a wave front moving through a medium in which the parameters μ, λ, ρ vary in a direction perpendicular to the motion. Because of the varying velocities across the front, the wave front as a whole will turn toward the region of lower velocity. The effect of compression on materials is to increase the elastic parameters μ, λ more than the density ρ, while the effect of an increase in temperature is to decrease μ, λ more than density ρ. Hence in a planet velocity should increase with depth, except possibly over a range where the effect of the temperature gradient outweighs that of the pressure gradient. Consequently ray paths should normally be concave toward the planetary surface, as shown in Figure 2.8, and the difference in time of travel of the wave from a given disturbance to different points will depend on the variation of velocity with depth.

To obtain the time of travel of a body wave in a spherical planet with elastic properties varying with depth, the planet can be considered as consisting of homogeneous concentric shells and the laws of refraction can

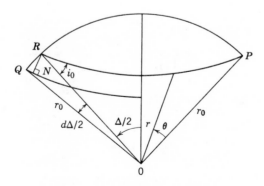

Figure 2.8: Geometry of a ray path.

be applied. The parameter p is defined as:

$$p = \frac{r \sin i}{v} \qquad (2.2.19)$$

where r is the radial coordinate, i is the angle of the ray to the normal, and v is the velocity. Equation (2.2.19) follows from Snell's law (see problem 2.10) and is constant for a particular ray.

Then the change in time T with angular distance Δ is obtained by:

$$\sin i_0 = \frac{NQ}{RQ} = \frac{v_0 \cdot \frac{1}{2} dT}{r_0^{\frac{1}{2}} d\Delta}$$

hence

$$p = \frac{dT}{d\Delta} \qquad (2.2.20)$$

Let θ be the angle at the center measured from the starting line OP on a ray such as that drawn in Figure 2.8. Then

$$\frac{r^2}{v} \cdot \frac{d\theta}{ds} = p$$

where ds is an element of arc length. Square this expression and replace $(ds)^2$ by $(dr)^2 + r^2(d\theta)^2$ to obtain

$$\frac{r^4}{p^2 v^2} = \left(\frac{dr}{d\theta}\right)^2 + r^2$$

or

$$d\theta = \pm \frac{p\, dr}{r[(r/v)^2 - p^2]^{1/2}}$$

Integrate with respect to r from the starting point to the deepest level of the ray to get an expression for Δ:

$$\Delta = 2p \int_{r_p}^{r_0} \frac{dr}{r[(r/v)^2 - p^2]^{1/2}} \qquad (2.2.21)$$

Eliminating $d\theta$ instead of ds obtains

$$\frac{p^2 v^2}{r^2} = 1 - \left(\frac{dr}{ds}\right)^2$$

or

$$ds = \pm \frac{r\, dr}{v[(r/v)^2 - p^2]^{1/2}}$$

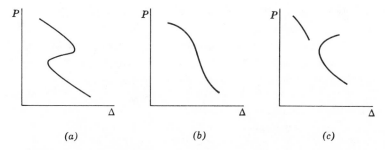

Figure 2.9: Time derivative versus distance curves: (a) with $dv/dr \ll 0$ layer; (b) normal: $dv/dr < 0$; (c) with $dv/dr > 0$ layer.

Then again integrate from the starting to the deepest point to get an expression for T:

$$T = 2 \int_{r_p}^{r_0} \frac{ds}{v}$$

$$= 2 \int_{r_p}^{r_0} \frac{(r/v)^2 \, dr}{r[(r/v)^2 - p^2]^{1/2}}$$

$$= p\Delta + 2 \int_{r_p}^{r_0} \frac{[(r/v)^2 - p^2]^{1/2}}{r} \, dr \qquad (2.2.22)$$

The normal value of dv/dr is rather small and negative; graphs of p versus Δ and T versus Δ obtained from (2.2.20-22) corresponding to this case are shown in Figures 2.9–10b. If there is a layer in which dv/dr is much more negative than usual, there will be a reversal in the p versus Δ curve and cusps in the T versus Δ curve, as shown in Figures 2.9–10a. A discontinuity in velocity will produce breaks in these curves, with two values of p and T corresponding to certain values of Δ.

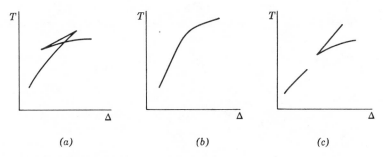

Figure 2.10: Time versus distance curves: (a) with $dv/dr \ll 0$ layer; (b) normal: $dv/dr < 0$; (c) with $dv/dr > 0$ layer.

If there is a layer in which dv/dr turns positive—that is, velocity decreases with depth—then there will be breaks in the p versus Δ and T versus Δ curves as shown in Figures 2.9–10c. In this case, certain values of distance Δ cannot exist, and there will be a "shadow zone," as shown in Figure 2.11.

Observed values of body-wave travel times T and its derivative $p = dT/d\Delta$ as a function of arc distance Δ from epicenters have been the principal method of obtaining the seismic velocities in Table 2.2. Also used is the derivative $dp/d\Delta = d^2T/d\Delta^2$. However, the existence of the low velocity layer in which dv/dr is reversed has necessitated the use of surface waves to obtain better upper mantle data.

If there is a discontinuity in elastic properties, there will be additional complications, since part of the wave will be refracted and part will be reflected at the interface, generally with some changes in the nature of the wave. The derivation of these changes is similar to that for electromagnetic waves in Section 6.1. For secondary or transverse waves, the effect for the component parallel to the interface (called SH) differs from that for the component normal to the interface (called SV). The principal transformations are:

Incident	Reflected	Refracted
SH	SH	SH
P	$SV, (P)$	$P(SV)$
SV	$P(SV)$	$SV, (P)$

where the lesser part of the energy is transmitted by the mode in parentheses. The proportion being transformed into each type of wave depends on the angle of incidence, in a manner similar to the reflected and refracted electromagnetic waves discussed in Section 6.1. The existence of the surface and mantle-core interfaces results in a considerable variety of waves. For example, with reference to the core-mantle interface, a wave starting out as a transverse S wave may travel only through the mantle (S); or may be reflected from the mantle-core boundary (ScS); or may pass through the core and be transformed into both longitudinal and transverse parts on

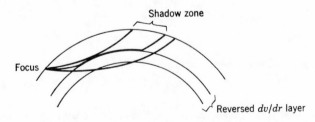

Figure 2.11: Effect of reversal in velocity gradient dv/dr on seismic-ray paths.

return (*SKS* and *SKP*); or may be reflected once at the core-mantle boundary internal to the core (*SKKS*); etc. Body waves resulting from these various reflections and refractions have been used to infer properties of the core-mantle boundary as well as velocities and densities of the inner and outer core as given in Tables 1.1 and 2.2 and Figure 2.18. [58, 199].

Surface Waves

The earth's surface and the crust-mantle interface (called the Mohorovicic discontinuity, or Moho) are important in a different manner in that an interface can constitute a wave guide: that is, groups of waves will be associated with the interface and travel along it. To simplify the mathematics, assume that the earth is homogeneous, and that we are interested in propagation distances such that the earth's surface can be considered a plane boundary. Let the $x_1 x_2$ plane be this boundary, and assume that (1) the direction of propagation is in the x_1 direction, and (2) motion is confined to the vicinity of the $x_1 x_2$ plane. Assumption (1) entails that all particles along a given line of constant x_3 and x_1 share the same motion, that is, $\partial/\partial x_2$ is zero. If we choose two functions φ, ψ in place of the displacements u_1, u_3 such that

$$u_1 = \frac{\partial \varphi}{\partial x_1} + \frac{\partial \psi}{\partial x_3}$$

$$u_3 = \frac{\partial \varphi}{\partial x_3} - \frac{\partial \psi}{\partial x_1}$$

(2.2.23)

then

$$\nabla^2 \varphi = \nabla \cdot \mathbf{u}$$

(2.2.24)

and

$$\nabla^2 \psi = \frac{\partial u_1}{\partial x_3} - \frac{\partial u_3}{\partial x_1}$$

(2.2.25)

that is, φ represents purely dilatational oscillation, whereas ψ represents pure rotation confined to vertical planes: called *P* and *SV* waves respectively. Furthermore, if motion in the u_2 direction occurs, it must be purely horizontal distortion. Hence we can write

$$\frac{\partial^2 \varphi}{\partial t^2} = \alpha^2 \nabla^2 \varphi$$

$$\frac{\partial^2 \psi}{\partial t^2} = \beta^2 \nabla^2 \psi$$

(2.2.26)

$$\frac{\partial^2 u_2}{\partial t^2} = \beta^2 \nabla^2 u_2$$

for the medium on one side of the boundary, and a similar equation for the medium on the other. Assume that the motion on any plane $x_3 = $ constant can be represented by a sinusoidal oscillation

$$\exp [i\kappa(x_1 - ct)]$$

where i is $\sqrt{-1}$ and κ is a component of a wave vector similar to that used in equation (1.2.29). The period of the wave then will be $2\pi\kappa/c$. Assume further that the requirement to confine the motion to the vicinity of the $x_1 x_2$ plane is expressed by a factor

$$\exp(-rx_3), \qquad \exp(-sx_3)$$

for $x_3 > 0$ and

$$\exp(r'x_3), \qquad \exp(s'x_3)$$

for $x_3 < 0$. Then we can write for the two mediums:

$$\varphi = A \exp[-rx_3 + i\kappa(x_1 - ct)]$$
$$\psi = B \exp[-sx_3 + i\kappa(x_1 - ct)] \tag{2.2.27}$$
$$u_2 = C \exp[-sx_3 + i\kappa(x_1 - ct)]$$

$$\varphi = D \exp[r'x_3 + i\kappa(x_1 - ct)]$$
$$\psi = E \exp[s'x_3 + i\kappa(x_1 - ct)] \tag{2.2.28}$$
$$u_2 = F \exp[s'x_3 + i\kappa(x_1 - ct)]$$

Substitution into (2.2.26) obtains

$$r = \kappa\sqrt{1 - c^2/\alpha^2}, \quad s = \kappa\sqrt{1 - c^2/\beta^2},$$
$$r' = \kappa\sqrt{1 - c^2/\alpha'^2}, \quad s' = \kappa\sqrt{1 - c^2/\beta'^2} \tag{2.2.29}$$

To determine the seven constants A through F and c, there are six boundary conditions:

1. The three displacements u_1, u_2, and u_3 are continuous.
2. The three stress components p_{3j} are continuous, where

$$p_{ij} = \delta_{ij}\lambda\Delta + 2\mu e_{ij} \tag{2.2.30}$$

Using (2.2.17, 18, 23), we find that both C and F must be zero; that is, there can be no displacement u_2, and hence no horizontal distortional waves *SH*.

The most important cases of these types of waves occur at the earth's surface, and are called *Rayleigh waves*. Since λ, μ, and ρ are zero in the upper medium, the boundary conditions become sufficient to determine the remaining constants D, E, and c. The velocity c falls between β and 0; that is, Rayleigh waves move more slowly than shear waves. (See problem 2.9.)

The next obvious complication consists of three homogeneous mediums separated by two parallel plane surfaces and propagation parallel to the surfaces. If the uppermost medium is again a vacuum, it works out in this

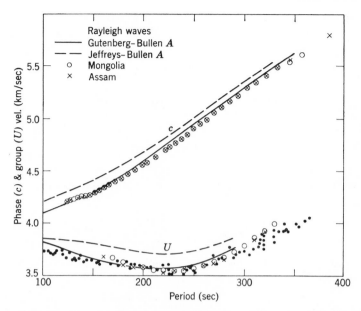

Figure 2.12: Experimental Rayleigh-wave dispersion data compared with theoretical predictions according to the Jeffreys and Gutenberg internal-velocity distribution and the Bullen A density distribution. From Press [323, p. 10].

case that SH waves are possible at the upper surface. Such waves are called *Love waves*.

In the actual earth, there are no homogeneous layers, but instead layers in which the velocity varies with depth. Hence we should expect the Rayleigh and Love wave theory to be modified in a manner that depends on wavelength, since the parameters r, s depend on the wave number κ by (2.2.29). Because the velocities generally increase with depth, the longer period waves should have higher phase (c) and group $(d(\kappa c)/d\kappa)$ velocities. In application the velocities for different periods are determined and then compared to the velocities calculated from a model. In Figure 2.12 is given such a comparison of velocity versus period curves, known as *dispersion curves* [58, 199, 323].

Note in Figure 2.12 that the surface waves discriminate sharply between two models based on body waves. The principal respect in which the two models differed was that Gutenberg's had a distinct low velocity layer, with a reversal in sign of dv/dr from 40 to 120 km depth [14, 294, 323, 324].

Free Oscillations

The suddenness of earthquakes results in most of their energy being emanated in wavelengths of a few kilometers or less. However, if an earthquake is big enough, it should be expected that some of the wavelengths will be long enough that the spherical form of the planet must be taken into account. Furthermore, the frequency of oscillation of such long wavelengths may be low enough that the effect of gravity $\partial V/\partial x_i$ in (2.2.11) is perceptible.

Expressing the displacement **u** in radial and tangential components (using θ for colatitude and φ for longitude), we get

$$
\left.\begin{array}{l} u_\theta \\ u_\varphi \\ u_r \end{array}\right\} \left.\begin{array}{l} = \\ = \\ = \end{array}\right\} \left.\begin{array}{l} \cos\theta\cos\varphi, \quad \cos\theta\sin\varphi, \quad -\sin\theta \\ -\sin\varphi, \qquad\quad \cos\varphi, \qquad\quad 0 \\ \sin\theta\cos\varphi, \quad \sin\theta\sin\varphi, \quad \cos\theta \end{array}\right\} \begin{pmatrix} u_1 \\ u_2 \\ u_3 \end{pmatrix} \tag{2.2.31}
$$

where u_1, u_2, u_3 are rectangular coordinates referred to polar and equatorial axes. If we further express the potential V in terms of a normal part V_0 and a disturbed part ψ, and the density ρ as

$$
\rho = \rho_0 - \rho_0 \Delta - \frac{d\rho_0}{dr} u_r \tag{2.2.32}
$$

the rectangular coordinate equations of motion (2.2.12) become, in spherical coordinates,

$$
\rho_0 \frac{\partial^2 u_r}{\partial t^2} = -\rho_0 \frac{dV_0}{dr}\Delta + \rho_0 \frac{d\psi}{dr} + \rho_0 \frac{\partial}{\partial r}\left(\frac{\partial V_0}{\partial r} u_r\right) + \frac{\partial}{\partial r}\left(\lambda\Delta + 2\mu\frac{\partial u_r}{\partial r}\right)
$$

$$
+ 2\frac{\mu}{r}\cdot\frac{\partial e_{r\theta}}{\partial\theta} + 2\frac{\mu}{r\sin\theta}\frac{\partial e_{r\varphi}}{\partial\varphi} + \frac{\mu}{r}(4e_{rr} - 2e_{\theta\theta} - 2e_{\varphi\varphi} + 2\cot\theta e_{r\theta})
$$

$$
\rho_0 \frac{\partial^2 u_\theta}{\partial t^2} = \frac{\rho_0}{r}\cdot\frac{\partial\psi}{\partial\theta} + 2\frac{\partial}{\partial r}(\mu e_{r\theta}) + \frac{1}{r}\frac{\partial}{\partial\theta}\left(\frac{\partial V_0}{\partial r}\rho_0 u_r + \lambda\Delta + 2\mu e_{\theta\theta}\right)
$$

$$
+ 2\frac{\mu}{r\sin\theta}\cdot\frac{\partial e_{\theta\varphi}}{\partial\varphi} \tag{2.2.33}
$$

$$
+ \frac{\mu}{r}\left[2\cot\theta\left(\frac{1}{r}\frac{\partial u_\theta}{\partial\theta} - \frac{u_\theta}{r}\cot\theta - \frac{1}{r\sin\theta}\frac{\partial u_\varphi}{\partial\varphi}\right) + 6e_{r\theta}\right]
$$

$$
\rho_0 \frac{\partial^2 u_\varphi}{\partial t^2} = \frac{\rho_0}{r\sin\theta}\cdot\frac{\partial\psi}{\partial\varphi} + 2\frac{\partial}{\partial r}(\mu e_{r\varphi}) + 2\frac{\mu}{r}\frac{\partial e_{\theta\varphi}}{\partial\theta}
$$

$$
+ \frac{1}{r\sin\theta}\frac{\partial}{\partial\varphi}\left(\frac{\partial V_0}{\partial r}\rho_0 u_r + \lambda\Delta + 2\mu e_{\varphi\varphi}\right) + \frac{6\mu}{r}e_{r\varphi} + \frac{4\mu}{r}\cot\theta e_{\theta\varphi}
$$

in which we have left out the term $0 = \rho_0(dV_0/dr) - (dp/dr)$ pertaining to the fluid reference earth.

From Poisson's equation there is also obtained

$$
\nabla^2\psi = 4\pi G\left(\rho_0\Delta + u_r\frac{d\rho_0}{dr}\right) \tag{2.2.34}
$$

where G is the constant of gravitation.

The logical functions to express vector quantities in a spherical body are the derivatives of a spherical harmonic:

$$\mathbf{u} = \begin{cases} L(r)\dfrac{\partial S_n}{\partial \theta} \\[2mm] \dfrac{M(r)}{\sin\theta} \cdot \dfrac{\partial S_n}{\partial \varphi} \\[2mm] U(r)S_n \end{cases} \tag{2.2.35}$$

where S_n is a surface spherical harmonic $P_{nm}(\cos\theta)e^{im\varphi}$. However, in any spherical shell of radius r the radial functions L, M of the tangential components can be transformed into another pair W, V such that all contribution to the dilatation, and hence all interaction with gravity, is confined to the function V, while W expresses rotation about a radial axis:

$$V = \frac{L + M}{2}$$
$$W = \frac{L - M}{2} \tag{2.2.36}$$

Just as in the unbounded plane wave case dilatational and rotational waves were found to have distinct velocities of propagation α and β, expressed by (2.2.17–18), so here in the spherically bounded case there are different frequencies of oscillation σ_S and σ_T for the dilatational and rotational components, so the displacement $\mathbf{u}$ may be expressed as:

$$\mathbf{u} = \begin{pmatrix} V(r)\dfrac{\partial S_n}{\partial \theta} \\[2mm] \dfrac{V(r)}{\sin\theta} \cdot \dfrac{\partial S_n}{\partial \varphi} \\[2mm] U(r)S_n \end{pmatrix} e^{i\sigma_S t} + \begin{pmatrix} W(r)\dfrac{\partial S_n}{\partial \theta} \\[2mm] \dfrac{-W(r)}{\sin\theta} \cdot \dfrac{\partial S_n}{\partial \varphi} \\[2mm] 0 \end{pmatrix} e^{i\sigma_T t} \tag{2.2.37}$$

The subscripts S, T signify *spheroidal*, connoting changes in shape of shells, and *toroidal*, connoting twisting within a shell, respectively.

The problem is: given a model with certain properties ρ, λ, and μ as a function of radius, determine for each wave number n the frequencies of oscillation σ_S, σ_T and the corresponding radial functions U, V, and W. Boundary conditions applicable to the problem are:

1. Regularity at the origin.
2. Vanishing of stresses at the deformed surface of the earth:

$$e_{r\theta} = e_{r\varphi} = 0 \qquad \text{at } r = a \tag{2.2.38}$$

3. Equality at the deformed surface of internal and external gravitational potentials, and of their respective gradients, which leads to:

$$\left[\frac{\partial \psi_n}{\partial r}\right]_{r=a} + \frac{(n+1)}{a}\,\psi_n = 4\pi G \rho_0 u_r \qquad (2.2.39)$$

The toroidal case should be simpler, since no perturbation of the gravitational field is involved. Substitution of the second term of (2.2.37) in (2.2.38) results in an identity for the first equation, while the second and third equations both reduce to:

$$\mu\left(\frac{d^2 W}{dr^2} + \frac{2}{r}\frac{dW}{dr}\right) + \frac{d\mu}{dr}\left(\frac{dW}{dr} - \frac{W}{r}\right) + \left[\sigma^2 \rho_0 - \frac{n(n+1)\mu}{r^2}\right]W = 0 \quad (2.2.40)$$

Assume for the moment both ρ_0 and μ to be constant, and define

$$k = \sigma\sqrt{\rho_0/\mu}$$

$$s = rk \qquad (2.2.41)$$

$$Q = Wks^{1/2}$$

where s is the new independent variable. Substituting for r, σ, ρ_0, μ, W in (2.2.40) obtains the equation

$$\frac{d^2 Q}{dr^2} + \frac{1}{s}\frac{dQ}{dr} + \left[1 - \frac{(n+\frac{1}{2})^2}{s^2}\right]Q = 0 \qquad (2.2.42)$$

which is Bessel's equation of order $n + \frac{1}{2}$. The solution (see, e.g., [260, p. 75]) is the Bessel function $J_{\pm(n+1/2)}$:

$$Q = J_{\pm(n+1/2)}(s) = \sum_{i=0}^{\infty} \frac{(-1)^i}{\Gamma(i+1)\Gamma(i \pm [n+\frac{1}{2}] + 1)}\left(\frac{s}{2}\right)^{\pm(n+1/2)+2i} \qquad (2.2.43)$$

where the gamma function Γ is defined as

$$\Gamma(x) = \int_0^{\infty} e^{-t} t^{x-1}\, dt \qquad (2.2.44)$$

or $(x - 1)!$ for a positive integer. Regularity at the origin constrains the solution in the sphere to positive values of n. The functions

$$j_n(s) = \sqrt{\frac{\pi}{2s}}\, J_{n+1/2}(s) \qquad (2.2.45)$$

are known as spherical Bessel functions. They often appear as functions of the radial coordinate in problems involving spherical boundaries [221, 260].

For the actual earth, the variation of density ρ_0 and rigidity μ with radius entails the use of numerical techniques, either by using spherical Bessel functions in homogeneous thin shells or directly integrating (2.2.40) numerically. A simplification of (2.2.40) convenient for numerical integration is

$$y_1 = W$$

$$y_2 = \mu\left(\frac{dW}{dr} - \frac{W}{r}\right)$$

(2.2.46)

The function y_1 is the radial factor of the displacement, and y_2, the radial factor of the stress. There results

$$y_1' = \frac{1}{r} y_1 + \frac{1}{\mu} y_2$$

$$y_2' = \left[\frac{\mu(n^2 + n - 2)}{r^2} - \sigma^2 \rho_0\right] y_1 - \frac{3}{r} y_2$$

(2.2.47)

where the primes denote derivatives with respect to r. Solving (2.2.47) numerically with $y_2 = 0$ at the core-mantle boundary and the surface, there results for each degree n a fundamental frequency σ corresponding to zero nodes in the radial function W, and an infinite set of discrete overtones of higher frequency, the kth overtone corresponding to k nodes in W. The standard notation for the kth overtone of the nth degree toroidal oscillation is $_kT_n$.

For the spheroidal oscillations the first term in (2.2.37) is taken to represent the displacement $\mathbf{u}$, and a similar representation must be made of the potential perturbation ψ:

$$\psi = P(r)S_n$$

(2.2.48)

Making the substitutions from (2.2.37) and (2.2.48) in (2.2.33), the first equation no longer disappears, while the second and third equations again reduce to the same equation:

$$\sigma^2\rho_0 U + \rho_0 P' - \frac{dV_0}{dr}\rho_0 X + \rho_0 \frac{d}{dr}\left(\frac{dV_0}{dr} U\right) + \frac{d}{dr}(\lambda X + 2\mu U')$$

$$+ \frac{\mu}{r^2}[4U'r - 4U + n(n+1)(-U - rV' + 3V)] = 0$$

(2.2.49)

$$\rho_0\sigma^2 Vr + \rho_0 P + \frac{dV_0}{dr}\rho_0 U + \lambda X + r\frac{d}{dr}\left[\mu\left(V' - \frac{V}{r} + \frac{U}{r}\right)\right]$$

$$+ \frac{\mu}{r}[5U + 3rV' - V - 2n(n+1)V] = 0$$

where

$$X = U' + \frac{2}{r} U - \frac{n(n+1)}{r} V \qquad (2.2.50)$$

the radial factor of the dilatation Δ. Substitution in (2.2.34) yields

$$P'' + \frac{2}{r} P' - \frac{n(n+1)}{r^2} P = 4\pi G(\rho_0' U + \rho_0 X) \qquad (2.2.51)$$

The simplifying transformations are

$$y_1 = U, \quad y_2 = \lambda X + 2\mu U', \quad y_3 = V,$$

$$y_4 = \mu\left(V' - \frac{V}{r} + \frac{U}{r}\right), \quad y_5 = P, \quad y_6 = P' - 4\pi G\rho_0 U \quad (2.2.52)$$

The y_i's are, respectively, the radial factors of the radial displacement; the radial stress; the tangential displacement; the tangential stress; the potential perturbation; and the potential perturbation gradient less the radial displacement contribution thereto. The resulting equations:

$$y_1' = -\frac{2\lambda}{(\lambda + 2\mu)r} y_1 + \frac{1}{\lambda + 2\mu} y_2 + \frac{\lambda n(n+1)}{(\lambda + 2\mu)r} y_3$$

$$y_2' = \left[-\sigma^2\rho_0 r^2 + 4\rho_0 \frac{dV_0}{dr} r + \frac{4\mu(3\lambda + 2\mu)}{\lambda + 2\mu}\right]\frac{y_1}{r^2} - \frac{4\mu}{(\lambda + 2\mu)r} y_2$$

$$+ \left[-n(n+1)\rho_0 \frac{dV_0}{dr} r - \frac{2\mu(3\lambda + 2\mu)n(n+1)}{\lambda + 2\mu}\right]\frac{y_3}{r^2}$$

$$+ \frac{n(n+1)}{r} y_4 - \rho_0 y_6$$

$$y_3' = -\frac{y_1}{r} + \frac{y_3}{r} + \frac{y_4}{r} \qquad (2.2.53)$$

$$y_4' = \left[-\frac{dV_0}{dr} \rho_0 r - \frac{2\mu(3\lambda + 2\mu)}{\lambda + 2\mu}\right]\frac{y_1}{r^2} - \frac{\lambda y_2}{(\lambda + 2\mu)r}$$

$$+ \left\{-\rho_0\sigma^2 r^2 + \frac{2\mu}{\lambda + 2\mu}[\lambda(2n^2 + 2n - 1) + 2\mu(n^2 + n - 1)]\right\}\frac{y_3}{r^2}$$

$$- \frac{3y_4}{r} - \frac{\rho_0 y_5}{r}$$

$$y_5' = 4\pi G\rho_0 y_1 + y_6$$

$$y_6' = -\frac{4\pi G\rho_0 n(n+1)}{r} y_3 + \frac{n(n+1)}{r^2} y_5 - \frac{2}{r} y_6$$

For a liquid core, the shear stress vanishes: $y_4 = 0$, and the other equations are modified somewhat. The surface boundary conditions are:

$$y_6 + \frac{n+1}{a} y_5 = 0; \qquad y_2 = y_4 = 0 \qquad (2.2.54)$$

where a is the surface radius. Solving (2.2.53) numerically results again in a set of frequencies with corresponding radial functions U, V. The fundamental for the nth degree is denoted $_0S_n$, and the kth overtone $_kS_n$ [9, 249, 385].

Some periods of oscillation, in minutes:

	$n = 2$			$n = 3$			$n = 4$	
k	$_kS_2$	$_kT_2$	k	$_kS_3$	$_kT_3$	k	$_kS_4$	$_kT_4$
0	54	44	0	36	29	0	26	22
1	25	13	1	18	12	1	14	10
2	16	7	2	17	7	2	12	7

The above periods are an appreciable fraction of a day for the lower modes. Hence an accurate solution should take into account the rotation of the earth; that is, in the equations of motion (2.2.11) a vector cross-product $-2\rho \boldsymbol{\omega} \times \mathbf{u}$, the Coriolis term, should be added on the right. The result in the solution is a "splitting" of the spectrum: that is, each of the periods in the foregoing table is replaced by two periods, corresponding to waves traveling in opposite directions with respect to the earth's rotation.

Analysis of records of the May 22, 1960, Chilean earthquake and the March 27, 1964, Alaskan earthquake has identified over forty $_0S_n$ modes, over twenty $_0T_n$ modes, and about six $_kS_n$, $k \geq 1$, modes of oscillation. The resulting improvement in determination of μ, λ, and ρ in the mantle has been considerable, the higher modes indicating mainly upper-mantle conditions and the lower modes, lower-mantle conditions [14, 324].

Results from Seismology

The main results of seismology are summarized in Table 2.2, obtained primarily by travel times of body waves and secondarily by the periods of free oscillations and dispersions of surface waves.

In addition to the mean velocities given in Table 2.2, considerable regional variation has been detected using both body waves and surface waves. P waves indicate velocities at the top of the mantle varying from 7.4 to 8.5 km/sec. In general, lower velocities are correlated with higher geologic activity. Velocities under ocean ridges are 7.4–7.7 km/sec, compared to an average of about 8.2 km/sec for ocean basins. In the western United States, velocities range from 7.5 to 8.2 km/sec; in the east, from 8.0 to 8.5 km/sec. Under Japan, they are 7.5–7.7 km/sec.

TABLE 2.2: MEAN SEISMIC VELOCITIES IN THE
EARTH

Depth (km)	r/R_E	V_p (km/sec)	V_s (km/sec)
60	0.991	8.15	4.6
100	0.984	8.0	4.4
150	0.976	7.85	4.35
200	0.969	8.05	4.4
300	0.953	8.5	4.6
400	0.937	9.0	4.95
500	0.921	9.6	5.3
600	0.906	10.1	5.6
800	0.874	10.9	6.15
900	0.859	11.3	6.3
1000	0.843	11.4	6.35
1200	0.812	11.8	6.5
1600	0.749	12.3	6.75
2000	0.686	12.8	6.95
2400	0.623	13.2	7.1
2800	0.560	13.7	7.25
2920	0.542	13.65	7.2
2920	0.542	8.0	
	0.433	8.9	
	0.325	9.6	
	0.217	10.1	
	0.195	10.5	
	≤ 0.173	11.1	

Based on F. Press in Clark [74, p. 215].

Surface waves also evidence appreciable regional variation in velocities in the form of variations in the dispersion curve, Figure 2.12. A summary of results as of 1961 is given in Figures 2.13–14. The existence of different curves for continent and ocean at periods as long as 100 seconds indicates differences in structure of the upper mantle to perhaps as deep as 100 kilometers.

In recent years considerably more seismic detail has been developed as a consequence of artificial earthquake sources; more widespread arrays of seismometers; and more elaborate techniques of analysis. Both surface waves and P waves have been used in these studies. In the radial direction, discontinuities in dv/dr have been inferred at depths of 120, 225 to 300, 670 to 700, and possibly 1200 and 1900 km. Laterally, distinct variations to 150 km depth, and possible variations to 800 km depth, have been detected.

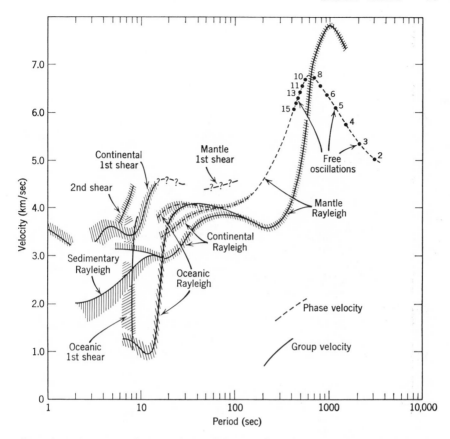

Figure 2.13: Summary of observed Rayleigh-wave dispersion. From Oliver [294, p. 82].

These variations have been most pronounced in the upper mantle, at about 100 km depth. The highest shear velocities V_s, about 4.8 km/sec, occur under continental shields, and the lowest, about 4.4 km/sec, under tectonically active areas. Under oceans the shear velocities average about 4.5 km/sec [14, 294, 323, 324].

These more precise and elaborate techniques have also enabled a great improvement in the accuracy of location and determination of the extent and direction of slip of earthquakes. From these results there has been inferred considerable detail about the structures and rates-of-slip of fault zones associated with both ocean ridge-transform fault and ocean trench-island arc systems, corroborating other evidence of sea-floor spreading at rates of 2 to 10 cm/yr [383, 384, 549].

This section has discussed only a part of the diverse subject of seismology;

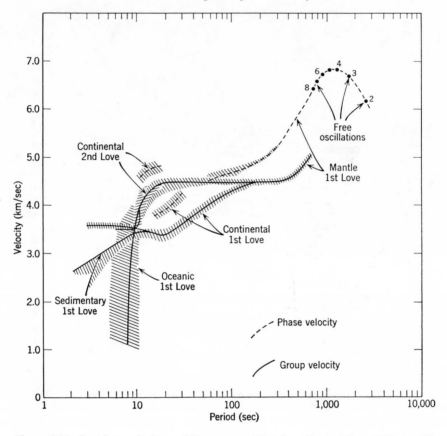

Figure 2.14: Summary of observed Love-wave dispersion. From Oliver [294, p. 83].

we have neglected such topics as earthquake source mechanisms; the distribution and frequency of earthquakes; anisotropy of elastic properties; the correlation of seismic velocity variations with gravity anomalies; determination of strain in the earth; the amount of energy involved (on the order of 10^{26} ergs/yr); etc. In the next section we take up the effects of imperfections in elasticity.

2.3   Anelasticity and Creep

The assumption of perfect elasticity in the earth is manifestly false. If it were true then the earth would still be reverberating from the effect of all earthquakes since its foundation. The imperfection in the elasticity takes many forms, all of which we are interested in, more or less. The simplest measure of anelasticity is the Q factor, which is defined by the part ΔE of the total energy stored E which is dissipated in a complete cycle, the cycle being a single oscillation in the system in which energy is alternately stored and released [215, 285]:

$$\frac{2\pi}{Q} = \frac{\Delta E}{E} = \frac{1}{E} \oint \frac{dE}{dt} \, dt \qquad (2.3.1)$$

An example of such an oscillation would be the cycle of vibration of one of the frequencies in an earthquake wave.

Simple Damped Oscillator Models

The simplest periodic phenomenon is a free oscillation in one dimension:

$$\ddot{x} + \sigma_0^2 x = 0 \qquad (2.3.2)$$

where σ_0^2 is the frequency of the oscillation. Now let us suppose there is a resistance to the motion proportionate to the velocity $\dot{x}$, expressed by a factor 2α:

$$\ddot{x} + 2\alpha\dot{x} + \sigma_0^2 x = 0 \qquad (2.3.3)$$

Both the amplitude and frequency of the oscillation might be changed by the damping α, so let us assume the solution to be of the form:

$$x = a(t) \cos \sigma t \qquad (2.3.4)$$

Differentiating (2.3.4) to obtain $\dot{x}$ and $\ddot{x}$, substituting in (2.3.3), and separately equating to zero the coefficients of $\sin \sigma t$ and $\cos \sigma t$ obtains:

$$x = A e^{-\alpha t} \cos \sqrt{\sigma_0^2 - \alpha^2} \, t \qquad (2.3.5)$$

where A is an arbitrary constant which we shall set equal to unity hereafter. The oscillation is thus damped out with a decay factor $e^{-\alpha t}$ and the frequency reduced (i.e., the period lengthened) from σ_0 to $\sqrt{\sigma_0^2 - \alpha^2}$. Expressing the instantaneous energy per unit mass as kinetic energy

$$E = \tfrac{1}{2}\dot{x}^2 \qquad (2.3.6)$$

we get

$$E = \sigma_0^2 \frac{e^{-2\alpha t}}{4} [1 + \cos 2(\sigma t - y)] \qquad (2.3.7)$$

where

$$\tan y = \frac{\sigma}{\alpha} = \frac{\sqrt{\sigma_0^2 - \alpha^2}}{\alpha} \qquad (2.3.8)$$

that is, the kinetic energy has a phase lag $2\alpha/\sigma$. Using the energy from (2.3.7) in the integration (2.3.1) with the peak energy stored $\sigma_0^2 \, e^{-2\alpha t}/4$ per cycle π/σ, we get

$$\frac{1}{Q} = \frac{2\alpha}{\sigma} \tag{2.3.9}$$

Now if there is a forced oscillation $k\sigma_0^2 \cos \kappa t$ added on the right of equation (2.3.3), we should expect that some of the energy cyclically stored and removed would also be dissipated. Since the acceleration frequency κ and amplitude $k\sigma_0^2$ are imposed on the oscillator from an external source, in a steady-state situation the displacement x should have the same frequency κ and a fixed amplitude, say b. However, it is possible that the damping α will cause a delay in response of the oscillator, expressible as a phase lag φ:

$$x = b \cos (\kappa t - \varphi) \tag{2.3.10}$$

Changing $\cos (\kappa t - \varphi)$ to $(\cos \varphi \cos \kappa t + \sin \varphi \sin \kappa t)$ in (2.3.10), differentiating to obtain $\dot{x}$ and $\ddot{x}$, substituting in (2.3.3), and separately equating to zero the coefficients of $\sin \kappa t$ and $\cos \kappa t$ obtains:

$$\tan \varphi = \frac{2\alpha\kappa}{\sigma_0^{\,2} - \kappa^2} \tag{2.3.11}$$

and

$$b = k\sigma_0^{\,2} \frac{(1 + \tan^2 \varphi)^{1/2}}{\sigma_0^{\,2} - \kappa^2 + \tan^2 \varphi} \tag{2.3.12}$$

that is, the phase lag φ depends on both the damping α and the forcing frequency κ, and goes to 90 degrees in the resonant case where $\kappa = \sigma_0$. In the situation $\alpha \ll \sigma_0$ and $\kappa \ll \sigma_0$:

$$\varphi \approx \frac{2\alpha\kappa}{\sigma_0^{\,2}} \tag{2.3.13}$$

$$b \approx k$$

Since energy constantly is being supplied to keep the velocity the same, to calculate the energy dissipation and hence the Q factor we cannot use the kinetic energy as in (2.3.6), but rather the work, force times displacement, and rate of doing work, force times velocity:

$$E = [k\sigma_0^{\,2} \cos \kappa t] \cdot [b \cos (\kappa t - \varphi)]$$
$$\dot{E} = [k\sigma_0^{\,2} \cos \kappa t] \cdot [-b\kappa \sin (\kappa t - \varphi)] \tag{2.3.14}$$

Using these in (2.3.1), we get:

$$\frac{1}{Q} = \frac{2\alpha\kappa}{\sigma_0^{\,2}} \tag{2.3.15}$$

In terms of the thermodynamics discussed in Section 1.2, the dissipation factor is related directly to the change in entropy per cycle, ΔS:

$$\frac{1}{Q} = \frac{T\Delta S}{2\pi E} \qquad (2.3.16)$$

Observations of Q

The proportionality of specific dissipation $1/Q$ to frequency κ predicted by (2.3.15) is borne out in experiments with liquids, where the dissipation is apparently due to a viscous drag as implied by (2.3.3). In experiments with solids, however, there is very little dependence of the dissipation $1/Q$ on frequency. Figure 2.15 shows the principal results. The $1/Q$'s for seismic waves are deduced from: (1) the increase in attenuation with distance from the source over that predicted by geometrical considerations; (2) the decrease in amplitude with time of spectral components of the free oscillations, as predicted by (2.3.5); and (3) the broadening of peaks in the free oscillations; if $\Delta\sigma$ is the difference between the half energy points in frequency, then

$$\frac{1}{Q} \approx \frac{2\Delta\sigma}{\sigma} \qquad (2.3.17)$$

As indicated by Figure 2.15, the Q's vary less than an order of magnitude over a range of frequencies of seven orders of magnitude between 10^{-4} and 10^6 cps. The variation in Q with frequency probably would be appreciably less for a single type of rock at uniform temperature and pressure than it is in Figure 2.15. The laboratory results in Figure 2.15 include all types of rock from granite to basalt. The seismic wave results range over all depths in the mantle, and hence over a great range of temperatures and pressures. If we assume $1/Q$ is not a function of frequency for uniform conditions, the

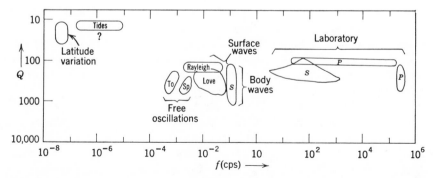

Figure 2.15: Specific dissipation in igneous rocks as a function of frequency. Based on Knopoff [215]; Bradley & Fort in Clark [74, p. 179]; and Anderson & Archambeau [15].

variation of observed $1/Q$ with frequency for surface waves and free oscillations can, in fact, be used to deduce the $1/Q$ at depth, since the function of depth varies with the wavelength. Let the subscript f refer to a particular frequency, and the subscript l refer to a particular level in an earth model of m layers; then we can write:

$$Q_f^{-1} = \frac{\sum\limits_{l=1}^{m} \Delta E_{lf}}{\sum\limits_{l=1}^{m} E_{lf}} = \frac{\sum E_{lf} Q_{lf}^{-1}}{\sum E_{lf}} = \sum_l A_{fl} \hat{Q}_l^{-1} \qquad (2.3.16)$$

whence a solution can be made for the $\hat{Q}_l$'s by least squares; in matrix notation, using a superscript T to denote a transpose,

$$\mathbf{q} = (\mathbf{A}^T \mathbf{A})^{-1} \mathbf{A}^T \hat{\mathbf{q}} \qquad (2.3.17)$$

where $\mathbf{A}$ is the matrix of A_{fl}'s and $\hat{\mathbf{q}}$, $\mathbf{q}$ are, respectively, column matrices of the Q_l^{-1}'s and Q_f^{-1}'s. In this manner, it has been deduced that Q has a minimum of about 80 at a depth of 80 km; that it increases rapidly between the depth of 400 km and 1000 km; and that it has an approximately constant value of 2000 in the lower mantle [14, 15, 215].

To extend Figure 2.15 to lower frequencies, we have the phenomena of the bodily tides, caused by attraction of the sun and moon, and the latitude variation: motion of the earth's rotation axis with respect to the crust, believed to be due to meteorological effects. However, both these phenomena may involve considerable dissipation at the fluid-solid interfaces of ocean-crust and core-mantle, and hence must be marked as of questionable applicability to the anelasticity of the mantle [257, 285].

Physical Explanations for Dissipation

Attempts to obtain mathematical models explaining the frequency independence of $1/Q$ have not been physically plausible. The ideas more pertinent to damping entail consideration of the imperfections in crystal structure: point defects, which include both impurities and vacancies; dislocations, across which the atoms are not aligned in accordance with the normal lattice structure; and grain boundaries: narrow zones of great irregularity between well-organized crystal blocks. When a material is stressed by an elastic wave, there will be (1) thermally activated displacement of the point defects to new sites in the lattice, called stress-induced ordering; (2) unpinning of dislocations from point defects and motion of dislocations through the crystal lattice; and (3) viscous sliding at grain boundaries. All of these processes are to some extent irreversible in nature, since they require the overcoming of a barrier to initiation, expressible by an activation energy G^*. At the end of each cycle of stress it is impossible to reproduce exactly the state at the start; hence there will be hysteresis effects and energy dissipation.

The requirement for an activation energy tends to make damping less frequency dependent and more amplitude dependent. It also makes it more temperature dependent, since associated with the activation energy G^* will be a decay time proportionate to $\exp(G^*/kT)$: the shorter this decay time, the more quickly dissipation takes place.

The fact that the Q's in Figure 2.15 are an order-of-magnitude lower than those obtained for pure samples of metal, which have a simpler crystal structure, supports the idea that grain boundary effects are important in rocks [148].

Creep

We are also interested in extending the model of nonelastic properties of rocks to much lower frequencies, or longer time scales, in order to explain their response to the forces evidenced by the geological record. At temperatures somewhat below melting, crystalline substances under shear stress appear to undergo a slow steady creep according to a law such as

$$\dot{e} = C(p) \exp\left(\frac{-G^*}{kT}\right) \tag{2.3.18}$$

where G^* is an activation energy, k is the Boltzmann constant, T is the absolute temperature, and C is an exponential, or, near melting, a power of the shear stress p. As melting is approached, however, the response of rocks under confining pressure to shearing stress is difficult to describe mathematically; failure usually occurs by rapid plastic deformation along narrow zones, which widen at pressures above 1 kilobar. After failure, cohesion is reestablished. At the temperatures and pressures which can be attained in the laboratory— on the order of 500°C and 5 kb—rocks usually fail by plastic flow at shear stresses between 100 and 1000 bars [151, 201].

Extrapolation of laboratory data to geological phenomena is discouraging, because over the long time scale creep much slower than observable in the laboratory could be quite significant. Hence there is a greater dependence on whatever theory of creep may be available. Again, effects at all three levels—point defects, dislocations, and grain boundaries—may be significant.

Diffusion Creep

The minimum level of creep occurs as a consequence of diffusion, described by (1.2.25–28): any crystal can change its shape by self-diffusion in such a way as to yield to an applied shearing stress. The rate of this diffusion, called

Herring-Nabarro creep, depends on the temperature, since thermal activation is required, and on the grain size, because of the time a vacancy or interstitial atom takes to move from one grain boundary to another.

Assume a single cubic crystal of one atomic type at uniform temperature. If there is a pressure gradient, then there will be a flow of lattice defects in whichever direction will relieve the inequality of pressure. This pressure effect, combined with the effect of any defect concentration gradients, can be represented by a chemical potential μ, as used in (1.2.16). Then the diffusive flux $\mathbf{j}$ (atoms per unit area per unit time) will be proportional to the gradient of this potential, similar to (1.2.26):

$$\mathbf{j} = \frac{n_L D}{kT} \nabla\mu \qquad (2.3.19)$$

where n_L is the number of lattice sites per unit volume, D is the self-diffusion coefficient, k is the Boltzmann constant, T is the absolute temperature, and μ is the work per atom required for the reversible addition of material to a region of the crystal, either interstitially or in vacancies. The thermal energy kT appears in the denominator of (2.3.19) because increase in the thermal agitation of the lattice hinders the diffusive flow (similar to increase of electrical resistance with temperature because of thermal agitation interfering with electron flow).

It is safe to assume that any irregularities of the flow $\mathbf{j}$ interior to the grain would be quickly removed, so that

$$\nabla \cdot \mathbf{j} \propto \nabla^2\mu = 0 \qquad (2.3.20)$$

Hence, like the gravitational potentials in Section 2.1, to know the potential μ everywhere in the crystal grain it suffices to know it all over the boundary. At the boundary there are two effects: (1) a chemical potential μ_0 of the source from which atoms are obtained, and (2) a stress p_{ii} with a component p_{rr} normal to the surface, so that for an atom of volume Ω there is a work $p_{rr}\Omega$ on attachment or removal. Thence for a spherical grain of radius R

$$\mu = \mu_0 - \Omega \sum_{i,j} \frac{p_{ij}x_i x_j}{R^2} \qquad (2.3.21)$$

The normal flux, using (2.3.19) and $n_L\Omega = 1$, is

$$j_n = \frac{dr/dt}{\Omega} = \frac{2D}{kT} \sum_{ij} \frac{p_{ij}x_i x_j}{R^3} \qquad (2.3.22)$$

where dr/dt is the rate of deformation of the surface, expressible in terms of the strain rate e_{ij} (see (2.2.2)) as

$$\frac{dr}{dt} = \sum_{i,j} \frac{e_{ij} x_i x_j}{R} \qquad (2.3.23)$$

From (2.3.22–23),

$$e_{ij} = \frac{2D\Omega}{kTR^2} p_{ij} \qquad (2.3.24)$$

Whence defining viscosity η as half the ratio of stress p_{ij} to strain rate e_{ij},

$$\eta = \frac{kTR^2}{4D\Omega} \qquad (2.3.25)$$

Using a factor C in place of the 4 to generalize to any geometry and (1.2.28) in place of the diffusion coefficient D,

$$\eta = \frac{kTR^2}{C\Omega D_0} \exp\left(\frac{E + p\Omega}{kT}\right) \qquad (2.3.26)$$

using (2.3.21) to define the activation energy G^* in terms of a part E expressing self-diffusion and a part $p\Omega$ accounting for the effect of pressure [135, 147, 172, 270].

The derivation of (2.3.25) given above neglected the effect of hydrostatic pressure on the volume of the grain and thus in effect assumed pure shear. More careful considerations obtain a value of about 8.4 for C. Experimental values of the parameters in (2.3.26) are about 1 to 10 cm²/sec for D_0, 3 to 6 eV for E, and 10 to 20 × 10⁻²⁴ cm³ for Ω. Using values in these ranges with the temperatures given by a curve such as Figure 2.17 and a grain radius R of 0.05 cm—a value of appreciable uncertainty in itself—gives several orders-of-magnitude variation in viscosity η, as shown in Figure 2.16. The curves are all similar, however, in that they predict that the viscosity in the upper mantle should be much less than in the crust or lower mantle [147].

Dislocation Climb

Except at very low stresses and temperatures close to melting, creep in metals is observed to depend much less on Herring-Nabarro diffusion than on motion of dislocations strongly dependent on stress p of a form such that in (2.3.18),

$$C(p) \approx HD_0 \left(\frac{p}{\mu}\right)^5 \qquad (2.3.27)$$

where μ is the rigidity. The parameter H depends on dislocation source density in the theoretical model of Weertman [429, 430], but experimental tests show a dependence on grain size, suggesting that grain boundary effects

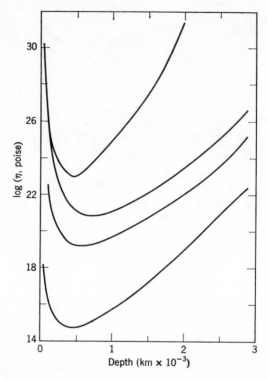

Figure 2.16: Effective viscosity due to diffusion creep in a polycrystalline material with $D_0 = 5 \text{ cm}^2/\text{sec}$ and $R = 0.05$ cm. From top to bottom the curves correspond to $E^* = 6$ eV, $V^* = 20 \text{ A}^3$; $E^* = 6$, $V^* = 10$; $E^* = 5$, $V^* = 10$; $E^* = 3$, $V^* = 10$, respectively. From Gordon [147, p. 2415].

are significant. Experiments with silicates indicate an even greater importance for grain boundary effects [270]. Dislocation climb is probably the dominant form of yielding in the upper mantle, whereas grain boundary effects have the greatest importance in the crust.

Geophysical Application

Hence it appears at present unfeasible to extrapolate theoretically from laboratory measurements to obtain the rheological parameters of the mantle. It can be said, however, that whatever the exact mechanism of creep, it is probably temperature and pressure dependent in such a way that there will exist a layer of weakness in the upper mantle. It also appears plausible that, at low shearing stresses on the order of a few bars, the material in the mantle behaves as a Newtonian viscous fluid. It therefore is feasible to attempt to explain geophysical evidences of creep by a strongly temperature-dependent viscous model. The principal observational data pertaining to the viscosity have been the rates of uplift of areas from which loads have been removed in the last few thousand years, such as those covered by the glaciers of the ice age or by recently evaporated lakes. These rates of uplift do indicate, in fact, that the apparent viscosity has a minimum on the order of 100 km deep, and increases rapidly with further depth—as would be expected if it were dependent on the closeness of the temperature to melting [267].

2.4   Planetary Heat Transfer

Thermal Conduction

The *specific heat at constant pressure*, C_p, of a substance is the amount of heat required to raise the temperature of 1 gram by 1°C.

The specific heat at constant pressure differs from the specific heat at constant volume, C_V, defined by (1.2.37), by the work of expansion $P \, \partial V/\partial T$:

$$C_p = \left(\frac{\partial E}{\partial T}\right)_p + P\left(\frac{\partial V}{\partial T}\right)_p$$

$$= \left(\frac{\partial H}{\partial T}\right)_p \tag{2.4.1}$$

where H is the enthalpy, defined by (1.2.12). For silicates, C_p is about 0.25 cal gm^{-1} °C^{-1}, or 10^7 ergs gm^{-1} °C^{-1}.

In heat transfer by thermal conduction, the rate of flow of energy per unit area per unit time is proportionate to the negative of the temperature gradient. For the flow of heat out of an element of matter this rule can be written as a surface integral over the element:

$$-\frac{\partial W}{\partial t} = -K \oint \nabla T \, dS \tag{2.4.2}$$

The proportionality factor K, the *thermal conductivity*, is about 0.008 cal cm^{-1} sec^{-1} °C^{-1} for silicates.

The rate of heat loss for the element of matter can be related to the rate of temperature change through the specific heat C_p, integrating over the volume of the element:

$$-\frac{\partial W}{\partial t} = -\int \rho \frac{\partial T}{\partial t} C_p \, d\tau \tag{2.4.3}$$

To convert (2.4.2) to a volume integral, apply Gauss's theorem:

$$-\oint K \nabla T \, dS = -\int K \, Div \cdot \nabla T \, d\tau = -\int K \nabla^2 T \, d\tau$$

Equating integrands yields the equation of thermal conduction:

$$\frac{\partial T}{\partial t} = \kappa \nabla^2 T \qquad (2.4.4)$$

where κ, the thermal diffusivity, is:

$$\kappa = \frac{K}{\rho C_p} \qquad (2.4.5)$$

If there is motion, the equation of heat conduction (2.4.4) must be modified to allow for the change of temperature by convection:

$$\frac{\partial T}{\partial t} = \kappa \nabla^2 T + \mathbf{v} \cdot \nabla T \qquad (2.4.6)$$

where $\mathbf{v}$ is velocity, $\dot{\mathbf{u}}$.

In the practical problem of a planet, there is in addition the rate of heat generation per unit volume $A(t)$ due to radiogenic materials:

$$\frac{\partial T}{\partial t} = \kappa \nabla^2 T + \mathbf{v} \cdot \nabla T + \frac{1}{\rho C_p} A(t) \qquad (2.4.7)$$

Converting (2.4.7) to spherical coordinates and assuming zero velocity and spherical symmetry obtains [239, 252]:

$$\rho C_p \frac{\partial T}{\partial t} = \frac{1}{r^2} \frac{\partial}{\partial r} \left(r^2 K \frac{\partial T}{\partial r} \right) + A(t, r) \qquad (2.4.8)$$

If $A(t, r)$ were zero and K and $C_p \rho$ constant, (2.4.8) could be solved in terms of spherical Bessel functions, the same as elastic waves in a homogeneous planet. The variability of these quantities makes it necessary to solve (2.4.8) numerically; furthermore, the consequence of radiative transfer is to make the conductivity K strongly temperature dependent by a relation such as [73]:

$$K = K_0 + \frac{16 n^2 s T^3}{3(\epsilon_0 + 120 \pi \sigma / n)} \qquad (2.4.9)$$

where n is the *index of refraction;* s, the *Stefan-Boltzmann constant,* (6.2.14); ϵ_0, the *opacity* at degrees Kelvin; and σ, the *electrical conductivity,* given by Figure 3.5. Of these parameters, the most uncertain is the opacity ϵ_0, which expresses the absorption and scattering of heat by the crystal lattice: the most likely values range from 5 to 20 cm^{-1}. The T^3 dependence is, roughly, a consequence of an energy gradient ∇E dependent on temperature: from the Stefan-Boltzmann law, (6.2.13),

$$\nabla E = \frac{\partial E}{\partial T} \nabla T = 4 s T^3 \nabla T \qquad (2.4.10)$$

Convection

Materials expand upon increase in temperature; for a small change in temperature δT, the change in density $\delta\rho$ is:

$$\delta\rho = -\rho\alpha\delta T \qquad (2.4.11)$$

The coefficient of thermal expansion α is about $2 \times 10^{-5}\,°C^{-1}$ for silicates.

A viscous material is one in which the stress, aside from hydrostatic pressure, is proportionate to the rate of deformation by the viscosity η:

$$p_{ij} = -p\delta_{ij} + 2\eta d_{ij} \qquad (2.4.12)$$

where

$$d_{ij} = \frac{1}{2}\left(\frac{\partial v_i}{\partial x_j} + \frac{\partial v_j}{\partial x_i} - \frac{2}{3}\delta_{ij}\frac{\partial v_i}{\partial x_i}\right) \qquad (2.4.13)$$

In (2.4.13), v_i is a component of velocity, **v**. Substituting (2.4.13) and (2.4.12) into the equations of motion obtains:

$$\rho\dot{v}_i = \rho\left(\frac{\partial v_i}{\partial t} + v_j\frac{\partial v_i}{\partial x_j}\right) = -\frac{\partial p}{\partial x_i} + \rho\frac{\partial V}{\partial x_i} + \eta\nabla^2 v_i \qquad (2.4.14)$$

called the *Navier-Stokes equation*. The assumption of incompressibility requires the divergence of the velocity to be zero:

$$\nabla\cdot\mathbf{v} = 0 \qquad (2.4.15)$$

If the density perturbation $\delta\rho$ from (2.4.11) is small enough, the only term in (2.4.14) in which it will be significant is that in which the density ρ is multiplied by the potential gradient $\partial V/\partial x_i$. Substituting $\rho_0 + \delta\rho$ for ρ in this term is called the *Boussinesq approximation*:

$$\frac{\partial v_i}{\partial t} + v_j\frac{\partial v_i}{\partial x_j} = \frac{-1}{\rho_0}\frac{\partial p}{\partial x_i} + (1 + \alpha\delta T)\frac{\partial V}{\partial x_i} + \nu\nabla^2 v_i \qquad (2.4.16)$$

the factor ν is called the *kinematic viscosity*:

$$\nu = \frac{\eta}{\rho_0} \qquad (2.4.17)$$

The problem of thermal convection in an incompressible viscous fluid of uniform properties κ, ρ_0, α, ν, with specified boundaries, gravitational potential V, and initial temperature $T = T_0 + \delta T$, is to determine the pattern of heat and material flow which is the solution of equations (2.4.6) and (2.4.16). The simplest question is the minimum temperature gradient ∇T necessary to start flow, that is, the minimum at which conduction is insufficient to carry away the heat. The first such problem solved was a horizontal layer of fluid of thickness d, potential gradient $-g$, and vertical temperature gradient β. Representing v_i by a Fourier series in three dimensions, Rayleigh [327] found that convection would occur for

$$\frac{g\alpha\beta}{\kappa\nu} d^4 > R = \frac{27}{14} \pi^4 = 657.5 \text{ for two free boundaries}$$

$$\text{or } 1100.7, \text{ one fixed, one free boundary}$$

$$\text{or } 1707.8, \text{ two fixed boundaries} \qquad (2.4.18)$$

Similar such *Rayleigh numbers R* have since been found for other boundary conditions, including spherical shells. The solutions obtained apply only if the gradient β slightly exceeds the minimum required for onset of convection. As the gradient β is further increased, there is a breakdown of the flow into a more and more complicated pattern.

The effect of adding a Coriolis term $2\boldsymbol{\omega} \times \mathbf{v}$ on the right of (2.4.16) is to increase the Rayleigh number R, an effect expressed by the dimensionless ratio $4\omega^2 d^4/\nu^2$, called the *Taylor number*. For Coriolis effects to be significant, the Taylor number must exceed unity [216].

The Coriolis effect is important in the more fluid parts of the earth such as in meteorological problems. However, if the viscosity as expressed by the factor ν in (2.4.16) is increased to the values appropriate to application to the mantle, a difference of about ten orders of magnitude, then the Coriolis becomes a negligibly smaller effect. Much more important is the likelihood that the heating is from sources distributed throughout the convective regime, the mantle, rather than from below the convecting layer. In geological time— about 4.5 Æ—the heat generated by radioactivity will be appreciable. The replacement of the Rayleigh number suggested is to eliminate the term β, the temperature gradient given in (2.4.18), and substitute a term that depends on (1) the amount of radioactive heat generation; (2) the amount of heat absorbed, expressed by the specific heat per unit volume, ρC_p; and (3) the amount of heat carried away, dependent on the thermal diffusivity, κ. To make this replacement of the proper dimensions of degrees/length a further factor of length would have to be applied to make total replacement

$$\beta \to \frac{Ad}{\rho C_p \kappa} \qquad (2.4.19)$$

The new Rayleigh number for internal heat generation then would be

$$Rh = \frac{g\alpha A}{\kappa^2 \nu \rho C_p} d^5$$

$$= \frac{g\alpha A}{\kappa^2 \eta C_p} d^5 \qquad (2.4.20)$$

using (2.4.17) [399]. The mathematical theory of convection with the heat source contained in the convecting material has not been worked out, but one would expect the critical Rayleigh numbers for transfer to different regimes of flow to be of the same general magnitude as they are for the layers heated from below: about 2000 for a spherical shell with the ratio of inner to outer radii of the mantle.

Let us summarize at this point the numbers we already have pertinent to this Rayleigh number.

$$g = 980 \text{ cm sec}^{-2}$$
$$\alpha \approx 2 \times 10^{-5} \, {}^\circ C^{-1}$$
$$d = 2.9 \times 10^8 \text{ cm} \qquad (2.4.21)$$
$$\kappa \approx 0.01 \text{ cm}^2 \text{ sec}^{-1}$$
$$C_p \approx 10^7 \text{ ergs gm}^{-1} \, {}^\circ C^{-1}$$

The two numbers missing are those for viscosity, η, and the rate of heat generation, A. As discussed in the section on anelasticity and creep, the significant rates of motion are still unobservable in the laboratory and we must use such geological phenomena as we have to deduce a viscosity. The phenomena used are the removal of the iceload of the ice age in the last few thousand years and the evaporation of water from a lake in comparable time. Treating the crust as an elastic layer over a layered viscous halfspace, uniform in its properties, the theory predicts that the time of decay of the depression in the elastic crust after removal of a load will be inversely proportional to the scale of the area depressed. Observations indicate, however, that this is not true; the decay time for the uplift of the Fenno-scandian area, about 1200 km across, is 5300 years, whereas the uplift for the area of Bonneville Lake (around the modern Salt Lake), about 180 km in diameter, is 4000 years. Hence, from the two phenomena we deduce viscosities differing by an order-of-magnitude. However, if it is assumed that the viscosity varies with depth, then we obtain the expected result that the smaller-scale depressions would depend more on viscosity at shallow depth than larger-scale depressions. These two phenomena as well as the details of higher order of variation in the Fennoscandian uplift lead to a model in which the viscosity is of the order of 5×10^{21} poises immediately below the crust; a minimum of about 3×10^{21} poises at depths of 200 to 400 km; and increasing to the order of 10^{23} poises at depths more than 1200 km [267]. (One poise is one gm cm^{-1} sec^{-1}.)

Another phenomenon that may give some indication of viscosity is the discrepancy of the actual oblateness of the earth from that corresponding to hydrostatic equilibrium. If we assume that it arises from a time lag of the adjustment of the earth as a whole to the slowing down of the rate of rotation of the earth due to tidal friction. We obtain from the discrepancy between the observed and theoretical oblateness of the earth a decay time on the order of 10^7 years, which in turn indicates a viscosity of 10^{26} gm cm^{-1} sec^{-1} [253]. An alternative explanation which could permit a much lower viscosity is that it is a consequence of the tendency of many random irregularities to align themselves about axes of maximum moment of inertia [541]. However, since the extrapolation from solid-state theory (Figure 2.16) indicates a considerable rise in viscosity with depth below 500 km, for numerical estimates let us adopt viscosities of:

$$\text{Upper mantle:}\ \eta \approx 10^{22}\ \text{gm cm}^{-1}\ \text{sec}^{-1}$$

$$\text{Lower mantle:}\ \eta \approx 10^{26}\ \text{gm cm}^{-1}\ \text{sec}^{-1}$$

$$(2.4.22)$$

Heat Sources

For the other parameter, A, we can, of course, take laboratory determinations of the chemical content of the radioactive elements in common rocks and from these calculate the ergs gm^{-1} yr^{-1} of the rock we would expect to be generated from this radioactive content. Averages of these determinations are shown in Table 2.3. The range for each rock type is generally peaked near the mean, with about 90 percent of the determinations between one-third and three times the mean. An exception is eclogite, which has a bimodal distribution.

The most prominent thing indicated by the table, as discussed in Section 1.1, is the tremendous upward concentration of the radioactive materials within the earth. The average radioactive content of the granite, for example,

TABLE 2.3: RADIOACTIVE CONTENT OF ROCKS

Rock	Chemical Content (ppm)			Heat Generation (10^{-6} cal gm^{-1} yr^{-1})	
	U	Th	K	Present	Original ($t = -4.5\ \AE$)
Granite	4.75	18.5	37,900	8.15	33.28
Diorite	2.0	(7.4)	18,000	3.40	14.47
Basalt	0.6	2.7	8,400	1.19	5.27
Periodotite	0.016	(0.06)	12	0.024	0.080
Dunite	0.001	(0.004)	10	0.001	0.007
Eclogite	0.048	0.18	360	0.074	0.328
	0.25	0.45	2,600	0.335	1.786
Chrondrites	0.012	0.04	845	0.038	0.286

Based on MacDonald [225, p. 194] and Lee [239].

is about 4000 times that of dunite.

The averages given in the table are rather crude in some cases. Much more consistent among different determinations than absolute abundances are the *ratios* of the radioactive elements. The Th/U ratio is generally about 4, whereas the K/U ratio is always in the vicinity of 10^4. Chondritic meteorites differ distinctly from earthly rocks in this respect, in that the K/U ratio is about 8×10^4. The present heat generation figures are calculated from the values of 0.71 cal gm^{-1} yr^{-1} for U^{238}, 4.3 cal gm^{-1} yr^{-1} for U^{235}, 0.2 cal gm^{-1} yr^{-1} for Th^{232} and 0.21 cal gm^{-1} yr^{-1} for K^{40}. These values are multiplied by the isotope abundance ratios of 0.9928 for U^{238}/U, 0.0072 for U^{235}/U, and 0.000119 for K^{40}/K to calculate the present heat generation. To get the original heat generation we then use the decay constants given in Table 1.8.

The uncertainty as to radioactive content of the rocks has led to the essential control on thermal models of the earth being the observed heat flow through the earth's surface. This flow averages approximately 1.4×10^{-6} cal cm^{-2} sec^{-1}. The radioactive content A then must be such that this observed heat is not exceeded if the thermal history of the earth is solved as a purely conductive problem (2.4.8). Solving the thermal history of the earth by (2.4.8) in this manner with the radioactive contents of the chondritic meteorites, which appear to have in the common elements a chemical content which may be that of the entire earth, does yield such agreement in the observed heat flow. More recently, however, it has been emphasized that the K/U ratio in meteorites differs appreciably from the K/U ratio in rocks. Furthermore, the atmospheric content of the products of the radioactive decay, the Ar^{40}/He^4 ratio, would agree better with a lower K/U ratio. The two models resulting from these two considerations are given in Table 2.4: the chondritic model and the model that reflects the K/U ratio of 10^4 of earthly rocks, known as the "Wasserberg" model [426]. The Th/U ratio of

TABLE 2.4: HEAT SOURCE MODELS OF THE MANTLE

Element	Half-life (Æ)	Chondritic Model			"Wasserberg" Model		
		Content (ppm)	Heat $(10^{-6}$ cal gm^{-1} yr$^{-1})$		Content (ppm)	Heat $(10^{-6}$ cal gm^{-1} yr$^{-1})$	
			Present	Original		Present	Original
U	4.5	0.012	0.009	0.046	0.045	0.033	0.174
Th	13.9	0.04	0.008	0.010	0.166	0.033	0.042
K	1.3	815.0	0.020	0.222	450.0	0.011	0.122
Total			0.037	0.278		0.077	0.338

the Wasserberg model is taken as 3.7. The basic absolute quantity thus is the uranium content. The value of 0.045 ppm is one which gives approximately the observed heat flow in the solution of (2.4.8) for the earth [239, 255].

By using the figure of 0.077×10^{-6} cal gm^{-1} yr^{-1} together with the conversion factors of 4.19×10^{7} ergs/cal, 3.15×10^{7} sec/yr and mean density of the mantle, 4.5 gm/cm^3, we get as our parameter $A(r, t)$:

$$A(0.8R, 0) \approx 0.5 \times 10^{-6} \text{ erg cm}^{-3} \text{ sec}^{-1}$$
$$A(0.8R, -4.5 \text{ Æ}) \approx 2.0 \times 10^{-6} \text{ erg cm}^{-3} \text{ sec}^{-1} \qquad (2.4.23)$$

Thermal-History Models

Using 2000 as the critical value of Rh and the numerical values for all the parameters except the length scale d, we get that the critical value is exceeded provided d exceeds

$$\text{Upper mantle: } d \geqslant (40 \times 10^{35})^{1/5} \text{ cm} \approx 200 \text{ km}$$
$$\text{Lower mantle: } d \geqslant (4 \times 10^{40})^{1/5} \text{ cm} \approx 1300 \text{ km} \qquad (2.4.24)$$

Thus it seems almost certain that even if we neglect the order-of-magnitude changes in viscosity with localized changes in temperature that there has been convection in the mantle. Convection affects the thermal history in two ways. The transport of heat by the advective term $\mathbf{v} \cdot \nabla T$ in (2.4.7) is probably less important than the transport of the heat sources $A(t)$, combined with the process of fractionation, which results in the upward migration of the U, Th, K because of their inability to fit in the earlier crystallizing portions of melts: a sort of zone melting process [529]. A thermal history calculation assuming a mantle part dunite, part basalt, in which U, Th, K are transferred upward as a consequence of melting of the basalt fraction, obtained the final temperature curve marked B in Figure 2.17. Disregard of such upward fraction results in the unrealistically high curve A. Also shown in Figure 2.17 are melting curves for dunite and basalt and an estimate of the actual temperature from the electrical conductivity of the mantle (see Section 3.2) [239].

Other difficulties we have not touched upon here are the effect of the removal of heat accompanying the phase transition which appears to exist between 400 and 900 km deep, and the original starting temperature of the earth. If we take the amount of matter in the earth and calculate the heat available from loss of gravitational energy (see problem 2.13) then we have a tremendous amount of energy available which is essentially controlled by the rate of accumulation of the earth and its atmosphere which determines in turn the balance point between the gain of heat from the gravitational source and the loss of heat by radiation. Also involved in the time and rate of formation of the earth are short-lived radioactive elements, the most important of these being an isotope of aluminum, Al^{26}, which has a half-life on the

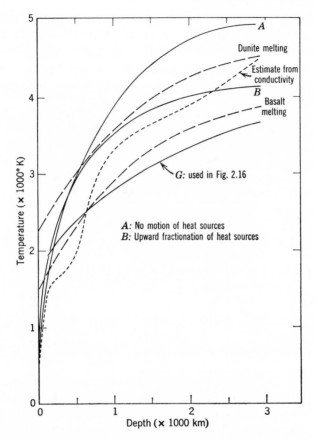

Figure 2.17: Temperature estimates in the mantle from thermal history calculations. From Lee [239, p. 259] and Gordon [147].

order of one million years. If the earth was formed within 10^6 years after the formation of Al^{26}, then there would be a large increment of heat from this source [59].

Heat-Flow Measurements

The measurement of heat flow out of the earth has developed only within the past 25 years. On land it requires a rather deep drill hole in which there must be measured at different points the difference in temperature. Samples of the material are taken to measure the thermal conductivity, and hence to obtain the heat flow, essentially by application of (2.4.2). The difficulties, aside from the expense of drilling a hole (which results in most land heat-flow measurements being in oil fields), are the necessity of allowing the hole to regain thermal equilibrium and the lateral transfer of heat by groundwater. Much more successful has been the measurement of heat flow in the oceans, where it is done by inserting a probe into the sediments in the bottom of the ocean, which are already in thermal equilibrium because of the mollifying effect of the ocean, and removing a core for the purpose of the conductivity measurements [238].

The results of heat-flow measurements indicate that the bulk of the measurements are in the range of about 0.8 to 2.0 $\times$ 10^{-6} cal cm^{-2} sec^{-1}. However, over localized areas the heat flow may increase to 6.0 $\times$ 10^{-6}. The areas which have been most characterized by these high heat flows are the crests of the ocean ridges. The distribution of heat-flow data is such that it is difficult to give a worldwide picture of distribution. Perhaps the most meaningful values we can give are those for seven types of areas [75]:

Continents:	Precambrian shield:	0.92 ± 0.17
Continents:	Paleozoic orogenic areas:	1.23 ± 0.4
Continents:	Post-Precambrian nonorogenic areas:	1.54 ± 0.58
Continents:	Mesozoic-Cenozoic orogenic areas:	1.92 ± 0.49
Oceans:	Trenches:	0.99 ± 0.61
Oceans:	Basins:	1.28 ± 0.53
Oceans	Ridges:	1.82 ± 1.56

$$\mu\text{cal cm}^{-2} \text{sec}^{-1}$$

2.5   Construction of a Model of the Mantle

The synthesis of the geochemical, geological, and geophysical information pertaining to the earth's interior described in the first two chapters can be done in stages: first, the construction of a static central model, a body that is in hydrostatic equilibrium and whose properties, density, temperature, chemical content, etc., are functions of the radius only; and second, a non-central model that entails lateral variations. The lateral variations are of interest not only in accounting for much of the observational data, but also, very likely, in explaining several properties of the central model.

Central Model of the Earth

The construction of the central model can be described briefly as: given the likely materials of the earth as indicated by the geochemical considerations, and their properties as measured in the laboratory, combined with the geophysical information we have of the variations of the conditions within the earth (the mass distribution, elastic properties, heat flow, etc.), can we construct a model that is consistent with chemical homogeneity of the material? If such homogeneity is not possible, then may the data be accounted for by phase transitions? Finally, where changes in physical properties are too great to be phase changes, what are the most likely changes in chemical substance?

As emphasized in the very beginning at Table 1.1, we are concerned mainly about the construction of a model of the mantle. The procedure to be followed is essentially that of Birch [31, 75]. The principal petrological datum is that the density of the material at the top of the mantle is about 3.3 gm/cm³. From (2.1.47) we have that the pressure P should change with radius according to:

$$\frac{dP}{dr} = g\rho \qquad (2.5.1)$$

in which we have substituted the gravity acceleration g for $-dV/dr$. The change in density with pressure is expressed by

$$\frac{d\rho}{dP} = \frac{\rho}{k} \qquad (2.5.2)$$

where k is the bulk modulus, originally appearing in (2.2.5). The bulk modulus can be measured, of course, in the laboratory for the likely materials of the earth at pressures which apply to the upper mantle. However, from the seismic wave theory of Section 2.2 and the velocities of seismic waves within the earth given by Table 2.2, we can derive directly the bulk modulus within the earth. Substituting from (2.2.5) for λ in (2.2.17) and using V_p in place of α for the compressional wave, V_s in place of β for the shear wave, we obtain

$$V_p^2 = \frac{(k + 4\mu/3)}{\rho}$$

$$V_s^2 = \frac{\mu}{\rho} \qquad (2.5.3)$$

then the bulk modulus k can be obtained by eliminating μ:

$$\frac{k}{\rho} = V_p^2 - \frac{4V_s^2}{3} = \varphi \qquad (2.5.4)$$

Finally combining (2.5.1, 2, 4) we get:

$$\frac{d\rho}{dr} = \frac{-g\rho}{\varphi} \qquad (2.5.5)$$

known as the *Adams-Williamson relationship*. With this relationship, the values of φ determined from observations, and the equation for the change in g,

$$\frac{dg}{dr} = 4\pi G\rho - \frac{2g}{r} \qquad (2.5.6)$$

we can start with the given density of 3.3 gm/cm³ and acceleration 980 cm/sec²
at the top of the mantle and numerically integrate downward through the
mantle to get the variation in density. As controls on this integration to
obtain density, we have the quantities given from geodesy at the end of
Section 2.1: the values of C, the moment of inertia about the rotation axis;
a, the radius; and GM, the gravitational constant times mass. For the central
problem we would prefer the mean moment of inertia I and the mean
radius R:

$$I = 8.0235 \times 10^{44} \, \text{gm/cm}^2$$

$$R = 6371040 \, \text{meters} \tag{2.5.7}$$

$$M = 5.976 \times 10^{27} \, \text{gm}$$

Integrating in this manner from the top to the bottom of the mantle, then
using the values in (2.5.7), subtracting out the crust as given in Table 1.1 plus
the mantle as just calculated, gives as the ratio $I_c/M_c R_c^2$ 0.57: closer to the
ratio for a hollow sphere than that for a uniform density sphere. Hence the
assumptions on which the calculation was based are incorrect. These assumptions were: homogeneity—that it was the same material and phase throughout; and adiabaticity—that the compression took place in such a manner that
there was no transfer of energy through flow of heat. This assumption was
made implicitly by using the bulk modulus k obtained from seismic waves:
seismic waves are of such high frequency that the transfer of heat in a cycle is
negligible. That the bulk modulus is the adiabatic we shall hereafter denote by
the subscript s: k_s. The effect of heat upon density is expressed, of course,
through the coefficient of thermal expansion α, and, hence, if there is a radial
gradient of temperature $\partial T/\partial r$, we can expect a corresponding radial gradient
of density, $\rho\alpha\partial T/\partial r$. To combine this with (2.5.5) for a static model, however,
we must use the isothermal bulk modulus, k_T, obtaining

$$\frac{d\rho}{dr} = -\frac{g\rho^2}{k_T} - \rho\alpha\frac{dT}{dr} \tag{2.5.8}$$

To use this isothermal relationship with the adiabatic data k_s we need the
change of temperature with pressure, the Clausius-Clapeyron relationship
(1.2.24). In this equation we replace the heat change Δq by the specific heat at
constant pressure times the temperature change, $C_p\Delta T$; and we replace the
specific volume change ΔV by the coefficient of thermal expansion times the
temperature change divided by the density, $\alpha\Delta T/\rho$, to obtain

$$\left(\frac{dT}{dP}\right)_s = \frac{\alpha T}{\rho C_p} \tag{2.5.9}$$

whence, using (2.5.1),

$$\frac{dT}{dr} = \left(\frac{\partial T}{\partial P}\right)_s \frac{dP}{dr} - \tau = -\frac{T\alpha g}{C_p} - \tau \qquad (2.5.10)$$

in which τ is the *superadiabatic gradient*, which we have shown with negative sign to accord with a temperature increase with depth. To relate the incompressibilities k_T and k_s we have,

$$V = V(P, T)$$

$$\left(\frac{dV}{dP}\right)_s = \left(\frac{dV}{dP}\right)_T + \left(\frac{\partial V}{\partial T}\right)_S \left(\frac{\partial T}{\partial P}\right)_S$$

$$-\frac{V}{k_s} = -\frac{V}{k_T} + \alpha V \frac{\alpha T}{\rho C_p}$$

Substituting (2.5.10) and

$$\frac{1}{k_T} = \frac{1}{k_s} + \frac{\alpha^2 T}{\rho C_p} \qquad (2.5.11)$$

in (2.5.8), and using (2.5.4), again we get

$$\frac{d\rho}{dr} = -\frac{g\rho}{\varphi} + \alpha\rho\tau \qquad (2.5.12)$$

Using values approximating those at a depth of about 30 km in the first term on the right of (2.5.10),

$$T = 750°K$$

$$\alpha = 2 \times 10^{-5}$$

$$C_P = 10^7 \text{ ergs cm}^{-3} °C^{-1}$$

$$g = 980 \text{ cm/sec}^2$$

we get a very small adiabatic temperature gradient $(\partial T/\partial r)_s$ of only about 0.15°C/km. This is much less than temperature gradients deduced from the observed surface heat flow of 1.5×10^{-6} cal cm^{-2} sec^{-1} and the conductivity K of about 10^{-2} cal cm^{-1} sec^{-1} °C^{-1}: more than 10°/km. Hence near the surface almost the entire temperature gradient must be superadiabatic. Deep in the mantle, however, where the temperature may be in excess of 3000°C and hence where the conductivity is much higher, as suggested by (2.4.9), the gradient must be quite close to adiabatic. Using the gradient 10°/km for τ and the value of 43 km²/sec² deduced for φ by using values in Table 2.2 and (2.5.4), we get that the second term in (2.5.12) is about equal to the first term. Going deep into the mantle g remains approximately constant, ρ increases but φ increases a good deal more. α, which is related to the density and compressibility through the Grüneisen constant γ by (1.2.41), will not change very much, whereas τ, because of the increase in thermal conductivity, will decrease appreciably. The variable that we will need to examine further to determine whether it changes significantly with pressure is the bulk modulus k.

The deduction of the appropriate change of incompressibility k with pressure can be done in several ways, such as thermodynamic theory or by something more fundamental. We follow Birch [31] by making the assumption that the change of compressibility with pressure for the silicates of the earth will follow similar to more compressible substances and their behavior under pressure in the laboratory. Mathematically, a change of incompressibility k with pressure is equivalent to adding second-degree terms, nonlinear terms, to the equation for strain e_{ij} (2.2.2):

$$e_{ij} = \frac{1}{2}\left(\frac{\partial u_i}{\partial x_j} + \frac{\partial u_j}{\partial x_i}\right) - \frac{1}{2}\sum_k \frac{\partial u_k}{\partial x_i} \cdot \frac{\partial u_k}{\partial x_j} \qquad (2.5.13)$$

For the case of hydrostatic strain of an isotropic medium we can write this in terms of a single component

$$e = \frac{\partial u}{\partial x} - \frac{1}{2}\left(\frac{\partial u}{\partial x}\right)^2 \qquad (2.5.14)$$

The relation between strain e and density ρ is

$$\frac{v_0}{v} = \frac{\rho}{\rho_0} = (1 - 2e)^{3/2} = (1 + 2f)^{3/2} \qquad (2.5.15)$$

where the negative of the strain f has been used to make it more convenient in the case of compression. For hydrostatic pressure alone we should expect that the strain energy can be expressed in the form of a power series in f with coefficients which are functions only of temperature

$$\psi = \sum_{i=2}^{\infty} a_i(T)f^i \qquad (2.5.16)$$

Whence from the expression $-PdV$ for a change $d\psi$ in the strain energy we get for the pressure

$$P = -\frac{df}{dv}\left(\frac{\partial \psi}{\partial f}\right)_T = \frac{1}{3v_0}(1 + 2f)^{5/2}\sum_{i=2}^{\infty} a_i i f^{i-1} \qquad (2.5.17)$$

From (2.2.12) the strain energy ψ at very small pressure will be $9k_0 f^2/2$. Substituting this for the first term in the series ψ and retaining only the $i = 2$ and $i = 3$ terms of the series, we obtain for P

$$P = 3k_0 f(1 + 2f)^{5/2}(1 - 2\xi f) \qquad (2.5.18)$$

or for the incompressibility k

$$k_T = k_0(1 + 2f)^{5/2}[1 + 7f - 2\xi f(2 + 9f)] \qquad (2.5.19)$$

The dimensionless parameter ξ is a function of temperature only and is a measure of the nonlinearity of the variation of incompressibility. From experimental data on the highly compressible alkali metals Li, K, Na, etc., Birch deduced that ξ was virtually 0. It is estimated that the dk/dP of silicates at the pressures existing in the mantle is between 3 and 4 [31].

For the variation of the thermal expansion α with pressure there is similarly obtained

$$\frac{\alpha}{\alpha_0} = 1 + \frac{qP}{k} \qquad (2.5.20)$$

The parameter q is normally about -4 [75].

Using this refined theory and starting the integration with $\rho = 3.32$ at the top of the mantle, we find that at depths less than 400 km the dominant factor is a rate of change of temperature dT/dr considerably above adiabatic. In other words, the parameter τ in (2.5.10, 12) is important. If this parameter exceeds a certain amount (6–10°C/km), the velocity decreases with depth. Such a decrease is observed to occur, in fact, in the large part of the earth, as discussed in Section 2.2. Below 400 km the relationship (2.5.12) breaks down; it is apparent that the phase transitions discussed in Section 1.2 must take place. This zone of change of a rate of increase of density ρ and compressibility k incompatible with (2.5.12) continues down to about 900 km. Below 900 km the changes in ρ and k are again consistent with a single substance. However, at these depths the compression is great enough that the nonlinear terms must be taken into account. A best fit to the seismic data is obtained with a value of about 0.2 for the nonlinear parameter ξ in (2.5.18, 19) [75].

For the composition of the mantle and the thermal regime some of the more important considerations are:

1. Because of the predominance of basaltic lava throughout geological time, the low melting fraction of the material of the mantle should be basaltic.

2. The absence of sizable gravity anomalies using a reasonable value for the coefficient of thermal expansion indicates relatively small variations in temperature at depths below about 400 km.

3. The distribution of heat flow values, as listed at the end of Section 2.4, limits the distribution of heat sources.

4. Variations in seismic characteristics between oceans and continents as deep as 400 km indicate that a good part of the upper mantle is essentially a transition zone.

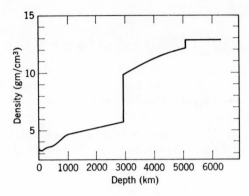

Figure 2.18: Density curve in the earth—pyrolite model. Based on Clark & Ringwood [75, p. 67].

Of the rocks described in Section 1.1, two appear most likely: first, eclo-gite, which can be a phase transition from basalt; and second, a combination of dunite and basalt, which has been called *pyrolite* by Ringwood [75, 340]. The lack of correlation between crustal thickness and the heat-flow variations make the basalt-eclogite phase transition very unlikely, however, as an explanation for the Moho. The difficulty in finding a reasonable model is that indicated by Tables 2.3 and 2.4. If basaltic material is to be important in the mantle, it must be depleted in the radioactive materials, uranium, thorium, and potassium, compared with the average basalts found at the surface. As mentioned in Section 2.4, however, there is quite a wide range of radiogenic contents of the basalts. To reconcile the values of heat flow for the oceans, shields, and continents with the differing contributions in the crusts likely in these different areas, a model which is uniform below 400 km must have on the order of 0.5 μcal cm^{-2} sec^{-1} from depths greater than 400 km. The temperature profiles resulting from these models of heat source distribu-tion together with heat transfer by thermal conduction only obtain tempera-ture profiles that manage to stay just short of melting in the upper mantle.

With the modifications in the calculation of mantle density described above, the ratio $I_c/M_cR_c^2$ obtained for the core is quite reasonable—about 0.39. The resulting density required in the core would correspond to a com-position of about 80 percent iron and 20 percent silica. The entire results for density are given in Figure 2.18.

Lateral Variations in the Earth's Interior

For the lateral irregularities on a large scale the data that are probably the most accurately known now are the variations of the gravitational field, as described in Section 2.1. If we take the topography and the gravity as expressed by the harmonic coefficients C_{lm}, S_{lm} in Table 2.1 and assume that these coefficients are due to the topography plus density irregularities supported elastically, then to have a determinate problem we must make a further assumption. The simplest assumption is that the shearing strain energy, the part of the strain energy W in (2.2.11) that depends on the rigidity, is a minimum summed throughout the mantle. If we assume zero interaction between different harmonics the resulting equations will be the same as those of the free oscillations (2.2.53), with the frequency $\sigma = 0$ and with the density variation appearing in the second equation through its effect on the compressive stress and in the sixth equation through its effect on the Poisson equation. The solution resulting is that the maximum shearing stress differences in the mantle are on the order of 100 bars. The maximum density irregularities $\Delta\rho$ are about 5×10^{-4} gm/cm^3 [204]. Using this $\Delta\rho$ with an extrapolated thermal expansion coefficient α of about $10^{-5}/°C$ in (2.5.10) and (2.4.11) yields temperature irregularities ΔT of only about 10°C.

The discussion of creep in Section 2.3, however, suggests that at elevated temperatures even 100 bars are difficult for silicates to sustain over geological times of a million years or more. If we take the indications of paleomagnetism, Figures 3.7 and 3.8, there are motions with velocity on the order of 10 km per million years or 1 cm/yr or 3×10^{-8} cm/sec. At such rates heat transfer would be dominated by convection since from (2.4.18)

$$Lv \gg \kappa = \frac{K}{\rho C_p} \qquad (2.5.21)$$

$$3 \times 10^8 \times 3 \times 10^{-8} \gg \frac{0.006}{4 \times 0.25}$$

The corresponding viscosity would be obtained by substituting ηv for μu in the elastic equations. Taking the 30-meter displacements as equivalent to the 100-bar stresses we have

$$\eta \approx \frac{u}{v}\mu = \frac{3 \times 10^3}{3 \times 10^{-7}} 10^{12} \approx 10^{22} \text{ gm cm}^{-1} \text{ sec}^{-1} \qquad (2.5.22)$$

which is about equal to the viscosity deduced from the Fennoscandian uplift for the uppermost 1000 km of the mantle.

It is a somewhat more difficult matter to make a realistic solution for a convecting mantle than to say that convection is probably significant. Many solutions that have been carried out are valid only at Rayleigh numbers just above critical (2.4.18) [68]. However, as discussed in Section 2.4, the Rayleigh number for the entire mantle is certainly well in excess of critical. The question then becomes: given that the convection is broken down into smaller cells of a scale d (2.4.24), is the flow steady and laminar, or is it unsteady and turbulent? In other words, once a system of flow exists, will it persist in the same pattern, or will it be continually breaking down and forming new patterns? The number that pertains to this question is the *Prandtl number Pr*:

$$Pr = \frac{\nu}{\kappa} \qquad (2.5.23)$$

where ν is the kinematic viscosity (2.4.17), and κ is the thermal diffusivity (2.4.5). The significance of the Prandtl number is most clearly brought out if we adopt in the Navier-Stokes equation (2.4.16) the distance d as the unit of length, the temperature change $d\beta$ across this distance as the unit of temperature, d^2/κ as the unit of time, and $\rho_0 d^3 \nu/\kappa$ as the unit of mass. Let us also replace $\partial V/\partial x_i$ by $-gx_i/r$ and subtract out the hydrostatic term $(\partial p_0/\partial r)/\rho_0 + g$ on the right of (2.4.16). The flow equation then becomes, using (2.4.18) for R, δp for $p - p_0$,

$$\frac{1}{Pr}\left(\frac{\partial v_i}{\partial t} + v_j \frac{\partial v_i}{\partial x_j}\right) = -\frac{\partial \delta p}{\partial x_i} + R\, \delta T\, \frac{x_i}{r} + \nabla^2 v_i \qquad (2.5.24)$$

Hence for a large Prandtl number Pr the inertial terms on the left of (2.5.24) are unimportant and the flow will be steady. For the values given by (2.4.21) and (2.4.22) the Prandtl number is indeed extremely large: on the order of 10^{23} to 10^{27}.

Using (2.5.24) with the left side zero and the heat-flow equation (2.4.6) with $\partial T/\partial t$ zero, Turcotte and Oxburgh [507] obtain solutions for $d = 1500$ km which yield surface velocities of about 4 cm/yr and heat fluxes approximating those across ocean ridges. However, there are still difficulties:

1. The Navier-Stokes equation may not be applicable to the upper mantle, because of the dependence of viscosity on stress through dislocation climb and grain boundary effects, as discussed in Section 2.3.

2. The probable great variation of viscosity with depth due to temperature and pressure dependence as in Figure 2.16 may drastically change the convective flow pattern from the analytic solution.

3. The rate of change in temperature $\partial T/\partial t$ is not zero, because of radiogenic heat.

4. The sources of radiogenic heat probably have been moved upward appreciably by fractionation, as discussed in Section 2.4.

5. The upper boundary of the convective system, the crust, is by no means smooth; there are great variations in stress, as manifest by the upheavals of mountain building, etc.

6. The phase transitions at depths 400–900 km have latent heats associated

with them which may significantly modify the superadiabatic temperature gradient.

7. The rough equality of heat flow on the continents and oceans suggests that there are a comparable number of heat sources in a given vertical section and hence that there has been relatively little horizontal motion, i.e., motion in each particular large region has occurred essentially within the vertical columns [253].

8. The seismic evidence suggests that the difference between continents and oceans extends fairly deep in the upper mantle, some 200 km or so. Hence the mechanism of continental drift is difficult to visualize. Although there could plausibly be a thin layer of 20 km or so sliding around on the surface, it is hard to think of a block a couple of hundred kilometers thick plowing its way through denser material.

9. The apparent geological pattern of growth of the continents by accretion over some 3×10^9 years is difficult to reconcile with their being shoved around a lot by convective currents.

In summary, we now have a good static central model of the earth, based mainly on geochemical and seismic evidence. However, there is definitely a need for a better understanding of the manner in which flow has occurred within the earth in order to account for the geological processes of mountain building, etc.; the extreme fractionation of materials; and the paleomagnetic and other evidences of large-scale motions at the surface, within the restraining conditions of the observed fields of gravity and heat flow. The marked evidence of sea-floor spreading, together with the relative newness of the sea floor, suggests that the ocean offers the more assimilable boundary conditions for theories of upper-mantle flow.

PROBLEMS

2.1. In the expression (2.1.17) for the gravitational potential of a planet, prove that locating the coordinate origin at the center of mass makes the coefficient $C_{00} = 1$ and the coefficients $C_{10} = C_{11} = S_{11} = 0$.

2.2. Derive the generation of zonal harmonics $P_{l0}(\cos \psi)$, as defined by substituting $\cos \psi$ for $\sin \varphi$ and $\sin \psi$ for $\cos \varphi$ in (2.1.16), from:

$$\frac{1}{q} = [r^2 + R^2 - 2rR \cos \psi]^{-1/2} = \frac{1}{r} \sum_{l=0}^{\infty} \left(\frac{R}{r}\right)^l P_{l0}(\cos \psi)$$

2.3. Prove

$$\int_0^\pi [P_{l0}(\cos \psi)]^2 \sin \psi \, d\psi = \frac{2}{2l + 1}$$

2.4. Prove the addition theorem for spherical harmonics; that is, a zonal harmonic $P_{l0}(\cos \psi)$ which is a function of arc distance ψ from a pole at φ', λ' transforms to

$$P_{l0}(\cos \psi) = P_{l0}(\sin \varphi')P_{l0}(\sin \varphi)$$

$$+ 2 \sum_m \frac{(l - m)!}{(l + m)!} P_{lm}(\sin \varphi')P_{lm}(\sin \varphi) \cos m(\lambda - \lambda')$$

where $\cos \psi = \sin \varphi' \sin \varphi + \cos \varphi' \cos \varphi \cos (\lambda - \lambda')$.

2.5. The order-of-magnitude of third-degree coefficients C_{3m}, S_{3m} in the earth's potential is about $\pm 1.0 \times 10^{-6}$. If these variations in the gravitational field are due to undulations in the core-mantle interface, what must be the order-of-magnitude (in kilometers) of the undulations, assuming a density jump about equal to that given by Figure 2.18: 5.4 gm/cm^3?

2.6. Derive an expression for Stoke's function $S(\cos \theta)$ as a sum of surface spherical harmonics, where $S(\cos \theta)$ is defined by

$$N = \frac{R}{4\pi g} \int\limits_{\text{sphere}} S(\cos \theta) \, \Delta g \, d\sigma$$

N = geoid height (2.1.43), g = mean acceleration of gravity

R = radius, θ = arc distance on sphere, Δg = gravity anomaly (2.1.44)

$d\sigma$ = element of surface area

2.7. (a) *Given*: mass $M = 5.97 \times 10^{27}$ gm, rotation $\omega = 0.729 \times 10^{-4}$ rad/sec, radius of earth $= 6.37 \times 10^3$ km, radius of core $= 3.39 \times 10^3$ km, second zonal harmonic of potential $J_2 = 0.001083$.

(b) *Assume*: (1) hydrostatic equilibrium; (2) constant density in mantle; (3) constant density in core.

(c) *Calculate*: (1) density of mantle; (2) density of core.

2.8. Assume that the wave in (2.2.15) is propagating spherically from a point. What will be the form of the wave equation? What will be the solution?

Assume that the wave equation (2.2.15) applies in only two dimensions, that is the wave is confined to a plane. Assume further that the wave propagates in a circle from a point. What will now be the form of the wave equation? Taking $y = R(r)T(t)$, what standard type of function will R be?

2.9. Using (2.2.17–26), and making the Poisson assumption $\lambda = \mu$ of (2.2.7), show that the velocity c of Rayleigh waves falls in the limits

$$0.9\beta < c < \beta$$

2.10. Using Snell's law ($v/\sin i = v'/\sin i'$ across an interface) prove that the parameter

$$p = \frac{r \sin i}{v}$$

where r is the radius of a concentric shell, i is an angle of incidence, and v is velocity, is constant for a given ray of a seismic wave.

2.12. Use the spherical Bessel functions of (2.2.45) to solve for the period of oscillation $_0T_2$ of the moon (radius 1.738×10^8 cm), assuming constant density $\rho = 3.32$ gm/cm^3 and elastic moduli $\lambda = \mu = 7.38 \times 10^{11}$ dynes/cm^2 (use a table of Bessel functions, e.g., pp. 457–459 of Abramovitz and Stegun, *Handbook of Mathematical Functions*, Dover, 1965).

2.13. If a particle of mass dm is brought from infinity to a mass M of radius r, the change in potential energy $GMdm/r$ is transformed into heat. Treating the origin of the earth as an accumulation of particles from infinity in this manner, how many calories per gram of heat are gained this way, if no heat is radiated?

Assume a constant rate of mass accumulation per surface area $d\tau/dt$ (dimensions $ML^{-2}T^{-1}$) and radiation of heat from the surface of a black body,

$$\dot{E} = \sigma T^4$$

where σ is the Stefan-Boltzmann constant 5.68×10^{-5} erg cm^{-2} °K^{-4} (see Section 6.2). Write equations for the mass and temperature as a function of time, assuming constant density, heat capacity, and no compression. Give the final mean temperature attained for a $d\tau/dt$ of 1 gm cm^{-2} sec^{-1} and a heat capacity of 0.25 cal gm^{-1} °C^{-1}.

2.14. Assume the temperature T at the earth's surface varies sinusoidally due to insolation. Assume that heat is transported to the interior by ordinary thermal conduction with numerical values for the parameters as given in Section 2.4. Derive an expression for the temperature at depth z for an amplitude ΔT of 20°C and a rate ω of 1 cycle/day. What is the amplitude and phase lag of the variation at a depth of 1 centimeter?

2.15. Assume a solid homogeneous planet of uniform thermal properties such that the thermal diffusivity κ is constant throughout. Further assuming no heat sources, the equation of heat conduction in spherical coordinates will be

$$\frac{\partial T(r, t)}{\partial t} = \frac{\kappa}{r^2} \frac{\partial}{\partial r}\left(r^2 \frac{\partial T}{\partial r}\right)$$

Solve the equation by assuming conductive equilibrium, whence the temperature T will have the form

$$T = R(r)\Theta(t) + \text{const}$$

and the radial function R will be a spherical Bessel function of zero order:

$$j_0(x) = \frac{1}{x}(a \cos x + b \sin x)$$

Take the boundary conditions as at the origin:

$$T(0, 0) = T_0$$

and at the surface $r = a$:

$$T(a, t) = 0$$

Assume $a = 6370$ km, $\kappa = 0.006$ cm²/sec, $T = 4000°C$, $T(a, t) = 0°C$.

How long will it take the temperature to drop to $300°C$ at the center? At a point 500 km deep?

Assuming conductivity $K = 3 \times 10^4$ ergs cm^{-1} sec^{-1} $°C^{-1}$, what will be the surface heat flow when $T = 300°C$ at 500 km depth?

2.16. Assume a perfect fluid mass of homogeneous density 5.5 gm/cm³, radius 6.37×10^8 cm, and a period of rotation of 100 min. Is this body stable: that is, assuming no outside influences, will it stay together?

Assume further that a chemical separation occurs within the planet such that a core of uniform density 12.8 gm/cm³ and a mantle of uniform density 4.2 gm/cm³ are formed. Conserving angular momentum, what will be the new period of rotation? Is the new arrangement stable: that is, will any matter become detached?

How much gravitational energy will be lost in the formation of the core? Assuming all this energy is converted into heat, no loss of heat by radiation, and a specific heat of 10^7 ergs gm^{-1} $°C^{-1}$, what will be the resulting mean increase in temperature?

2.17. Derive a formula for the hydrostatic pressure inside a homogeneous planet (neglect rotational and thermal effects). What is the pressure at the center of the moon (mass and radius given in Table 4.1), assuming it to be homogeneous?

2.18. It states on page 87 that horizontal shear (*SH*) waves, called Love waves, are possible at the free surface of a layer *M* over a half space *M'*. Prove this by extending the treatment on pages 85–86 to include the additional layer. What condition does the existence of surface *SH* waves impose on the shear (*S*) wave velocities in mediums *M* and *M'*?

REFERENCES

The outstanding treatise on the mathematical treatment of the physics of the earth's interior has long been *The Earth*, now in its fourth edition, by *Jeffreys* [199]. Much of the material discussed in this chapter was originally developed, though, by *Love* [249]. Considerable newer work is explained by *Takeuchi* [385]. Other general works giving more data are *Gutenberg* [152] and *MacDonald* [253], as well as the symposium volumes edited by *Odishaw* [289], *Hurley* [187], *Gaskell* [522], and *Runcorn* [552]. An adequate mathematical background is attainable from texts such as *Margenau & Murphy* [260] or *Kraut* [221].

Much of Section 2.1 is based on *Jeffreys* [199]. The principal modern text on gravity and geodesy is *Heiskanen & Moritz* [171]. The book by *Garland* [127] is helpful. The most recently published results for the variations of the gravity field are summarized and compared by *Kaula* [207].

The principal textbook on seismology is by *Bullen* [58]. Seismic methods and results of recent years are reviewed by *Press* [323, 324], *Anderson* [143], and *Oliver*

[294]. Inhomogeneities are discussed by *Toksöz et al.* [506]. The treatment of the free oscillations is that of *Alterman et al.* [9]; it is also derived by *Takeuchi* [385].

The recent advances in inferring location and slip of earthquakes have been principally by *Sykes* [383, 384] and *Brune* [549].

Reviews of anelastic dissipation in general are given by *Knopoff* [215] and *Gordon & Nelson* [148]; its particular application to seismic waves, by *Anderson & Archambeau* [15] and *Anderson* [14]. Various empirical models of creep have been synthesized by *MacDonald* [257]. The theory of diffusive creep is derived by *Herring* [172]; it is also discussed in the text of *Girifalco* [135]. Dislocation climb is derived by *Weertman* [429], and the general theory of dislocations is explained in the text by *Weertman & Weertman* [430]. The geophysical application of creep theories is discussed by *Gordon* [147] and *McKenzie* [270]. Various experimental results on the mechanical behavior of rocks are given in the symposium volumes edited by *Griggs & Handin* [151] and *Judd* [201]. Some data are also given in the handbook by *Clark* [74]. The most advanced treatment of deducing viscosity from crustal rebound is by *McConnell* [267].

The discussion of thermal histories dependent primarily on conductive transfer is based mainly on *MacDonald* [252, 255] and *Lee* [239]. The theory of the radiative transfer contribution is given by *Clark* [73]. Effects of igneous differentiation are discussed by *McConnell et al.* [487]. The most extensive compilation of heat-flow data is by *Lee & Uyeda* [240]. Important discussions of chemical content affecting heat sources are by *Gast* [128] and *Wasserburg et al.* [426]. The fundamental paper on laminar convective flow was by *Rayleigh* [327]; more recent work is fully explained in the book by *Chandrasekhar* [48]. The theory has since been extended by *Roberts* [342], *Turcotte & Oxburgh* [507], and *McKenzie* [572]. The difficulties of making realistic application of convective theory to the mantle are discussed by *Knopoff* [216], *Tozer* [399], and *Verhoogen* [417]. A collection of papers on heat flow is *Lee* [238].

The development of a central model of the mantle is based mainly on the work by *Birch* [31], as updated in a few respects by *Clark & Ringwood* [75]; see also *Ringwood* [340] and *Anderson* [14]. The calculations of stress implications of the gravity field are from *Kaula* [204]. Papers of varying degrees of speculativeness on the mechanical and thermal irregularities of the mantle are by *Runcorn* [350], *Orowan* [305], *Elsasser* [111], *MacDonald* [256], *McKenzie* [269], plus others in the volumes edited by *Blackett et al.* [35] and *Hurley* [187].

Chapter 3

PLANETARY MAGNETISM

In Chapters 1 and 2 we discussed observations and experiments pertaining to the earth's interior and developed physical and chemical models of planetary interiors with no reference to one of the main subjects of physics, electromagnetism (other than the relation of electrical to thermal conductivity). The reason why this neglect was possible is that the electromagnetic influences on the state of solid matter are quite slight.

However, of the terrestrial planets at least the earth has a fluid core composed largely of material of appreciable conductivity. The earth also has a magnetic field of pronounced broad-scale variations that would be expected to be associated with a fluid conductive core. We shall first discuss these variations, and then explore their theoretical explanation. The final section, on paleomagnetism, deals with particular effects of the magnetic field on matter deposited on the earth's surface which have become very important in connection with the geologic record, as already mentioned in Section 1.4.

As before, the earth takes a much greater part of our attention than the other planets; in this instance, however, it is because the earth is apparently much more active, and not merely because it is more accessible.

3.1 Spatial and Temporal Variations of Planetary Magnetic Fields

Expression of the External Magnetic Field

The magnetic field at the earth's surface normally is expressed in terms of a vector of magnitude F with a radial component positive downward, A, and a horizontal component H. Because the classical technique of observing the magnetic field utilized the deflection of a magnetized needle, there are also used the angle with respect to the horizontal, the inclination I, and the angle about the vertical with respect to North, the declination D. Equations (3.1.1) and (3.1.2) give the relationships between the rectangular components of the magnetic field vector and the angular quantites I and D.

$$\left.\begin{array}{c} X \\ Y \\ Z \end{array}\right\} = F \left\{\begin{array}{c} \cos I \cos D \\ \cos I \sin D \\ \sin I \end{array}\right\} \tag{3.1.1}$$

$$H = F \cos I \tag{3.1.2}$$

In units of magnetic induction (the same numerically as units of field strength, since the permeability of the air is virtually unity) the strength of the earth's magnetic field is less than one gauss (Γ). The conventional unit used is the gamma (γ), defined as 10^{-5} Γ.

The earth's magnetic field is similar to the gravitational field in that it can be expressed at the earth's surface as the gradient of scalar potential. The magnetic field differs significantly from the gravitational field, however, in that (1) a larger proportion of the field—about 0.1 percent—is of external, rather than internal, origin; and (2) the internally generated field undergoes perceptible changes with time, on the order of 0.1 percent per year.

The external field originates from the interaction of the charged particles of the solar field with the earth's field and atmosphere, and has a broad spectrum of variations ranging from milliseconds up to eleven years (arising from the principal cycle of solar activity). It is of interest with respect to the earth's interior in that the externally caused variations induce electric currents in the mantle which in turn give rise to temporal variations of the magnetic field usable to deduce mantle conductivity, as discussed at the end of Section 3.2.

The spherical harmonic expression customarily used for the internally generated geomagnetic field, analogous to (2.1.17), is

$$V = R \sum_{l=1}^{\infty} \left(\frac{R}{r}\right)^{l+1} \sum_{m=0}^{l} P_l{}^m(\theta)(g_l{}^m \cos m\lambda + h_l{}^m \sin m\lambda) \qquad (3.1.3)$$

where θ is the colatitude ($\pi/2 - \varphi$) and $P_l{}^m(\theta)$ is a Legendre associated function (equation 2.1.16) normalized so that

$$\int_0^\pi [P_l{}^m(\theta)]^2 \sin \theta \, d\theta = \frac{4}{2l + 1} \qquad (3.1.4)$$

known as the *Schmidt partial normalization*. F is, then, the magnitude and X, Y, Z are the components of ∇V in the specified directions [71, 191].

Observations of the Earth's Magnetic Field

The measurement of the geomagnetic field is carried out as a combination of frequently repeated observations at fixed stations and occasional field surveys to obtain spatial variations, by ship or aircraft or satellite. A variety of techniques are employed. The older magnetometers utilized the torques generated by the interaction of the field with permanent magnets of electric coils. The newer magnetometers are either the flux-gate type, dependent on the change in weak fields, of the permeability of a highly sensitive material; or the proton-precession type, dependent on the rate of precession about the earth's field of protons whose spins have been aligned by a much stronger artificial field [191].

TABLE 3.1: SPHERICAL HARMONIC COEFFICIENTS OF THE
GEOMAGNETIC FIELD, EPOCH 1960.0

l	m	$g_l{}^m$ (γ)	$\dot{g}_l{}^m$ (γ/yr)	$h_l{}^m$ (γ)	$\dot{h}_l{}^m$ (γ/yr)
1	0	−30426	18.9		
1	1	−2174	7.3	5761	−1.9
2	0	−1548	−24.8		
2	1	3000	−0.8	−1949	−14.0
2	2	1574	0.8	201	−17.7
3	0	1323	−0.4		
3	1	−2009	−10.5	−442	1.9
3	2	1275	3.4	233	4.0
3	3	877	−1.9	−118	−9.0
4	0	957	0.8		
4	1	797	5.4	149	−0.9
4	2	527	−1.9	−266	−1.7
4	3	−400	−0.2	−4	3.2
4	4	273	0.8	−262	−5.5
5	0	−241	3.5		
5	1	353	−0.7	0	1.8
5	2	231	2.5	124	2.9
5	3	−33	0.6	−104	−0.8
5	4	−147	0.0	−98	−0.4
5	5	−79	1.6	75	−0.2

From Cain et al. [61].

A recent analysis obtained the results given in Table 3.1 and Figures 3.1 and 3.2 for the intensity and rate of change of the geomagnetic field [61].

The principal characteristics of the earth's magnetic field as deduced from several such analyses since the first one by Gauss in 1830 are [178, 180, 191]:

1. The field is predominantly a dipole (i.e., representable as a first-degree harmonic) of about 0.6 Γ strength at an angle of 11.5° ($\tan^{-1} \sqrt{(g_1{}^1)^2 + (h_1{}^1)^2}/g_1{}^0$) to the rotation axis.

2. The nondipole part of the field ($l \geq 2$) has a total intensity of about 0.05 Γ—one-tenth the main field—and coefficients that decrease markedly with increasing degree l.

3. The dipole field is decreasing in intensity about 15 γ/yr moving westward at a rate of about 0.07°/yr [$d(\tan^{-1} h_1{}^1/g_1{}^1)/dt$]. These trends have persisted throughout the 135 years of detailed analyses.

4. The nondipole field is changing more rapidly: about 50 γ/yr (rms), with a maximum of about 200 γ/yr. In terms of harmonic coefficients, the general

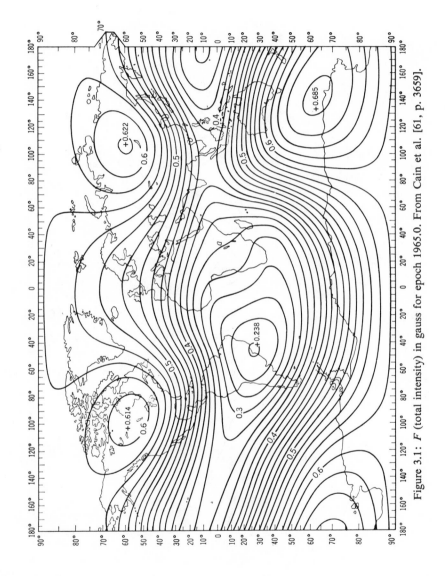

Figure 3.1: F (total intensity) in gauss for epoch 1965.0. From Cain et al. [61, p. 3659].

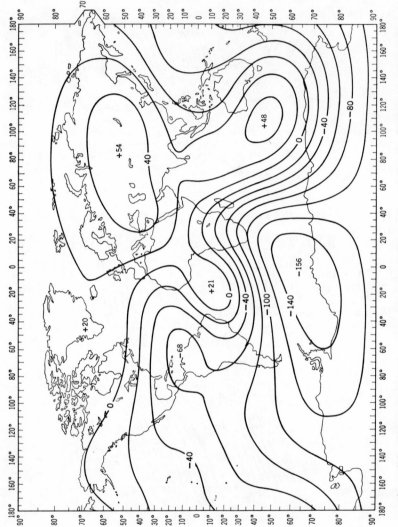

Figure 3.2: *F* (total intensity) secular change in gammas per year. From Cain et al. [61, p. 3664].

increase in magnitude for degrees 2, 3, and 4 indicated by Table 3.1 has persisted since at least 1900. In terms of spatial representation, the change has been such that the nondipole features of the magnetic field in Figure 3.1 have moved westward steadily at a rate averaging about 0.1°/yr, but varying appreciably from one latitude to another. There is a more rapid westerly drift of the secular variation field—the features in Figure 3.2—on the order of 0.3°/yr. The generally lower rates of change in the Pacific and higher rates around Antarctica have always existed.

By the techniques of paleomagnetism discussed in Section 3.3, more information about the field in the historical and geologic past has been deduced [83, 95, 96]:

1. Over the past 2500 years, the dipole intensity has decreased at an average of about 7 γ/yr, so that the field was 50 percent more intense in 500 B.C. However, about 5000 years ago the field had about the same intensity as now. About 10,000 years ago, the time scales associated with the secular variation were about the same as it is now.

2. In the last million years, the dipole field has maintained the same polarity it has now, wobbling with periods up to 10^5 years and amplitudes greater than 15 degrees about an average orientation displaced 5 degrees toward the Pacific from the present rotation axis. Throughout this time, the nondipole field in the Pacific has been relatively mild, as it is at present.

3. In the last 20 million years, there have been at least 60 reversals in polarity of the dipole field. The duration of the reversal process—i.e., the time during which there is no pronounced dipole—appears to be less than 10,000 years. During this period the average orientation of the pole was still within 5 degrees of the present rotation axis, and the wobbles were within 20 degrees of this average.

4. In the last 1.0 Æ, there have been many reversals of polarity; however, for two periods of about 50 million years each (Permian and Jurassic), the number of determinations of the same polarity is exceptionally high. During this time the apparent magnetic pole has wandered far from the present rotation axis, with inconsistencies between continents, as discussed in Section 3.3.

The geomagnetic field thus has characteristics that unavoidably suggest an origin in the liquid core: broad spatial variations of a global scale, and temporal variations on a time scale of 10^5 years for the dipole field and 10^3 years for the nondipole field. (In addition, there are local variations of up to a few hundred gamma, associated with magnetic material in the crust.)

Information about the magnetic fields of other planets is deducible, in principle, from space-probe magnetometer measurements; nonthermal electromagnetic radiation; and modulation of the solar wind by the planet due to an increase of its effective cross-section by a magnetic field. For the terrestrial planets, however, the only definite information is the negative results obtained by planetary probes. Mariner V detected a magnetopause near Venus which set an upper limit on its field strength of 0.001 to 0.01 times the earth's [537]; the U.S.S.R. Venus probe set the limit even lower, 0.0003 times the earth's [534]. Mariner IV detected no field for Mars at a radial distance of 2 planetary radii, setting an upper limit on intensity of only 0.0003 times of the earth's [178, 211, 584]. Recently the lunar satellite Anchored-IMP failed to detect any lunar magnetic field. Furthermore, in passing behind the moon, it failed to detect any perceptible effect of the moon on the inter-planetary magnetic field. This latter observation indicates that if the moon has an electrically conducting interior, it must be insulated from steady-state interaction with the solar wind by a surface layer of extremely low conductivity, less than 10^{-7} mho/cm [504].

3.2 Hydromagnetism and the Dynamo Theory

We take as the starting point Maxwell's equations, which are derived in any standard text on classical electromagnetism, such as Jackson [190] or Corson and Lorrain [81].

Fundamental Equations of Hydromagnetism

From the Biot-Savart law relating current and magnetic induction and Ampère's law of force between current loops, the force per unit volume **F** exerted by a current density **J** and a magnetic-flux density **B** is, in electromagnetic units:

$$F = J \times B \qquad (3.2.1)$$

Thus if an electromagnetic field exists in a viscous medium, then to the equations of motion (2.4.15) there must be added (3.2.1):

$$\frac{d\mathbf{v}}{dt} = -\frac{1}{\rho}\nabla p + \nabla V + \nu\,\nabla^2\mathbf{v} + \frac{1}{\rho}\mathbf{J} \times \mathbf{B} \qquad (3.2.2)$$

To eliminate either **J** or **B**, use Maxwell's second, third, and fourth equations:

$$\text{Ampère's law:} \qquad \nabla \times \mathbf{B} = 4\pi\mu\mathbf{J} \qquad (3.2.3)$$

$$\text{Faraday's law:} \qquad \nabla \times \mathbf{E} = -\frac{\partial \mathbf{B}}{\partial t} \qquad (3.2.4)$$

and the absence of free poles:

$$\nabla \cdot \mathbf{B} = 0 \qquad (3.2.5)$$

where μ is the magnetic permeability and **E** is the electric field, related to **J** and **B** by Ohm's law in the form:

$$J = \sigma(E + v \times B) \tag{3.2.6}$$

where σ is the conductivity. In equation (3.2.3), there has been neglected on the right the displacement current $\dot{E}/\epsilon$, where ϵ is the dielectric constant, as is justified for low-frequency phenomena such as are important in the earth's core [62].

Sometimes in place of the flux density **B** it is more convenient to use the magnetic field **H**, defined by:

$$H = \frac{B}{\mu} \tag{3.2.7}$$

Take the curl of (3.2.3):

$$\nabla \times (\nabla \times B) = 4\pi\mu\nabla \times J \tag{3.2.8}$$

Substitute from (3.2.6) for **J**:

$$\nabla \times (\nabla \times B) = 4\pi\mu\sigma\nabla \times (E + v \times B) \tag{3.2.9}$$

and substitute from (3.2.4) for $\nabla \times E$:

$$\nabla \times (\nabla \times B) = 4\pi\mu\sigma\left[-\frac{\partial B}{\partial t} + \nabla \times (v \times B)\right] \tag{3.2.10}$$

The condition (3.2.5) makes the left of (3.2.10) become $-\nabla^2 B$ (see problem 3.1). Rearranging (3.2.10) yields an appearance similar to (3.2.2):

$$\frac{\partial B}{\partial t} = \nabla \times (v \times B) + \nu_m \nabla^2 B \tag{3.2.11}$$

where the "magnetic viscosity" ν_m is:

$$\nu_m = \frac{1}{4\pi\mu\sigma} \tag{3.2.12}$$

The effect of the magnetic viscosity ν_m on the magnetic field **B** in (3.2.11) is similar to the effect of the kinematic viscosity ν in (2.4.16) on the velocity field **v**. If the velocity **v** were zero in (3.2.11), then the solution for a continuum with boundaries of dimension L would be a decay of the flux density B proportionate to $\exp(-t\nu_m/L^2)$. The existence of hydromagnetism depends on a decay time L^2/ν_m long compared to the time in which deformation of the medium adds to the field through the first term on the right of (3.2.11).

An infinite decay time L^2/ν_m is equivalent to a zero magnetic viscosity ν_m, so that the second term on the right of (3.2.11) becomes zero, and

$$\frac{\partial B}{\partial t} = \nabla \times (v \times B) \tag{3.2.13}$$

This situation, by (3.2.12), corresponds to infinite conductivity σ; according to (3.2.13), the field changes only with motion of the medium, and hence is said to be "frozen" in the medium.

Using (3.2.3), the force (3.2.1) can be written

$$\mathbf{J} \times \mathbf{B} = \frac{1}{4\pi\mu} (\nabla \times \mathbf{B}) \times \mathbf{B} \qquad (3.2.14)$$

Using the vector identity

$$\tfrac{1}{2}\nabla(\mathbf{B} \cdot \mathbf{B}) = (\mathbf{B} \cdot \nabla)\mathbf{B} - (\nabla \times \mathbf{B}) \times \mathbf{B} \qquad (3.2.15)$$

this becomes

$$\mathbf{J} \times \mathbf{B} = -\nabla\left(\frac{B^2}{8\pi\mu}\right) + \frac{1}{4\pi\mu} (\mathbf{B} \cdot \nabla)\mathbf{B} \qquad (3.2.16)$$

The magnetic force thus can be said to be equivalent to a magnetic hydrostatic pressure

$$p_M = \frac{B^2}{8\pi\mu} \qquad (3.2.17)$$

plus a term equivalent to an additional tension along the lines of force. These magnetically caused stresses have an effect on a fluid similar to making it more viscous, and thus to decrease turbulence and to make any flow smoother, more laminar. In the horizontal layer problem, (2.4.18), it in effect reduces the Rayleigh number relative to critical. As discussed in Section 9.3, a magnetic pressure such as (3.2.17) can have a significant inhibiting effect on condensation from an interstellar cloud.

Substituting (3.2.16) in (3.2.2) and neglecting the mechanical and gravitational terms, we have

$$\frac{d\mathbf{v}}{dt} = -\frac{1}{\rho}\nabla\left(\frac{B^2}{8\pi\mu}\right) + \frac{1}{4\pi\mu\rho} (\mathbf{B} \cdot \nabla)\mathbf{B} \qquad (3.2.18)$$

If we substitute $\mathbf{B_0} + \mathbf{B_1}$ for $\mathbf{B}$ and $\mathbf{v_1}$ for $\mathbf{v}$ in (3.2.13) and (3.2.18), where $\mathbf{B_1}$, $\mathbf{v_1}$ are small disturbances, and neglect the products of small quantities, then we obtain (see problem 3.4) that disturbances can be propagated along the magnetic field lines at velocity

$$v_A = \left(\frac{B^2}{4\pi\mu\rho}\right)^{1/2} \qquad (3.2.19)$$

known as the *Alfvén velocity* [1, 82].

The Earth: Effect of Rotation, the Dynamo

The closeness of the magnetic dipole axis to the axis of rotation, discussed in Section 3.1, suggests that the rotation has an important effect on the hydromagnetic regime in the earth's core. It therefore seems appropriate that the fields of velocity **v** and magnetism **B** be referred to axes fixed in the earth. Hence the equations of motion (3.2.2) must be modified to refer to rotating axes by replacing the potential of gravitation V by a potential of gravity U, including the centrifugal force term $\frac{1}{2}\omega^2 s^2$ (2.1.33), and by adding a Coriolis term $2\boldsymbol{\omega} \times \mathbf{v}$ (see problem 4.2). Making in addition the substitution from (3.2.14), we have as the system of equations to be solved:

$$\frac{d\mathbf{v}}{dt} = -\frac{1}{\rho}\nabla p + \nabla U - 2\boldsymbol{\omega} \times \mathbf{v} + \nu \nabla^2 \mathbf{v} + \frac{1}{4\pi\mu\rho}(\nabla \times \mathbf{B}) \times \mathbf{B} \quad (3.2.20)$$

$$\frac{\partial \mathbf{B}}{\partial t} = \nabla \times (\mathbf{v} \times \mathbf{B}) + \nu_m \nabla^2 \mathbf{B} \quad (3.2.11)$$

Equation (3.2.11) was derived using the absence of free poles, (3.2.5), but for the velocity field we must impose the continuity of matter (assumed incompressible),

$$\nabla \cdot \mathbf{v} = 0 \quad (3.2.21)$$

In the spherically bounded core, the fields **v** and **B** are most appropriately represented as vector spherical harmonics, with spheroidal (in geomagnetism called "poloidal") and toroidal parts, as was the elastic displacement field **u** in (2.2.34). But if the first term on the right of (3.2.11) is more important than the second, then the problem immediately is much more difficult because interactions between the two fields, and hence between different harmonics, are necessary to maintain the magnetic field $\mathbf{B}/\mu$. We therefore wish to compare the decay time L^2/ν_m with the time scale observed in geomagnetic phenomena, such as the westerly drift.

The length scale L we can take to be the radius of the core, about 3×10^8 cm. The magnetic permeability μ of a substance that is hot enough to be molten is essentially that of a vacuum, 1 emu. The electric conductivity σ of a metal at temperatures above the Debye temperature decreases with increase in the temperature due to the greater scattering, such as was deduced in connection with deriving the Lindemann melting law. Thus the conductivity of iron would be about an order-of-magnitude less than that observed at normal temperatures: that is, about 3×10^{-6} emu. The 20 percent admixture of silica to iron in the core, inferred in Section 2.5, may reduce the conductivity another order-of-magnitude [582]. Using 3×10^{-6} emu we get a decay time L^2/ν_m of about 10^5 years: much more than the circuit time of 4×10^3 years deduced from the secular drift of about 0.1°/yr. Thus the advective term $\nabla \times (\mathbf{v} \times \mathbf{B})$ in (3.2.11) must be much more important than the diffusive term.

However, it is of interest to determine the minimum velocity field **v** necessary to maintain a magnetic field $\mathbf{B}/\mu$ against energy loss due to ordinary electrical resistance, or Joule heating, J^2/σ. The equation appropriate to this problem would be (3.2.10) with the rate $\partial \mathbf{B}/\partial t$ set zero:

$$\nabla \times (\mathbf{v} \times \mathbf{B}) = -\nu_m \nabla^2 \mathbf{B} \qquad (3.2.22)$$

A detailed numerical attack on this problem was made by Bullard and Gellman [57] who assumed that the magnetic field could be represented by a sum of vector spherical harmonics,

$$\mathbf{B} = \mu \sum_{\beta} (\mathbf{S}_\beta + \mathbf{T}_\beta) \qquad (3.2.23)$$

where $\mathbf{S}_\beta$ is a spheroidal and $\mathbf{T}_\beta$ is a toroidal vector spherical harmonic of a particular degree and order, l and m, and variation with radius r as defined by (2.2.37). The velocity field was similarly expressed as

$$\mathbf{v} = \sum_{\alpha} (\mathbf{S}_\alpha + \mathbf{T}_\alpha) \qquad (3.2.24)$$

The degree and order of each term in the velocity field to be taken into account were specified, as well as its radial variation, in the form of a simple polynomial in r. Left as unknowns to be solved were the magnitudes of the velocity terms, plus the magnitudes of the unobservable toroidal terms of the magnetic field, $\mathbf{T}_\beta$, coupled to the observables $\mathbf{S}_\beta$ by the specified velocity field.

The simplest likely velocity field generating the main dipole term S_1 of the magnetic field required both a T_1 and an $S_2{}^2$ motion in the velocity field. Such a system roughly satisfies the requirement of conservation of angular momentum, which here appears mathematically as the Coriolis term $2\boldsymbol{\omega} \times \mathbf{v}$ in the equations of motion (3.2.20). A T_1, $S_2{}^2$ velocity field couples the S_1 magnetic term to T_2 and $T_2{}^2$ plus higher-order terms in the magnetic field. Since the number of terms thus coupled is infinite, computer limitations prevent a mathematically rigorous proof that the specified system is possible. The main conclusions reached by Bullard and Gellman were that the toroidal fields in the core coupled to the dipole field of surface intensity 0.6 Γ must have a magnitude of about 100 Γ; and that the maximum velocities required to maintain such a field are about 0.01 cm/sec radially and 0.04 cm/sec horizontally. The average velocity yields a westerly drift of 0.13°/yr [57]. These results depended on the assumed conductivity of 3×10^{-6} emu. In addition, more recent calculations including higher-degree terms have failed to obtain a convergence toward a particular solution—indicating that for the material parameters selected, a major part of the ohmic dissipation must occur in higher-degree motions [469].

Although these numerical results leave in doubt the existence of a homogeneous dynamo in the real earth, it has been proven that they can exist for certain artificial models [474].

The manner in which magnetic and velocity fields interact, and the role of

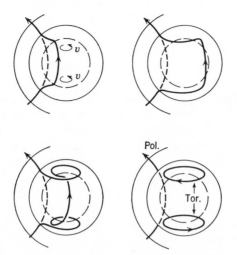

Figure 3.3: Generation of a toroidal T_2 magnetic field by interaction between a poloidal S_1 field with a T_1 velocity field. From Elsasser [109, p. 604].

the earth's rotation therein, is not easily perceived in the rather mathematical formulation of a vector spherical harmonic representation. In the case of a core rotating relative to the mantle, starting with the poloidal magnetic term S_1, it is possible to visualize how a velocity term T_1 applied thereto will generate the magnetic term T_2, as sketched in Figure 3.3. However, the completion of the chain T_2 magnetic $\to S_2{}^{2C}$ velocity $\to T_2{}^{2C}$ magnetic $\to T_1$ velocity $\to T_2{}^{2S}$ magnetic $\to S_2{}^{2C}$ velocity $\to S_1$ magnetic is not so easily visualized in terms of stretching and snapping of magnetic field lines by velocity flows.

On a more local scale, a mechanism whereby a rising eddy can generate magnetism is pictured in Figure 3.4 [307]. If there is thermal convection, there will exist a series of streams rising in some places and sinking elsewhere. Consider a rising stream in the northern hemisphere; at the bottom of the column fluid converging horizontally from the south will turn to the east relative to the rotating frame because it has more angular momentum than an element attached to the frame, while fluid from the north will turn to the west because it has less. Both of these turns will impart a counterclockwise rotation to the rising fluid. Now if there is a toroidal magnetic field with field lines normal to the axis of the convective stream, the field lines will be

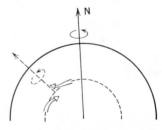

Figure 3.4: Rotation of fluid about a rising convection stream.

lifted and simultaneously twisted. If the twist is 90 degrees, there is created a loop of magnetic force in a plane perpendicular to the original lines. A consideration of the effects produced by a sinking current leads to the conclusion that the components of the loops about meridian lines will cancel, but that the components about parallel lines reinforce each other: that is, the resulting net loops lie in meridional planes. Since these loops are all in the same direction, they will tend to coalesce and form a poloidal dipole field.

The smaller the eddies generating the aforedescribed process, the quicker they will die out because of viscosity, that is, have a short decay time L^2/v. However, the dipole (as well as other long wave variations) formed by the coalescence of the magnetic loops they create is much more persistent—a long L^2/v_m. The model is steady state only in a statistical sense, since individual small eddies die out relatively quickly.

If there existed adequate estimates of the field intensities and velocities in the core, then the energy dissipation entailed could be calculated.

Dot multiply equation (3.2.6) by $\mathbf{J}/\sigma$:

$$\frac{J^2}{\sigma} = \mathbf{J} \cdot \mathbf{E} + \mathbf{J} \cdot (\mathbf{v} \times \mathbf{B}) \tag{3.2.25}$$

The term on the left of (3.2.25) is the rate of ohmic dissipation per unit volume. To transform the right into terms of the magnetic and velocity fields, replace $\mathbf{J}$ by (3.2.3):

$$\frac{J^2}{\sigma} = \frac{1}{4\pi\mu} [(\nabla \times \mathbf{B}) \cdot \mathbf{E} + (\nabla \times \mathbf{B}) \cdot (\mathbf{v} \times \mathbf{B})] \tag{3.2.26}$$

Use the vector identity

$$(\nabla \times \mathbf{B}) \cdot \mathbf{E} = \mathbf{B} \cdot (\nabla \times \mathbf{E}) - \nabla \cdot (\mathbf{E} \times \mathbf{B}) \tag{3.2.27}$$

plus (3.2.4) to replace the first term on the right of (3.2.26):

$$\frac{J^2}{\sigma} = \frac{1}{4\pi\mu} \left[-\frac{1}{2} \frac{\partial B^2}{\partial t} - \nabla \cdot (\mathbf{E} \times \mathbf{B}) + (\nabla \times \mathbf{B}) \cdot (\mathbf{v} \times \mathbf{B}) \right] \tag{3.2.28}$$

The first term on the right of (3.2.28) is minus the rate of change of the magnetic energy per unit volume, $B^2/8\pi\mu$. To the last term on the right apply the vector identity

$$(\nabla \times \mathbf{B}) \cdot (\mathbf{v} \times \mathbf{B}) = \mathbf{v} \cdot [\mathbf{B} \times (\nabla \times \mathbf{B})] \tag{3.2.29}$$

and substitute for the factor in brackets from the equations of motion (3.2.20):

$$\frac{1}{4\pi\mu} \mathbf{v} \cdot [\mathbf{B} \times (\nabla \times \mathbf{B})] = -\rho \mathbf{v} \cdot \left(\frac{d\mathbf{v}}{dt} + \frac{1}{\rho} \nabla p - \nabla U + 2\boldsymbol{\omega} \times \mathbf{v} - v \nabla^2 \mathbf{v} \right)$$

$$\tag{3.2.30}$$

The terms on the right are, respectively: (1) the rate of change of kinetic energy; (2) the rate at which pressure forces increase energy; (3) the rate of release of gravitational energy; (4) the rate of conversion of rotational energy; and (5) the rate of viscous dissipation, all per unit volume. To obtain the total energy exchanges, substitute (3.2.30) in (3.2.28), integrate throughout the volume of the core, and apply Gauss's theorem (see problem 3.2) to the second term on the right of (3.2.28):

$$\int_V \frac{J^2}{\sigma} d\tau = -\int_V \frac{\partial}{\partial t} \left(\frac{B^2}{8\pi\mu}\right) d\tau - \int_S \frac{\mathbf{E} \times \mathbf{B}}{4\pi\mu} dS$$

$$+ \int_V \rho\mathbf{v} \cdot \left(\frac{\partial \mathbf{v}}{\partial t} - \mathbf{v} \cdot \nabla\mathbf{v} - \frac{1}{\rho}\nabla p + \nabla U + 2\boldsymbol{\omega} \times \mathbf{v} + \nu \nabla^2\mathbf{v}\right) d\tau$$

$$(3.2.31)$$

where $d\tau$ is an element of volume and dS an element of surface area. The second term on the right is the flux of electromagnetic energy across the core-mantle boundary; because of the relatively low conductivity of the mantle, this energy exchange is small compared to some others [57, 180].

From the numerical values obtained in the Bullard and Gellman model of 100 Γ for B, 0.02 cm/sec for v, and 10 gm/cm³ for ρ, the magnetic-field energy density $B^2/8\pi\mu$ is 400 ergs/cm³, but the kinetic energy density $\rho v^2/2$ is only 4×10^{-3} erg/cm³. Hence the energy rates in (3.2.31) would be dominated by the magnetic term. Using the decay time L^2/ν_m of about 10^5 years to deduce a rate and integrating over the volume $4\pi L^3/3$ of 10^{26} cm³, we get a rate of energy dissipation of about 10^{16} ergs/sec. However, these numbers apply only to the principal low-degree term of the model. The failure of the numerical calculations to converge, together with the much shorter time scale indicated by the westerly drift, suggests that the energy dissipation in higher-degree eddies is probably orders-of-magnitude more important: perhaps as much as the 10^{18} ergs/sec. The likelihood of a lower conductivity also indicates higher energy requirements.

Possible sources of the energy dissipated in the core which have been suggested are:

1. *Radioactivity.* The energy generation of about 10^{-8} erg cm⁻³ sec⁻¹, or 10^{-9} cal gm⁻¹ yr⁻¹, required is somewhat less than the minimum rate for dunite in Table 2.3. However, only a minor fraction—on the order of 10^{-2}—would be available for conversion into magnetic energy instead of flowing out of the core as heat.

2. *Cooling and Crystallization.* If the core is cooling because of the considerable thermal conductivity of the mantle, then energy will be released in a manner conducive to convection by crystallization of iron from the melt at

the interface between the liquid and solid core. However, if the energy require-ments are as much a 10^{18} ergs/sec, then the estimated cooling rate would have to be on the order of 10^3 °C/Æ [416].

3. *Gravitational Energy.*   If the core were still forming by separation of the denser core material from the mantle, then ample energy would be available. However, the most recent considerations of core formation by separation from the mantle have concluded that it would be a self-accelerating process that would go to completion in a relatively short time [32, 400].

4. *Precession.*   The moments-of-inertia ratios $(C - A)/C$ differ between the earth as a whole and the core by about 0.0008; hence, by (4.3.26), there would be a difference in the rates of precession of the core and the earth as a whole if they were uncoupled. In actuality they are coupled by friction and magnetic induction, so that in effect the mantle exerts a torque on the core. Mathematically, this effect appears as an extra term $(\boldsymbol{\omega} \times \dot{\boldsymbol{\varphi}}) \times \mathbf{r}$ in the equa-tions of motion (3.2.20), where $\dot{\boldsymbol{\varphi}}$ is the precession vector. This term, known as a *Poincaré force*, arises by allowing for the precession in transforming from inertial to body-fixed coordinates. Since the relative precession is only about one-fourth the total precession, only one-fourth of this force needs to be balanced by other terms in (3.2.20):

$$\tfrac{1}{4} |(\boldsymbol{\omega} \times \dot{\boldsymbol{\varphi}}) \times \mathbf{r}| \approx |2\boldsymbol{\omega} \times \mathbf{v}| \approx \left| \frac{1}{4\pi\mu\rho} (\nabla \times \mathbf{B}) \times \mathbf{B} \right| \qquad (3.2.32)$$

Whence an estimate of the characteristic velocity is:

$$v = \frac{|\boldsymbol{\omega} \times \dot{\boldsymbol{\varphi}}|}{8 |\boldsymbol{\omega}|} R \approx \tfrac{4}{3} \times 10^{-4} \,\text{cm/sec} \qquad (3.2.33)$$

and of the magnetic field:

$$B/\mu \approx (\pi\rho |\boldsymbol{\omega} \times \dot{\boldsymbol{\varphi}}| R^2)^{1/2} \approx 29\,\Gamma \qquad (3.2.34)$$

Since the field appears as a vector cross-product in (3.2.32), this value must be regarded as the geometric mean of the poloidal and toroidal components. An estimate of the poloidal component B_P at the core-mantle boundary can be made by requiring that its cross-product with the velocity be sufficient to balance the ohmic dissipation of the field, as in (3.2.22):

$$B_P \leq \frac{1}{4\pi\mu\sigma R} \cdot \frac{B}{v} \approx 17\,\Gamma$$

using values from (3.2.33–34) and 3×10^{-6} for σ. This value is somewhat more than that obtained by extrapolating the surface field down to the core, about 4Γ, which implies considerable shielding. If we adopt $7\,\Gamma$ as a com-promise, a B_T of $120\,\Gamma$ results.

The velocity (3.2.33) is at right angles to the rotation vector, and hence predominantly radial. The horizontal components of velocity we would expect to be somewhat larger; we can estimate them by taking the **B**'s on the right of (3.2.32) to be the two toroidal components:

$$v_T \approx \frac{B_T{}^2}{8\pi\mu\rho\,|\omega|\,R} \approx 2.3 \times 10^{-3}\,\text{cm/sec} \tag{3.2.35}$$

about one-tenth the mean secular drift rate. The total work done by the mantle on the core can be estimated as the product of the magnetic stress $B^2/4\pi\mu$ by the toroidal velocity v_T integrated over the surface:

$$W \approx \frac{B^2}{4\pi\mu}\,v_T(4\pi R^2) \approx 2.3 \times 10^{17}\,\text{ergs/sec} \tag{3.2.36}$$

Thus, of the possible energy sources for the geomagnetic dynamo, precession appears definitely to be significant [258, 486]. Whether it is the only important energy source remains to be seen. A model of the dynamo accounting for its more detailed manifestations, such as the secular drift, is needed to deduce what other mechanisms are involved as well as a better estimate of the electrical conductivity.

Flow Patterns in the Core

As discussed, the advective term $\nabla \times (\mathbf{v} \times \mathbf{B})$ in $\partial\mathbf{B}/\partial t$, (3.2.11), seems appreciably more important that the diffusive term $\nu_m\,\nabla^2\mathbf{B}$ in the main part of the core. We should expect some influence of both the mechanical viscosity ν and magnetic viscosity, however, on the boundary layer at the core surface in which there is a transition between a rigid coupling of the core to the mantle and the free flow characterized by (3.2.13). This layer is also important to any effect of precession on the dynamo. A detailed consideration shows that the boundary layer will also depend on the velocity with which disturbances propagate—that is, the Alfvén velocity v_A (3.2.19)—and obtains a thickness of $(\nu\nu_m)^{1/2}/v_A$ [343, 375, 376]. Using the viscosity for molten iron observed at surface pressure, 0.005 cm²/sec, together with the conductivity 3×10^{-6} emu and core surface magnetic field intensity of 4 Γ yields a boundary layer of only 68 cm. While there may be an increase in the mechanical viscosity by two or three orders of magnitude, it seems clear that the boundary layer is thin, and hence that knowledge of the external field and its rates of change will lead to some knowledge of the velocity field by (3.2.13). Since the mantle is too warm to contain any ferromagnetic sources, the external field at the core surface is known by extrapolating downward the scalar potential (2.1.3) and its rate of change.

Taking into account the fact that the radial component v_r of the velocity field is zero everywhere on the core-mantle boundary, and hence that the horizontal derivatives are zero, and using the incompressibility (3.2.21), we get from (3.2.13),

$$\frac{\partial B_r}{\partial t} = -B_r\left(\frac{1}{r}\cdot\frac{\partial v_\theta}{\partial \theta} + \frac{v_\theta \cot\theta}{r} + \frac{1}{r\sin\theta}\frac{\partial v_\lambda}{\partial \lambda}\right)$$

$$-\frac{v_\theta}{r}\frac{\partial B_r}{\partial \theta}\frac{1}{r\sin\theta}\cdot\frac{\partial B_r}{\partial \lambda} \tag{3.2.37}$$

The horizontal components of velocity, v_θ and v_λ, can be expressed as a two-dimensional vector which is the sum of an irrotational and a rotational velocity field,

$$\mathbf{v} = -\nabla_T\psi + \mathbf{r}\times\nabla\chi \tag{3.2.38}$$

where the subscript T denotes the horizontal component of the gradient. ψ and χ in turn can be expressed conveniently as scalar spherical harmonic expansions.

Application of (3.2.37) and (3.2.38) to the downward extrapolated field leads to a current system that is mainly horizontal—that is, mainly in the component ψ—plus a strong upcurrent south of Africa and a strong downcurrent centered on eastern Europe. The maximum horizontal velocity is about 10 km/yr [202].

Secular Change

Two principal hypotheses have been suggested for the secular change of the geomagnetic field, including the westward drift. One is that they are hydromagnetic waves: that is, the free oscillations obtained solving the equations (3.2.11) and (3.2.20) in terms of vector spherical harmonics are analogous to the elastic free oscillations of the mantle. The other is that they are the consequence of electromagnetic coupling between the mantle and the main part of the core, together with conservation of angular momentum in the eddies that rise to the surface of the core.

In the hydromagnetic-wave hypothesis, the secular variation does not necessarily entail transport of material. Instead, there is a propagation of wave disturbances. The motions of irregularities in the external field correspond to the motions of wave forms in the core, and hence the rates of motion of particular harmonics in the field should be the phase velocities of the corresponding modes of oscillation in the magnetic field of the core.

The velocities of hydromagnetic waves in the core will be considerably modified from the Alfvén velocity, (3.2.19), by the rotation of the earth. In the equations of motion (3.2.20), neglect the body force plus viscous terms, $\nabla U + \nu\nabla^2\mathbf{v}$. Solutions for the free oscillations are then obtainable by assuming that the main part of the flux density $\mathbf{B}$ is symmetric about the rotation axis (i.e., expressible as $j_0(\boldsymbol{\omega} \times \mathbf{s})/\omega$, where $\mathbf{s}$ is the vector from the axis), assuming the remainder of the magnetic field and the velocity $\mathbf{v}$ are small, and neglecting products of small quantities. There is one boundary condition: the velocity normal to the boundary is zero. The result of the calculation is a set of normal modes for the magnetic field. However, there is no indication that there should be a selective excitation of westward traveling waves [259].

In the electromagnetic-coupling hypothesis, the magnetic field and the material in the core are moving together, and the apparent westward drift is explained as a rotation of the part of the core giving rise to the variations which is slower than the rotation of the mantle. This situation would occur if the rotation of the mantle was coupled with the rotation of the deeper main part of the core, from which the dipole predominantly originates, while the outer core would rotate less slowly because of conservation of angular momentum in a convecting system involving up and downcurrents. The mantle would rotate with the main part of the core rather than the outer part if the coupling between mantle and core was predominantly electromagnetic through the interaction of the magnetic field with the conducting medium of the mantle rather than mechanical through the viscous drag at the core-mantle boundary [56, 345].

The electromagnetic-coupling hypothesis is of interest in that it should be of additional observational verification because variations in the strength of the coupling should result in variations in the rotation of the earth. So far, both the observational data and the numerical parameters of the hydromagnetic model have not been of sufficient precision to relate the two phenomena clearly [345, 346].

Electrical Conductivity of the Mantle

The existence of an electromagnetic coupling depends on the electrical conductivity σ of the mantle. If the magnetic-flux density $\mathbf{B}$ is time varying, then by Faraday's law (3.2.4) there will exist an electrical field $\mathbf{E}$ and, by Ohm's law (3.2.6), a current density $\mathbf{J}$. The mantle conductivity is small enough, however, that we can ignore its effect on the magnetic field, which is thus representable as the gradient of a scalar potential, such as (3.1.3). However, we now want (3.1.3) extended to take into account the time variation and the response of the mantle to externally, as well as internally, generated fields [235, 268, 335]:

$$V = R \sum_{l=1}^{\infty} \sum_{m=1}^{l} P_l{}^m(\theta) \left\{ \left[\left(\frac{R}{r}\right)^{l+1} g_l{}^m + \left(\frac{r}{R}\right)^l g_l{}'^m \right] \cos m\lambda \right.$$

$$\left. + \left[\left(\frac{R}{r}\right)^{l+1} h_l{}^m + \left(\frac{r}{R}\right)^l h_l{}'^m \right] \sin m\lambda \right\} e^{i\omega t} \qquad (3.2.39)$$

In obtaining solutions for a conducting mantle, it is convenient to use a vector potential **A** defined by:

$$\nabla \times \mathbf{A} = \mathbf{B} \qquad (3.2.40)$$

whence, by (3.2.4),

$$\mathbf{E} = -\frac{\partial \mathbf{A}}{\partial t} - \nabla\varphi \qquad (3.2.41)$$

in which φ is an arbitrary scalar function. **B** is left unchanged by a transformation

$$\mathbf{A} \to \mathbf{A}' = \mathbf{A} + \nabla\Lambda \qquad (3.2.42)$$

where Λ is a scalar; to keep **E** unchanged as well,

$$\varphi \to \varphi' = \varphi - \frac{\partial\Lambda}{\partial t} \qquad (3.2.43)$$

It is convenient to choose Λ so that

$$\nabla \cdot \mathbf{A} = 0 \qquad (3.2.44)$$

since then $\partial\varphi/\partial t$ must be zero, and hence φ is ignorable in a time-varying solution. Applying Ampere's law (3.2.3) and Ohm's law (3.2.6) (with **v** zero), to (3.2.40) and (3.2.41) yields

$$\nabla \times (\nabla \times \mathbf{A}) = -4\pi\mu\sigma\frac{\partial \mathbf{A}}{\partial t} \qquad (3.2.45)$$

From (3.2.39) $\nabla \times \mathbf{A}$ is representable as a gradient of a scalar,

$$\nabla \times \mathbf{A} = \mu\nabla V \qquad (3.2.46)$$

whence, taking the permeability μ as a constant in the mantle,

$$\mathbf{A} = \mathbf{r} \times \nabla\psi \qquad (3.2.47)$$

and

$$\nabla^2\psi = 4\pi\sigma\mu\frac{\partial\psi}{\partial t} \qquad (3.2.48)$$

in which **r** is the position vector and ψ is a scalar. So there is obtained again the scalar diffusion equation, as in (2.3.4). Assuming constant σ, as well as μ, (3.2.48) is solvable in spherical coordinates as the product of spherical Bessel functions and surface spherical harmonics. However, in this case we are interested in the variation of σ radially, and its effect on different frequencies of variation in the external magnetic field. Hence, after substituting

$$\psi = R_l(r)P_l^m(\theta)\, e^{i(m\varphi+\omega t)} \qquad (3.2.49)$$

and separating variables in a manner similar to (2.1.2–5), there is obtained an equation in R_l to be solved either numerically or assuming a particular form

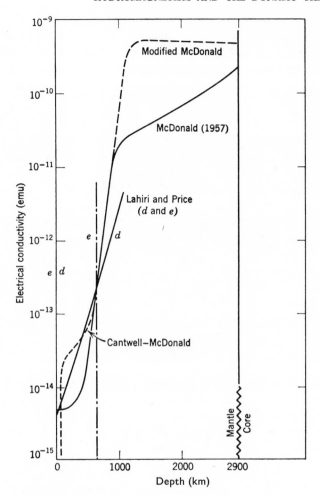

Figure 3.5: Electrical conductivity in the mantle. Based on Eckhardt et al. [104. p. 6285].

for the radial variation of σ:

$$r^2 \frac{d^2R_l}{dr^2} + 2r \frac{dR_l}{dr} - l(l + 1)R_l = 4\pi\sigma\mu i\omega r^2 \qquad (3.2.50)$$

The variations in the surface magnetic field obtained by substituting (3.2.49) into (3.2.47) and (3.2.47) into (3.2.40) can be compared to observed values and an adjustment made to determine the radial variation in σ that best fits the data. The electrical conductivity as deduced from the temporal variations of the external field is given in Figure 3.5 [104]. It has an increase of about four orders-of-magnitude between 400 and 800 km deep, the same zone in which other properties of the mantle undergo considerable change. It thus is thought to be associated with the increase in conductivity of the silicates with rearrangement of their crystal structure.

3.3 Paleomagnetism

Ferromagnetism

Paleomagnetism has undergone a great development since 1950. The basic physical phenomenon upon which paleomagnetism depends is that of *ferromagnetism*. Certain materials are observed to have a spontaneous magnetic field: in the absence of an external magnetic field they will still be magnetized. Such magnets are, of course, quite familiar. If a magnetic field H is imposed on a ferromagnetic substance, the ferromagnetic substance will acquire a magnetic field M related to the field H by

$$M = \chi H \qquad (3.3.1)$$

where χ is the magnetic susceptibility defined with respect to unit mass. The susceptibility χ is a function of temperature according to the rule

$$\chi = \frac{N\langle \mu^2 \rangle}{k(T - \theta)} \qquad (3.3.2)$$

where N is the number of atoms per unit volume, μ is the magnetic moment per atom, k is the Boltzmann constant, and θ is known as the Curie temperature. The Curie temperature is itself a function of an arbitrary parameter λ:

$$\theta = \frac{\lambda N\langle \mu^2 \rangle}{3k} \qquad (3.3.3)$$

The theoretical derivation of λ depends on quantum-mechanical theory in which an apparent internal magnetic field $\lambda\mu$ is caused by an interaction between the spins of electrons of neighboring atoms. The existence of the Curie temperature is due to the thermal agitation overcoming this tendency toward magnetization. In actual laboratory samples the susceptibility normally is considerably less than that predicted by theory due to the division of a sample into blocks of differing magnetization called domains. Although there is correlation between the susceptibility and the grain size of crystals, the domains do not appear to have any necessary relationship to the crystal grains. Ferromagnetic substances also have a saturation point, a maximum imposed field H above which there is no increase in the magnetization that can be attained. The principal magnetic minerals are given in Table 3.2. As is evident from the table, there is a sharp reduction in the magnetization possible with the addition to the iron of other elements, oxygen and sulfur,

TABLE 3.2: MAGNETIC PROPERTIES OF MINERALS

Mineral	Formula	Curie Point (°C)	Saturation, M (emu/gm @ 24°C)	Maximum Field, H (Oe)
Magnetite	Fe_3O_4	578	92–93	20
Hematite	Fe_2O_3	675	0.5	7600
Pyrrhotite	$Fe_{1-x}S$ ($x < 0.13$)	310	62	15–20
Iron	Fe	770	21,500	1.8

Based on Lindsley et al. in Clark [74, p. 546].

and the compounds are properly called ferrimagnetic rather than ferromagnetic because the magnetic properties are really the result of unequal and opposing atomic spin moments. Both magnetite, which has a spinel structure, and hematite, which has a rhombohedral structure, are anisotropic in their magnetic properties. The strength of the magnetization depends on the relative direction of the crystal structure and the imposed field H [188, 213].

In application magnetite is by far the most important of the magnetic minerals and the apparent degree of magnetization of a sample normally depends on the proportion of magnetite content, the suceptibility being slightly less than the proportion of magnetite in the rock. Magnetization is found in many types of rocks: sedimentary, both mechanical and chemical; igneous, both extrusive and intrusive; and metamorphic. This variety of locale is the consequence of several different ways in which remanent magnetism, the imposition of magnetism by an external field, can occur:

1. *TRM. Thermoremanent magnetization* is probably the most important. It is the magnetization that occurs when a rock cools from above to below the Curie temperature. The temperatures of the Curie points given in Table 3.2 are all obviously intermediary between the temperatures of lavas or plutonic intrusions, and the normal temperatures at the earth's surface. A rock that acquired magnetism by TRM will typically have a magnetization of about 2.5×10^{-3} emu/gm. This TRM is quite stable; by tests on samples in the laboratory it is unaffected by temperatures up to about 450°C.

2. *CRM. Chemical remanent magnetization* includes all types of magnetization that arise from changes of a chemical nature occurring at temperatures below the Curie point, such as crystallization in metamorphic rocks and chemical recombination of iron oxides in sediments. CRM is thought to occur by the process of nucleation, the aligning of the elements of a crystal in the process of crystallization. The intensity of CRM in a field comparable to that of the earth is about one-tenth that of TRM.

3. *DRM.   Detrital remanent magnetization.* In the deposition of a sediment from a fluid, the particles that are of magnetic susceptibility have some freedom to align themselves with the magnetic field. There will be some scatter with this alignment, of course, depending on the degree of turbulence and the strength of the couple between the particle and the field, in turn depending on the mechanical shape of the particles.

4. *VRM.   Viscous remanent magnetization,* refers to a modification of the magnetization due to thermal effects at temperatures well below the Curie point. This is mainly of concern as modifying the magnetization acquired by TRM or CRM [77, 188].

Application to the Earth

If we assume the earth's magnetic field to be a dipole perfectly aligned with its rotation axis, then a particle acquiring remanent magnetism will align itself in its meridian and thus have zero declination D, and it will have an inclination I, depending on its latitude. It will also have an intensity of magnetization M, dependent on the strength of the field F at the time of deposition. If we can reconstruct the original orientation of a magnetized sample obtained from a geological formation, then, assuming the perfect dipole field, we can determine the location of the North Pole at the time of deposition from the direction of magnetization of the sample.

The validity of the aforedescribed procedure depends, of course, on how closely the earth's magnetic field approximates the perfect dipole aligned with the rotation axis. Remanent magnetization of relatively recent geologic deposits indicates that this has been true for the last few million years, provided that we allow for complete reversal of the field at intervals on the order of 500,000 years. This reversal process takes only about 10,000 years. This recent remanent magnetization also indicates that the present separation of the dipole from the rotation axis of 11.5 degrees is exceptionally large; normally it is less. The application of remanent magnetization from much more remote geological times to the determination of the direction of the pole depends on the assumption that the dominant character of the magnetic field is that of a dipole aligned with the rotation axis. As discussed in the previous section, this is still not assured theoretically. It is difficult to imagine, however, how an ordering mechanism other than the rotation could lead to a field of comparable strength [77, 519].

Because of the many possible sources of error, paleomagnetists have placed great emphasis on sampling procedures and application of statistical tests. A single paleomagnetic result is generally that of what is called a *rock unit,* a deposit of rocks within one geological period in one geographical area on the order of some tens to hundreds of kilometers in extent. This rock unit in turn is sampled at as many exposures as possible, each exposure known as a *site.*

At each site are taken several *samples*, the orientation of each sample being separately determined in order to reconstitute the original horizontal plane and direction of north. Finally, in the laboratory each sample normally is cut into three or four specimens to determine the magnetization and make checks of internal consistency. A typical rock unit may comprise five sites, or forty samples, or a hundred specimens. For the results of a rock unit to be acceptable it must comprise at least five samples; it must yield a pole position which has a 95 percent probability ring of less than 25°; and it must have a stability indicated either by its nonalignment with the present field or by laboratory tests [188].

As of October, 1963, there were established about 90 Precambrian rock units, 240 Paleozoic (0.23–0.6 Æ) rock units, 125 Mesozoic (0.06–0.23 Æ) rock units, and 195 Cenozoic rock units. As with most geophysical measurements, the distribution geographically is far from ideal, with a great concentration of measurements in Europe and North America [188].

Results of Paleomagnetic Determinations

The usual method of reporting paleomagnetic results is in the form of a plot of the apparent pole position on an equal-area projection. Figure 3.6 is an example of all such plots for one particular period, the Permian period. This figure demonstrates a general characteristic that applies to all periods: there is a much closer agreement among points on the same continent than on different continents. An exception to this rule is India, for which the paleomagnetic poles plot differently than those for Europe and northern Asia. Figure 3.7 is a combination of such plots for the five continents for which there are rock units for six or more geological periods. In nearly all cases the points shown for Europe and northern Asia and for North America are based on several rock units, but those for Africa and South America often are based on only one or two rock units. The figure generally is interpreted on the basis of a combination of polar wandering and continental drift. According to all data, 500 million years ago the Pole was somewhere in the middle of the Pacific Ocean. Since then it has migrated toward the present North Pole by way of Siberia, coming within 60 degrees about 400 million years ago, and within 20 degrees about 100 million years ago. In addition, the paleomagnetic data indicate the North America and Europe were much closer together and in a considerably lower latitude in Paleozoic time. It further indicates, more sketchily, that South America and Africa were close together, near the South Pole, and that Antarctica, Australia, and India, were also considerably farther south. The breakup of these relationships and the drift to the present position is interpreted to have occurred at the end of the Paleozoic, about 200 million years ago [188, 554].

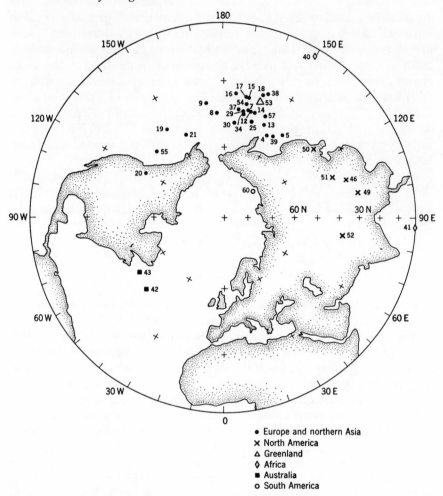

Figure 3.6: Paleomagnetic poles for the Permian period. Based on Irving [188, p. 119].

Variations in Intensity and Polarity

Pertinent to the question of the correctness of the assumption of the earth's field being predominantly a rotationally aligned dipole, the information on past intensity of the magnetic field, from measurements of magnetization M and susceptibility χ, is much sketchier than the information on direction. The measurements that have been published indicate that the field was perceptibly weaker in the past, perhaps about 10 percent of the present field. However, it is very indefinite as to how much the magnetization M may have decreased due to the VRM [188]. The information on polar

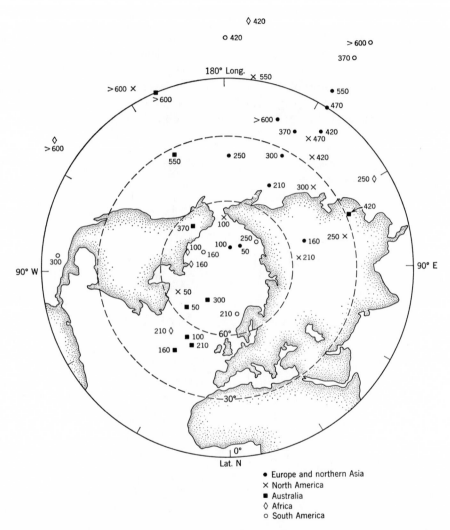

Figure 3.7: Approximate continental mean paleomagnetic poles. Approximate time past in 10^6 years. Based on Irving [188, pp. 110–128].

reversal is more definite, particularly for the past four million years. From well-established sequences of lava flows, dated by the K-Ar method in Iceland, France, Hawaii, the continental United States, and the Soviet Union, polar reversals occurred about 0.85, 1.85, 1.95, 2.4, 3.0, 3.1, and 3.35 million years ago. In these cases laboratory examination of the rocks in which the apparent reversal occurred reveals no characteristic suggesting a reverse polarity upon magnetization. For the older paleomagnetic data, the indications are that polar reversals occurred less frequently, and a puzzling fact is that all thirty-five of the paleomagnetic poles shown in Figure 3.6 have the same polarity as the present field, even though the poles probably extended over the entire 50 million years of the Permian period [83, 85, 95, 96, 188].

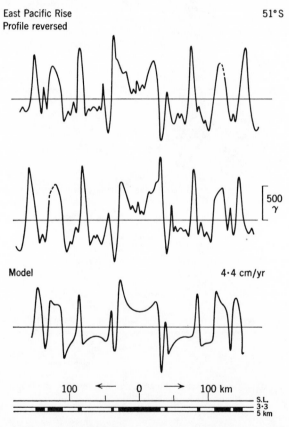

Figure 3.8: Comparison of magnetic anomaly profile observed across East Pacific Rise at 51°S with reversed profile and calculations from z model of field intensity, susceptibility, and thickness of magnetized layer 1.7 km. From Vine [419, p. 1409].

Use of Magnetic Anomaly Patterns

The reversals of the geomagnetic field have been used to date different strata in sedimentary cores and, most interestingly, to correlate magnetic anomalies at different locations in the ocean floor. It was first suggested by Vine and Matthews [420] that there existed an approximate symmetry of magnetic anomaly patterns about oceanic ridges caused by the magnetization of new oceanic crust as it cooled at the ridge and the subsequent spreading of crust to each side of the ridge. An example of such a pattern across the East Pacific Rise is given in Figure 3.8. If the spatial pattern in Figure 3.8 is compared to the time scale established from lava flows, the two patterns match for an average rate of spreading of 4.4 cm/yr, provided an extra pair of reversals about 0.7 and 0.8 $\times$ 10^6 years ago are added. Similar patterns are observed in several other locations, with rates of motion varying from 1 to 4.5 cm/yr. Also observed in magnetic anomaly patterns are transcurrent faults up to 1200 km in length [419, 420, 557].

Paleoclimatology

The findings of paleomagnetism have stimulated a good deal of new activity in paleoclimatology, the determination of past climates, and hence latitudes, from biological and meteorological indications, such as: the existence of coral, which requires temperatures above 18°C if it is of a type depending on algae symbiosis; the existence of carbonate deposits which normally occur only below latitudes of 30 degrees; the absence of rings in trees, which indicates a low latitude tropical climate; the existence of laterite soils indicating, again, a warm, rainy climate; the existence of evaporites such as gypsum and wind-deposited sediments, both indicating hot, dry climates; striations in the rock such as would be caused by glaciers; the ratios of certain isotopes such as O^{18}/O^{16} which depend upon temperature; the balance between various species of organisms; etc. Again, the information available is much greater for North America and Europe than elsewhere. In the case of these continents the paleoclimatological evidence does corroborate the paleomagnetic evidence in indicating that the climate in these areas was equatorial in the late Paleozoic, about 250 million years ago [188].

PROBLEMS

3.1. Prove the vector identity

$$\nabla \times (\nabla \times \mathbf{B}) = \nabla(\nabla \cdot \mathbf{B}) - \nabla^2 \mathbf{B}$$

3.2. Prove Gauss's theorem:

$$\int_V \nabla \cdot \mathbf{x} \, dv = \oint_S \mathbf{x} \cdot \mathbf{n} \, ds$$

where the integration on the left is over a volume V enclosed by a surface S, over which the integration on the right is made; $\mathbf{x} \cdot \mathbf{n}$ is the outward normal component of the field.

3.3. Prove the vector identity

$$\nabla \times (\mathbf{v} \times \mathbf{B}) = (\mathbf{B} \cdot \nabla)\mathbf{v} - (\mathbf{v} \cdot \nabla)\mathbf{B}$$

Discuss the physical interpretation obtained by substituting this expression in the equation for $\partial \mathbf{B}/\partial t$ (3.2.12). How does it express the carrying along of the field by the fluid? How does it express stretching of lines of force?

3.4. In equations (3.2.13) and (3.2.18) substitute $\mathbf{B}_0 + \mathbf{B}_1$ for $\mathbf{B}$ and $\mathbf{v}_0 + \mathbf{v}_1$ for $\mathbf{v}$. Assume $\mathbf{B}_1 \ll \mathbf{B}_0$ and $\mathbf{v}_0 = 0$. Neglecting the products of small quantities, show that a small disturbance $\mathbf{B}_1$, $\mathbf{v}_1$ will be propagated at the Alfvén velocity (3.2.19).

3.5. Prove Cowling's theorem: an axially symmetric motion of a hydromagnetic system cannot maintain a dynamo.

3.6. Estimate the order-of-magnitude of each of the terms in the equations of motion (3.2.20), using the numerical values associated with the Bullard and Gellman model. Which terms are most important? It is stated in the text that the effect of the magnetic field is to make the flow stiffer, more laminar. What magnetic Rayleigh number might express this effect, analogous to the thermal Rayleigh number (2.4.18)?

3.7. To the equations of motion with only magnetic-force terms (3.2.18), add the Coriolis term $-2\boldsymbol{\omega} \times \mathbf{v}$. Assume the vectors $\boldsymbol{\omega}$ and $\mathbf{B}$ are parallel. Derive the result that the Alfvén velocity, (3.2.19), will be modified to

$$v_A = \frac{l\omega}{2\pi} \pm \left[\frac{B^2}{8\pi\rho} + \left(\frac{l\omega}{2\pi} \right)^2 \right]^{1/2}$$

where l is the wavelength of the disturbance traveling with velocity v_A.

REFERENCES

The most extensive treatise on geomagnetism is that by *Chapman & Bartels* [71], which recapitulates all work up to 1940. The most recent detailed and comprehensive work is by *Rikitake* [335]. Other reviews summarizing the observational data are *Hide & Roberts* [180] and *Jacobs* [191]. Particular emphasis on information pertaining to other planets is made by *Kern & Vestine* [211] and by *Hide* [178]. The detailed determination of the field we used here is that by *Cain et al.* [61]. Results for the magnetic field measurements near Mars are interpreted by *Van Allen et al.* [584]; near the moon, by *Sonett et al.* [504]; near Venus, by *Vinogradov et al.* [534] and by *Van Allen et al.* [537].

The appropriate introduction to hydromagnetism is through a text on electromagnetism, such as *Jackson* [190]. Texts entirely on hydromagnetism are *Alfvén &*

Fälthammar [1], *Cowling* [82], and *Roberts* [497]. An extensive review by *Elsasser* [109] is also helpful. The fundamentals are also developed by *Chandrasekhar* [68], with a view to problems of marginal stability. The application to the earth is treated in detail in *Rikitake* [335] and *Takeuchi* [385].

The principal detailed calculation of the earth's hydromagnetic dynamo was by *Bullard & Gellman* [57]. Other dynamo hypotheses are by *Elsasser* [110], *Parker* [307], *Hide* [177], and *Herzenberg* [474]; more general reviews are given by *Hide & Roberts* [180], *Jacobs* [191], and *Gibson & Roberts* [469]. The inference of motions in the core from the secular variation is treated in *Bullard et al.* [56], *Roberts & Scott* [343], and *Kahle et al.* [202]. *Bullard et al.* [56], *Rochester* [345], and *Rochester & Smylie* [346] investigate core-mantle coupling, while *Hide* [179] and *Malkus* [259] develop the theory of hydromagnetic waves in the core as a possible explanation for the westward drift. Boundary effects are discussed by *Stewartson* [375, 376] and by *Malkus* [258, 486], who also investigates the possibility of precessional torques being the energy source for the dynamo. *Verhoogen* [416] investigates thermal energy sources. *Stacey* [582] discusses conductivity.

The inference of electrical currents in the mantle from variations in the magnetic field is treated by *Lahiri & Price* [235], *McDonald* [268], *Eckhardt et al.* [104], and *Rikitake* [335].

The discussion of paleomagnetism is based largely on the book by *Irving* [188]. The most extensive description of techniques is a symposium volume edited by *Collinson et al.* [77]. Long-period variations of the geomagnetic field inferred from land data are described by *Cox & Doell* [83], *Doell & Cox* [95], *Doell et al.* [96], *Cox et al.* [519], *Dagley et al.* [85], *Smith* [373], and *Creer* [554]; oceanic data, by *Vine & Matthews* [420], *Vine* [419], *Opdyke et al.* [302], *Vogt & Ostenso* [510], and *Heirtzler et al.* [557]. See also the symposium volume edited by *Blackett et al.* [35].

Chapter 4

DYNAMICS OF THE EARTH-MOON SYSTEM

The present state of the solar system is that of a few widely separated chunks whose courses are evidently the result of a very long process of sorting out and settling down. The interaction between these chunks is primarily that of Newtonian gravitation. Because of the great difference in masses between different bodies of appreciable interaction, the principal manifestations of this interaction are orbits that differ very little from the perfect ellipses which the theory predicts in the case of only two bodies. Consequently, the mathematical development of the orbital behavior of natural bodies in the solar system normally takes the form of perturbations of a perfect Keplerian ellipse.

There are small but significant departures from Keplerian motion, however, which indicate, first, that peculiar circumstances within the framework of Newtonian mechanics—many more near-resonances than would occur by chance, etc.—are important in determining the present arrangement of the solar system, and second, that non-Newtonian interactions dependent on the nature of planetary constitutions have resulted in appreciable long-term transfers of energy and angular momentum.

The plan of this chapter is first to develop the essentials of Newtonian theory in terms of Keplerian motion plus small perturbations thereof, and then to apply this theory to the system for which the most detailed data is available: the earth-moon system. The main purposes are to limit the circumstances of origin and long-term evolution and to deduce properties of the earth and moon affecting their own motions and motions of artificial satellites. In Chapter 5 we make similar application to the planetary system. Also a small part of the earth-moon system—its dust—we shall leave to Chapter 5, since its serious consideration involves the capture of material from the interplanetary medium.

4.1 Generalities on Celestial Mechanics

Elliptic Motion

Assume that we have a particle of negligible mass attracted by another point mass M in accordance with Newton's law. Assume further that the

158

origin of coordinates is at the mass M. Newton's law for the acceleration of the particle can be expressed in vectorial form, using μ for GM, as:

$$\ddot{\mathbf{r}} = -GM\frac{\mathbf{r}}{r^3} = -\mu\frac{\mathbf{r}}{r^3} \qquad (4.1.1)$$

The acceleration vector $\ddot{\mathbf{r}}$ is therefore colinear with the position vector $\mathbf{r}$. If we define the equatorial plane as the plane determined by the position vector and the velocity vector $\dot{\mathbf{r}}$, the particle will never depart from the equatorial plane because there is no component of acceleration out of the plane. Hence, in converting from rectangular to spherical coordinates,

$$\mathbf{x} = r\begin{cases} \cos\varphi\cos\lambda \\ \cos\varphi\sin\lambda \\ \sin\varphi \end{cases}$$

we can set equal to zero the latitude φ and its derivatives with respect to time $\dot{\varphi}$ and $\ddot{\varphi}$. Differentiating twice with respect to time we obtain (4.1.1) in polar coordinates:

$$x = r\cos\lambda$$
$$y = r\sin\lambda$$
$$\dot{x} = \dot{r}\cos\lambda - r\dot{\lambda}\sin\lambda$$
$$\dot{y} = \dot{r}\sin\lambda + r\dot{\lambda}\cos\lambda$$
$$\ddot{x} = \ddot{r}\cos\lambda - 2\dot{r}\dot{\lambda}\sin\lambda - r\ddot{\lambda}\sin\lambda - r(\dot{\lambda})^2\cos\lambda = -\mu\cos\lambda/r^2$$
$$\ddot{y} = \ddot{r}\sin\lambda + 2\dot{r}\dot{\lambda}\cos\lambda + r\ddot{\lambda}\cos\lambda - r(\dot{\lambda})^2\sin\lambda = -\mu\sin\lambda/r^2$$

The point from which the longitude λ is measured is arbitrary, so we can also set λ zero, but not $\dot{\lambda}$ or $\ddot{\lambda}$. The equations of motion thus become:

$$\ddot{r} - r(\dot{\lambda})^2 = -\frac{\mu}{r^2} \qquad (4.1.2)$$

$$r\ddot{\lambda} + 2\dot{r}\dot{\lambda} = 0 \qquad (4.1.3)$$

If we multiply (4.1.3) by r, it is evident that it is immediately integrable to:

$$r^2\dot{\lambda} = h \qquad (4.1.4)$$

where h is constant. Equation (4.1.4) states that *angular momentum*, $r^2\dot{\lambda}$, is conserved. To integrate (4.1.2), replace $1/r$ by u. Then:

$$\frac{du}{dr} = -\frac{1}{r^2}$$

From (4.1.4):

$$\frac{dt}{d\lambda} = \frac{r^2}{h}$$

whence

$$\frac{du}{d\lambda} = \frac{du}{dr} \cdot \frac{dr}{dt} \cdot \frac{dt}{d\lambda} = -\frac{1}{r^2}\dot{r}\frac{r^2}{h} = -\frac{\dot{r}}{h}$$

and

$$\frac{d^2u}{d\lambda^2} = \frac{d}{dt}\left(-\frac{\dot{r}}{h}\right)\frac{dt}{d\lambda} = -\frac{\ddot{r}}{h}\frac{r^2}{h} = -\frac{\ddot{r}}{u^2h^2}$$

or

$$\ddot{r} = -h^2u^2\frac{d^2u}{d\lambda^2} \tag{4.1.5}$$

Substituting from (4.1.4) for $\dot{\lambda}$ and from (4.1.5) for $\ddot{r}$ in (4.1.2), and replacing r by $1/u$ everywhere, yields

$$\frac{d^2u}{d\lambda^2} + u = \frac{\mu}{h^2} \tag{4.1.6}$$

Equation (4.1.6) is readily integrated as

$$\frac{1}{r} = u = A\cos(\lambda - \lambda_0) + \frac{\mu}{h^2} \tag{4.1.7}$$

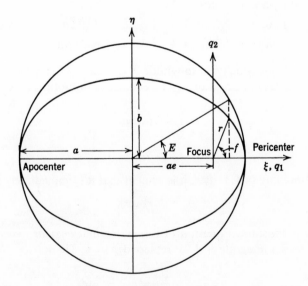

Figure 4.1: Orbital ellipse.

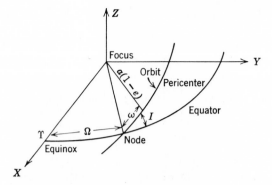

Figure 4.2: Orbital orientation.

If in the equation for an ellipse (see Figure 4.1), with origin at the center,

$$\frac{\xi^2}{a^2} + \frac{\eta^2}{b^2} = 1 \tag{4.1.8}$$

we substitute $ae + r \cos f$ for ξ, $\sin f$ for η, and $a^2(1 - e^2)$ for b^2, and solve the resulting quadratic equation for r, there is obtained for the positive root:

$$r = \frac{a(1 - e^2)}{(1 + e \cos f)}$$

or

$$\frac{1}{r} = \frac{1}{a(1 - e^2)} + \frac{e}{a(1 - e^2)} \cos f \tag{4.1.9}$$

Comparing (4.1.7) and (4.1.9), we see (4.1.7) is the equation of an ellipse with origin at the focus and:

$$\lambda - \lambda_0 = f \tag{4.1.10}$$

$$A = \frac{e}{a(1 - e^2)} \tag{4.1.11}$$

$$h = \sqrt{\mu a(1 - e^2)} \tag{4.1.12}$$

The size of the orbit of the particle thus can be expressed by the *semimajor axis*, a, of the ellipse; the shape, by the *eccentricity*, e; and the location of the particle in the ellipse by f, called the *true anomaly*. Equations (4.1.9–12) also apply to hyperbolic motion with $a < 0$ and $e > 1$.

Position in the orbital plane also can be expressed by the **q** coordinate system, shown in Figure 4.1. To completely specify the location of the particle, we need the three Euler angles shown in Figure 4.2: the *longitude of the node*,

Ω; the *inclination*, I; and the *argument of pericenter*, ω. These angles constitute the rotation:

$$\mathbf{R}_{xq} = \qquad \mathbf{R}_3(-\Omega) \qquad \cdot \qquad \mathbf{R}_1(-I) \qquad \cdot \qquad \mathbf{R}_3(-\omega)$$

$$= \begin{pmatrix} \cos\Omega & -\sin\Omega & 0 \\ \sin\Omega & \cos\Omega & 0 \\ 0 & 0 & 1 \end{pmatrix} \begin{pmatrix} 1 & 0 & 0 \\ 0 & \cos I & -\sin I \\ 0 & \sin I & \cos I \end{pmatrix} \begin{pmatrix} \cos\omega & -\sin\omega & 0 \\ \sin\omega & \cos\omega & 0 \\ 0 & 0 & 1 \end{pmatrix}$$

$$(4.1.13)$$

which defines rotation from the **q** to the **x** coordinate system. In the notation $\mathbf{R}_i(\alpha)$, i denotes the axis of rotation and α denotes the angle rotated, being positive for a counterclockwise rotation as viewed from the positive end of the axis toward the origin.

Another way of locating the particle in the ellipse that is sometimes more convenient is the *eccentric anomaly*, E. The eccentric anomaly, as shown in Figure 4.1, is the angle subtended at the center of a circle of radius a, tangent to the ellipse, at the point on the circle whose ξ coordinate is the same as that of the point on the ellipse. From Figure 4.1 we get

$$q_1 = \xi - ae = a(\cos E - e) \tag{4.1.14}$$

Using (4.1.8) we then obtain

$$q_2 = \eta = a\sqrt{1 - e^2} \sin E \tag{4.1.15}$$

$$r = \sqrt{q_1{}^2 + q_2{}^2} = a(1 - e \cos E) \tag{4.1.16}$$

For the rate of motion of the particle in its orbit, we can use (4.1.4) changing λ to f. Equation (4.1.4) is more readily integrated if the true anomaly is replaced by the eccentric anomaly. Differentiate (4.1.9) to obtain dr/df:

$$\frac{dr}{df} = -r^2 \frac{d(1/r)}{df} = \frac{r^2 e}{a(1 - e^2)} \sin f$$

Substitute q_2 for $r \sin f$ from Figure 4.1:

$$dr = \frac{req_2}{a(1 - e^2)} df \tag{4.1.17}$$

From differentiating (4.1.15–16) we obtain

$$dr = \frac{e}{\sqrt{1 - e^2}} q_2 \, dE \tag{4.1.18}$$

Using (4.1.17–18) to eliminate dr, (4.1.16) for r, and (4.1.12) for h, (4.1.4) becomes

$$a^2\sqrt{1 - e^2}(1 - e \cos E) \, dE = \sqrt{\mu a(1 - e^2)} \, dt \qquad (4.1.19)$$

(4.1.19) integrates to:

$$E - e \sin E = M \qquad (4.1.20)$$

where

$$M = n(t - t_0)$$

and

$$n = \mu^{1/2} a^{-3/2} \qquad (4.1.21)$$

The time t_0 is the time of passing pericenter. The quantity M is known as the *mean anomaly*, and the quantity n as the *mean motion*. Equation (4.1.20) is known as *Kepler's equation* and (4.1.21) as *Kepler's third law* [86, 206, 282].

Perturbed Equations of Motion

The foregoing developments apply solely to motion in a purely central field, but our interest in dynamics is largely due to the fact that the force fields are perceptibly noncentral. If the forces are gravitational, then they can be represented as gradients of scalars, and (4.1.1) can be replaced by

$$\ddot{\mathbf{r}} = \nabla V \qquad (4.1.22)$$

where the scalar potential V has a noncentral form. Even for this noncentral field, however, the Keplerian ellipse and its orientation can be regarded as a coordinate system, alternative to rectangular or polar coordinates. At any instant the situation of an orbiting body can be described by the inertially fixed rectangular components of position (x, y, z) and velocity $(\dot{x}, \dot{y}, \dot{z})$. In place of these six numbers the six numbers of the Keplerian ellipse $(a, e, I, M, \omega, \Omega)$ may be used. The relationship between the two systems can be expressed by the rotation from a coordinate system in the orbital plane referred to perigee to the inertially fixed system:

$$\begin{aligned}
\mathbf{x} &= \mathbf{R}_{xq}(\Omega, I, \omega)\mathbf{q}(a, e, M) \\
\dot{\mathbf{x}} &= \mathbf{R}_{xq}(\Omega, I, \omega)\dot{\mathbf{q}}(a, e, M)
\end{aligned} \qquad (4.1.23)$$

where the rotation matrix $\mathbf{R}_{xq}$ is defined by (4.1.13) and:

$$\mathbf{q} = \left\{ \begin{array}{c} a(\cos E - e) \\ a\sqrt{1 - e^2} \sin E \\ 0 \end{array} \right\} = \left\{ \begin{array}{c} r \cos f \\ r \sin f \\ 0 \end{array} \right\} \qquad (4.1.24)$$

from (4.4.14–15) and Figure 4.1; and

$$\dot{\mathbf{q}} = \left\{ \begin{array}{c} -\sin E \\ \sqrt{1 - e^2} \cos E \\ 0 \end{array} \right\} \frac{na}{1 - e \cos E} = \left\{ \begin{array}{c} -\sin f \\ e + \cos f \\ 0 \end{array} \right\} \frac{na}{\sqrt{1 - e^2}} \qquad (4.1.25)$$

from (4.4.14–19).

The Keplerian ellipse $(a, e, I, M, \omega, \Omega)$ corresponding to the position $\mathbf{r}$ and velocity $\dot{\mathbf{r}}$ of a particle at a particular time is known as the *instantaneous*, or *osculating, orbit*. If the potential field V differs from a central field, this ellipse will be continually changing. However, if the field differs very slightly from a central field—as is the case for any situation of significant duration—we should expect that the parameters of the ellipse would change slowly, and hence that the ellipse would constitute a coordinate system convenient for representing the position and velocity of the particle. The problem is to convert (4.1.22) from rectangular coordinates to Keplerian ellipse coordinates, or *elements*, as they are more conventionally called. First we convert (4.1.22) from vectorial to subscript notation, and second we change the equations of motion (4.1.22) from three second-order equations to six first-order equations by treating the velocity components as variables in the same manner as the position components:

$$\frac{d}{dt} x_i = \dot{x}_i, \qquad i = 1, 2, 3 \qquad (4.1.26)$$

$$\frac{d}{dt} \dot{x}_i = \frac{\partial V}{\partial x_i}, \qquad i = 1, 2, 3 \qquad (4.1.27)$$

where x_i, $\dot{x}_i$ denote inertially fixed rectangular components of position and velocity respectively. The rates of change dx_i/dt and $d\dot{x}_i/dt$ in (4.1.26–27) can be expressed as functions of the rates of change dS_k/dt of the six Keplerian elements, where S_k represents any of a, e, i, M, ω, or Ω.

$$\sum_{k=1}^{6} \frac{\partial x_i}{\partial S_k} \cdot \frac{dS_k}{dt} = \frac{\partial x_i}{\partial S_k} \cdot \frac{dS_k}{dt} = \dot{x}_i, \qquad i = 1, 2, 3 \qquad (4.1.28)$$

$$\sum_{k=1}^{6} \frac{\partial \dot{x}_i}{\partial S_k} \cdot \frac{dS_k}{dt} = \frac{\partial \dot{x}_i}{\partial S_k} \cdot \frac{dS_k}{dt} = \frac{\partial V}{\partial x_i}, \qquad i = 1, 2, 3 \qquad (4.1.29)$$

where $\partial x_i/\partial S_k$ is obtained by differentiating (4.1.23–24) and $\partial \dot{x}_i/\partial S_k$ by differentiating (4.1.23–25). In the central formulas of (4.1.28–29) we have followed the convention that summation takes place over subscripts repeated in a product. The summation symbol will be omitted hereafter. To complete the conversion, for each element S_l in turn: (1) multiply (4.1.28) by $-\partial \dot{x}_i/\partial S_l$; (2) multiply (4.1.29) by $\partial x_i/\partial S_l$; and (3) add the resulting equations together:

$$-\frac{\partial \dot{x}_i}{\partial S_l} \cdot \frac{\partial x_i}{\partial S_k} \cdot \frac{dS_k}{dt} + \frac{\partial x_i}{\partial S_l} \cdot \frac{\partial \dot{x}_i}{\partial S_k} \cdot \frac{dS_k}{dt} = -\frac{\partial \dot{x}_i}{\partial S_l} \dot{x}_i + \frac{\partial x_i}{\partial S_l} \cdot \frac{\partial V}{\partial x_i} \quad (4.1.30)$$

or

$$[S_l, S_k]\frac{dS_k}{dt} = \frac{\partial F}{\partial S_l} \quad (4.1.31)$$

summing over k, where

$$[S_l, S_k] = \frac{\partial x_i}{\partial S_l} \cdot \frac{\partial \dot{x}_i}{\partial S_k} - \frac{\partial \dot{x}_i}{\partial S_l} \cdot \frac{\partial x_i}{\partial S_k} \quad (4.1.32)$$

known as *Lagrange's brackets*, and

$$F = V - T \quad (4.1.33)$$

F is known as the *force function*; it is the negative of the *Hamiltonian* used in physics. V is the negative of the potential energy, and T is the kinetic energy:

$$T = \tfrac{1}{2}\dot{x}_i\dot{x}_i \quad (4.1.34)$$

summing over i.

There are now two principal problems: (1) the formulation of the Lagrangian brackets $[S_l, S_k]$; and (2) the transformation of the potential V from rectangular or polar coordinates to Keplerian elements.

The form of (4.1.32) indicates that $[S_l, S_k]$ is the negative of $[S_k, S_l]$ and that $[S_k, S_k]$ vanishes, so there are fifteen different Lagrangian brackets to be determined by differentiating (4.1.23). A property of the Lagrangian brackets which facilitates their evaluation is their time invariance (see problem 4.1). The complete set of nonzero results are:

$$[\Omega, I] = -[I, \Omega] = -na^2(1 - e^2)^{1/2} \sin I$$

$$[\Omega, a] = -[a, \Omega] = (1 - e^2)^{1/2} \cos I \, na/2$$

$$[\Omega, e] = -[e, \Omega] = -na^2 e \cos I/(1 - e^2)^{1/2}$$

$$[\omega, a] = -[a, \omega] = (1 - e^2)^{1/2} na/2 \qquad (4.1.35)$$

$$[\omega, e] = -[e, \omega] = -na^2 e/(1 - e^2)^{1/2}$$

$$[a, M] = -[M, a] = -na/2$$

Substituting these expressions in (4.1.31) and solving the six simultaneous equations for the dS_k/dt yields:

$$\frac{da}{dt} = \frac{2}{na} \frac{\partial F}{\partial M}$$

$$\frac{de}{dt} = \frac{1 - e^2}{na^2 e} \frac{\partial F}{\partial M} - \frac{(1 - e^2)^{1/2}}{na^2 e} \frac{\partial F}{\partial \omega}$$

$$\frac{d\omega}{dt} = \frac{-\cos I}{na^2 (1 - e^2)^{1/2} \sin I} \frac{\partial F}{\partial I} + \frac{(1 - e^2)^{1/2}}{na^2 e} \frac{\partial F}{\partial e}$$

$$\frac{dI}{dt} = \frac{\cos I}{na^2 (1 - e^2)^{1/2} \sin I} \frac{\partial F}{\partial \omega} - \frac{1}{na^2 (1 - e^2)^{1/2} \sin I} \frac{\partial F}{\partial \Omega} \qquad (4.1.36)$$

$$\frac{d\Omega}{dt} = \frac{1}{na^2 (1 - e^2)^{1/2} \sin I} \frac{\partial F}{\partial I}$$

$$\frac{dM}{dt} = -\frac{1 - e^2}{na^2 e} \frac{\partial F}{\partial e} - \frac{2}{na} \frac{\partial F}{\partial a}$$

It is customary to express the force function as:

$$F = \frac{\mu}{r} + R - T \qquad (4.1.37)$$

where R, comprising all terms of V except the central term, is known as the *disturbing function*. To express $\mu/r - T$ in the Keplerian elements, use (4.1.25) and (4.1.9):

$$\frac{\mu}{r} - T = \frac{\mu}{r} - \frac{1}{2} (\dot{q}_1{}^2 + \dot{q}_2{}^2)$$

$$= \frac{\mu}{r} - \frac{n^2 a^2}{2(1 - e^2)} [\sin^2 f + e^2 + 2e \cos f + \cos^2 f]$$

$$= \frac{\mu}{r} - \frac{\mu}{2a(1 - e^2)} [(2 + 2e \cos f) - (1 - e^2)]$$

$$= \frac{\mu}{r} - \frac{\mu}{r} + \frac{\mu}{2a} = \frac{\mu}{2a} \qquad (4.1.38)$$

Hence in all equations of (4.1.36) F can be replaced by R except in the last, which becomes, using (4.1.21),

$$\frac{dM}{dt} = n - \frac{1 - e^2}{na^2 e} \cdot \frac{\partial R}{\partial e} - \frac{2}{na} \cdot \frac{\partial R}{\partial a} \qquad (4.1.39)$$

The symmetries and similarities of the brackets in (4.1.35) suggest that further simplifications may be made by change of variables from Keplerian. Let us try to find a set L, G, H such that

$$[M, L] = 1, \quad [M, G] = 0, \quad [M, H] = 0$$
$$[\omega, L] = 0, \quad [\omega, G] = 1, \quad [\omega, H] = 0 \qquad (4.1.40)$$
$$[\Omega, L] = 0, \quad [\Omega, G] = 0, \quad [\Omega, H] = 1$$

The only nonzero bracket in (4.1.35) involving the inclination, I, is the first. From (4.1.32) we must have:

$$[\Omega, H]\frac{\partial H}{\partial I} = [\Omega, I] = -na^2(1 - e^2)^{1/2} \sin I \qquad (4.1.41)$$

whence

$$H = na^2(1 - e^2)^{1/2} \cos I \qquad (4.1.42)$$

As a check, we find (remembering n is $\mu^{1/2}a^{-3/2}$):

$$[\Omega, H]\frac{\partial H}{\partial e} = [\Omega, e] \qquad (4.1.43)$$

$$[\Omega, H]\frac{\partial H}{\partial a} = [\Omega, a] \qquad (4.1.44)$$

Similarly from $[\omega, G]$ $(\partial G/\partial e)$ and $[M, L]$ $(\partial L/\partial a)$:

$$G = na^2(1 - e^2)^{1/2} \qquad (4.1.45)$$

$$L = na^2 = \mu^{1/2}a^{1/2} \qquad (4.1.46)$$

We thus obtain the somewhat simpler *Delaunay equations*:

$$\dot{L} = \frac{\partial F}{\partial M} \qquad \dot{M} = -\frac{\partial F}{\partial L}$$

$$\dot{G} = \frac{\partial F}{\partial \omega} \qquad \dot{\omega} = -\frac{\partial F}{\partial G} \qquad (4.1.47)$$

$$\dot{H} = \frac{\partial F}{\partial \Omega} \qquad \dot{\Omega} = -\frac{\partial F}{\partial H}$$

The Lagrangian and Delaunay forms—(4.1.36) and (4.1.47)—are not the only forms of the equations of motion, and are indeed limited by their dependence on the accelerations being representable as gradients of a scalar potential. A form of more general application is the *Gaussian*:

$$\dot{a} = \frac{2a^2}{h} \left[eS \sin f + p \frac{T}{r} \right]$$

$$\dot{e} = \frac{p}{h} [S \sin f + T(\cos E + \cos f)]$$

$$\dot{I} = \frac{1}{h} rW \cos u$$

$$\dot{\Omega} = \frac{1}{h \sin I} rW \sin u \qquad\qquad (4.1.48)$$

$$\dot{\omega} = \frac{p}{h} \left[-\frac{1}{e} S \cos f + \frac{1}{e} T \left(1 + \frac{r}{p} \right) \sin f - \frac{\cot I}{p} rW \sin u \right]$$

$$\dot{M} = \frac{p}{h} \left[-\beta S \cos f + \frac{2}{a\eta} Sr + \beta T \left(1 + \frac{r}{p} \right) \sin f - \frac{r}{p} W \sin u \cot I \right] - \dot{\omega}$$

where S, T, W are the radial, transverse, and normal components of acceleration; also

$$p = a(1 - e^2)$$

$$h = \sqrt{\mu a(1 - e^2)}, \qquad \text{the angular momentum}$$

$$\eta = \sqrt{1 - e^2}$$

$$\beta = \frac{1 - \eta}{e}$$

and

$$u = \omega + f$$

To integrate the equations of motion (4.1.22) or (4.1.36) or (4.1.47) or (4.1.48), the best technique depends on, first, the nature of the disturbances, as expressed by the disturbing function R of (4.1.37) or the orthogonal force components S, T, W in (4.1.48); and second, the purpose of the integration. For some disturbances and purposes, such as the trajectory of an artificial satellite, the problem is simple (since computers were developed): numerical integration suffices. For other disturbances and purposes, the problem is still unsolved: this is particularly true of many aspects of orbital evolution important to an understanding of the long-term behavior of the solar system [146, 206, 318].

Disturbing Functions

Even for many cases of the simplest disturbance—the gravitational attraction of another body besides the central body—a full deterministic solution

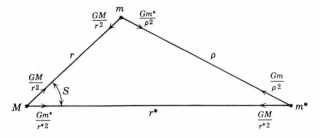

Figure 4.3: Three-body problem.

has not been attained. Since the perturbation is gravitational, it may be treated as a disturbing function R, known as a *third-body* disturbing function. In Figure 4.3, let M be the central body; m, the body whose orbit we wish to determine; m^*, the third body which is the source of the disturbing attraction r, r^*, and ρ the intervening distances; and S the angle at the central body as indicated in Figure 4.3. If we referred positions and velocities of the three bodies to the center of mass of the system, then the accelerations could be expressed as indicated by the arrows in Figure 4.3. However, in practice the coordinate origin is more conveniently taken as the central body M. Then in expressing the acceleration of the orbiting body m the accelerations of the central body must be subtracted:

$$\ddot{x}_i = -\frac{G(M + m)}{r^2} \cdot \frac{x_i}{r} - \frac{Gm^*}{\rho^2} \cdot \frac{x_i - x_i^*}{\rho} - \frac{Gm^*}{r^{*2}} \cdot \frac{x_i^*}{r^*} \quad (4.1.49)$$

To express the acceleration $\ddot{x}_i$ as the derivative of a potential, $\partial V/\partial x_i$, we integrate (4.1.49) with respect to x_i to get:

$$V = G\left(\frac{M + m}{r} + \frac{m^*}{\rho} - \frac{m^*\mathbf{x}^* \cdot \mathbf{x}}{r^{*3}}\right) \quad (4.1.50)$$

To eliminate the third side length ρ, use the law of cosines, and develop in a binomial series:

$$\frac{m^*}{\rho} = m^*(r^2 + r^{*2} - 2rr^* \cos S)^{-1/2}$$

$$= \frac{m^*}{r^*} \sum_{i=0}^{\infty} \binom{-\frac{1}{2}}{i}\left[\left(\frac{r}{r^*}\right)^2 - 2\frac{r}{r^*}\cos S\right]^i \quad (4.1.51)$$

where $\binom{-\frac{1}{2}}{i}$ denotes the binomial coefficient. This representation is appropriate for $r < r^*$; if $r > r^*$, division by r is appropriate. Collecting together all terms containing each power of r/r^*, $(r/r^*)^n$ (see problem 2.2), we get for (4.1.50):

$$V = G \frac{M + m}{r} + R \qquad (4.1.52)$$

where

$$R = G \frac{m^*}{r^*} \sum_{n=2}^{\infty} \left(\frac{r}{r^*}\right)^n P_{n0}(\cos S) \qquad (4.1.53)$$

Finally, to separate the coordinates of m and m^* referred to M, we can apply the addition theorem (see problem 2.4) to $P_{n0}(\cos S)$.

$$R = G \frac{m^*}{r^*} \sum_{n=2}^{\infty} \left(\frac{r}{r^*}\right)^n \sum_{m=0}^{n} (2 - \delta_{0m}) \frac{(n - m)!}{(n + m)!} P_{nm}(\sin \delta) P_{nm}(\sin \delta^*)$$
$$\times \cos m(\alpha - \alpha^*) \quad (4.1.54)$$

where δ_{om} is the Kronecker delta (1 if $m = 0$, 0 if $m \neq 0$) and (δ, α), (δ^*, α^*) are declination and right ascension of m, m^*, respectively. Declination δ is the same as latitude φ, whereas right ascension α differs from longitude λ as used in Section 2.1 in that it is measured from an inertially fixed, rather than a body-fixed, point [47, 86, 282, 318].

Integration

If the accelerations from (4.1.49) directly or from gradients of (4.1.52, 54) are used in a numerical integration, then on the order of 100 integration steps per revolution of m must be taken—which limits the total integration to something like 1000 to 10,000 revolutions before round-off error is excessive. If m is a planet we are thus limited to about 10^{-5} of its total lifetime. However, most of the effort is used up calculating short-periodic variations which are not of interest. If the disturbing function or accelerations can be averaged over the revolution, then the duration of the integration can be greatly lengthened. This averaging obviously can be done numerically. If $r \ll r^*$ or $r^* \ll r$ so that a form such as (4.1.54) converges rapidly, then the averaging can be done more efficiently analytically, by converting the spherical coordinates r, δ, α and r^*, δ^*, α^* to Keplerian elements, in a manner similar to that described in Section 4.2 for variations of the gravitational field, and dropping the terms containing the mean anomaly M. Then for the third-body disturbance problem the length of the integration step will be limited by the rate of change of the other orbital elements—which for m^*/M on the order of 10^{-3}, will be on the order of 10^{-3} times the mean motion n. Hence the total integration can be carried on the order of 1000 times as long, or still 10^{-2} of the total lifetime.

So for a better understanding of the long-term properties of dynamical problems, resort must be had to analytical techniques. Normally such techniques start from a form of the equations of motion which isolate the rapid change $\dot{M}$, but which also has the simplest possible form, such as the Delaunay equations (4.1.47). Equations of this form are known as *canonical*, and may be abbreviated as

$$\dot{p}_i = \frac{\partial F}{\partial q_i}, \qquad \dot{q}_i = -\frac{\partial F}{\partial p_i} \qquad (4.1.55)$$

where the p_i's (called *action variables*) are L, G, H and the q_i's (called *angle variables*) are M, ω, Ω. The first and obvious attack on equations such as (4.1.55) is to manipulate them so that the variables can be separated, similar to the solution of Laplace's equation in spherical coordinates (2.1.2). Failing this, it may be possible to transform to a different set of variables p_i', q_i' with force function F' for which the solution is known. The fact that the motions (p_i, q_i) and (p_i', q_i') are both derived from single scalars F and F' respectively suggests that the transformation between the two can also be expressed in terms of a single scalar. With the aid of Hamilton's principle (see problem 4.3) this is shown to be true.

The course of the analytical solution of most problems is thus to successively eliminate the more rapidly changing angle variables so that a manageably few (it is hoped) variables remain. Thus, for example, in the three-body problem of Figure 4.3 with $m \ll m^* \ll M$ and $r \approx r^*$, if we refer m's orbit to the plane of m^*'s orbit, it can be shown that the first action variable L must be virtually constant because of the short period of the corresponding angle variable M, and the third action variable H must be virtually constant because of the short period of the angle variable $\Omega - \alpha^*$, where α^* is the longitude of m^* measured from the same inertially fixed point as is Ω. These virtual constancies are the result of the corresponding disturbing forces $\partial R/\partial M$, $\partial R/\partial \Omega$ cycling too rapidly to build up appreciable integrated effects on the orbit: they are "averaged out." The remaining motion consists of oscillations of the second action variable G dependent on the location of the pericenter ω. Since ω in turn depends on G, these oscillations may be large enough so that ω does not go through a full cycle from 0 to 2π, but instead librates. Physically the situation is one in which the energy—equivalent to L—and the component of angular momentum normal to m^*'s orbital plane—equivalent to H—are essentially conserved, but the total angular momentum—equivalent to G—has wide oscillations. Geometrically, the mean distance a stays nearly constant, but the eccentricity e and inclination I may have wide oscillations of opposite phase; that is, $\dot{e}$ has opposite sign to $\dot{I}$ [47, 146, 318].

4.2 Orbital Dynamics of the Earth-Moon System

The dominant characteristics of any dynamical system not undergoing rapid change are determined by the distribution of the masses on which the gravitational attraction depends. If these masses are collected together in a few discrete bodies tightly enough that motion within any body is very small compared to motions of the bodies relative to each other, then assuming the bodies to be perfectly rigid should obtain a good first approximation to their motion, and any effects of nonrigidity should be susceptible to treatment as perturbations of such motion. We thus break down the sizable topic of the dynamics of the earth-moon system, including their satellites into rigid and nonrigid sections.

Artificial Satellite Orbits

The simplest dynamical problem in the earth-moon system is that of the artificial satellite, its simplicity arising first from the nature of our interest in it—more as a means of measuring the natural environment than as a phenomenon whose history we wish to deduce for its own sake—and second from its negligible effect on other bodies. The main characteristics of a satellite's motion are determined by the gravitational field, most conveniently expressed in spherical harmonics (2.1.17). To relate this field to the motion of the satellite we want to convert coordinates from spherical $\{r, \varphi, \lambda\}$ to the Keplerian elements $\{a, e, I, M, \omega, \Omega\}$ which can be considered as an alternative coordinate system. This conversion has two main parts: (1) the effect of rotation, expressed by the three Euler angles $\Omega - \theta$, I, and ω, where Ω, I, ω are shown in Figure 4.2 and θ is the Greenwich sidereal time, the angle between the inertially fixed vernal equinox ($\alpha = 0$) and the body-fixed prime meridian ($\lambda = 0$); and (2) the effect of change from circular to elliptic coordinates shown in Figure 4.1, necessary because the true anomaly f does not change uniformly with respect to the independent variable, time.

The effect of a general rotation $\Omega - \theta$, I, ω on a spherical harmonic is a formidable piece of algebra; however, in the present problem it is somewhat simplified by the fact that we are interested only in the potential on the

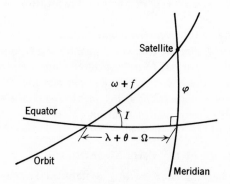

Figure 4.4: Orbit-equator-meridian spherical triangle.

"equator," the orbital plane, of the new system. Using the relationships between the parts of the spherical triangle in Figure 4.4, and (2.1.15–16), there is eventually obtained:

$$V = \frac{GM}{r} \sum_{l,m} \left(\frac{R}{r}\right)^l \sum_{p=0}^{l} F_{lmp}(I)$$

$$\cdot \left\{ \begin{bmatrix} C_{lm} \\ -S_{lm} \end{bmatrix}_{l-m\,\text{odd}}^{l-m\,\text{even}} \cos\left[(l-2p)(\omega+f) + m(\Omega-\theta)\right] \right.$$

$$\left. + \begin{bmatrix} S_{lm} \\ C_{lm} \end{bmatrix}_{l-m\,\text{odd}}^{l-m\,\text{even}} \sin\left[(l-2p)(\omega+f) + m(\Omega-\theta)\right] \right\} \quad (4.2.1)$$

where

$$F_{lmp}(I) = \sum_{t} \frac{(2l-2t)!}{t!(l-t)!(l-m-2t)!2^{2l-2t}} \sin^{l-m-2t} I$$

$$\cdot \sum_{s=0}^{m} \binom{m}{s} \cos^s I \sum_{c} \binom{l-m-2t+s}{c}\binom{m-s}{p-t-c}(-1)^{c-k} \quad (4.2.2)$$

in which k is the integer part of $(l-m)/2$, t is summed from zero to the lesser of p or k, and c is summed over all values making the binomial coefficients nonzero. The radius R in (4.2.1) is conventionally taken to be the mean equatorial radius a_e, which we shall substitute hereafter.

The second transformation, circular to elliptic, replaces r and f in (4.2.1) by a, M, and e. Again, the general case involves a lot of algebra, but there is a considerable simplification for the most important terms, which we would expect to be those from which the most rapidly changing angle, M, to be missing. These terms would be obtained if we apply a simple averaging with respect to M of the potential V in equation (4.2.1):

$$\bar{V} = \frac{1}{2\pi} \int_0^{2\pi} V \, dM \quad (4.2.3)$$

Using (see problem 4.4)

$$dM = \frac{r^2}{a^2(1-e^2)^{1/2}} df \quad (4.2.4)$$

we get

$$\bar{V} = \frac{GM}{a} \sum_{l,m} \left(\frac{a_e}{a}\right)^l \sum_{p=1}^{l-1} F_{lmp}(I)G_{lpq}(e)$$

$$\cdot \left\{ \begin{bmatrix} C_{lm} \\ -S_{lm} \end{bmatrix}_{l-m\,\text{odd}}^{l-m\,\text{even}} \cos\left[(l-2p)\omega + m(\Omega-\theta)\right] \right.$$

$$\left. + \begin{bmatrix} S_{lm} \\ C_{lm} \end{bmatrix}_{l-m\,\text{odd}}^{l-m\,\text{even}} \sin\left[(l-2p)\omega + m(\Omega-\theta)\right] \right\} \quad (4.2.5)$$

where

$$G_{lpq}(e) = \frac{1}{(1 - e^2)^{l-1/2}} \sum_{d=0}^{p'-1} \binom{l-1}{2d+l-2p'}\binom{2d+l-2p'}{d}\left(\frac{e}{2}\right)^{2d+l-2p'} \tag{4.2.6}$$

in which

$$p' = \min(p, l - p), \qquad q = 2p - l \tag{4.2.7}$$

The development given here is somewhat abstract, but necessary to gain full use of the satellite orbits to determine the gravitational potential V; it is worthwhile to derive the Keplerian form for specific cases lmp (see problem 4.6).

The most important perturbations we would expect to arise from the largest coefficient C_{lm} or S_{lm}. As discussed in Section 2.1, the largest is C_{20}, or $-J_2$. Looking at (4.2.5), we see that it gives rise to only one long-period term that corresponding to $p = 1$:

$$\bar{V}_{20} = -J_2 \frac{GMa_e^2}{a^3} F_{201}(I)G_{210}(e)$$

$$= -J_2 \frac{GMa_e^2}{a^3} \cdot \frac{3 \sin^2 I - 2}{4(1 - e^2)^{3/2}} \tag{4.2.8}$$

Using $\mu/2a + \bar{V}_{20}$ for F in the equations of motion (4.1.36), we get no long-term variation in the action variables, a, e, I, but do obtain a contribution to mean anomaly motion $\dot{M}$ as well as precessions $\dot{\Omega}$ and $\dot{\omega}$ of the node and perigee:

$$\dot{\Omega} = -\frac{3nJ_2a_e^2}{2(1 - e^2)^2 a^2} \cos I$$

$$\dot{\omega} = \frac{3nJ_2a_e^2}{4(1 - e^2)^2 a^2}(5 \cos^2 I - 1) \tag{4.2.9}$$

In (4.2.9), n^2 has been substituted for GM/a^3, by (4.1.21). A more "physical" derivation of the precession of $\dot{\Omega}$ can be obtained considering the satellite to be distributed uniformly around its orbit and using the relationship (2.1.32) between the oblateness and moments of inertia to derive the torque T in Euler's equation (4.3.2) (see problem 4.7).

Equation (4.2.9) indicates that a close satellite orbit can be closely represented as a secularly precessing ellipse. Hence the perturbations due to the small terms C_{lm}, S_{lm} can be represented as linear forced oscillations: that is, the potential V_{lm} can be substituted for F in (4.1.36) and the equations integrated assuming a, e, I constant and $M, \omega, \Omega, \theta$ secularly changing on the right. For instance:

$$\Delta\bar{\Omega}_{lm} = \frac{1}{na^2(1-e^2)^{1/2}\sin I} \cdot \frac{GM}{a}\left(\frac{a_e}{a}\right)^l \sum_{p=1}^{l-1} \frac{G_{lpq}(e)\,\partial F_{lmp}(I)/\partial I}{[(l-2p)\dot{\omega}+m(\dot{\Omega}-\dot{\theta})]}$$

$$\cdot\left\{\begin{bmatrix} C_{lm} \\ -S_{lm}\end{bmatrix}\begin{smallmatrix}l-m\,\text{even}\\l-m\,\text{odd}\end{smallmatrix} \sin\,[(l-2p)\omega+m(\Omega-\theta)]\right\}$$

$$-\left\{\begin{bmatrix} S_{lm} \\ C_{lm}\end{bmatrix}\begin{smallmatrix}l-m\,\text{even}\\l-m\,\text{odd}\end{smallmatrix} \cos\,[(l-2p)\omega+m(\Omega-\theta)]\right\} \quad (4.2.10)$$

The unavoidable appearance of the much higher rate $\dot{\theta}$ in the denominator indicates that the perturbations due to tesseral harmonics ($m \neq 0$) will be appreciably smaller than those due to zonal harmonics ($m = 0$).

In addition to the long-period terms discussed so far, there will be an infinite set of short-period terms of argument $[(l-2p)\omega + (l-2p+q)M + m(\Omega - \theta)]$, $(l-2p+q) \neq 0$, with an eccentricity function $G_{lpq}(e)$ of $O(e^{|q|})$ as a factor. Most of these can be ignored, but there will always occur terms for which

$$(l-2p)\dot{\omega} + (l-2p+q)\dot{M} + m(\dot{\Omega}-\dot{\theta}) < 1\text{ cycle/2 days} \quad (4.2.11)$$

These terms can be quite significant because they affect the semimajor axis a, as indicated by the first line of (4.1.36), which in turn affects the mean anomaly M through Kepler's law (4.1.21):

$$\Delta_2 M_{lmpq} = \int \frac{\partial n}{\partial a}\Delta_1 a_{lmpq}\,dt$$

$$= -\frac{3GMa_e{}^l F_{lmp}G_{lpq}(l-2p+q)}{a^{l+3}[(l-2p)\dot{\omega}+(l-2p+q)\dot{M}+m(\dot{\Omega}-\dot{\theta})]^2} \quad (4.2.12)$$

$$\times \text{ sinusoidal terms}$$

The integration in (4.2.12) depends on the rate in (4.2.11) not being *too* close to zero. If the starting value is close enough to an equilibrium point, it can occur that the argument will not go through a complete cycle, but will librate; this can be the case, for example, for some of the 24-hour communication satellites, for which $\dot{\omega} + \dot{M} + \dot{\Omega} - \dot{\theta}$ is often less than one cycle/year (see problem 4.15).

Perturbations of the type of (4.2.10) have been used to deduce considerable detail about the earth's gravitational field, as shown by Figure 2.5. The difficulties are mainly statistical: lack of sufficient orbital variety to distinguish between different terms lm, km, $l - k$ even, having the same arguments in (4.2.5); lack of sufficiently well-distributed tracking to yield uniform observation over all cycles $[(l-2p)\omega + m(\Omega - \theta)]$; and errors in tracking station positions [80, 206].

The principal dynamical neglect is atmospheric drag. At the altitudes of geodetically useful satellites, the force of drag per unit mass can be expressed by (see problem 4.8):

$$F_d = \frac{C_D}{2}\left(\frac{A}{m}\right)\rho v^2 \tag{4.2.13}$$

where C_D, about 2.4 for a sphere, is a "shape" factor; A/m is the area/mass ratio of the satellite; ρ is atmospheric density; and v is velocity relative to the atmosphere. Since the drag force is always contrary to the velocity vector, its effect is not "averaged out" by the rotation of the earth or the orbit, and an energy loss results. This loss causes a contraction of the orbit and a speeding up of the satellite to counteract the increased gravitational pull, in accordance with Kepler's law (4.1.21). The atmospheric density decreases very rapidly with altitude, enough so that even for rather moderate eccentricities the drag can be considered almost related to the perigee radius, r_p; from (4.1.38):

$$\Delta v^2 = 2\Delta T_p = GM\Delta\left[\frac{2}{r_p} - \frac{1}{a}\right] = GM\Delta\left[\frac{(1+e)}{a(1-e)}\right] \tag{4.2.14}$$

Since $\Delta T < 0$ and $\Delta a < 0$, necessarily $\Delta e < 0$, so that the orbit becomes more circular [212].

Recently the perturbations of artificial satellites of the moon have been used to determine the moons' gravitational field. The dynamics developed so far are equally applicable to this problem, although there are differences of an order-of-magnitude in some of the parameters (e.g., the rotation rate $\dot{\theta}$) and the data analysis problem differs appreciably [208].

Motion of the Moon

These dynamics are also applicable to the moon itself, a natural satellite. However, it is far enough out that the disturbances due to the third-body effect of the sun, (4.1.50), are much more important than the variations in the earth's gravitational field. If we express the disturbing function of the sun by its spherical harmonic form, (4.1.54), and apply to $P_{lm}(\sin\delta)\begin{Bmatrix}\sin\\\cos\end{Bmatrix}m\alpha$ and $P_{lm}(\sin\delta^*)\begin{Bmatrix}\sin\\\cos\end{Bmatrix}m\alpha^*$ the same development as was applied to $P_{lm}(\sin\varphi)\begin{Bmatrix}\sin\\\cos\end{Bmatrix}m\lambda$ of (2.1.17), we get a form similar to (4.2.5)

$$R^* = \frac{Gm^*}{a^*}\sum_{lmpqhj}\left(\frac{a}{a^*}\right)^l(2-\delta_{om})\frac{(l-m)!}{(l+m)!}F_{lmp}(I)F_{lmh}(I^*)$$

$$\cdot H_{lpq}(e)G_{lhj}(e^*)\cos\left[(l-2p)\omega + (l-2p+q)M\right.$$

$$\left. - (l-2h)\omega^* - (l-2h+j)M^* + m(\Omega - \Omega^*)\right] \tag{4.2.15}$$

In (4.2.15), $F_{lmp}(I)$ and $F_{lmh}(I^*)$ are expressed by (4.2.2); $H_{lpq}(e)$ is a new function arising from r^l instead of r^{-l-1}, but still of $O(e^{|q|})$; and $G_{lhj}(e^*)$ is given by (4.2.6) only for the long-periodic case $(l - 2h + j)$ zero. However, there are several practicable simplifications to (4.2.15): (1) a/a^* is 1/386, so that $l = 2$ terms are dominant; (2) $GMJ_2a_e{}^2a^{-3}/GM^*a^2a^{*-3}$ is 1/19,830, so that the appropriate reference plane is the ecliptic, the earth-sun orbit, whence only $lmh = 201$ and 220 terms are nonzero; and (3) e^* is only 0.0168, so that $j = 0$ terms are dominant. Equation (4.2.15) thus becomes:

$$R_2{}^* = \frac{Gm^*a^2}{a^{*3}} \sum_{p,q} \{-\tfrac{1}{2}F_{20p}(I)H_{2pq}(e) \cos [(2 - 2p)\omega + (2 - 2p + q)M]$$

$$+ \tfrac{1}{4}F_{22p}(I)H_{2pq}(e) \cos [(2 - 2p)\omega + (2 - 2p + q)M + 2(\Omega - \alpha^*)]\}$$

$$(4.2.16)$$

As with oblateness effects on close satellites, the secular effects will arise from the term $pq = 10$; we need only to substitute $m^*a^2/2a^{*3}$ for $J_2Ma_e{}^2/a^3$ in (4.2.8–9). Making the further substitution of n^{*2} for Gm^*/a^{*3}, and n^2 for GM/a^3 (from (4.1.21)), we get

$$\dot{\Omega} \approx -\frac{3}{4}\frac{n^{*2}}{n} \cos I = -\tfrac{3}{4}m^2n \cos I$$

$$\dot{\omega} \approx \frac{3}{8}\frac{n^{*2}}{n} [5 \cos^2 I - 1] = \tfrac{3}{8}m^2n[5 \cos^2 I - 1]$$

$$(4.2.17)$$

where m is the ratio of the sidereal month to the sidereal year, 0.0748. Using 5.15 degrees for I, (4.2.17) yields that the node Ω should recede at a rate of 1 cycle/239.2 sidereal months, or 1 cycle/17.92 years; and that the perigee ω should advance at a rate of 1 cycle/9.00 years. The observed periods are 18.60 and 8.86 years respectively. Most of the discrepancy is due to neglected higher-order effects of the sun rather than to J_2, the planets, etc.

If we also neglect the e of 0.0549 in (4.2.16) and set I equal to zero, then the only nonzero term for $m = 2$ becomes:

$$R_{22}{}^* = \frac{3Gm^*a^2}{4a^{*3}} \cos 2(\alpha - \alpha^*) \qquad (4.2.18)$$

then, since α contains M, there is from the first line of (4.1.36) a bimonthly perturbation of the semimajor axis, which in turn gives rise to a bimonthly perturbation of the mean anomaly by a derivation similar to (4.2.12):

$$\Delta_2 M_{22} = \tfrac{9}{8}m^2 \sin 2(\alpha - \alpha^*)$$

$$= 0.00628 \sin 2(\alpha - \alpha^*) \qquad (4.2.19)$$

This perturbation is known as the *variation*; the exact solution incorporating the variation found by G. W. Hill in the latter part of the nineteenth century is the basis of the theory elaborated by E. M. Brown which is used for the accurate calculation of the moon's orbit today. The precision of this calculation is now on the order of 10 meters for the moon's position, entailing several hundred Fourier series terms to express all the significant higher-order interactions of the solar perturbations [47, 49, 51, 318].

4.3   Rotational Dynamics: Rigid

Free Oscillations

Although the orbital perturbation of the moon by the earth's oblateness J_2 is relatively minor, the torque exerted by the moon (and sun) on the earth's bulge—better expressed now in terms of the moments of inertia C, A, related to J_2 by (2.1.32)—is significant in causing a variation of the earth's rotation with respect to inertial space. The pertinent equations are Euler's equations, which state that the rate of change of the angular momentum **H**, inertially referred, is equal to the torque **T**. Let the force vector be **F**, then Newton's law (4.1.1) can be expressed for a particle of mass m:

$$\mathbf{F} = m \frac{d}{dt} \dot{\mathbf{x}} \tag{4.3.1}$$

The torque **T** is $\mathbf{x} \times \mathbf{F}$; applying the operation $\mathbf{x} \times$ to (4.3.1), we get

$$\mathbf{T} = \dot{\mathbf{H}} \tag{4.3.2}$$

where, since $\dot{\mathbf{x}} \times \dot{\mathbf{x}}$ is zero,

$$\mathbf{H} = m\mathbf{x} \times \dot{\mathbf{x}} \tag{4.3.3}$$

Equation (4.3.2) can also apply to a continuous body, with proper definition of the angular momentum **H**. Let us switch to subscript notation. Then a component H_i of **H** *can* be written as an integration over mass elements $dm = \rho \, dV$:

$$H_i = \int_{\text{vol}} \rho \epsilon_{ijk} x_j \dot{x}_k \, dv$$

$$= C_{il}\omega_l \tag{4.3.4}$$

where ω_j is the component of rotation about the j axis, *provided that* the moments of inertia C_{il} are defined as:

$$C_{il} = \int_{\text{vol}} \rho \epsilon_{ijk} \epsilon_{klm} x_j x_m \, dv = \int_{\text{vol}} \rho(x_k x_k \delta_{il} - x_i x_l) \, dv \tag{4.3.5}$$

(since $\dot{x}_k$ is $\epsilon_{klm}\omega_l x_m$). In (4.3.4–5) repetition of a subscript in a product indicates summation.

Given a body of certain specifications, we can more easily calculate the moments of inertia C_{il} and rotation ω_l with respect to body-fixed axes than with respect to inertially fixed axes. However, usually the torque **T** in (4.3.2) is more easily calculated with respect to inertial axes. The principal relations between two sets of axes we have described are the Euler angles Ω, I, ω shown in Figure 4.2 and used in the rotation matrix $\mathbf{R}_{qx}$, (4.1.13). In the present context, the **x** coordinate system is inertially fixed and the **q** coordinate system is body fixed. The total rate of change $\dot{\mathbf{H}}_{\text{space}}$ will be a combination of (1) the change referred to body-fixed axes $\dot{\mathbf{H}}_{\text{body}}$, and (2) the effect of the motion of these axes with respect to inertially fixed space. This motion of the body axes is best written as the rotation **ω** about inertially fixed axes momentarily coinciding with the body axes. Then if we are given precession rates $\dot{\Omega}$, $\dot{I}$, $\dot{\psi}$ we can write

$$\boldsymbol{\omega} = \mathbf{R}_3(\psi)\left\{ \begin{pmatrix} 0 \\ 0 \\ \dot{\psi} \end{pmatrix} + \mathbf{R}_1(I)\left[\begin{pmatrix} \dot{I} \\ 0 \\ 0 \end{pmatrix} + \mathbf{R}_3(\Omega)\begin{pmatrix} 0 \\ 0 \\ \dot{\Omega} \end{pmatrix} \right] \right\}$$

$$= \begin{Bmatrix} \dot{\Omega} \sin I \sin \psi + \dot{I} \cos \psi \\ \dot{\Omega} \sin I \cos \psi - \dot{I} \sin \psi \\ \dot{\Omega} \cos I + \dot{\psi} \end{Bmatrix} \tag{4.3.6}$$

then

$$\dot{\mathbf{H}}_{\text{space}} = \dot{\mathbf{H}}_{\text{body}} + \boldsymbol{\omega} \times \mathbf{H} \tag{4.3.7}$$

The simplest case of the Euler equation is when the torque **T** is 0. Taking a body such as the earth: $C_{11} = C_{22} = A$; $C_{33} = C$; $C_{ij} = 0$, $i \neq j$; and assuming A, C, fixed, (4.3.2) and (4.3.7) become

$$\begin{Bmatrix} A\dot{\omega}_1 \\ A\dot{\omega}_2 \\ C\dot{\omega}_3 \end{Bmatrix} + \begin{Bmatrix} (C - A)\omega_2\omega_3 \\ (A - C)\omega_3\omega_1 \\ 0 \end{Bmatrix} = 0 \tag{4.3.8}$$

which yields that ω_3 is a constant. Defining

$$n = \frac{C - A}{A} \omega_3 \tag{4.3.9}$$

gives two equations for ω_1, ω_2 which can be used to separate the variables by differentiation; the end result:

$$\begin{Bmatrix} \omega_1 \\ \omega_2 \end{Bmatrix} = \alpha \begin{Bmatrix} \cos \\ \sin \end{Bmatrix} (nt + \beta) \tag{4.3.10}$$

The period $2\pi/n$ will be, from (4.3.9), $2\pi A/\omega_3(C - A)$, or for the earth 305 days; a perfectly rigid earth would oscillate with this period in response to a random shock [86, 199, 451].

Precession and Nutation

To calculate forced oscillations, the applied torque must be calculated; it will depend on both the disturbing body and the moments of inertia of the planet.

We require the torque on a planet of moments of inertia A, A, C (where C is about the axis of rotation) by an external body of mass m at distance r at inclination I to the equator of the planet, as sketched in Figure 4.5. The torque T about an axis in the equatorial plane exerted on the planet by an external body m at $(r^*, \varphi^*, \lambda^*)$ can be expressed as the integral of the torques on mass elements dM of the planet. However, if the system is isolated, angular momentum is conserved, i.e., $\dot{H}$ is zero. Hence by Euler's equation (4.3.2), the torque at the external body must be opposite and equal to that on the planet, and we can write

$$T(r^*, \varphi^*, \lambda^*) = r^* F_{\varphi^*}$$

$$= m \frac{\partial U}{\partial \varphi^*} \tag{4.3.11}$$

where U is the total potential of the planet per unit mass of the external body. Since we assumed that the distribution of mass in the planet was expressible by the moments of inertia A, A, C, then the only term in the potential (2.1.17) contributing to the derivative in (4.3.11) is the second-degree zonal term, the coefficient for which is connected to the moments of inertia by (2.1.32) (in which $a = R$):

$$U = \frac{G(C - A)}{r^{*3}} P_{20}(\sin \varphi^*) \tag{4.3.12}$$

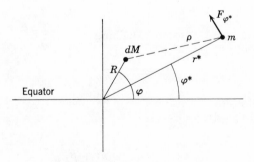

Figure 4.5: Geometry for torque.

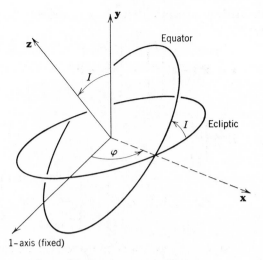

Figure 4.6: Geometry of precession.

However, the body is continually moving around the planet in orbital motion; we require the torque averaged over this motion. Hence the zonal harmonic $P_{20}(\sin \varphi^*)$ should be transformed to orbital elements, the same as for the orbital perturbation problem. From (4.2.1):

$$U = \frac{G}{r^{*3}}(C - A)\sum_{p=0}^{2} F_{20p}(I) \cos [(2 - 2p)(\omega + f)] \qquad (4.3.13)$$

Neglecting the eccentricity of the orbit, the averaged potential becomes:

$$\langle U \rangle = \frac{G}{r^{*3}}(C - A)F_{201}(I) \qquad (4.3.14)$$

whence

$$\langle T \rangle = m \frac{\partial \langle U \rangle}{\partial I} = \frac{Gm}{r^{*3}}(C - A)\frac{\partial F_{201}}{\partial I}$$

$$= \frac{3}{4}\frac{Gm}{r^{*3}}(C - A) \sin 2I \qquad (4.3.15)$$

Using (4.2.2) to evaluate F_{201}.

To obtain the rate of precession of the earth's rotation axis, let the direction of the earth's rotation axis be $\mathbf{z}$ and the direction of the normal to the ecliptic be $\mathbf{y}$ (see Figure 4.6). Then the direction $\mathbf{x}$ of the equator-ecliptic line of intersection will be:

$$\mathbf{x} = \frac{\mathbf{y} \times \mathbf{z}}{\sin I} \qquad (4.3.16)$$

Referred to inertially fixed axes with the 3-axis normal to the ecliptic, the three directions are:

$$\mathbf{x} = \mathbf{R}_3(-\varphi) \begin{Bmatrix} 1 \\ 0 \\ 0 \end{Bmatrix} = \begin{Bmatrix} \cos\varphi \\ \sin\varphi \\ 0 \end{Bmatrix} \tag{4.3.17}$$

$$\mathbf{y} = \begin{Bmatrix} 0 \\ 0 \\ 1 \end{Bmatrix} \tag{4.3.18}$$

$$\mathbf{z} = \mathbf{R}_3(-\varphi)\mathbf{R}_1(-I) \begin{Bmatrix} 0 \\ 0 \\ 1 \end{Bmatrix} = \begin{Bmatrix} \sin I \sin\varphi \\ -\sin I \cos\varphi \\ \cos I \end{Bmatrix} \tag{4.3.19}$$

The total angular velocity $\boldsymbol{\omega}$ is a combination of the constant rotation n about $\mathbf{z}$ and the motion of the $\mathbf{z}$-axis about $\mathbf{y}$:

$$\boldsymbol{\omega} = n\mathbf{z} + \mathbf{z} \times \dot{\mathbf{z}} \tag{4.3.20}$$

The angular momentum is:

$$\mathbf{H} = Cn\mathbf{z} + A\mathbf{z} \times \dot{\mathbf{z}} \tag{4.3.21}$$

To obtain the Euler equations, take the right of (4.3.7) and equate it to the torque T:

$$Cn\dot{\mathbf{z}} + A\mathbf{z} \times \ddot{\mathbf{z}} = -T\mathbf{x} \tag{4.3.22}$$

The minus sign appears on the right because the torque exercised by the disturbing body in the ecliptic on the equator will be clockwise.

Precession is a steady rate $\dot{\varphi}$ of φ and a fixed inclination I. Hence differentiate (4.3.19):

$$\dot{\mathbf{z}} = \begin{Bmatrix} \sin I \cos\varphi \\ \sin I \sin\varphi \\ 0 \end{Bmatrix}\dot{\varphi}, \qquad \ddot{\mathbf{z}} = \begin{Bmatrix} -\sin I \sin\varphi \\ \sin I \cos\varphi \\ 0 \end{Bmatrix}\dot{\varphi}^2 \tag{4.3.23}$$

since $\ddot{\varphi}$ is specified to be zero.

We are still at liberty to choose the 1-axis from which the angle φ to $\mathbf{x}$ is measured; to simplify matters, let us make it the $\mathbf{x}$-axis itself before substituting from (4.3.17, 19, 22) in (4.3.23) to get:

$$Cn \begin{Bmatrix} \sin I \\ 0 \\ 0 \end{Bmatrix}\dot{\varphi} + A \begin{Bmatrix} -\sin I \cos I \\ 0 \\ 0 \end{Bmatrix}\dot{\varphi}^2 = -T \begin{Bmatrix} 1 \\ 0 \\ 0 \end{Bmatrix} \tag{4.3.24}$$

Since $\dot\varphi$ is much smaller than n the $A\dot\varphi^2$ term in (4.3.24) will be much smaller than the $Cn\dot\varphi$ term. So neglect the second term in (4.3.24) and write the first line as:

$$Cn \sin I\dot\varphi = -T \tag{4.3.25}$$

or, substituting from (4.3.15) for T:

$$\dot\varphi = \frac{3}{2} \frac{Gm}{r^3} \cdot \frac{C - A}{Cn} \cos I \tag{4.3.26}$$

In "planetary" units (G, earth's mass, earth's radius all unity), the time unit is 806.8 seconds, or n is 0.0588. Using

$$n = 0.0588$$

$$-\frac{C - A}{MR^2} = J_2 = 0.0010827$$

$$C = 0.332$$

$$m_m = 0.0123$$

$$r_m = 60.27$$

$$I = 23.5 \text{ deg}$$

$$m_s = 333,000$$

$$r_s = 23,400$$

there results

$$\dot\varphi = \frac{3}{2} \cdot \frac{-0.0010827}{0.332 \times 0.0588} \left(\frac{0.0123}{60.27^3} \cos 23.5° + \frac{333,000}{23,400^3} \cos 23.5° \right)$$

$$= -0.0830(5.12 + 2.38) \times 10^{-8}$$

$$= -6.23 \times 10^{-9} = 6.68 \times 10^{-7} \text{ rad/day} = 2.44 \times 10^{-4}/\text{yr}$$

and

$$P = \frac{2\pi}{\dot\varphi} = 25,800 \text{ yr} \quad [86,199,451] \tag{4.3.27}$$

Lunar Librations

The moon's rotation $\dot\theta$ about its own axis equals the mean motion in its orbit. However, because of the inclination of the moon's orbit with respect to its equator, and because the rate f is nonuniform, by (4.1.59), the earth can exert a torque on the moon. If this torque were zero, then there would apply three relationships, known as *Cassini's laws*:

1. $\dot\theta = \dot M + \dot\omega + \dot\Omega$.
2. Inclination = constant.

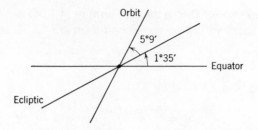

Figure 4.7: Relationship between planes pertaining to the moon's orientation.

3. The lunar figure pole, ecliptic pole, and lunar orbit pole are in one great circle (see Figure 4.7).

Departure of the actual orientation of the moon from Cassini's laws is known as *physical libration.*

To set up the Euler equations, define the 1-axis as being the body axis in the mean direction of the earth and the 3-axis as being the rotation axis. Then, to the first order,

$$A\dot{\omega}_1 - (B - C)\omega_2\omega_3 = 0$$

$$B\dot{\omega}_2 - (C - A)\omega_3\omega_1 = \frac{3GM}{r^3}(A - C)\nu \qquad (4.3.28)$$

$$C\dot{\omega}_3 \qquad\qquad = \frac{3GM}{r^3}(B - A)\mu$$

where μ, ν are the direction cosines of the earth with respect to the 2- and 3-axes respectively; A, B, C are the moments of inertia about the 1-, 2-, and 3-axes, and it has been assumed $(A - B) \ll (C - A)$ or $(C - B)$.

Just as with the earth, there are both free-oscillation and forced-oscillation solutions to (4.3.28). The latter are considerably more complicated, however, by the extent to which the variations of the earth-moon orbit, as they enter through μ, ν, and r, must be taken into account.

The theory of the physical librations, together with observations of variations from the purely optical libration due to the orbit, is used to deduce the ratios of moment of inertia differences $(B - C)/A$, $(A - C)/B$, $(B - A)/C$ (not independent) in (4.2.31). The quantity $(C - A)/MR^2$ is now evaluated from its effect on the motion of artificial satellites around the moon. The combination of the determinations yields a ratio B/MR^2 close to that for a homogeneous body, 0.4. In the past, the $(C - A)/MR^2$ was deduced from the motion of the node $\dot{\Omega}$ of the moon's orbit, after subtracting therefrom the solar, planetary, earth J_2, etc., effects. The resulting B/MR^2 was implausibly large. However, the error now appears attributable to an inadequate treatment of effects on the determination of $\dot{\Omega}$ from observations of the moon's latitude and longitude of the irregular variations in the earth's rotation, mentioned in Section 4.5 [103, 224, 225].

Summary

The rigid-body dynamics described in Sections 4.2–3 are of value both as enabling measurement of several parameters pertaining to the earth and moon, and as providing a reference framework for the nonrigid dynamics taken up in the next chapter.

Table 4.1 is a compilation of useful parameters. "Planetary units" are units such that the gravitational constant G, planet mass M, and radius R are all unity.

4.4   Effects of Elasticity and Fluidity

In the response of the earth and the moon to their mutual attraction and to the attraction of the sun, we can categorize different levels of nonrigidity:

1. Both the moon and the solid part of the earth are elastic in their response to small stresses.

2. The earth has a fluid atmosphere, oceans, and core.

3. Imperfections in elasticity, viscosity in the fluid parts, and interface frictions—either solid-fluid or solid-solid—can be expected to result in dissipation of energy.

Bodily Tides

We start by considering a perfectly elastic earth. The disturbing potential due to an external body, sun or moon, is that given by (4.1.54). However, since we are now interested in relative displacements of points within the earth, it is appropriate to replace the inertially referred δ, α by the body referred φ, λ, which in turn necessitates replacing α^* by $\alpha^* - \theta$, where θ is the Greenwich sidereal time. The acceleration derived fron this potential is small—about $10^{-7}g$—so the elastic response of the earth may be considered linear. If we further assume that all significant variation of elastic properties is radial, then the invariance of degree l of a spherical harmonic under rotation (see problem 4.11) requires that the potential U_{Tlm} arising from elastic displacement of masses in response to a tidal potential term U_{lm} in (4.1.54) is a function of degree only. Combining these two conditions then if we rewrite the disturbing potential (4.1.54) as

$$U(r) = \sum_l U_l(r) \qquad (4.4.1)$$

at the surface of the earth, $r = R$, we can write

$$U_T(R) = \sum_l k_l U_l(R) \qquad (4.4.2)$$

TABLE 4.1: PARAMETERS OF THE EARTH-MOON SYSTEM

Parameter	Symbol	Dimensions	Cgs Units	Earth Planetary Units	Moon Planetary Units
Gravitational constant	G	$M^{-1}L^3T^{-2}$	6.67×10^{-8}	1.0	1.0
Earth					
Mass	M or m^*	M	5.977×10^{27}	1.0	81.3
Mean radius	a_e or R	L	6.371×10^8	1.0	3.67
Mean acceleration	g	LT^{-2}	9.80×10^2	1.0	
Surface density	ρ	ML^{-3}	2.80	0.122	
Present mean rotation	$\dot{\theta}$	T^{-1}	7.29×10^{-5}	0.0588	
Potential Love number	k_2		0.30		
Displacement Love number	h_2		0.60		
Present polar moment of inertia	C	ML^2	8.043×10^{44}	0.3319	
Mean moment of inertia	I	ML^2	8.025×10^{44}	0.3309	
Moon					
Mass	m^* or M	M	7.35×10^{25}	0.0123	1.0
Mean radius	a_e or R	L	1.738×10^8	0.2725	1.0
Mean acceleration	g	LT^{-2}	1.62×10^2		1.0
Surface density	ρ	ML^{-3}	3.34		0.239
Present mean rotation	$\dot{\theta}$	T^{-1}	2.6617×10^{-6}		0.002758
Potential Love number	k_2		0.020		
Displacement Love number	h_2		0.033		
Present orbit					
Semimajor axis	a^*	L	3.84×10^{10}	60.3	221.7
Eccentricity	e^*		0.0549		
Mean inclination to earth's equator			0.416		
Inclination to ecliptic			0.0899		
Anomalistic motion		T^{-1}	2.6505×10^{-6}	2.138×10^{-3}	2.746×10^{-3}
Perigee motion		T^{-1}	2.26×10^{-8}	1.84×10^{-5}	2.34×10^{-5}
Nodal motion		T^{-1}	-1.14×10^{-8}	-0.93×10^{-5}	-1.18×10^{-5}
Present obliquity	ϵ		0.4092		

From Kaula [205].

where k_l is a constant dependent on the elastic properties. Since R/r^* is small, let us restrict attention to the lowest degree term, $l = 2$:

$$U_T(R) \approx k_2 U_2(R) \qquad (4.4.3)$$

$U_T(R)$ is thus a second-degree harmonic arising from masses within the surface R; hence, in accordance with (2.1.17), exterior to R it must be proportionate to r^{-3}:

$$U_T(r) = \left(\frac{R}{r}\right)^3 U_T(R) = \left(\frac{R}{r}\right)^3 k_2 U_2(R) = \left(\frac{R}{r}\right)^5 k_2 U_2(r) \qquad (4.4.4)$$

The potential $[1 + k_2(R/r)^5]U_2(r)$ may be considered as a disturbing potential T, as discussed in Section 2.1. In determining its effect δg on a gravity meter at the earth's surface, we must take into account the vertical displacement of the surface, as we did in calculating the gravity anomaly Δg in (2.1.45). However, since the surface of the elastic earth is not an equipotential, we cannot take the displacement as given by (2.1.43); instead, let us introduce another parameter h_l and, neglecting $l > 2$, write:

$$N_T = h_2 \frac{U_2}{g} \qquad (4.4.5)$$

Then from (2.1.44), using $[1 + k_2(R/r)^5]U_2(r)$ for T,

$$\delta g = -\frac{\partial T}{\partial n} + \frac{\partial g}{\partial r} N_T$$

$$= -(2 - 3k_2)\frac{U_2}{r} - \frac{2g}{r} h_2 \frac{U_2}{g}$$

$$= -(1 - \tfrac{3}{2}k_2 + h_2) 2\frac{U_2}{r} \qquad (4.4.6)$$

Another measurable quantity would be the variations in height $\delta \zeta$ of an equipotential with respect to the earth's surface, such as the height of a pond with respect to its bottom. The tide would raise the surface $(1 + k_2)U_2/g$, but then $h_2 U_2/g$ must be subtracted for the rise of the bottom:

$$\delta \zeta = (1 + k_2 - h_2)\frac{U_2}{g} \qquad (4.4.7)$$

Accurate observations of the stars, such as those made by the latitude variation observations, will show a tilt $\delta \xi$ of the earth's surface with respect to inertial space. This tilt is caused by the enhancement $(1 + k_2)$ of the potential plus a horizontal displacement, which is taken into account by a third number l_2 subtracted from the factor:

$$\delta\xi = (1 + k_2 - l_2)\frac{1}{R}\frac{\partial U_2}{\partial\psi} \tag{4.4.8}$$

where ψ is arc distance. The three numbers h_2, k_2, l_2 are known as *Love numbers*, after the English physicist A. E. H. Love. For a specific model of the earth, such as constituted by Table 2.1 plus Figure 2.14, they can be calculated using the same equations (2.2.45) as are used for the free oscillations, but with the frequency σ set zero and with the first boundary condition one that appropriately relates a potential (y_5 radial factor) with its gradient (y_6 radial factor):

$$y_6(R) + \frac{n+1}{R}\,y_5(R) = (2n+1)g \tag{4.4.9}$$

Setting $n = 2$ and using "planetary" units as defined in Table 4.1, we have

$$h_2 = y_1$$
$$l_2 = y_3 \tag{4.4.10}$$
$$1 + k_2 = y_5$$

The calculated Love numbers agree fairly well with those observed with a gravity meter $[1 - (3k_2/2) + h_2]$ and tiltmeter $(1 + k_2 - h_2)$. The greatest discrepancies occur for stations near the coast, apparently due to the loading of the crust by the ocean tide. However, even for sites away from the coast there are significant variations in $[1 - (3k_2/2) + h_2]$: from about 1.10 to 1.26. Observed values of $(1 + k_2 - h_2)$ range from about 0.54 to 0.82, centering at 0.68 [199, 274].

Latitude Variation

The elasticity of the earth will affect the free period of oscillation of the rotation axis, derived in (4.3.7–10). In the elastic case, we must consider the possibility that time-varying changes in the earth's shape will cause the axis of rotation to depart from the axis of figure. If the coordinate axis is taken to be the rotation axis, for absolute rigidity, then products of inertia will appear in the Euler equations. Substitute (4.3.4, 7) into (4.3.3) and convert to subscript notation:

$$\frac{d}{dt}(C_{ij}\omega_j) + \epsilon_{ijk}\omega_j C_{kl}\omega_l = T_i \tag{4.4.11}$$

Considering C_{11}, C_{22}, C_{33}, and ω_3 to be large, all other quantities small, putting T_i zero, and neglecting all small products and increments in (4.4.11), obtains

$$\dot{C}_{13}\omega_3 + C_{11}\dot{\omega}_1 - \omega_3{}^2C_{23} + \omega_2\omega_3(C_{33} - C_{22}) = 0$$

$$\dot{C}_{23}\omega_3 + C_{22}\dot{\omega}_2 + \omega_3{}^2C_{13} + \omega_3\omega_1(C_{11} - C_{33}) = 0 \qquad (4.4.12)$$

$$C_{33}\dot{\omega}_3 \qquad\qquad\qquad\qquad\qquad\quad = 0$$

Define the direction cosines of the actual instantaneous axis of rotation as:

$$\left.\begin{matrix} l \\ m \\ n \end{matrix}\right\} = \begin{cases} \omega_1/\omega_3 \\ \omega_2/\omega_3 \\ \omega_3/\omega_3 \end{cases} \qquad (4.4.13)$$

and let

$$C_{11} = C_{22} = A, \quad C_{33} = C, \quad C_{13} = -G', \quad C_{23} = -F'$$

whence the first two lines of (4.4.12) become (dropping the subscript from ω):

$$-\dot{G}' + A\dot{l} + \omega F' + m\omega(C - A) = 0$$

$$-\dot{F}' + A\dot{m} - \omega G' + l\omega(A - C) = 0 \qquad (4.4.14)$$

The displacements due to rotation are the same as those due to a potential $\frac{1}{2}\omega^2 s^2$ (see (2.1.33)), where s is the distance from the instantaneous axis; this increment to the rotation potential will be

$$\Delta U_{\text{rot}} = \tfrac{1}{2}\omega^2 \Delta s^2 = \tfrac{1}{2}\omega^2[(x - lz)^2 + (y - mz)^2 - (x^2 + y^2)]$$

$$= -\omega^2 z(lx + my) \qquad (4.4.15)$$

The extra gravitational potential produced by elastic deformation will thus be

$$U_{\text{rot}_T} = -\omega^2 k_2 z(lx + my)\left(\frac{R}{r}\right)^5$$

$$= -\omega^2 k_2 R^2 \frac{1}{3}\left(\frac{R}{r}\right)^3 P_{21}(\sin\varphi)(l\cos\lambda + m\sin\lambda) \qquad (4.4.16)$$

But in the gravitational potential (see problem 4.12)

$$U_{21} = G\left(\frac{1}{r}\right)^3 P_{21}(\sin\varphi)(G'\cos\lambda + F'\sin\lambda) \qquad (4.4.17)$$

whence

$$F' = -\frac{m\omega^2 k_2 R^5}{3G}, \qquad G' = -\frac{l\omega^2 k_2 R^5}{3G} \qquad (4.4.18)$$

Substituting for F', G', $\dot{F}'$, and $\dot{G}'$ in (4.4.14) obtains

$$\left(A + \frac{k_2\omega^2 R^5}{3G}\right)l + \left(C - A - \frac{k_2\omega^2 R^5}{3G}\right)\omega m = 0$$

$$\left(A + \frac{k_2\omega^2 R^5}{3G}\right)\dot{m} - \left(C - A - \frac{k_2\omega^2 R^5}{3G}\right)\omega l = 0 \qquad (4.4.19)$$

which can be solved in the same manner as (4.3.10) to yield a period

$$P = \frac{A + k_2\omega^2 R^5/3G}{C - A - k_2\omega^2 R^5/3G} \text{ days} \qquad (4.4.20)$$

The effect of elasticity is thus to lengthen the period. Substituting numbers from Table 4.1 gives a period of 448 days. Power-spectrum analysis of observations of latitude variation gives, in addition to a sharp peak at 365 days (a forced oscillation), a rather broad peak centering at about 437 days—corresponding to a k_2 of 0.284, which is within the uncertainty of the earth tide determinations [199, 285].

Ocean Tides

The close agreement of the Love numbers observed with those obtained by the elastic calculation using (2.2.45) is somewhat illusory, since for the periods involved the oceans appear to decrease k_2 by about 0.06, while the fluid core increases it by about 0.08. Both of these effects are difficult theoretical problems [199, 285, 377, 418].

To take into account the ocean tide and its interaction with the elastic earth, let us start with a coordinate system l referred to the local vertical, as defined by Figure 4.8. In the figure, u_3 is the rotation axis. Hence referred to l

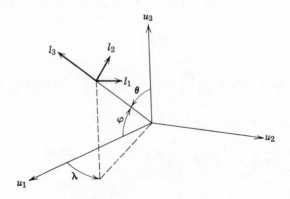

Figure 4.8: Coordinate references for ocean tide problem.

coordinates, the rotation vector, in terms of the colatitude θ, becomes:

$$\boldsymbol{\omega} = \left\{ \begin{array}{c} 0 \\ \omega \sin \theta \\ \omega \sin \theta \end{array} \right\} \tag{4.4.21}$$

The *inertially referred* equations of motion

$$\rho \dot{l}_i = \frac{\partial W}{\partial l_i} + \frac{\partial p_{ij}}{\partial l_j} \tag{4.4.22}$$

where W is the body-force potential, ρ is density, and p_{ij} is the stress tensor for zero-rigidity and incompressibility, $p_{ii} = -p$, $p_{ij} = 0$, $i \neq j$, and p is hydrostatic pressure ("$-$," because "$+$" corresponds to a dilation). Converting (4.4.22) to refer to rotating earth-fixed coordinates, we get

$$\frac{\partial \dot{l}_i}{\partial t} + 2\epsilon_{ijk}\omega_j l_k = \frac{\partial}{\partial l_i}\left(W + V - \frac{p}{\rho}\right) \tag{4.4.23}$$

where $2\epsilon_{ijk}\omega_k l_k$ is the Coriolis term and V is the potential of centrifugal acceleration:

$$V = \frac{\omega^2}{2}(u_1{}^2 + u_2{}^2) \tag{4.4.24}$$

The body-force potential W is a combination of the fixed-potential U_0, the varying disturbing potential arising from the sun and the moon U_2, and the tidal potential due to the response of the earth, U_T:

$$W = U_0 + U_2 + U_T, \qquad U_0 \gg U_2 + U_T \tag{4.4.25}$$

Define

$$\zeta \equiv \text{tide height with respect to mean sea level}$$

Assume that we are interested only in time-varying solutions of (4.4.23). Then $U_0 + V$ may be omitted on the right. Furthermore, to eliminate the pressure, write (4.4.23) to apply *always* at the surface, where $p = 0$. The surface, however, has a time-varying displacement ζ with respect to a fixed level (assuming solid earth absolutely rigid, see below), which we must take into account in its effect on the potential W:

$$\Delta W = \frac{\partial W}{\partial r} \zeta \approx \frac{\partial U_0}{\partial r} \zeta = -g\zeta \tag{4.4.26}$$

Then for a working potential we have:

$$\psi \equiv U_2 + U_T - g\zeta \tag{4.4.27}$$

and (4.4.23) becomes:

$$\frac{\partial l_i}{\partial t} + 2\epsilon_{ijk}\omega_j l_k = \frac{\partial \psi}{\partial l_i} \tag{4.4.28}$$

Define

$$h \equiv \text{ocean depth}$$

Consider an element of ocean with depth h and horizontal dimensions $2\delta l_1$ and $2\delta l_2$. The amount of water per unit time entering the element in the positive i direction is Δw_{Ii}; leaving in the same direction, Δw_{Oi}. Assuming incompressibility, we can write:

$$\Delta w_{I1} + \Delta w_{I2} + \Delta w_{I3} = \Delta w_{O1} + \Delta w_{O2} + \Delta w_{O3} \tag{4.4.29}$$

Taking into account variations in both depth h and velocity $\mathbf{l}$, and taking the ocean bottom as a fixed reference, we have

$$\Delta w_{I1} = \left(l_1 - \frac{\partial l_1}{\partial l_1}\delta l \right)\left(h - \frac{\partial h}{\partial l_1}\delta l_1 \right)2\delta l_2$$

$$\approx \left(hl_1 - \frac{\partial(hl_1)}{\partial l_1}\delta l_1 \right)2\delta l_2$$

Similarly,

$$\Delta w_{O1} = \left(hl_1 + \frac{\partial(hl_1)}{\partial l_1}\delta l_1 \right)2\delta l_2$$

$$\Delta w_{I2} = \left(hl_2 - \frac{\partial(hl_2)}{\partial l_2}\delta l_2 \right)2\delta l_1 \tag{4.4.30}$$

$$\Delta w_{O2} = \left(hl_2 + \frac{\partial(hl_2)}{\partial l_2}\delta l_2 \right)2\delta l_1$$

and

$$\Delta w_{I3} = 0$$

$$\Delta w_{O3} = 4\frac{\partial \zeta}{\partial t}\delta l_1 \delta l_2$$

So (4.4.29) becomes

$$\frac{\partial \zeta}{\partial t} = -\left[\frac{\partial(hl_1)}{\partial l_1} + \frac{\partial(hl_2)}{\partial l_2} \right] \tag{4.4.31}$$

Considering that

$$\frac{\partial}{\partial l_1} = \frac{1}{a\sin\theta}\frac{\partial}{\partial \lambda} \quad \text{and} \quad \frac{\partial}{\partial l_2} = -\frac{1}{a}\frac{\partial}{\partial \theta}$$

where a is the earth's radius, (4.4.31) indicates that

$$O(l_3) = O\left(\frac{\partial \zeta}{\partial t}\right) = \frac{h}{a} O(l_1, l_2) \ll (l_1, l_2) \tag{4.4.32}$$

Hence the l_3 term of (4.4.28) must be negligible in its effect on the tide height compared to the l_1, l_2 terms through (4.4.31), and we can neglect both the third equation and l_3 as it appears in the first two. Writing out the first two equations of (4.4.28), using (4.4.21):

$$\frac{\partial l_1}{\partial t} - 2\omega \cos \theta l_2 = \frac{\partial \psi}{\partial l_1}$$

$$\frac{\partial l_2}{\partial t} + 2\omega \cos \theta l_1 = \frac{\partial \psi}{\partial l_2} \tag{4.4.33}$$

Assume

$$\zeta \propto e^{i\sigma t}$$

$$\psi \propto e^{i\sigma t}$$

and

$$l_2 = U\, e^{i\sigma t} \tag{4.4.34}$$

$$l_1 = V\, e^{i\sigma t}$$

Then (4.4.33) becomes

$$i\sigma V - (2\omega \cos \theta)U = \frac{\partial \psi}{\partial l_1}$$

$$i\sigma U + (2\omega \cos \theta)V = \frac{\partial \psi}{\partial l_2} \tag{4.4.35}$$

Solve (4.4.35) for U and V:

$$\left.\begin{matrix} U \\ V \end{matrix}\right\} = \begin{pmatrix} 2\omega \cos \theta & -i\sigma \\ -i\sigma & -2\omega \cos \theta \end{pmatrix} \begin{pmatrix} \partial\psi/\partial l_1 \\ \partial\psi/\partial l_2 \end{pmatrix} \frac{1}{\sigma^2 - 4\omega^2 \cos^2 \theta} \tag{4.4.36}$$

and substitute in (4.4.31) (applying (4.4.34)):

$$i\sigma\zeta = \frac{\partial}{\partial l_1}\left[h\left(i\sigma \frac{\partial \psi}{\partial l_1} + 2\omega \cos \theta \frac{\partial \psi}{\partial l_2}\right)\Big/(\sigma^2 - 4\omega^2 \cos^2 \theta)\right]$$

$$- \frac{\partial}{\partial l_2}\left[h\left(2\omega \cos \theta \frac{\partial \psi}{\partial l_1} - i\sigma \frac{\partial \psi}{\partial l_2}\right)\Big/(\sigma^2 - 4\omega^2 \cos^2 \theta)\right] \tag{4.4.37}$$

Equation (4.4.37) has never been fully solved for the actual earth, mainly because of the complications involving variations of the depth h. Equation (4.4.37) is really a differential equation in ζ since, by (4.4.27), ζ is in the potential function ψ, not only directly through the $-g\zeta$ term, but also indirectly through its contribution to U_T. The latter will have the following components:

1. The potential of the attraction of the water tide, ζ, say U_ζ.
2. The elastic response of the earth to the disturbing potential, $k_2 U_2$.
3. The effect on the potential due to the upward displacement $h_2 U_2/g$ of the ocean bottom (since the equations apply at the free surface).
4. The elastic response of the earth to the water tide, $\Sigma k_l' U_{\zeta l}$.
5. The effect of the displacement of the sea bottom $\Sigma h_l' U_{\zeta l}/g$.

If we represent ψ and ζ as a sum of spherical harmonics of degrees l,

$$\psi = \sum_l \psi_l, \qquad \zeta = \sum_l \zeta_l \tag{4.4.38}$$

then Love number theory can be applied to the elastic response and the potential U_ζ calculated from the formula for a surface layer $\rho_W \zeta$, (2.1.25):

$$U_\zeta = 4\pi G a \sum_l \left(\frac{a}{r}\right)^{l+1} \frac{\rho_W \zeta_l}{2l+1} \tag{4.4.39}$$

where ρ_W is the density of water. Then, taking $\frac{4}{3}\pi G a^3 \bar\rho/a^2 \approx g$, where $\bar\rho$ is mean density, 5.5 gm/cm³:

$$\psi = g \sum_l \left[(1 + k_l' - h_l') \frac{3}{2l+1} \frac{\rho_W}{\bar\rho} - 1 \right] \zeta_l + (1 + k_2 - h_2) U_2 \tag{4.4.40}$$

since

$$\frac{\partial U_0}{\partial r} h_l \frac{T}{g} = -g h_l \frac{T}{g} = -g h_l N \tag{4.4.41}$$

where T is any disturbing potential. Numerical values which have been obtained for standard elastic models of the earth are:

$$k_2 \approx 0.30, \qquad h_2 \approx 0.60,$$

$$k_2' \approx -0.31, \quad h_2' \approx -1.03, \quad k_3' \approx -0.20, \quad h_3' \approx -1.05$$

Hence the effective potential U_2 is reduced about 30 percent by elastic yielding, and the displacement effect $-g\zeta$ is reduced about 30 percent by the ocean loading plus elastic response.

Return to (4.4.37) and assume:

$$\begin{aligned}
&\text{(1) } h = \text{constant} \\
&\text{(2) ocean loading negligible} \rightarrow \rho_W = 0 \\
&\text{(3) a rigid earth} \rightarrow k_2 = h_2 = 0 \\
&\text{(4) location at the pole} \rightarrow \cos\theta = 1, \frac{\partial}{\partial l_i}\cos\theta = 0
\end{aligned} \tag{4.4.42}$$

Then we have left (where l_1, l_2 are any two arbitrary rectangular axes at the pole, such as those used for latitude variation):

$$\zeta = \frac{h}{\sigma^2 - 4\omega^2}\left(\frac{\partial^2 \psi}{\partial l_1{}^2} + \frac{\partial^2 \psi}{\partial l_2{}^2}\right) \tag{4.4.43}$$

or, using (4.4.40),

$$\nabla^2 \zeta + \frac{4\omega^2 - \sigma^2}{hg}\zeta = \nabla^2 \bar{\zeta} \tag{4.4.44}$$

where ∇^2 is $(\partial^2/\partial l_1{}^2) + (\partial^2/\partial l_2{}^2)$ and $\bar{\zeta}$ is the equilibrium tide, U_2/g. In (4.4.44), $\nabla^2 \bar{\zeta}$ is in effect the forced oscillation; setting it zero results in an equation for free oscillations which requires boundary conditions to solve, but which in any case will have the result that the tide ζ will be proportionate to the depth h.

Removing assumption (4) in (4.4.42) to obtain a global solution, the coordinate system must be converted from the local rectangular l to spherical coordinates, and the element of surface area $\delta l_1\,\delta l_2$ replaced by $a^2 \sin\theta\,d\theta\,d\lambda$; (4.4.31) becomes

$$\frac{\partial \zeta}{\partial t} = -\frac{1}{a}\left[\frac{\partial}{\partial \mu}\left(\sqrt{1-\mu^2}\,hl_2\right) + \frac{\partial}{\partial \varphi}\left(\frac{hl_1}{\sqrt{1-\mu^2}}\right)\right] \tag{4.4.45}$$

where

$$\mu \equiv \cos\theta \tag{4.4.46}$$

Then (4.4.35) becomes

$$i\sigma V - 2\omega\mu U = \frac{1}{a\sqrt{1-\mu^2}}\cdot\frac{\partial\psi}{\partial\varphi}$$

$$i\sigma U + 2\omega\mu V = \frac{\sqrt{1-\mu^2}}{a}\cdot\frac{\partial\psi}{\partial\mu} \tag{4.4.47}$$

and (4.4.37) becomes

$$a^2\zeta = \frac{\partial}{\partial\mu}\left[\frac{h(1-\mu^2)}{\sigma^2 - 4\omega^2\mu^2}\cdot\frac{\partial\psi}{\partial\mu} - \frac{2\omega\mu h}{i\sigma(\sigma^2 - 4\omega^2\mu^2)}\frac{\partial\psi}{\partial\lambda}\right]$$

$$+ \frac{\partial}{\partial\lambda}\left[\frac{2\omega\mu h}{i\sigma(\sigma^2 - 4\omega^2\mu^2)}\cdot\frac{\partial\psi}{\partial\mu} + \frac{h}{(1-\mu^2)(\sigma^2 - 4\omega^2\mu^2)}\frac{\partial\psi}{\partial\lambda}\right] \tag{4.4.48}$$

Setting $\omega = 0$ separates the variables and, as might be expected, the solution yields that ζ is representable as a sum of spherical harmonics. With $\omega \neq 0$, even for constant h the solution entails considerable mathematical manipulation. The case $\sigma = 2\omega$ was first done by Laplace, who assumed infinite series of the form

$$\zeta - \bar{\zeta} = \sum A_i \sin^{2i} \theta \; e^{i(\sigma t + 2x)}$$

For values of the parameter

$$\beta = \frac{4\omega^2 a^2}{gh}$$

of 10, 20, and 40, he obtained $\zeta/\bar{\zeta}$ of 11.26, -1.82, and -7.43: that is, even for a constant depth, the tide varies significantly from equilibrium [100, 183, 236].

4.5   Energy-Dissipating Processes

Periodic Variations in the Earth's Rotation

The free-oscillation peak at 437 days in the latitude variation spectrum apparently is due to random disturbing effects. The peak is rather broad, leading to a Q of about 30 by (2.3.17). It is still not definite, however, whether the peak broadening is due to interactions between loosely coupled components of the disturbing impulses or to true dissipation, and, if the latter, whether it occurs in the ocean or the mantle. The phase lags in the earth tide measurements by gravimeter $[1 - (3k_2/2) + h_2]$ average about 5 degrees, equivalent to a Q of about 11, by (2.3.13–15).

Another source of information about mass and energy transfers in the earth is its rotation. *Universal time* (UT) is defined by the earth's rotation; in comparison to *ephemeris time* (ET), defined by orbital motions, and *atomic time* (A1), defined by oscillations in the cesium atom, UT shows annual and semiannual variations characterized by:

$$ET - UT = 0.0028^s \sin (\alpha_\odot - 38°)$$

$$+ \; 0.0009^s \sin 2(\alpha_\odot - 110°) \qquad (4.5.1)$$

where $\alpha_\odot$ is the longitude of the sun from the vernal equinox measured along the ecliptic. Differentiating (4.5.1) with respect to time and dividing by 13,750 will give the variation of the rotation rate ω in radians/unit time. Assuming that angular momentum $C\omega$ is conserved, we have a choice of either varying the moment of inertia C by moving masses relative to the rotation axis or changing the rotation rate of the solid earth by transfer of angular momentum to (or from) the atmosphere or ocean. Measurements of seasonal variations in zonal wind velocities appear to explain most of the annual term, but not the semiannual. North-south shifts of air masses sufficient to account for the semiannual term recently have also been observed in satellite orbits as a semiannual variation in oblateness J_2, but appear to entail atmospheric pressure changes somewhat larger than observed (see problem 4.13) [261, 285].

Secular Changes in the Earth's Rotation

There are longer-term irregular changes in ET − UT apparently associated with coupling between core and mantle. More clearly established from observations of the sun and the moon over the last 280 years is a growing secular difference ET − UT. This difference is expressed in terms of discrepancies $\Delta L_\odot$ and $\Delta L_\mathbb{)}$ of the observed longitudes of the sun and moon, respectively, from the calculated longitudes:

$$\Delta L_\odot = a_\odot + b_\odot T + f_\odot(T)$$
$$\Delta L_\mathbb{)} = a_\mathbb{)} + b_\mathbb{)} T + f_\mathbb{)}(T)$$

(4.5.2)

where T is ET. $a_\odot$, $b_\odot$, $a_\mathbb{)}$, and $b_\mathbb{)}$ are empirical constants; nonzero values for these are indistinguishable from corrections to the longitudes at epoch and either mean motions (or semimajor axes, by (4.1.21)) or mean rates of rotation of the earth. The information of interest rests in the remainders $f_\odot(T)$ and $f_\mathbb{)}(T)$, nonzero values of which require one or more of:

1. Variation in the gravitational constant, G.
2. Numerical errors in the orbital calculation.
3. Variations in the earth's rotation rate.
4. Transfer of energy between rotation and orbital motion,

Of these effects, 1 and 3 would affect sun and moon alike; 2 and 4 would affect the sun and moon differently, but only 4 would be expected to make $f_\odot$ and $f_\mathbb{)}$ proportionate to T^2. The results obtained from analysis of the observations since 1680 are:

$$f_\mathbb{)} = (5''.22 \pm 0''.30)T^2, \qquad f_\odot = (1''.23 \pm 0''.04)T^2$$

(4.5.3)

for T in centuries. Expressing $f_\mathbb{)}$ and $f_\odot$ as a combination of accelerations $\dot{\omega}$ in the earth rotation and $n_\mathbb{)}$, $n_\odot$ in orbital motion, we have:

$$f_\mathbb{)} = \frac{1}{2}\left(\dot{n}_\mathbb{)} - \frac{n_\mathbb{)}}{\omega}\dot{\omega}\right)T^2$$

$$f_\odot = \frac{1}{2}\left(\dot{n}_\odot - \frac{n_\odot}{\omega}\dot{\omega}\right)T^2$$

(4.5.4)

To make (4.5.4) solvable for the three unknowns $\dot{n}_\mathbb{)}$, $\dot{\omega}$, $\dot{n}_\odot$, let us assume for the moment that angular momentum H is conserved in the earth-moon system; if the assumption is correct, then $\dot{n}_\odot$ will be zero, and we do not have to write the more complicated condition involving the sun. Let m be the mass of the moon and M the mass of the earth; then:

$$H = \frac{Mm}{M+m}r^2 f + C\omega$$

$$\approx m[GM]^{2/3}n_\mathbb{)}^{-1/3} + C\omega$$

(4.5.5)

neglecting the eccentricity of the moon's orbit and using (4.1.21) (Kepler's law, neglecting the mass of the moon). Differentiate (4.5.5), substitute numbers from Table 4.1, and set $\dot{H}$ zero:

$$\dot{n}_{\rangle} = 0.0227\dot{\omega} \tag{4.5.6}$$

With the ratios $n_{\rangle}/\omega$ of 0.0366 and $n_{\odot}/\omega$ of 0.00274, (4.5.3, 4, and 6) yield, as hoped,

$$\dot{\omega} = -750''/\text{cen}^2$$

$$\dot{n}_{\rangle} = -17.0''/\text{cen}^2 \tag{4.5.7}$$

$$\dot{n}_{\odot} = 0.40''/\text{cen}^2$$

However, the anticipated magnitude of the acceleration $\dot{n}_{\odot}$ is less than that of perceptible errors in $f_{\rangle}$ and $f_{\odot}$. Hence the customary procedure is to utilize the best observed quantity, which is the effective discrepancy in acceleration of sun and moon, known as the *weighted discrepancy difference WDD*:

$$WDD = f_{\rangle}(T) - \frac{n_{\rangle}}{n_{\odot}} f_{\odot}(T)$$

$$= \frac{1}{2}\left(\dot{n}_{\rangle} - \frac{n_{\rangle}}{n_{\odot}} \dot{n}_{\odot}\right) T^2 \tag{4.5.8}$$

whence

$$\dot{n}_{\rangle} = -22''.4/\text{cen}^2 = -1.09 \times 10^{-23} \text{ rad/sec}^2$$

$$\dot{\omega} = -986''/\text{cen}^2 = -4.81 \times 10^{-22} \text{ rad/sec}^2 \tag{4.5.9}$$

From this point, we shall not refer to $n_{\odot}$, so we let $n_{\rangle}$ be replaced by n [93, 285].

An interesting confirmation of the rates (4.5.9) has recently been obtained as far back as the middle Devonian period (0.38 Æ ago) from a banded structure which appears on certain fossil corals. These fine bands (20 to 60 per millimeter) have variations in intensity indicating both the number of days in the year (a measure of $\Delta\omega$) and the number of days in the month (a measure of $\Delta\omega/n$). Use of both these data in equations for conservation of angular momentum obtains the rates (4.5.9) with negligible change in the earth's moment of inertia C [431].

Tidal Friction in the Earth

For angular momentum to be transferred from the earth to the moon, there must be, according to Euler's equation (4.2.1), a nonzero average torque T exerted by the moon on the earth. If the tidal response (4.4.2) of the earth to the moon were instantaneous, then there would be zero net torque since the tidal bulge would always be symmetric about the earth-moon line. However,

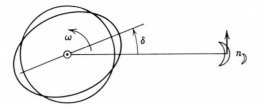

Figure 4.9: Lag of tidal bulge.

if there is imperfect elasticity with energy dissipation as always occurs in real materials, then, as derived in Section 2.3, there will be a phase lag φ. In the case of the earth's rotation a lag will appear as the occurrence of the maximum tidal bulge for a given point *after* that point has passed the earth-moon line, since $\omega \gg n$ (see Figure 4.9). Hence the moon will exert a torque T on this bulge which opposes ω, thus slowing down the earth's rotation. The equal and opposite torque exerted by the bulge on the moon will add to the moon's energy and angular momentum so that it moves farther out in its orbit and slows down.

For the magnitude of the torque we can take the derivative of either term in (4.5.5)

$$T = C\dot{\omega} = 3.98 \times 10^{23} \text{ dynes cm} \qquad (4.5.10)$$

For the energy of rotation lost by the earth we have:

$$\dot{E} = \frac{d}{dt}(\tfrac{1}{2}C\omega^2) = C\omega\dot{\omega} = -2.8 \times 10^{19} \text{ ergs/sec} \qquad (4.5.11)$$

and gained by the orbit, using (4.1.22, 37):

$$\dot{E} \approx -\frac{d}{dt}\left(m\frac{GM}{2a}\right) = \frac{GMm}{2a^2}\dot{a}$$

$$= -m\frac{na^2}{3}\dot{n} = 1.0 \times 10^{18} \text{ ergs/sec} \qquad (4.5.12)$$

Hence 2.7×10^{19} ergs/sec must be dissipated in the earth.

The locus of this energy dissipation in the earth is not entirely certain; it is most likely to occur in the oceans, but also may occur by friction between blocks in the crust or by solid friction in the mantle. The dissipation of energy in the oceans is believed to occur almost entirely in shallow seas where restricted entry results in rapid tidal currents. To calculate the tidal dissipation in a shallow sea, there are three possible integrations (as indicated in Figure 4.10): $\dot{W}_{\mathbb{D}} + \dot{W}_{\odot}$ is the mean rate of work per unit surface area done by the moon and sun on the surface of the oceans; $\dot{W}_a$ is the energy flux per unit time and unit area across the entry to shallow seas; and $\dot{W}_b$ is the rate of

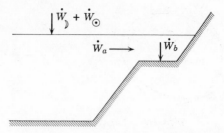

Figure 4.10: Tidal energy dissipation in the ocean. From Munk & MacDonald [285, p. 209].

work per unit surface area done by currents on the sea bottom. Whence

$$\dot{E} = \int_{\substack{\text{total sea surface}}} (\dot{W}_{)} + \dot{W}_{\odot})\, dS$$

$$= \int_{\substack{\text{entrance to shallow seas}}} \dot{W}_a\, dS$$

$$= \int_{\substack{\text{area of shallow seas}}} \dot{W}_b\, dS \qquad (4.5.13)$$

The integration over the total sea surface is indefinite because it depends on knowledge of the actual tide height over all the oceans, whereas the other two integrations are indefinite because of poor knowledge of the velocities of tidal currents. However, $\dot{W}_a$ depends on the first power of the velocity, of currents, while $\dot{W}_b$ depends on the third power, so that the $\dot{W}_a$ calculation generally is considered more reliable.

The energy flux into and out of the entrance to a sea is a product of the departure from normal pressure Δp and velocity u:

$$\dot{W}_a = \langle u\, \Delta p \rangle \qquad (4.5.14)$$

The occurrence of dissipation then appears as a lag φ of the velocity u behind the pressure Δp, which depends on the height a of the tide:

$$\Delta p = \rho g a \cos \omega t$$
$$u = u_0 \cos (\omega t - \varphi) \qquad (4.5.15)$$

A calculation of the energy flux $\dot{W}_a$ worldwide has obtained 1.7×10^{19} ergs/sec as the estimated mean dissipation rate [280, 285, 390].

Orbital Evolution from Tidal Friction

To obtain the lag angle δ in Figure 4.9 and the variations of the lunar orbit, we need to calculate tidal potential U_T, which in turn depends on the disturbing potential U_2. From the considerations discussed in Section 2.3, in particular (2.3.1), we should expect the rate of energy dissipation (4.5.11) to equal the net average rate of doing work averaged over a cycle. This work may be considered either as being done by the moon on the earth or by the earth on the moon. The latter seems a simpler calculation, so let us put

$$\dot{E} = \langle \dot{W} \rangle = \langle \text{force} \times \text{velocity} \rangle = m^* \left\langle \frac{\partial U_T}{\partial x_i} \dot{x}_i \right\rangle \qquad (4.5.16)$$

The potential U_T appearing in the last formula of (4.5.16) will be that associated with the tide—that is, the tidal potential U_T of (4.4.4). If we are to take into account the lag angle δ in Figure 4.9, then (4.4.4) should be rewritten to include time as an argument:

$$U_T(r, t + \Delta t) = \frac{R^5}{r^2(t)r^3(t + \Delta t)} k_2 U_2(r, t) \qquad (4.5.17)$$

where

$$\Delta t = \frac{\delta}{\omega - n}$$

To be able to write the derivative of U_T in (4.5.16), we need to be able to express U_T, and hence U_2, in terms of the moon's orbital elements (or, conversely, obtain the moon's velocity in earth-fixed coordinates). If we express U_2 in the earth-fixed form of (4.1.54), the important term in the simplification represented by Figure 4.9 is $lm = 22$, the harmonic associated with an equatorial ellipticity. Taking the lag angle δ into account converts the argument of the potential from $2(\lambda - \lambda^*)$ to $2(\lambda - \lambda^* + \delta)$: the δ is subtracted from λ^*, the source longitude, not λ, the disturbed body longitude. Hence we obtain as the pertinent adaption of (4.1.54):

$$U_T = k_2 G \frac{m^* R^5}{r^{*3} r^3} \frac{1}{12} P_{22}(\sin \varphi) P_{22}(\sin \varphi^*) \cos 2(\lambda - \lambda^* + \delta) \quad (4.5.18)$$

If the eccentricity and inclination of the moon's orbit are neglected, then there is motion only in λ and we can write for the combination of (4.5.16) and (4.5.18):

$$\dot{E} = m^* \left\langle \frac{\partial U_T}{\partial \lambda} \dot{\lambda} \right\rangle$$

$$= -k_2 G m^{*2} \frac{R^5}{r^{*3} r^3} \frac{9}{12} 2[\sin 2(\lambda - \lambda^* + \delta)](n - \omega)$$

$$= -k_2 G m^{*2} \frac{R^5}{r^6} \frac{3}{2} (\omega - n) \sin 2|\delta| \qquad (4.5.19)$$

The minus sign appears because the lag δ should have the same sign as the rate $n - \omega$. Note that the setting equal of λ and λ^* is not done until *after* the derivative is taken; in these equations the moon is playing a double role as a body whose orbit is perturbed and as a source of gravitational potential, and the derivative must be taken with respect to the coordinate of the perturbed orbiting body—the equations would be equally valid if it were a body different from the source of the potential. Substituting numbers from Table 4.1 in (4.5.19):

$$\dot{E} = 3.65 \times 10^{20} \sin 2\delta \text{ ergs/sec} \tag{4.5.20}$$

Allowing for the inclination reduces $\dot{E}$ to 3.08×10^{20} ergs/sec, whence

$$\frac{1}{Q} = \frac{2.7 \times 10^{19}}{3.08 \times 10^{20}} = \frac{1}{11.5} \tag{4.5.21}$$

which is close to the mean $1/Q$ deduced from earth tide measurements, and

$$2\delta = \varphi = 5.0 \text{ deg} \tag{4.5.22}$$

For the change in the semimajor axis, we can use (4.5.18) as the disturbing function in the first of the equations of motion (4.1.36). Making the same substitutions as in deriving (4.5.19), we get

$$\dot{a} = \frac{2}{na} \left\langle \frac{\partial U_T}{\partial M} \right\rangle$$

$$= \frac{3k_2}{na} Gm^* \frac{R^5}{r^6} \sin 2|\delta| \tag{4.5.23}$$

Substituting from Kepler's equation (4.1.21) for n and setting a for r—that is, neglecting the eccentricity of the orbit—we get

$$\dot{a} \approx 3k_2 m^* \left(\frac{G}{M} \right)^{1/2} \cdot \frac{R^5}{a^{11/2}} \sin 2|\delta| \tag{4.5.24}$$

Transforming (4.5.24) into a differential equation for dt in terms of da, we get for the time T for the semimajor axis to change from a_1 to a_2:

$$T = \int dt$$

$$= \int_{a_1}^{a_2} \frac{M^{1/2}}{m^* G^{1/2}} \cdot \frac{a^{11/2}}{3k_2 R^5} \cdot \frac{da}{\sin 2|\delta|}$$

$$= \frac{2}{39} \frac{M^{1/2}}{m^* G^{1/2}} \frac{\Delta a^{13/2}}{k_2 R^5 \sin 2|\delta|} \tag{4.5.26}$$

To obtain the rate of change of the eccentricity, it does not suffice to use the angular momentum relationship (4.1.12) with the already deduced rates $\dot{H}$

and $\dot{n}$ or $\dot{a}$, first because those rates were deduced assuming the eccentricity zero, and second because the parts of U_T dependent on the orbital eccentricity and inclination are also important. Instead, the tidal potential U_T of (4.5.17) must include all $l = 2$ terms, and must be converted to a form suitable for use in the Keplerian equations of motion, (4.1.36), similar to the spherical harmonic potential, (2.1.56–60):

$$U_T = k_2 G \frac{m^* R^5}{a^{*3} a^3} \sum_m (2 - \delta_{0m}) \frac{(2 - m)!}{(2 + m)!} \sum_{p,q} F_{2mp}(I) F_{2mp}(I^*)$$

$$\cdot G_{2pq}(e) G_{2pq}(e^*) \cos [v^*_{2mpq} - \varphi_{2mpq} - m\theta^* - (v_{2mpq} - m\theta)] \quad (4.5.27)$$

where

$$v_{2mpq} = (2 - 2p)\omega + (2 - 2p + q)M + m\Omega \quad (4.5.28)$$

In using U_T for the disturbing function in R in (4.1.36), the derivatives must be taken with respect to the nonasterisked quantities and the two not set equal until after differentiating. In this manner are obtained the energy dissipations and orbital changes consequent on the change in distance between earth and moon and their north-south relative motion. Also the effects of dissipation in the moon may be taken into account. If the moon had similar elastic properties to the mantle and a Q the same as the earth, (i.e., if Q was not frequency or amplitude dependent), its effect on the eccentricity would be about two-thirds that of the earth. The principal results are that the semi-major axis is increasing at about 3 cm/yr; the eccentricity at about $+0.012 \times 10^{-9}$/yr; and the inclination at $-0.52° \times 10^{-9}$/yr. If it is assumed that the same tidal Q has always prevailed, then integrating back in time brings the moon back to the earth only about 1.6 Æ ago, at an appreciable inclination to the earth's equator. Hence either the moon was created relatively recently, or tidal dissipation has been considerably less in the past than it is now [88, 142, 199, 205, 254].

Spin-Orbit Coupling

Another phenomenon that evidently is a consequence of tidal friction is the coincidence of the moon's mean rate of rotation $\omega_{\mathbb{D}}$ and its orbital mean rate n: as the rotation $\omega_{\mathbb{D}}$ is slowed down to about n, we would expect the dominant effect to be the torque exerted by the earth on the moon's equatorial bulge, $B - A$. However, since the eccentricity of the orbit causes the instantaneous angular motion f with respect to the earth to vary from the uniform rate n, we should also expect that the existence of this situation would depend on some relationship between the orbital eccentricity e and the magnitude of the restoring torque, which, from (4.3.28) will be proportionate to $(B - A)/C$. For an eccentric orbit and initial rotation $\omega_{\mathbb{D}}$ greater than mean motion n, we would expect $\omega_{\mathbb{D}}$ to decrease until it was still greater than n but sometimes

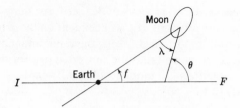

Figure 4.11: Fixed lunar bulge.

less than the instantaneous rate f—a situation that would cause a reversal in the location of the always lagging tidal bulge in Figure 4.9, which we must now consider as applying to the moon. This bulge reversal will cause a reversal of the torque $m^* \, \partial U_T / \partial \lambda$ exerted by the earth on the lunar tidal bulge, where U_T is defined by (4.5.18) with the roles of moon and earth interchanged. In the instantaneous rate of motion λ of the earth in a moon-fixed reference system, we must replace n by the instantaneous rate f, and $\omega_{\mathbb{Y}}$ by the instantaneous rate $\dot\theta$ (see Figure 4.11). Then for the averaged torque, if we neglect the inclination, we get from (4.5.18):

$$
\langle T \rangle = m^* \left\langle \frac{\partial U_T}{\partial \lambda} \right\rangle
$$

$$
= -k_2 G m^{*2} \frac{3}{2} \left\langle \frac{R^5}{r^6} \sin 2(\lambda - \lambda^* + \delta) \right\rangle
$$

$$
= -D \left\langle \left(\frac{R}{r} \right)^6 \sin 2\delta \right\rangle
$$

$$
= -\frac{D}{Q} \frac{n}{2\pi} \int_0^{2\pi/n} \left(\frac{R}{r} \right)^6 \operatorname{sgn}(\dot\theta - f)\, dt
$$

$$
= -\frac{D}{2\pi Q (1 - e^2)^{1/2}} \int_0^{2\pi} \left(\frac{R}{r} \right)^4 \operatorname{sgn}(\dot\theta - f)\, df \qquad (4.5.29)
$$

where we have replaced the constant factors by D and $\sin 2\delta$ by $\operatorname{sgn}(\dot\theta - f)/Q$, and have used (4.2.4) to replace dt.

In the trapping situation, the range of the integration in (4.5.29) must be split into two pieces because of the sign reversal of $\dot\theta - f$. Let us define the zero points of $\dot\theta - f$ by the slowly varying quantity

$$
\eta = \theta - M \qquad (4.5.30)
$$

Then, using (4.2.4) again, the integration limits are at

$$
f = \pm \left(\frac{\pi}{2} - \chi \right) \qquad (4.5.31)
$$

where

$$\sin \chi = \frac{\dot{\eta}}{2en} - \frac{3e}{4} \tag{4.5.32}$$

The integral of (4.5.29) becomes

$$\langle T \rangle = \frac{2D}{\pi Q} (4e \cos \chi - \chi) \tag{4.5.33}$$

All of the time-varying quantities involved in this evaluation of the integral are governed by the ordinary Keplerian equations except θ, which connects lunar fixed longitudes to an inertial reference. The equation governing θ in the short run is the Euler equation in longitude, the third of (4.3.28). Let us rewrite it in terms of the small quantity η, with the torque $\langle T \rangle$ on the right:

$$C\ddot{\eta} + \tfrac{3}{2}(B - A)\frac{GM}{r^3} \sin 2\eta = \langle T \rangle \tag{4.5.34}$$

Multiply (4.5.34) by $\dot{\eta}$ and substitute n^2 for GM/r^3 (from (4.1.21)):

$$\frac{d}{dt}\left[\frac{C\dot{\eta}^2}{2} - \tfrac{3}{4}(B - A)n^2 \cos 2\eta\right] = \dot{E} \tag{4.5.35}$$

where E is the energy of a system including the earth and the distribution of mass in the moon, both referred to axes which are centered in the moon and which rotate at a constant rate n, the mean rate of orbital motion. From (4.5.33),

$$\dot{E} = \frac{2D}{\pi Q} (4e \cos \chi - \chi)\dot{\eta} \tag{4.5.36}$$

The rate of dissipation of this energy thus goes to zero at synchronous rotation, $\dot{\eta} = 0$. Near this critical point the angle χ is small, from (4.5.32). Hence letting $\sin \chi \approx \chi$ and substituting from (4.5.32), we get

$$\dot{E} = \frac{D}{\pi e Q}\left(9.5e^2\dot{\eta} - \frac{\dot{\eta}^2}{n}\right) \tag{4.5.37}$$

The solution of (4.5.35) (see problem 4.15) gives $\dot{\eta}$ as a function of $(B - A)/C$. The main conclusion is that the synchronous rotation $\omega_{\text{☽}} = n$ of the moon depends on the orbit once having been in the condition [141]:

$$\left[\frac{3}{2}\left(\frac{B - A}{C}\right)\right]^{1/2} > \frac{9.5\pi e^2}{2\sqrt{2}} \tag{4.5.38}$$

PROBLEMS

4.1. Prove the time invariance of the Lagrangian brackets; i.e., that

$$\frac{\partial}{\partial t} [S_l, S_k] = 0$$

where S_l, S_k are any two orbital elements and $[S_l, S_k]$ is defined by (4.1.32).

4.2. Derive the equations of motion for a particle in rectangular coordinates **u** rotating about the u_3 axis at a rate $\dot\theta$ with respect to inertial axis **x** by (1) using vector notation; (2) using tensor notation; (3) using the rotation matrix connecting the **u** and **x** systems:

$$\mathbf{u} = \mathbf{R}_3(\theta)\mathbf{x}$$

Which term in the resulting equation is the centrifugal acceleration? Which is the "Coriolis" acceleration?

4.3. Given a force function F and canonical variables connected therewith by (4.1.55), prove Hamilton's principle for

$$\delta \int_{t_1}^{t_2} \left(\sum_i p_i \dot q_i + F \right) dt = 0$$

that is, between fixed points $(\mathbf{p}, \mathbf{q})$ at times t_1 and t_2, variations of the integral will be zero for small variations $(\delta\mathbf{p}, \delta\mathbf{q})$ and $(\delta\dot{\mathbf{p}}, \delta\dot{\mathbf{q}})$ of the path.

4.4. Using the equations of elliptic motion, (4.1.4–21), derive the differential relationship between mean anomaly M and true anomaly f:

$$\frac{df}{dM} = \frac{a^2}{r^2} (1 - e^2)^{1/2}$$

4.5. Derive equation (4.2.6) for the long periodic eccentricity function $G_{l_{pq}}(e)$. Use (4.1.9).

4.6. Derive an expression for the potential term V_{22} in terms of Keplerian elements $\{a, e, I, M, \omega, \Omega\}$ using Figure 4.4: that is, do not use (4.2.2).

4.7. Replace a satellite in a circular orbit of inclination I by a ring of the same total mass, and replace the equatorial bulge of the earth by a mass ring giving the same difference $C - A$ in moments of inertia. Calculate the torque T exercised by the equatorial ring on the satellite ring, and thence the rate of change $\dot{\mathbf{H}}$ of angular momentum of the satellite ring. Convert the moment of inertia difference $C - A$ to J_2 and calculate $\dot\Omega$ from $\dot{\mathbf{H}}$; compare the results with (4.2.9).

4.8. Derive an expression for the drag force F_d, (4.2.13), by assuming the satellite to be a flat plate of area/mass ratio A/M and the drag to occur by elastic collisions between atmospheric molecules and the plate.

4.9. The earth's rotation shows an annual variation from a uniform rate which can be approximated by an expression for the lead in time τ of

$$\tau = 0.028^s \sin(\lambda_\odot - 38°)$$

where $\lambda_\odot$ is the longitude of the mean sun measured from the beginning of the year.

If this variation is due to variations in the moments of inertia, what must be the corresponding variations in the gravitational harmonic coefficient J_2?

What would be the perturbations of a close satellite orbit due to these variations in J_2?

If the variation in rotation rate is due to the motion of air masses, what would be the magnitude of the corresponding variations in atmospheric pressure?

4.10. The J_2 of Mars is about 0.00197, and its equator is inclined about 25.2 deg to its orbit. Using the mass, radius, and rotation from Table 5.1 and assuming Mars homogeneous, derive the rate of precession of Mars' rotation axis due to the torque exercised by the sun.

4.11. Prove the invariance of degree of a spherical harmonic under rotation: that is, if $V_{lm}(\varphi, \lambda)$ is a harmonic referred to one set of axes, then it will equal a sum of harmonics $V_{lm'}(\varphi', \lambda')$ referred to another set:

$$V_{lm}(\varphi, \lambda) = \sum_{m'} D_{lmm'} V_{lm'}(\varphi', \lambda')$$

4.12. Prove that the gravitational harmonic V_{21} is a function of the products of inertia F', G'

$$V_{21} = G\left(\frac{1}{r}\right)^3 P_{21}(\sin\varphi)(G'\cos\lambda + F'\sin\lambda)$$

where

$$G' = \int_{\text{vol}} \rho xz \, dv, \qquad F' = \int_{\text{vol}} \rho yz \, dv$$

4.13. The amplitude of the latitude variation—the motion of the principal axis of inertia with respect to the rotation axis of the earth—is about 5 meters for the combination of the annual forced oscillation and the 14-month free oscillation. What is the magnitude of the corresponding perturbation J_{21} of the gravitational field? Should all or part of this perturbation affect close satellite orbits? If so, what will be the principal periodicity of the orbital perturbations and what will be the order-of-magnitude of the orbital oscillations?

4.14. Calculate the energy rate $\dot{E}$ due to tidal torques exercised on the earth by the sun, using (4.5.19) and assuming the same lag as in (4.5.22). What are the corresponding rates $\dot{\omega}$ and $\dot{n}_\odot$?

4.15. Given an equation of the "pendulum" form,

$$\dot{\psi}^2 = K + L\cos 2\psi, \qquad K < L$$

derive an expression for the period T of libration of ψ in terms of the elliptic integral of the first kind:

$$F(k, \psi) = \int_0^\psi \frac{d\psi}{(1 - k^2 \sin^2 \psi)^{1/2}}$$

What will be the value of k^2 in this function? What will be the midpoint ψ_0 and extremes ψ_m of this libration?

REFERENCES

The basic physics of Chapters 4 and 5 is classical mechanics, as set forth in books such as *Goldstein* [146]. Texts applying classical mechanics to planetary and satellite motions—that is, books on celestial mechanics—are *Moulton* [282], *Plummer* [318], *Brouwer & Clemence* [47], and *Danby* [86].

The theory of the motion of the moon applied nowadays was principally the work of *Brown* [52]. General explanations of the theory are given by *Brown* [51], *Plummer* [318], *Brouwer & Clemence* [47], and *Brouwer & Hori* [49]. Instructions as to its application—as well as other matters in this chapter—are given in the "Explanatory Supplement," written by the *Nautical Almanac Offices* [288]. See *Eckert* [105] and *Eckert et al.* [106] for the most recent development of the theory.

The discussion of orbital dynamics of artificial satellites is based mainly on *Kaula* [206]. Many papers on satellite orbits were published 1958–1964; no entirely satisfactory review exists. See *Cook* [80] for a review with emphasis on determination of the earth's gravitational field, and *King-Hele* [212] for the dynamics of atmospheric drag effects. A summary of the most recent results for the earth's field is given by *Kaula* [207]; of similar analyses of orbits around the moon, by *Kaula* [208].

Rigid-body rotation of the earth is treated in the most detail by *Woolard* [451]. The theory and calculation of the moon's libration is developed by *Koziel* [224] and *Eckhardt* [103]; recent results are described in *Koziel* [225].

The analysis of imperfections and irregularities in the dynamics of the earth-moon system has occupied much of some important treatises, such as *Love* [249], *Jeffreys* [199], and *Munk & MacDonald* [285]. Recent collections of articles on the earth-moon system are *Kopal* [217], *Kuiper & Middlehurst* [232], *Middlehurst & Kuiper* [279], and *Marsden & Cameron* [262].

Earth tides are the subject of a recent book by *Melchior* [274]. Love number calculations for the earth are given by *Longman* [247] and for the moon by *Harrison* [162]. The ocean tide theory given here is based mainly on *Hough* [183]; see also *Lamb* [236]. A review of the development of ocean tide theory is given by *Doodson* [100]. The precessional and nutational interaction between the mantle and core, which has been skipped in this text, is reviewed by *Vicente* [418]; the most important subsequent paper is by *Stewartson & Roberts* [377].

Most of the discussion of the variations in the earth's rotation is based on *Munk & MacDonald* [285]. More recent information on periodic variations is given by *Markowitz et al.* [261]. A more recent evaluation of the historical data on the secular retardation has been made by *Dicke* [93]; the paleontological data are discussed by *Wells* [431]. The theory of tidal dissipation in shallow seas was developed by *Taylor* [390]; its most recent application was by *Miller* [280].

The original work on the evolution of the moon's orbit as a consequence of tidal friction was by G. H. Darwin, and is collected in the second volume of his works, *Darwin* [88]. More recent work has been by *Gerstenkorn* [133], *MacDonald* [254], *Kaula* [205], *Goldreich* [141, 142], and *Ruskol* [498].

Chapter 5

DYNAMICS OF THE SOLAR SYSTEM

The main parts of the solar system are given in Table 5.1. In addition to the principal bodies listed in the table, there are many smaller members of the solar system in three principal categories: asteroids, comets, and dust. Because of observational uncertainties, it is inappropriate to include them in the table; all that can be said is that their contribution to the mass of the solar system within observable limits—say, within Jupiter's orbit—is orders-of-magnitude smaller than the earth. These small bodies are still of considerable interest, however, relevant to the origin and evolution of the solar system.

5.1 The Planetary System

By the "planetary system" we mean the bodies listed in Table 5.1. We shall also take up in this section the various satellite systems of the planets.

The approximate orbital elements of the planets are listed in Table 5.2.

Orbits of the Planets

The motions of the planets are one of the earliest subjects of successful scientific investigation. These investigations combined long series of careful observations with elaborate and detailed calculations. It is still true, however, that in some cases the calculations disagree with observations by appreciably more than their likely errors. The difficulties generally are considered to fall in two categories: (1) the definition and determination of the parameters that form the basis of the reference framework which connects the theory and observation and of the numerical calculation of orbits, known as the *system of astronomical constants*; and (2) the complexities of the orbit computation itself. Although these difficulties are largely matters of geometry and of working out the consequences of Newtonian attraction, their precise solution is desirable if other inferences are to be drawn from the remaining discrepancies from observation or from the values of planetary or orbital parameters themselves. For example, the interpretation of the longitude residuals $f_\odot(T)$ and $f_\mathrm{D}(T)$ in (4.5.2–3) as caused by the transfer of angular momentum from the earth's rotation to the moon's orbital motion was originally suggested in the eighteenth century, but was not generally accepted until about a century

TABLE 5.1: MAIN PARTS OF THE SOLAR SYSTEM

Body	Mean Density (gm/cm³)	Total Mass (earth masses)	Mean Radius (km)	Moment of Inertia / Mass × Radius² (C/MR^2)	Period of Rotation (days)	Number of Identified Satellites	Ratio Satellite / Primary Mass
Sun	1.4	333441.	696000	0.06	25.36	—	—
Mercury	6.03	0.0556	2434	?	59.7	0	—
Venus	5.11	0.8161	6056	?	−243.09	0	—
Earth	5.52	1.0123	6370	0.333	1.00	1	0.0123
Mars	4.16	0.1076	3370	0.389	1.03	2	?
Jupiter	1.34	318.3637	69900	0.25	0.40	12	0.00019
Saturn	0.68	95.2254	58500	0.22	0.43	10	0.00026
Uranus	1.55	14.5805	23300	0.23	0.89	5	?
Neptune	1.58	17.2642	25000	0.29	0.53	2	0.00128
Pluto	4.(?)	0.18	3000	?	6.39	0	—

Based on Allen [4, p. 143], Vaucouleurs [413], Ash et al. [20] and Shapiro [502].

TABLE 5.2: ORBITAL ELEMENTS OF THE PLANETS

Planet	P (yr)	a (AU)	e	I (to ecliptic)	M (1900)	$\dot{M}$ (cen^{-1})	Ω (1900)	$\dot{\Omega}$ (cen^{-1})	ω (1900)	$\dot{\omega}$ (cen^{-1})
Mercury	0.241	0.3871	0.206	0.1221	1.785	2610.0	0.822	0.021	0.502	0.006
Venus	0.615	0.7233	0.007	0.0591	3.711	1022.0	1.324	0.016	0.950	0.009
Earth	1.000	1.0000	0.017	—	6.260	628.3	—	—	1.766	0.030
Mars	1.881	1.5237	0.093	0.0322	5.580	334.1	0.852	0.013	4.980	0.019
Jupiter	11.865	5.2037	0.049	0.0228	4.275	53.0	1.737	0.017	4.770	0.010
Saturn	29.650	9.5803	0.051	0.0434	3.148	21.19	1.970	0.016	5.905	0.019
Uranus	83.744	19.1410	0.046	0.0135	1.281	7.50	1.283	0.009	1.667	0.021
Neptune	165.451	30.1982	0.005	0.0309	0.741	3.79	2.282	0.019	4.770	−0.007
Pluto	247.687	39.4387	0.250	0.2995	1.621	2.54	1.925	0.025	1.985	0.0000+

(The Ω is measured from equinox, and hence $\dot{\Omega}$ includes 0.025 cen^{-1} arising from precession of the equinox.)
Based on Nautical Almanac Offices [288] and Cohen & Hubbard [76].

later because inadequacies in the derivation of the higher-order perturbations made $f_{\mathrm{D}}(T)$ appear to be caused by the sun.

Astronomical Constants

The system of astronomical constants, together with numerical values, adopted by the International Astronomical Union in 1964 is given in Table 5.3. The last prior revision to the system was in 1896. Revisions are rarely

TABLE 5.3: THE I.A.U. SYSTEM OF ASTRONOMICAL CONSTANTS

Constants	Numerical Values
Defining constants:	
Number of ephemeris seconds in one tropical year (1900)	$s = 31\ 556925.9747$
Gaussian gravitational constant, defining the AU (units: rad/day)	$k = 0.017202\ 09895$
Primary constants:	
Measure of one AU in meters	$A = 149600 \times 10^6$
Velocity of light in meters/sec	$c = 299792.5 \times 10^3$
Equatorial radius for earth in meters	$a_e = 6378160$
Dynamical form factor for earth	$J_2 = 0.001082\ 7$
Geocentric gravitational constant (units: $m^3\ s^{-2}$)	$GE = 398603 \times 10^9$
Ratio of the masses of moon and earth	$\mu = 1/81.30$
Sidereal mean motion of moon in rad/sec (1900)	$n_{\mathrm{D}}{}^* = 2.661699\ 489 \times 10^{-6}$
General precession in longitude per tropical century (1900)	$p = 5025''.64$
Obliquity of the ecliptic (1900)	$\epsilon = 23°27'08''.26$
Constant of nutation (1900)	$N = 9''.210$
Derived constants:	
Solar parallax	$\pi_{\odot} = 8''.794$
Light time for unit distance	$\tau_A = 499^s.012$
Constant of aberration	$\kappa = 20''.496$
Flattening factor for earth	$f = 1/298.25$
Heliocentric gravitational constant (units: $m^3\ s^{-2}$)	$GS = 132718 \times 10^{15}$
Ratio of masses of sun and earth	332958
Ratio of masses of sun and earth + moon	$1/m = 328912$
Perturbed mean distance of moon in meters	$a_{\mathrm{D}} = 384400 \times 10^3$
Constant of sine parallax for moon	$\sin \pi_{\mathrm{D}} = 3422''.451$
Constant of Lunar inequality	$L_{\mathrm{D}} = 6''.440$
Constant of parallactic inequality	$P_{\mathrm{D}} = 124''.986$

From Wilkins [441].

made in order to facilitate comparisons of elaborate fundamental calculations; if a particular application requires a more accurate value than that given in the adopted set, it generally can be handled as a differential correction or as a special calculation of a limited number of variables for a limited duration. Thus some values in Table 5.3 are no longer the best; for example, analysis of trajectories of Ranger probes yields 3.98601×10^{14} m^3 s^{-2} as a better value of GE, while a more accurate value of the astronomical unit (AU) is 149,597, 700 ± 400 km. This value is the mean of two recent determinations of the light time τ_A, 499.0048 and 499.0036 sec, times the velocity of light, 299,792.5 km/sec.

In the case of planetary masses, recent improvements by analysis of radar-ranging and space-probe trajectories have been so great that in most cases there is appreciable change from the official values adopted by the I.A.U. in 1964. Two such solutions are given in Table 5.4.

The names used in Table 5.3 are the names customarily used by astronomers working with ephemerides, etc. Since some of the names are rather cryptic, they are explained below.

The selection of constants as "defining" or "primary" depends mainly on the most accurate means of measurement. Time measurements have always been the most accurate, so those constants that are given with the most significant figures are related to mean motions: s, k, and n_{D}. The parameters s and k might better be characterized as conversion factors, rather than constants. If we further specify

$$d = 86400 \qquad \text{(sec time/day)}$$
$$\zeta = 206264.80625 \quad \text{(sec arc/rad)}$$
$$\pi = 3.1415926536$$

TABLE 5.4: SUN/PLANET MASS RATIOS

| | I.A.U. Adopted | Improved Solutions | |
	(Wilkins [441])	(Ash et al. [20])	(Anderson [17])
Mercury	6 000 000	6 021 000 $\pm$ 53 000	6 005 000 $\pm$ 18 000
Venus	408 000	408 250 120	408 522.6 0.6
Earth + moon	329 390	328 900 60	328 900 1.8
Mars	3 093 500	3 111 000 $\pm$ 9 000	3 098 600 600
Jupiter	1 047.355		1 047.44 0.02
Saturn	3 501.6		3 499.1 0.4
Uranus	22 869		22 930 6
Neptune	19 314		19 070 21
Pluto	360 000		400 000 $\pm$ 40 000

then we have two expressions for the mean motion $n_{\bigodot}$ in inertially referred longitude of the earth around the sun in rad/sec:

$$n_{\bigodot} = \frac{k}{d} \frac{(1 + m)^{1/2}}{(1 + 3 \times 10^{-8})^{3/2}}$$

$$n_{\bigodot} = \frac{2\pi - 0.01 p/\zeta}{s} \tag{5.1.1}$$

By (5.1.1), k is the mean motion a particle of negligible mass at a mean distance of 1 AU from the sun would have if there were no other planets. The term 3×10^{-8} appears in (5.1.1) because of a 7 percent error in the mass m at the time Gauss established k as a constant. The actual mean distance of the earth from the sun is larger by another factor 2×10^{-7} due to planetary perturbation. The quantity p appears in (5.1.1) because the tropical year defined by the number of seconds s is the time of a complete revolution with respect to the *equinox*, the point at which the earth-sun orbit, called the *ecliptic*, crosses the equator. However, as derived in Section 4.3, this point is moving at the precession rate $-p$/cen. Hence to obtain an inertially referred longitude the precession rate must be added. Note that the varying quantity ω, the earth's rotation rate, does not appear in the system; the "day" in terms of which the rate k is expressed is an exact multiple of the second defined by the tropical year 1900.

It is only recently, however, that directional measurements have been supplanted by radar ranging in determining position and by artificial probes in determining relative masses, so only in 1964 were A, GE, and μ adopted as primary constants, and $\pi_{\bigodot}$, κ, $\sin \pi_{\mathbb{D}}$, and $L_{\mathbb{D}}$ became secondary.

$$\pi_{\bigodot} = \frac{\zeta a_e}{A}$$

$$\kappa = \frac{\zeta k A}{c}$$

$$\sin \pi_{\mathbb{D}} = \frac{\zeta a_e}{a_{\mathbb{D}}} = \frac{\zeta a_e n_{\mathbb{D}}^{2/3}(1 + \beta)}{[(1 + \mu)GE]^{1/3}} \tag{5.1.2}$$

$$L_{\mathbb{D}} = \zeta \frac{\mu}{1 + \mu} \cdot \frac{\pi_{\mathbb{D}}}{\sin \pi_{\mathbb{D}}}$$

In the third equation of (5.1.2), β expresses the effect of the sun on the mean distance of the moon from the earth; its value is 0.00090768.

Several constants are included in Table 5.3 because they affect observations from the earth of directions referred to the stars, which constitute an inertially fixed framework defined by a catalog of accurately observed fundamental stars. These constants are p, ϵ, N (all affecting the direction of the earth's rotation axis), κ (for the effect of the earth's orbital motion), $\pi_\odot$, $\pi_\rangle$ (for displacement of a station from the earth's center in observing the sun and moon, respectively), and $L_\rangle$ (for displacement of the earth from the earth-moon barycenter).

The constant of parallactic inequality $P_\rangle$ is the coefficient of the monthly perturbation in longitude of the moon arising from the P_{3_0} term in the Legendre polynomial development of the sun's disturbing function, (4.1.53).

The constant of nutation N is the amplitude of the principal periodic perturbation of the earth's rotation axis by the moon, associated with the 18.6-year period of the moon's node. It is taken as a primary constant because the fluid core causes N to differ perceptibly from the value calculated by the rigid-body theory from (4.3.22) [17, 20, 288, 441].

Planetary Orbit Integration

In integrating the motion of the planets, we have two distinct requirements: (1) in historical time, to calculate the orbits as accurately as possible to compare with observations; and (2) in geological time, to describe the evolution of the orbits as part of the evolution of the solar system. A calculated orbit meeting requirement (1) is called an *ephemeris*, and is satisfactorily obtained by numerical integration. For the requisite accuracy, the integration must be done for the several planets simultaneously, because the departures of any planet's motion from a Keplerian ellipse can have a perceptible effect on its perturbation of other planets through the disturbing function (4.1.50 or 4.1.54). Since there is a wide variation in the masses and periods of the planets, there is a wide choice of such matters as orbital elements, integration step length, etc. in the application of this requirement of simultaneity. The largest simultaneous integration thus far carried out was for the five outer planets with a 40-day step for 120,000 years [76]. The most interesting result of the calculation was the appearance of a commensurability between Pluto and Neptune that prevents their approaching within 18 AU of each other. To obtain ephemerides for the inner planets, the orbits of the outer planets resulting from the afore described numerical integration can be taken as fixed: the manner of integration, however, either must be analytic or must be one that isolates the anomalistic motion in one variable if comparable duration of the integration is to be attained with the much shorter periods.

To extend the integration of the orbit long enough to obtain several revolutions of node and perihelion, and hence any significant variation in the eccentricity and inclination, only analytical techniques suffice. In such analytic solutions Pluto is neglected, since its orbit intersects Neptune's, as are all short periodic (i.e., functions of anomaly or longitude) terms beyond the first order except the major near commensurability $5M_S - 2M_J$, where S and J denote Saturn and Jupiter respectively, which has a period of about 14,400 years. It is believed that the results are valid for several million years [48, 50]. Figure 5.1 is a representation of the variation in the eccentricity for the last million years.

In these analytic solutions the equations of motion are essentially those of the Keplerian elements, (4.1.36), modified to remove indeterminacy in the origin of the angles if inclination or eccentricity go to zero:

$$\lambda = M + \omega + \Omega$$
$$\tilde{\omega} = \omega + \Omega$$

(5.1.3)

The development of the disturbing function is similar to (4.1.54) summed over several disturbing planets j^*, modified to take advantage of the small

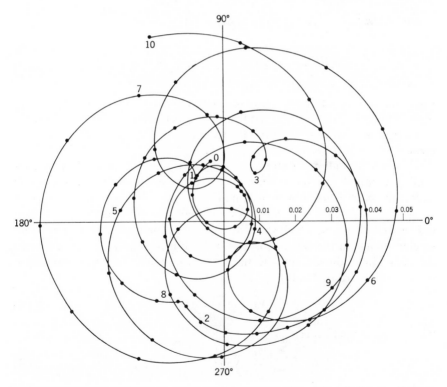

Figure 5.1: Variations of the eccentricity e of the earth's orbit with perihelion longitude $\tilde{\omega}$ for the last 10^6 years. From Brouwer & Clemence [48, p. 50].

eccentricities and inclinations. For the disturbing function term R_{ij} pertaining to the perturbation of planet i by planet j, we have the form

$$R_{ij} = \sum A e^{q_1} e^{*q_2} (\tan I)^{q_3} (\tan I^*)^{q_4}$$
$$\cdot \cos [(k_1 + k_3 + k_5)\lambda + (k_2 + k_4 - k_5)\lambda^*$$
$$- k_1 \tilde{\omega} - k_2 \tilde{\omega}^* - k_3 \Omega - k_4 \Omega^*] \quad (5.1.4)$$

In R_{ij}, the sum $q_1 + q_2 + q_3 + q_4$ is called the *degree*. In the first approximation, only terms of degree 0 are considered; in the second approximation, terms of degree 1 are added; and so forth. In integrating the Lagrangian equations at each approximation, the major difference from the technique applied to earth satellites described in Section 4.2 is that the node Ω and perihelion $\tilde{\omega}$ cannot be assumed to be moving secularly. Hence it can be shown by induction that in the end the formal solution will be made up of terms of the form

$$m^{*s} A \frac{t^p}{(l n_0 + l' n_0^*)} r e_0^{q_1} e_0^{*q_2} (\tan I_0)^{q_3} (\tan I_0^*)^{q_4}$$
$$\cdot \frac{\sin}{\cos} (l\lambda_0 + l'\lambda_0^* - k_1 \tilde{\omega} - k_2 \tilde{\omega}^* - k_3 \Omega - k_4 \Omega^*) \quad (5.1.5)$$

where $s, p, r, q_1, q_2, q_3, q_4$ are positive integers or zero. Such a solution is valid only within a certain limited time from the epoch, because of the power of t which appears—analogous to the limited validity of a Taylor series development.

Although the full description of the orbit (other than anomaly) by conventional series development is limited in the duration to which it is applicable to less than 10^8 years, similar techniques can place bounds on the range of variation of elements for a much longer time. The most restrictive of these is Poisson's theorem, which states that to the second order there can be no secular change in the semimajor axis a. In terms of the Delaunay elements the same limitation will apply to the action variable L. For the perturbation of L we have, from (4.1.47),

$$\Delta L = \int_{t_0}^{t_e} \frac{\partial F}{\partial M} \, dt \quad (5.1.6)$$

whence, to second order,

$$F = F_0(t) + \sum_{j=1}^{3} \left[\frac{\partial F_0}{\partial p_j} \Delta p_j(t) + \frac{\partial F_0}{\partial q_j} \Delta q_j(t) \right] + \cdots \quad (5.1.7)$$

In (5.1.7), the p_j's are L, G, H and the q_j's are M, ω, Ω, so we can write to the requisite order

$$\Delta p_j(t) = \int_{t_0}^{t} \frac{\partial F_0}{\partial q_j} \, du, \qquad \Delta q_j(t) = - \int_{t_0}^{t} \frac{\partial F_0}{\partial p_j} \, du \qquad (5.1.8)$$

Substituting (5.1.8) into (5.1.7) and thence in (5.1.6), it can be shown that if F_0 has the form

$$F_0 = \sum_i C_i(L_0, G_0, H_0) \cos \{b_i[M_0 + \dot{M}(t - t_0)] + c_i[\varphi_0 + \dot{\varphi}(t - t_0)]\}$$

$$(5.1.9)$$

where φ is any angle other than M, then the derivative of any term in (5.1.7) of the form $(\partial^2 F_0/\partial p_j \, \partial M)\Delta p_j$ or $(\partial F_0/\partial p_j)(\partial \Delta p_j/\partial M)$ which might give rise to secular or long periodic variation of L will be canceled out by another equal term of opposite sign $(\partial F_0/\partial q_j)(\partial \Delta q_j/\partial M)$ or $[\partial^2 F_0/(\partial q_j \, \partial M)]\Delta q_j$. (See problem 5.2.) Poisson's theorem indicates that no significant change in the semimajor axis of the planets can have occurred since their motions became governed predominantly by gravitation (other than possible close encounter between Pluto and Neptune, which is ruled out on other grounds) [155].

For limitations on the variation of the eccentricity and inclination, there is only a collective condition known as the Laplace-Lagrange theory, which states that, to the second order, for N planets

$$\sum_{i=1}^{N} m_i n_i a_i^2 e_i^2 = \text{const}$$
$$\sum_{i=1}^{N} m_i n_i a_i^2 \tan^2 I_i = \text{const} \qquad (5.1.10)$$

This theory is thus an appreciable limitation on the variation of the orbits of the major planets but not on those of the smaller inner planets [47, 48, 50, 53, 76, 155].

Properties of Orbits in the Solar System

The considerable elaborations of the modern mathematical theory of stability have been applied to the evolution of the solar system, without attaining any significant bounds to the conditions of origin more restrictive than those obtained from the formal series developments of conventional celestical mechanics. Hence it seems more promising to describe the properties of the planetary system in more specific detail in the hope of finding features that suggest particular mechanisms. Since some of these features may pertain to satellite systems rather than to the planetary system itself, it is appropriate at this point to list satellite orbit characteristics, as has been done in Table 5.5.

TABLE 5.5: SATELLITES

Planet and Satellite Name	Ratio Satellite Mass / Planet Mass	Orbit Semimajor Axis / Planet Radius (a/R)	Orbit Sidereal Period (yr)	Eccentricity (e)	Inclination (I)	Radius (R) (km)
Earth						
Moon	1.23×10^{-2}	60.27	0.064 8	0.0549	0.0899*	1738
Mars						
Phobos		2.755	0.000 873†	0.017	0.020	6
Deimos		6.919	0.003 452	0.003	0.031	3
Jupiter						
V		2.539	0.001 364	0.003	0.000	70
(I) Io	3.81×10^{-5}	5.905	0.004 841	0.003	0.000	1670
(II) Europa	2.48×10^{-5}	9.346	0.009 72	0.000	0.000	1460
(III) Ganymede	8.17×10^{-5}	14.99	0.019 59	0.0015	0.000	2550
(IV) Callisto	5.09×10^{-5}	26.36	0.045 70	0.0075	0.000	2360
VI		160.7	0.686	0.158	0.496*	50
VII		164.4	0.710	0.270	0.488*	10
X		164	0.722	0.14	0.50*	10
XII		290	-1.727	0.109	2.56*	8
XI		313	-1.896	0.207	2.86*	7
VIII		326	-2.205	0.475 ± 0.18	2.63 ± 0.08*	8
IX		332	-2.076	0.275 ± 0.15	2.74 ± 0.09*	6

	Mass	Distance	Period	e	i	Radius
Saturn						
Ring C		1.23 – 1.52	(0.000 88)			—
Ring B	≤5 × 10⁻⁵	1.54 – 1.98		0.0	0.0	
Ring A		2.05 – 2.34	(0.001 35)			
Janus		2.67	0.002 1			200
Mimas	6.69 × 10⁻⁸	3.111	0.002 581	0.020	0.026	300
Enceladus	·1.27 × 10⁻⁷	3.991	0.003 750	0.004	0.000	300
Tethys	1.14 × 10⁻⁶	4.939	0.005 168	0.000	0.019	500
Dione	1.82 × 10⁻⁶	6.327	0.007 486	0.002	0.000	500
Rhea	4.0 × 10⁻⁶	8.73	0.012 37	0.001	0.006	700
Titan	2.41 × 10⁻⁴	20.48	0.043 62	0.029	0.006	2440
Hyperion	2.0 × 10⁻⁷	24.83	0.058 2	0.104	0.010	200
Iapetus	2.0 × 10⁻⁶	59.67	0.217 2	0.028	0.257	500
Phoebe		216.8	−1.507	0.166	2.6	100
Uranus						
Miranda	1.0 × 10⁻⁶	5.494	0.003 870	≪0.01	0.00	100
Ariel	1.4 × 10⁻⁵	8.079	0.006 90	0.0028	0.00	300
Umbriel	5.9 × 10⁻⁶	11.25	0.011 35	0.0035	0.00	200
Titania	5.0 × 10⁻⁵	18.46	0.023 84	0.0024	0.00	500
Oberon	2.9 × 10⁻⁵	24.69	0.036 86	0.0007	0.00	400
Neptune						
Triton	1.32 × 10⁻³	15.85	−0.016 08	0.000	2.79	2000
Nereid	3.0 × 10⁻⁷	249.5	0.982	0.749	0.48	100

* Asterisked inclinations refer to planetary orbit; all other inclinations, to planetary equator.
† Phobos is the only satellite whose period of revolution is less than the period of rotation of its planet.
Based on Brouwer & Clemence [48], Nautical Almanac Offices [288], Danby [86], and Allen [4, p. 147].

Of features suggesting particular mechanisms, starting with the more obvious, we can enumerate:

1. The regularity of planetary orbits. All planet orbits have small eccentricities, small inclinations, and (viewed from the north pole) counterclockwise orbital motion, as is the rotation of the sun.

2. The similarity of the various satellite systems to the planetary system. Most satellites have small eccentricities and inclinations, some of them very small indeed. Of the 16 satellites with semimajor axes of less than 20 planet radii, 14 have an eccentricity less than 0.008; 6, less than 0.001; and 2, less than 0.00005. Fifteen of these satellites have an inclination to the planet equator of less than 2 deg, and 11 have less than 20 min. Furthermore, we have

$$\frac{\sum \text{planet masses}}{\text{sun mass}} \approx 10^{-3} \approx \frac{\sum \text{satellite masses}}{\sum \text{planet masses}} \qquad (5.1.11)$$

3. The *Titius-Bode law*. The ratio of successive planetary semimajor axes is rather constant: if we count the asteroids as a planet and disregard Pluto, we get for this ratio about

$$\frac{a_{n+1}}{a_n} \approx 1.75 \pm 0.20 \qquad (5.1.12)$$

4. The concentration of angular momentum in the planets. If the sun condensed from dust which had moved with Keplerian velocities, its rotation would be 200 times as great. However, over 0.99 of the angular momentum is concentrated in the major planets which constitute little more than 0.001 of the total mass. (See Table 9.6.)

5. The positive correlation of rotation rate with the mass of the planet. The angular momentum density defined as the quantity

$$D = \frac{H}{M} = \frac{C\omega}{M} \qquad (5.1.13)$$

varies almost directly proportionate to $M^{5/6}$, as indicated in Figure 5.2. The principal exceptions to this rule are the terrestrial planets which have the greatest likelihood of having undergone significant tidal friction [254].

6. The occurrence of many more near commensurabilities in the solar system than can be attributed to chance. Among the several planets and satellites of the solar system, there are 46 pairs of bodies whose ratio of mean motions is less than 7. Between 1/7 and 1 there are 17 ratios of integers 1 to 7. For any small limit ϵ, there are several more pairs of mean motions with a ratio differing less than ϵ from one of these integer ratios than would be obtained by chance, as shown in Table 5.6.

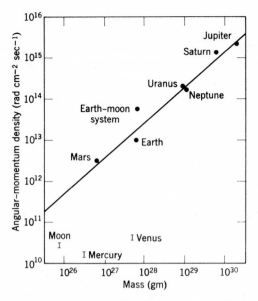

Figure 5.2: Angular-momentum density of planets. From MacDonald [254, p. 522].

In addition to the mean motion pairs summarized in Table 5.6, there are commensurabilities connecting three satellites of Jupiter; Io, Europa, and Ganymede:

$$\frac{n_1 - 3n_2 + 2n_3}{n_1} \leq 10^{-9} \tag{5.1.14}$$

and the four large satellites of Uranus:

$$\frac{n_1 - n_2 - 2n_3 + n_4}{n_1} \approx 0.00328 \tag{5.1.15}$$

Perhaps the most remarkable is that which exists between the motions of Neptune and Pluto:

$$3\dot{\lambda}_p - 2\dot{\lambda}_N - \dot{\tilde{\omega}}_p \approx 0 \tag{5.1.16}$$

TABLE 5.6: NUMBER OF MEAN MOTION RATIOS n_2/n_1 WITHIN A LIMIT ϵ OF AN INTEGER RATIO

ϵ	0.0119	0.0089	0.0059	0.0030	0.0015
Number observed	33	26	20	12	6
Chance	17	13	9	3	2

From Roy & Ovenden [347].

In numerical integrations carried over 120,000 years this rate oscillated about zero with a period of 19,670 years in such a way as to prevent Pluto ever coming within 18 AU of Neptune [76].

There are apparent couplings between mean motions and rotation rates: for the rotation of Mercury

$$\omega \approx \frac{3n}{2} \tag{5.1.17}$$

and for the rotation of Venus:

$$\omega \approx 5n_E - 4n_V \tag{5.1.18}$$

where n_E and n_V are the mean motions of the earth and Venus, respectively [78, 143]. In addition, there are many commensurabilities involving the asteroids [155, 396].

Resonances

Possible explanations for the aforestated characteristics of the planetary system can be categorized according to ascending complexity and hence uncertainty of interaction:

(a) gravitational;
(b) tidal;
(c) collisional;
(d) hydromagnetic.

It is desirable to explain as much as possible by the first two categories, since, for the latter two to operate, the solar system would have to be greatly different in condition from what it is now. The features that seem most likely of explanation are the small eccentricities and inclinations and the commensurabilities, since they all appear to constitute stable states which can be attained without any major transfers of energy or angular momentum (i.e., transfers very small compared to the total energy or momentum of a planetary orbital motion). The angular momentum density distribution shown in Figure 5.2 is possibly explicable as a consequence of collisional processes in the creation of planets out of smaller bodies, in which the rotational angular momentum is acquired as a small differential between orbital angular momenta (see problem 5.3). For the overall distribution of mass and angular momentum in the solar system, items 3 and 4, a model of the origin of the solar system is necessary, with significant nonmechanical processes in operation, as discussed in Section 9.3.

The mathematical treatment of a commensurability, where only purely gravitational forces are effective, is an elaboration of the stability theory

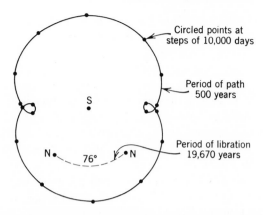

Circled points at
steps of 10,000 days

Period of path
500 years

Period of libration
19,670 years

S

N   76°   N

Figure 5.3: Path of Pluto in a reference frame rotating with Neptune, showing libration of path with respect to the sun-Neptune line. From Cohen & Hubbard [76, p. 12].

applicable to a pendulum. In the case of Pluto's orbit as perturbed by Neptune, there is said to exist a case of resonance, since the critical angle $3\lambda_p - 2\lambda_N - \tilde{\omega}_p$ never goes through a full cycle, but instead librates ± 38 deg about 180 deg. As a consequence, Pluto never approaches within 18 AU of Neptune, despite its perihelion distance, $a_p(1 - e_p)$, being within Neptune's orbit, a_N (see Table 5.2). If we take a reference frame rotating with Neptune about the sun, Pluto's path is as shown in Figure 5.3. The orientation of this path with respect to the Sun-Neptune line varies with the ± 38 deg libration as indicated in the figure. Exact commensurability—that is, $3\dot{\lambda}_p - 2\dot{\lambda}_N - \dot{\tilde{\omega}}_p = 0$—occurs only when Neptune is at the extreme of its libration with respect to the path of Pluto. At this point, the main effect of Neptune on Pluto which is not averaged out in a 500-year period is an along-track acceleration exerted at the nearest small loop in Pluto's path.

To study this libration analytically, we require all terms of the disturbing function of the form (5.1.4) or the form (4.2.15) which contain arguments

$$i(\delta - \pi) = i(3\lambda_p - 2\lambda_N - \tilde{\omega}_p)$$
$$= i[2\omega + 3M + 2(\Omega - \lambda^*)] \qquad (5.1.19)$$

where i is any integer. In (5.1.19), we have defined δ so that it oscillates about zero, and on the second line have used asterisked symbols to designate elements of Neptune's orbit and unasterisked symbols for Pluto's orbit. From the second line and (4.2.15), we see that the coefficient must be $O(e^{|i|})$ and hence that the terms with $i = 1$ will most likely be dominant. The nonappearance of the longitude of the node (except as part of the longitude of perihelion), together with the results of the numerical integration, indicates that perturbations out of the orbital plane are not important. Hence we can reduce the variables to δ, ω, a, and e, and write

$$R \approx -C\,(a^*/a)\,e\cos\delta \qquad (5.1.20)$$

where the eccentricity of Neptune's orbit has been neglected. The manner in which the ratio a^*/a appears is a practical difficulty; a series such as (4.2.15) would converge very slowly. In some treatments of this sort, a numerical averaging is applied. In any case, given the restriction that Pluto never comes close to Neptune, C is a positive function of order m^*/M ($\sim 10^{-4}$) times the central term GM/a.

The existence of a resonance implies that in the terms on the right of the equations of motion (4.1.36 and 39) variations of the elements are significant. From (4.1.36 and 39), (5.1.19), and (5.1.20):

$$\dot{a} = \frac{6}{na}\frac{\partial R}{\partial \delta} \qquad\qquad = \frac{6C}{na}e\sin\delta$$

$$\dot{e} = 3\frac{1-e^2}{na^2 e}\frac{\partial R}{\partial \delta} - \frac{(1-e^2)^{1/2}}{na^2 e}\frac{\partial R}{\partial \omega} = 3\frac{1-e^2}{na^2}C\sin\delta$$

$$\dot{\omega} = \frac{(1-e^2)^{1/2}}{na^2 e}\frac{\partial R}{\partial e} \qquad\qquad = -\frac{(1-e^2)^{1/2}}{na^2 e}C\cos\delta \quad (5.1.21)$$

$$\dot{\delta} = 3n - \frac{1-2e^2}{na^2 e}\frac{\partial R}{\partial e} - \frac{6}{na}\frac{\partial R}{\partial a} - 2\dot{\lambda}^*$$

$$= 3n + \left(6\frac{\partial C}{\partial a}e + \frac{1-2e^2}{ae}C\right)\frac{\cos\delta}{na} - 2\dot{\lambda}^*$$

Thence

$$\ddot{\delta} = \frac{\partial \dot{\delta}}{\partial a}\dot{a} + \frac{\partial \dot{\delta}}{\partial e}\dot{e} + \frac{\partial \dot{\delta}}{\partial \delta}\dot{\delta}$$

Using Kepler's third law (4.1.21),

$$\ddot{\delta} \approx -\frac{27C}{a^2}e\sin\delta \qquad (5.1.22)$$

since, from Table 5.2, $e^2 \gg Ca/GM$. In this crudest approximation, then, δ satisfies a simple pendulum equation (problem 4.15). A complete solution takes into account the other variations in (5.1.21). One solution using a transformation from the Delaunay equations (4.1.47) confirms the 20,000-year libration in δ and obtains a secular motion of $\tilde{\omega}$ with a period of 15.5×10^6 years [182].

The asteroid orbits also demonstrate some resonance effects, as discussed in Section 5.3.

5.2   Energy-Dissipating Processes

Major Planet Q's

In recent years, much about the properties of satellite orbits and the couplings between planetary rotation and orbital motion has been explained as the consequence of tidal friction. The treatments are extensions of the methods described in Section 4.5. The properties of significance are the smallness of several of the eccentricities, inclinations, and *semimajor axes,* as listed in Table 5.5. The existence of satellites so close to the major planets sets a severe upper bound on the planetary dissipation factor $1/Q$; since these satellites all have periods greater than that of planetary rotation, perceptible dissipation in the planets would have long since driven off the satellites, as has happened in the case of the earth and moon. Assuming that the satellites have been in orbit since the origin of the solar system 4.5×10^9 years ago, and using this duration as the time in (4.5.26), sets lower limits of more than 50,000 on the Q's for Jupiter, Saturn, and Uranus. It might be hoped that secular accelerations determined from observations of some of the satellites would furnish further evidence of tidal friction. In practice, however, the accelerations estimated either have the wrong sign or only give a loose lower bound on Q: e.g., 10^4 for Jupiter from the absence of a perceptible acceleration for Io.

However, confirmation of small planetary $1/Q$ compared to satellite $1/Q$ is obtained from the very small eccentricities: if the satellite acquires a rotation equal to its orbital angular rate, then the resulting tides can transfer only energy, not angular momentum, since there is only variation in distance, not any systematic along-track lag giving rise to a couple. If angular momentum, proportionate to $[a(1 - e^2)]^{1/2}$, (4.1.12), is conserved while the semimajor axis a decreases with the energy, then eccentricity e also must decrease until it is virtually zero and the effect negligible. Dissipation in the satellite has a similar damping effect on the inclination [139, 145].

Orbit-Orbit Coupling

As the satellites move outward at differing rates due to tidal friction in the rotating planet, their mean motions eventually will attain a commensurable relationship such as (5.1.14 or 15). Their gravitational interaction will then transfer angular momentum from one satellite to another, so that thereafter they will move outward together with periods coupled. If we assume that tidal acceleration is significant only in the inner satellite, then the situation is similar to (5.1.22), with the addition of a small term $dn_T{}^*/dt$ for the tidal acceleration:

$$\frac{d^2\delta}{dt^2} = -k^2 \sin \delta - 2\frac{dn_T{}^*}{dt} \tag{5.2.1}$$

where k^2 is $27Ce/a^2$. Assume a small δ negligibly different from sin δ; then the solution of (5.2.1) is:

$$\delta = K \sin kt - \frac{2}{k^2} \frac{dn_T{}^*}{dt} \qquad (5.2.2)$$

where K is a constant. Hence, the effect of the tidal torque on δ is a phase shift. To obtain the energy transfer between satellites and thence the acceleration dn/dt of the outer body, use Kepler's law and substitute the averaged δ in the first equation of (5.1.21):

$$\frac{dn}{dt} = -\frac{3n}{2a} \langle \dot{a} \rangle$$

$$= \frac{18Ce}{a^2 k^2} \frac{dn^*}{dt}$$

$$= \frac{2}{3} \frac{dn^*}{dt} \qquad (5.2.3)$$

Hence once a close commensurability (i.e. small δ) is attained, it is maintained. Furthermore, since $dn^*/dt < 0$, a similar substitution in the second equation of (5.1.21) obtains a positive $\langle \dot{e} \rangle$, this reinforcing the commensurability.

The solution discussed here is for the case n/n^*, which is approximately $2/3$; the same sort of analysis would apply to other ratios, such as $1/2$. Also there can be orbit-orbit coupling which involves the inclination and node instead of the eccentricity and perimeter. The most marked such coupling is between the satellites Mimas and Tethys of Saturn. Integration of their orbits back in time obtains a zero inclination of one body $1.14 \times 10^{11}Q$ sec ago, or 2×10^8 yr using the minimum Q of 7×10^4 estimated from the semimajor axes [140, 546].

Spin-Orbit Coupling

In the process of tidal deceleration of rotation described by (4.5.29–34), it is possible that the eccentricity e and moments-of-inertia difference $(B - A)/C$ may be large enough to cause a stabilization of the rotation rate ω at a ratio to the orbital rate n higher than 1:1. In an eccentric orbit, the torque caused by the gravitational attraction of the central body for a tidal bulge will tend to impart a rotation rate ω approaching that of the angular rate f at pericenter. Once a commensurability has been attained, then stabilization of the rotation rate would depend on the torque exerted on the fixed bulge $(B - A)/C$. Figure 5.4 shows the geometry pertinent to such spin-orbit coupling, of which the most marked case is Mercury, (5.1.17). The same Euler equation in longitude, the third of (4.3.28), applies, as was used in the case of the moon,

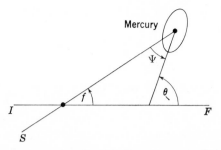

Figure 5.4: Spin-orbit coupling geometry. From Goldreich & Peale [143, p. 426].

(4.5.34); however, now in place of (4.5.30) we make the substitution

$$\eta = \theta - \frac{kM}{2} \qquad (5.2.4)$$

where k is any integer. In place of (4.5.34) we thus obtain

$$C\ddot{\eta} + \frac{3}{2}\frac{GM_\odot}{r^3}(B - A) \cdot \sin 2\eta(\cos 2f \cos kM + \sin 2f \sin kM)$$
$$\cdot \cos 2\eta(\cos 2f \sin kM - \sin 2f \cos kM) = 0 \quad (5.2.5)$$

If $\dot{\theta}$ is close to $kn/2$ and $(B - A)/C \ll 1$, η changes very slightly in one orbit. Averaging the functions of r, f, M over an orbit obtains the same power series $G_{lpq}(e)$ as appeared in developing the spherical-harmonic gravity field of the earth (4.2.5) or the third-body disturbing function (4.2.15); using Kepler's law (4.1.21), we get:

$$C\ddot{\eta} + \tfrac{3}{2}n^2(B - A)G_{20(k-2)}(e) \sin 2\eta = 0 \qquad (5.2.6)$$

Solutions of (5.2.6) as the pendulum equation (problem 4.15) obtain stable librations about spin rates of $kn/2$ dependent on the magnitude of $G_{20(k-2)}(e)$. For the case of Mercury, we have

$$G_{201}(e) = \frac{7e}{2} - \frac{123e^3}{16} + \cdots \approx 0.654 \qquad (5.2.7)$$

If there are tidal torques, then the averaged tidal torque $\langle T \rangle$ must be added to the right of (5.2.6). The tidal torque from (4.5.29) is

$$\langle T \rangle = -\frac{3k_2 GM_\odot^2 R^5}{2r^6} \sin 2|\delta| \qquad (5.2.8)$$

The possibility of stable libration then depends on

$$|\langle T \rangle| < \tfrac{3}{2}n^2(B - A)G_{20(k-2)}(e) \qquad (5.2.9)$$

Substituting $1/2Q$ for $\sin 2\,|\delta|$ and numbers for other variables ($k_2 = 0.05$) obtains for Mercury:

$$\frac{B - A}{C} > \frac{7.1 \times 10^{-8}}{Q\,|G_{20(k-2)}(e)|} \tag{5.2.10}$$

The dissipation factor Q for an oceanless planet like Mercury must be well over 10; hence stability of resonant spin states near $k = 2$ requires only plausibly small values of $(B - A)/C$.

The probability of capture into a resonant spin state, however, depends on the nature of the dependence of the tidal torque $\langle T \rangle$ on the rate $\dot{\eta}$. Assume that tidal friction is slowing the spin of the planet from a rate much higher than the orbital motion n, and that the tidal torque $\langle T \rangle$ added to the right of (5.2.6) is constant. The first integral of (5.2.6) is then

$$C\frac{\dot{\eta}^2}{2} - \tfrac{3}{4}(B - A)n^2 G_{20(k-2)}(e)\cos 2\eta = \langle T \rangle\eta + E_0 \tag{5.2.11}$$

where $E = E_0 + \langle T \rangle\eta$ is the energy.

In Figure 5.5, the upper curve is a plot of $\dot{\eta}^2/2$ versus η, using (5.2.11), with a greatly exaggerated magnitude of $\langle T \rangle$. If the torque $\langle T \rangle$ were constant, then the spin would follow the curve from left to right until it reached $\eta_{\max}$, or zero $\dot{\eta}$. It then would return along exactly the same curve, and there would be no capture. If, however, the torque had a sign dependence on $\dot{\eta}$—as we have generally taken it to have in Section 4.5—of a plausible form such as

$$\langle T \rangle = -K\left(V + \frac{\dot{\eta}}{n}\right) \tag{5.2.12}$$

then the return to the left after reaching $\eta_{\max}$ would be along the lower curve in Figure 5.5. Hence there would be a finite probability of capture proportionate to $\delta E/\Delta E$, where δE and ΔE, shown in Figure 5.5, are:

$$\Delta E = -K\int_{\eta_1}^{\eta_2}\left(V + \frac{\dot{\eta}}{n}\right)d\eta$$

$$\delta E \approx \frac{2K}{n}\int_{\eta_1}^{\eta_2}\dot{\eta}\,d\eta \tag{5.2.13}$$

If we assume the right side of (5.2.11) to be negligibly small for the purpose of evaluating $\dot{\eta}$, then we obtain, taking $\eta_2 - \eta_1 = \pi$,

$$P = \frac{\delta E}{\Delta E} = \frac{2}{1 + \pi V/2[3(B - A)G_{20(k-2)}(e)/C]^{1/2}} \tag{5.2.14}$$

Since $(B - A)/C$ is very small for any planet, the constant part V of the tidal torque must be very small for any finite probability of capture to exist. If the

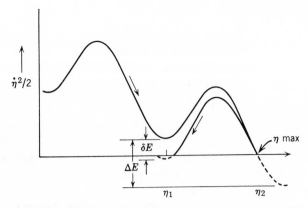

Figure 5.5: Schematic diagram of $\dot{\eta}^2/2$ versus η for $\langle T \rangle = -K(V + \dot{\eta}/\eta)$. From Goldreich & Pearle [143, p. 428].

tidal torque is of any type whose entire sign dependence is on the rate, (i.e., $V = 0$), then a plausible $(B - A)/C$, such as 10^{-5}, for Mercury would be quite sufficient to stabilize its rotation in the $k = 3$ state [78, 143].

The trapping torque also may be exercised by another orbiting body, as well as the central body, as appears to be the case for the spin-orbit coupling of Venus, (5.1.18). In this case the capture probability depends also on the mass and distance of the torquing body. Extending the theory (5.2.4–14) to the case of Venus we conclude that the $(B - A/C$ of Venus must be implausibly large, 10^{-4}, in order to stabilize the rotation in resonance at a period of -243.16 days. The physics of the essential problem—the dissipation of sufficient energy of libration, δE, around the resonant angular velocity—needs to be examined more closely. The explanation most recently suggested is a fluid core viscously coupled to the mantle in Venus; maximum capture probability occurs if the core responds to angular velocity changes with a time lag of about 3×10^4 years [143, 144].

5.3 Small Bodies of the Solar System

In this category are included comets, asteroids, meteors, and dust. They are of interest as indicators of properties of the interplanetary medium; as likely sources of meteorites; and as examples of certain dynamical phenomena pertinent to the origin and evolution of the solar system. In this section we shall describe the mechanical properties of these small bodies and their orbits, and discuss the dynamical problems associated with them.

Comets

As of 1960, 566 comets had been discovered and observed well enough to establish an orbit. These orbits, after perturbation by the planets, are classifiable as [321]:

Elliptic, $P < 200$ years	94
Elliptic, $P > 200$ years	117
Near parabolic	290
Hyperbolic	65
Total	566

No perturbations attributable to comets having been detected—even between halves of a split comet—estimates of their mass must be made from their size and brightness. Such estimation is difficult because of variation in intrinsic brightness with distance r from the sun proportionate to about r^{-4}; 10^{17} grams is generally given as an upper limit.

If integration of the orbits is carried backward from the elements established by observation, it is found that most orbits observed as hyperbolic have entering elements on the elliptic side of parabolic. In one study, 29 of 33 hyperbolic orbits were changed to elliptic. The most hyperbolic value of $1/a$ which remained was -66×10^{-6} [295]. In another study, 14 of 21 orbits changed back to elliptic [40]. It has not yet been established that any orbit was definitely hyperbolic beyond the uncertainty of the observations. What does seem certain is that the majority of comet orbits have energies $-2\mu/a$ close to zero, and hence large semimajor axes. Table 5.7 gives the number of comets per 0.00005 interval of $1/a$ observed 1850–1952 for which the mean error for $1/a$ was estimated to be less than ±0.00010, or which were observed for more than six months.

The average published mean error of $1/a$ was ±0.00003, with a considerable spread. These errors are large enough that all the negative values in the table could be erroneous; the distribution n of calculated $1/a$ *could* have been (but was not necessarily) the result of a distribution of all positive $1/a$ with a sharper peak in the interval 0.00000 to $+0.00004$. On the other hand, there tends to be a bias toward small $1/a$ because these comets are generally brighter and their orbits more interesting to calculate. If these two factors are taken into account, the true distribution of $1/a$ could very plausibly be the hypothetical "elliptic" distribution n_E given in the table. An equally probable "hyperbolic" distribution n_H is given to show that it is much less likely that the true $1/a$ is distributed symmetrically about 0, let alone predominantly hyperbolic.

To provide the listed number n_E per century, the total population of comets per interval of $1/a$ must be vastly greater for small $1/a$, since the frequency of appearance of a given comet is inversely proportional to its period, $a^{3/2}$. Hence we apply a factor $(1/a)^{-3/2}/100$, using the mid-value of the interval, to obtain a hypothetical total of comets in each interval of $1/a$ with eccentricity sufficiently large to come within range of observability. The sphere of

TABLE 5.7: DISTRIBUTION $1/a$ OF COMETS

$1/a$ (AU^{-1})		Actual Calculated Distribution (obs/cen) (n)	Hypothetical Distributions		
			"Hyperbolic" (obs/cen) (n_H)	"Elliptic" (obs/cen) (n_E)	"Elliptic" Total $[(1/a)^{-3/2} n_E/100]$
−0.00015 to	−0.00011	1	0	0	
−0.00010	−0.00006	1	1	0	
−0.00005	−0.00001	4	7	0	
0.00000	+0.00004	15	15	26	2,900,000
+0.00005	+0.00009	8	8	5	86,000
+0.00010	+0.00014	3	2	1	7,600
+0.00015	+0.00019	1	1	1	4,600
+0.00020	+0.00024	1	1	1	3,100
+0.00025	+0.00049	1.0	1.0	1.0	1,400
+0.00050	+0.00074	0.8	0.8	0.8	520
+0.00075	+0.00099	0.6	0.6	0.6	250
+0.00100	+0.00199	0.25	0.25	0.17	30
+0.00200	+0.00499	0.05	0.05	0.08	4.7
+0.00500	+0.00999	0.05	0.05	0.043	0.67
+0.01000	+0.01999	0.015	0.015	0.017	0.093
+0.02000	+0.03999	0.002	0.002	0.004	0.004

Based on Oort [296].

observability is about 2 AU, hence the eccentricity required for observability is more than $1 - 2(1/a)$. Thus if comets also have a distribution in eccentricity e that is similar for all $1/a$, then we have a further factor which relatively enhances the number of small $1/a$ in the hypothetical population.

Finally, the interval of 50×10^{-6} in Table 5.7 is considerably smaller than the root-mean-square change $\Delta(1/a)$ per perihelion passage, which is about $\pm 700 \times 10^{-6}$. If we started out with a population of comets of perihelion distance $a(1 - e)$ less than 2 AU and $1/a$ as listed in the last column of Table 5.7, then the rms perturbation of $\pm 700 \times 10^{-6}$ would cause many of the comets to be lost, and the remainder of the distribution on the elliptic side of zero to be somewhat smoothed out. Since the perturbation is essentially an impulse close to perihelion—much more severely so than the satellite drag discussed in Section 4.2, (4.2.14)—a comet that stays elliptic will return to nearly the same perihelion location. If the observed population consists of such return comets, the distribution of $1/a$ would have long since had its peak considerably smoothed out. Hence it is necessary that the comets of small $1/a < 0.0001$ be new to the inner regions of the solar system, which in turn requires that they have received some perturbation near aphelion. The only known sources of perturbations at distances on the order of 10^5 AU (0.5 parsec) are stars; from the known density and motions of stars near the sun, it is estimated that in 10^6 years 20 solar masses of stars pass within 2×10^5 AU of the sun, each taking a time on the order of 3×10^4 years to do so [295, 296].

The directions of cometary orbits at first glance appear rather randomly distributed. On taking a sufficiently large sample, however, the locations of perihelia of long-period comets show a correlation with the plane of maximum stellar population called the *galactic plane*. These locations are summarized in Table 5.8, which divides the celestial sphere into equal areas [404]. The distribution of perihelion directions also shows some correlation with the motion of the sun relative to the nearby stars, which is in the direction $l_I\ 22°$, $b_I\ 25°$. Since it takes a comet of 0.00002 $1/a$ about 5×10^6 years to go from aphelion to perihelion, the distribution should have no apparent relationship to stars close to the sun at present.

Dependence on passing stars to perturb comets to within 2 AU of the sun entails (1) a total number of comets several orders-of-magnitude larger than that given in Table 5.7 since such a perturbation for a comet at more than 5×10^4 AU will have a very small probability: this population has been estimated as 10^{11}; and (2) very few observable comets of semimajor axis between 1000 and 10,000 AU, since near perihelion these comets will be perturbed to different energies, while near aphelion there are rarely any stars to perturb the comets toward the sun.

TABLE 5.8: DISTRIBUTION OF COMET PERIHELIA
IN GALACTIC COORDINATE SYSTEM I*

Galactic longitude	180°		270°		0°		90°	180°
Latitude 90°	13		12		16		12	
42° / 0°	25	14	18	20	(34)	26	27	26
-42°	9	12	20	32	34	24	22	15
-90°	6		7		5		18	

* Relatable to ecliptic system by Euler angles 280°, 62°, 0°: $\mathbf{i}_G = \mathbf{R}_1(62°)\,\mathbf{R}_3(280°)\mathbf{i}_E$. Based on Tyror [404].

Comets that have definitely elliptical orbits appear to be less bright than near-parabolic comets, as if they had been depleted chemically. Some comets—Encke, D'Arrest, Wolf I—which have relatively close perihelia are observed to suffer an acceleration corresponding to a mass loss on the order of 0.002 to 0.005 per revolution [435].

Dynamics of Comet Orbits

The dynamical problems associated with comets can be put in two categories: (1) those associated with their current or recent history; and (2) those associated with their origin. As with other matters in the solar system, the difficulties in solving problems in category (1) has prevented a serious attack on problems in category (2).

In the recent history of a comet, we are concerned about perturbations near perihelion by planets and perturbations near aphelion by stars. Since Jupiter is so much more massive than the other planets, we should expect to get a good approximation to the actual motion by considering only Jupiter's perturbations. We are thus concerned again with the three-body problem, (4.1.49–50), but in an entirely different manner than in previous applications. The primary question now is the change in energy, or $1/a$, on a single passage; the secondary question is what parameters of the orbit remain invariant, or nearly so, in order that we may predict in at least a statistical manner the future course of the orbit. Let us express the force function F—the negative of the energy—in the form it would have if the origin of the coordinate system were at the center of mass of Jupiter and the sun. Then, from (4.1.37 and 50), neglecting the mass m of the comet,

$$F = \frac{GM}{2a} + \frac{Gm^*}{\rho} \tag{5.3.1}$$

To determine the rate of change of energy we have, using (4.1.55),

$$\frac{dF}{dt} = \frac{\partial F}{\partial q_i} \dot{q}_i + \frac{\partial F}{\partial p_i} \dot{p}_i + \frac{\partial F}{\partial t} = \frac{\partial F}{\partial t} \tag{5.3.2}$$

The explicit derivative $\partial F/\partial t$ depends on the motion in longitude α^* of Jupiter:

$$\frac{\partial F}{\partial t} = \frac{\partial F}{\partial \alpha^*} \dot{\alpha}^* = -\frac{Gm^*}{\rho^2} \frac{\partial \rho}{\partial \alpha^*} \dot{\alpha}^* \tag{5.3.3}$$

From the law of cosines,

$$\rho^2 = r^2 + r^{*2} - 2rr^* \cos S \tag{5.3.4}$$

And from the spherical triangle in Figure 5.6,

$$\cos S = \cos (\Omega - \alpha^*) \cos (\omega + f) - \cos I \sin (\Omega - \alpha^*) \sin (\omega + f)$$

$$(5.3.5)$$

whence, assuming Jupiter's orbit circular,

$$\frac{\partial F}{\partial \alpha^*} = - \frac{\partial F}{\partial \Omega} \tag{5.3.6}$$

But from (4.1.47) $-\partial F/\partial \Omega$ is $-\dot{H}$. Thence

$$\frac{dF}{dt} = \frac{\partial F}{\partial t} = -\dot{H}\dot{\alpha}^* \tag{5.3.7}$$

and, replacing $\dot{\alpha}^*$ by n^* as appropriate for assuming Jupiter's orbit circular, we must have:

$$F' = F + Hn^* = \text{const} \tag{5.3.8}$$

Replace H by its expression from (4.1.42) and F by its expression from (5.3.1)

$$F' = \frac{GM}{2a} + \frac{Gm^*}{\rho} + n^*na^2(1 - e^2)^{1/2} \cos I = \text{const} \tag{5.3.9}$$

Before and after each passage Gm^*/ρ is very small compared to other terms in (5.3.9). Neglecting this term, dividing (5.3.9) by $GM/2$, and using Kepler's law, (4.1.21), for both the comet and Jupiter, we get

$$\frac{1}{a} + \frac{2}{a^{*3/2}} \sqrt{a(1 - e^2)} \cos I \approx \text{const} \tag{5.3.10}$$

known as *Tisserand's criterion*, long used to determine whether an observed comet is a return of a previously observed comet. We can use Tisserand's

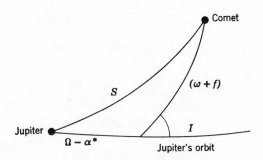

Figure 5.6: Jupiter orbit:comet orbit:Jupiter-comet plane spherical triangle.

criterion together with (4.1.47) to calculate the change $\Delta(1/a)$ in a passage:

$$\Delta\left(\frac{1}{a}\right) \approx -\frac{2n^*}{GM}\Delta H$$

$$\approx -\frac{2n^*}{GM}\int_{t_p-\Delta t}^{t_p+\Delta t}\frac{\partial F}{\partial \Omega}\,dt$$

$$\approx 4n^*a^*\frac{m^*}{M}\int_{t_p-\Delta t}^{t_p+\Delta t}\frac{r}{\rho^3}\frac{\partial(\cos S)}{\partial \Omega}\,dt \qquad (5.3.11)$$

using (5.3.1 and 4). The time limits Δt should be such that the term Gm^*/ρ in (5.3.9) neglected in (5.3.10) is negligibly small. Integrations of (5.3.11) or other forms of $\Delta(1/a)$, plus the application of statistical distributions, are unavoidably messy, but in general they obtain the result suggested by (5.3.11) that $\Delta(1/a)$ is of the order of m^*/M: that is, 10^{-3}; more precisely, as previously mentioned, $\pm0.7 \times 10^{-3}$ rms for a in AU [415, 436]. Using (5.3.10) and assuming $\Delta \cos I$ small compared to Δe and $a^*\Delta(1/a)$, we get

$$O(\Delta e) = -O[\Delta(1/a)] \qquad (5.3.12)$$

Whence for perihelion distance $q = a(1 - e)$,

$$O(\Delta q) \ll a^2O[\Delta(1/a)] \qquad (5.3.13)$$

and aphelion distance $Q = a(1 + e)$,

$$O(\Delta Q) = 2a^2\Delta(1/a) \qquad (5.3.14)$$

that is, a perturbation at perihelion causes a major change in aphelion and little change in perihelion distance. Hence as long as a cometary orbit is not perturbed to hyperbolic, it will continue to return to be perturbed again.

The perturbation at aphelion by a star has an opposite effect of greatly changing the perihelion distance while little affecting the aphelion distance.

There are two main theories of origin of comets. One theory, based mainly on the fact that the energies $1/a$ are predominantly elliptic—that is, assuming that the n_E column in Table 5.7 is applicable—is that the comets were always part of the solar system; that their aphelions were perturbed outward by planetary perturbations; and that their perihelions in turn were perturbed outward by stellar perturbations. Manifestly such a process will be inefficient in that most comets will be lost permanently. However, the total mass of the 10^{11} or so comets required is still a good deal less than the mass of one major planet. In support of this theory attempts have been made to explain residuals in the orbits of Uranus, Neptune, and Pluto by a cloud of comets beyond 40 AU of about 10 to 20 earth masses [438]. This theory was originated by Oort [295].

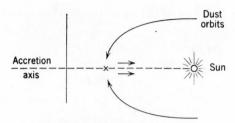

Figure 5.7: Accretion hypothesis of comet formation.

The other theory, based mainly on the fact that the energies $1/a$ are very small—that is, assuming that the n_H column in Table 5.7 is applicable—is that the comets are collected from interstellar dust. As the sun moves through a dust cloud, the dust particles describe hyperbolic orbits about the sun in a reference frame fixed with the sun, as shown in Figure 5.7. The particles thus are "focused" on the axis of the sun's motion. Impacts of particles at the axis will destroy the transverse components of velocity and reduce the energies of motion from hyperbolic to elliptic. Within a certain distance of the sun, the radial component of velocity will be less than the escape velocity, $\sqrt{2GM/r}$ (see problem 5.4), and thus conglomerations of these particles will be drawn back toward the sun. The main weaknesses of this theory are that the energy dissipated in the loss of transverse velocity would be expected to vaporize the dust, and that observed comet orbits are not nearly as often hyperbolic as elliptic. This theory was originated by Lyttleton [250].

Asteroid Orbits

The orbits of about 1600 asteroids are known; probably over 30,000 more are within reach of modern telescopes. The largest asteroid, Ceres, has a radius of 385 km; nine others are estimated to have radii of 100 km or more. Perhaps 200 have radii of more than 25 km. The mass of one asteroid, Vesta, has been estimated from orbital perturbations; combination with a radius of comparable observational uncertainty gets a density of about 8 gm/cm³ [559]. The rates of rotation of 27 asteroids are known: these periods of rotation range from 2.1^h to 16.8^h. Why asteroids rotate so rapidly is a problem; they are yet another strong contradiction of the rule shown by Figure 5.2.

The total mass of asteroids is estimated to be 10^{25} grams. Virtually all this mass is in asteroids with orbits of small eccentricity and inclination and semi-major axes between 2.1 and 3.1 AU. The most prominent dynamical property of the main body of asteroids is the distribution of their mean motions expressed as a ratio n/n^* to the mean motion of Jupiter, shown in Figure 5.8.

The mean motions in Figure 5.8 are, in terms of the theory of Section 4.1, the total mean motion $\dot{M} + \dot{\omega} + \dot{\Omega}$. If we define

$$\lambda = M + \omega + \Omega \qquad (5.3.15)$$

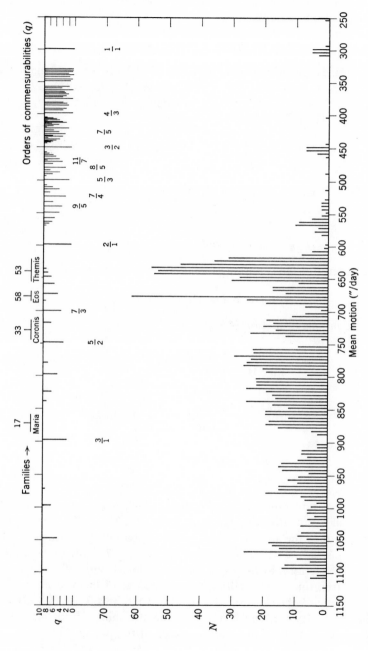

Figure 5.8: Distribution of asteroids in intervals of 5 "/day of mean motion $n \approx 0.0168$ of ratio n/n^*. From Brouwer [46, p. 158].

then for an asteroid that has a mean motion ratio n/n^* near the integral ratio k/j, the angle of interest q_1 is:

$$q_1 = j\lambda - k\lambda^* \tag{5.3.16}$$

In the third-body disturbing function form of (4.2.15) the combination of (5.3.16) occurs exactly only for $j = k$, when $(l - 2p) = (l - 2h) = m$. However, the situation is closely approximated in any case where $(l - 2p)/(l - 2h)$ is j/k. Then if

$$s = \frac{(l - 2p)}{j} \tag{5.3.17}$$

and

$$\psi = \frac{s(jM - kM^*) + \varphi}{2} \tag{5.3.18}$$

where

$$\varphi = s(j\omega - k\omega^*) + m(\Omega - \Omega^*) \tag{5.3.19}$$

a significant term of the disturbing function can be written

$$R = f(a, e, I)g(a^*, e^*, I^*) \cos 2\psi \tag{5.3.20}$$

From the equations of motion (4.1.36)

$$\dot{a} = \frac{2}{na} \frac{\partial R}{\partial M} = \frac{-2sj}{na} fg \sin 2\psi \tag{5.3.21}$$

whence

$$\ddot{\psi} = \frac{sj\ddot{M}}{2} = -\frac{sj}{2} \frac{3n}{2a} \dot{a} = \frac{3(sj)^2}{2a^2} fg \sin 2\psi \tag{5.3.22}$$

which integrates to

$$\dot{\psi}^2 = K - \frac{3(sj)^2}{2a^2} fg \cos 2\psi \tag{5.3.23}$$

The constant of integration K is an energy, which is the sum of a kinetic energy $\dot{\psi}^2$ and a potential energy $[3(sj)^2/2a^2]fg \cos 2\psi$. If this energy K is small enough, then the angle ψ cannot go through a full cycle, since $\dot{\psi}^2$ must be positive; instead, ψ will librate about the value $\pi/2$. Now in a group of asteroids characterized by mean motions in the vicinity of a particular kn^*/j, at a given time we would expect to see most of them in the vicinity where $\dot{\psi}$ is changing the slowest: that is, near where $\ddot{\psi}$ is 0. By (5.3.22), this requires 2ψ to be 0 or π, and hence $|\psi|$ to be at a minimum or maximum. The former would apply if the asteroid were not trapped in a libration; the latter, if it were trapped. The probability of trapping would depend on the magnitude of the potential "well" $3(sj)^2fg \cos 2\psi/2a^2$ relative to other disturbing potentials. We would expect this "well" to be deeper for semi-major axes closer to Jupiter's: that is, smaller values of n/n^*. This appears to be the case in Figure 5.8: the smaller ratios on the right have peaks in the distribution, whereas the larger ratios of 8/5 or more appear to coincide with hollows, indicating that $|\psi|$ is at a maximum. These hollows are known as the *Kirkwood gaps*. For these cases where a gap occurs at the commensurability, a refinement of Figure 5.8 obtains maxima near [46]

$$n = \frac{k}{j} n^*(1 \pm 0.03) \qquad (5.3.24)$$

For the larger ratios of n/n^*—smaller ratios of a/a^*—we would expect the $l = 2$ terms of the form (4.2.15) to be dominant, and hence $s(j - k)$ to be even, so that the difference $\omega - \omega^*$ would be zero for 2ψ to be zero; this effect is also observed. Also, since Jupiter's orbit is essentially the reference plane, the $sk = 2$ terms corresponding to $lmh = 220$ in (4.2.15) must have the largest coefficients. The asteroid inclinations being small, the $lmp = 220$ terms also must have the largest factor $F_{lmp}(I)$. Hence to obtain a difference

$$q = k - j \qquad (5.3.25)$$

a higher-order term must give rise to the near commensurability. The parameter q is in fact called the order of the commensurability, and is plotted along the top of Figure 5.8, since the most pronounced effects should be associated with the lowest orders. Substitution of $(1 - 2 \sin^2 \psi)$ for $\cos 2\psi$ in (5.3.23) obtains the standard form for the pendulum equation. However, the solution in the form of elliptic integrals (see problem 4.15) is not too meaningful, since for the large a/a^* involved there normally will be several significant terms of the form of (5.3.20). Hence the usual procedure is to transform the Delaunay elements, (4.1.47), and associated force function F so that the slowly changing difference q_1 of (5.3.16) is one of the angle variables; eliminate one or two pairs of variables analytically by series development, if possible; and then proceed by numerical integration, sometimes even averaging the force function numerically around the asteroid orbit and Jupiter's orbit.

In addition to the clustering of asteroid elements about certain values of the semimajor axis a, indicated by Figure 5.8, there are (after removal of periodic perturbations) clusterings with respect to eccentricity e, inclination I, and, in a few cases, $\tilde{\omega} + \Omega = \omega + 2\Omega$. Such a clustering is called a *family*. The $\omega + 2\Omega$ grouping is perhaps most interesting. If we set the inclination I equal to zero in the formulae for secular motion due to third-body perturbation, (4.2.17), we get zero for $\dot{\omega} + 2\dot{\Omega}$. Hence if a family were created by the breakup of a single asteroid, we should expect that they would drift apart much more slowly in $\omega + 2\Omega$ than in any other angle elements or combination thereof. Backward extrapolation of $\omega + 2\Omega$ for a couple of families does, in fact, indicate a coming together within the last 10^6 years [45].

Collisions

The possibility of collision between asteroids is of interest pertinent to the origin of meteorites. If we consider N asteroids of radius R to be uniformly distributed in a torus of volume V, then the probability of a collision per unit time will be

$$P = \pi R^2 \frac{U}{V} N \qquad (5.3.26)$$

where U is the average relative velocity. Taking U to be 5 km/sec (roughly one-third the Kepler orbit velocity), R to be 1 km and V to be 10^{41} cm^3 gives about 6×10^{-18} N/yr. The main limitation on N is that the total surface area of the asteroids not exceed a limit set by the *Gegenschein*, a diffuse glow of maximum intensity in a direction almost exactly opposite the sun in the night sky. This limit is estimated to be 8×10^{10} km^2. Hence if the asteroids were all of 1-km radius, the occurrence of a collision would be an extremely rare event. An increase in the probability is obtained by assuming a distribution of radii R of the form

$$dN = CR^{-p} \, dR \qquad (5.3.27)$$

A lower limit of about 10^{-5} cm on R is set by the Poynting-Robertson effect, described below. The value of p that appears to best fit the data is about 3.28. However, the data pertain to asteroids that are considerably larger than the bulk of the population important as contributors to collisions. Also p may be a function of position in the asteroid belt, because of varying probabilities of collision.

In addition, the meteorite origin question raises the problems of (1) the relative size of bodies to produce significant fragmentation, discussed in Section 7.1; and (2) the portion of bodies deflected into orbits which result in subsequent collision with the earth. The latter problem is severe for the chondritic meteorites, which, as discussed in Section 8.4, have relatively short cosmic-ray exposure ages. Hence special attention has been paid to those asteroids that have a high probability of collision with the earth. Thirty-four asteroids have been identified having orbits intersecting Mars' orbit; of these, eight, called the *Apollo group*, also cross the earth's orbit, as shown in Figure 5.9. These asteroids are also of interest as possibly being the remnants of comets.

For the dynamics of close approach to, and collision with, a planet, we require a generalization of the elliptic-orbit theory of Section 4.2 to hyperbolic

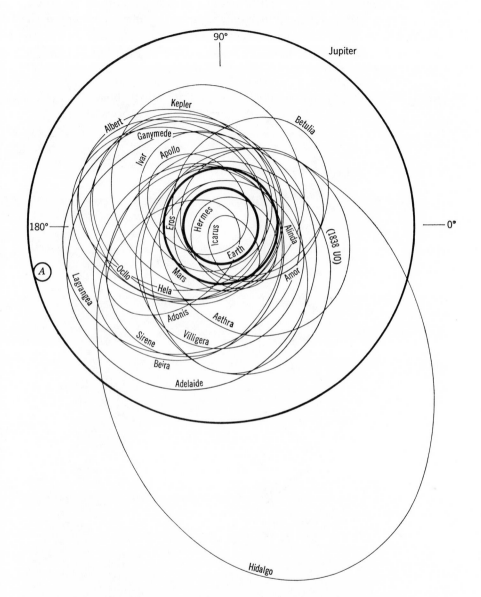

Figure 5.9: Asteroids with cometary orbits. From Richter [334, p. 26].

orbits. Equations (4.1.9) for r and (4.1.38) for v^2 still apply; from the latter, setting $r = \infty$ obtains the semimajor axis a as a function of approach velocity u:

$$a = -\frac{\mu}{u^2} \tag{5.3.28}$$

Then from the rectangular coordinate equation for a hyperbola

$$\tan \psi = -\frac{b}{a} = \sqrt{e^2 - 1} \tag{5.3.29}$$

and from the right triangle OAF in Figure 5.10

$$\sin \psi = \frac{d}{ae}$$

$$e^2 - 1 = \tan^2 \psi = \frac{\sin^2 \psi}{1 - \sin^2 \psi} \tag{5.3.30}$$

$$= \frac{d^2}{(ae)^2 - d^2}$$

whence

$$e = \left[1 + \left(\frac{d}{a} \right)^2 \right]^{1/2} \tag{5.3.31}$$

and

$$\sin \psi = \frac{1}{[(a/d)^2 + 1]^{1/2}} \tag{5.3.32}$$

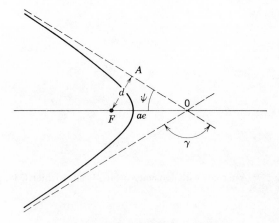

Figure 5.10: Hyperbolic orbits.

so for the deflection angle γ

$$\sin \tfrac{1}{2}\gamma = \sqrt{1 - \sin^2 \psi} = \left(1 + d^2 \frac{u^4}{\mu^2}\right)^{-1/2} \tag{5.3.33}$$

In Figure 5.10, the capture effective radius σ is the distance d, and R is the distance of closest approach, the pericenter:

$$R = a(1 - e) \tag{5.3.34}$$

Substitute for e from (5.3.31) and for a from (5.3.28):

$$R = \frac{\mu}{u^2}\left[\left(1 + \frac{4u^4\sigma^2}{\mu^2}\right)^{1/2} - 1\right] \tag{5.3.35}$$

Let s be the velocity of escape, $\sqrt{2\mu/R}$ (problem 5.4), replace μ by $Rs^2/2$ in (5.3.35), and solve for σ:

$$\sigma = R\sqrt{1 + s^2/u^2} \tag{5.3.36}$$

Instead of relative velocity of approach u we normally have the Keplerian elements of the asteroid orbit and the planet orbit. Let the x-axis of a rectangular coordinate system be the radial coordinate through the planet orbit at the point of closest approach; the z-axis, the normal to the planet orbit; and the y-axis, the tangent to the planet orbit neglecting its eccentricity. Then the components of relative velocity will be, using (4.1.4):

$$u_x = \dot{r} = \left(v^2 - \frac{h^2}{r^2}\right)^{1/2} \approx \left(v^2 - \frac{h^2}{a^{*2}}\right)^{1/2}$$

$$u_y = r\dot{f}\cos I - n^*a^* \approx \frac{h}{a^*}\cos I - n^*a^* \tag{5.3.37}$$

$$u_z = r\dot{f}\sin I \approx \frac{h}{a^*}\sin I$$

whence, using (4.1.12, 21, and 37):

$$u^2 = v^2 + \frac{h^2}{a^{*2}}(\cos^2 I + \sin^2 I - 1) - 2n^*h\cos I + n^{*2}a^{*2}$$

$$= \mu\left[\frac{2}{a^*} - \frac{1}{a}\right] - 2\mu\sqrt{a(1 - e^2)}\frac{\cos I}{a^{*3/2}} + \frac{\mu}{a^*}$$

$$= \frac{3\mu}{a^*} - \mu\left[\frac{1}{a} + 2\sqrt{a(1 - e^2)}\frac{\cos I}{a^{*3/2}}\right] \tag{5.3.38}$$

But the quantity inside the brackets of (5.3.38) is the same as the Tisserand

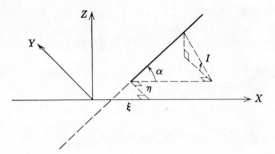

Figure 5.11: Close approach.

criterion, (5.3.10), earlier derived as constant: that is, on a close approach the total velocity u is unchanged—as would also be expected from the symmetry of the hyperbola in Figure 5.10.

From Figure 5.11 we get (see problem 5.5):

$$d^2 = \frac{\xi^2}{1 + \cot^2 \alpha \csc^2 I} \tag{5.3.39}$$

The deflection angle γ is calculable from (5.3.36) using the planet μ^* for μ, u^2 from (5.3.38) and d^2 from (5.3.39). Then for the final components $u_x{}'$, $u_y{}'$, $u_z{}'$:

$$\left.\begin{array}{c} u_x{}' \\ u_y{}' \\ u_z{}' \end{array}\right\} = \left\{\begin{array}{c} u_x \\ u_y \\ u_z \end{array}\right\} \cos \gamma - \left\{\begin{array}{c} x \\ y \\ z \end{array}\right\} \frac{\sin \gamma}{d} u \tag{5.3.40}$$

The changed elements v^2, h, I, and thence a, e can be found by inverting (5.3.37).

The value ξ of radial difference at intersection of the node will be at the true anomaly $f = -\omega$, so that, from (4.1.9),

$$\xi = \frac{a(1 - e^2)}{1 + e \cos \omega} - a^* \tag{5.3.41}$$

The possibility of significant close approach thus will depend on ω being in a certain interval $\Delta\omega$. Assuming a uniform rate $\dot{\omega}$, and assuming a certain distance $d_{\max}$ as significant for a planet, the interval $\Delta\omega$ can be expressed in terms of u, u_x, and I to obtain a probability of close approach per revolution:

$$P = \frac{d_{\max}^2 u}{\pi \sin I \, |u_x|} \tag{5.3.42}$$

Thus given orbital elements a, e, I of a small body, and a set of planets with specified d_{max}'s, an algorithm can be constructed to calculate the distribution of lifetimes per planet with mean T_i; to select a planet at random by weighting proportionate to $1/T_i$; to select at random a time t and distance d of close approach to this planet; and either to terminate with collision or to deflect, yielding new elements a, e, I and leading to a repetition of the process [18, 298, 303, 432, 433].

If the body has an orbit of appreciable eccentricity and inclination, then the aforedescribed process may have to be modified to take into account the oscillations of e and I and the nonuniform motion of perihelion, ω, as discussed at the end of Section 4.1.

The results of such statistical, or "Monte Carlo," calculations demonstrate the effectiveness of Jupiter's great capture radius, (5.3.36): the time constant for any Jupiter-crossing orbit is relatively short, about 10^6 years, while for Mars-only crossers it is on the order of 10^9 years. The time constant for the Apollo asteroids is about 10^7 years, which is in attractive agreement with the cosmic-ray exposure ages of meteorites (Section 8.4). However, there are at least three difficulties with the Apollo asteroids as sources of stony meteorites.

First, the fact that none of the eight Apollo asteroids has ever been accidentally rediscovered makes it improbable that the total number of earth-crossing asteroids of radius more than 0.5 km is over 50 (see problem 5.7). Hence the Apollo asteroids fail by about two orders-of-magnitude in providing sufficient mass yield of meteorites (see Section 8.1).

Second, if the Apollo asteroids are ordinary asteroids perturbed into earth-crossing orbits, then the population of ordinary asteroids would have to be so large that 10 to 100 times as many meteorites would be obtained directly from the main belt as would be obtained from Apollo asteroids. Such meteorites would have exposure ages on the order of 10^8 to 10^9 years, much longer than those observed. Hence a more plausible origin for both Apollo asteroids and stony meteorites is the extinct and disintegrating nuclei of comets, in particular that small part of the comet population with aphelia inside Jupiter's orbit [303, 433].

Third, twice as many chondritic meteorites are observed to fall in the afternoon as in the morning. Such a distribution requires that the majority of the meteorites overtake the earth—i.e., that their orbits have larger semimajor axes than the earth, and that they are close to perihelion at time of collision. Monte Carlo calculations further indicate that to attain a bias as high as 2:1, the perihelion must be quite close to 1.0 AU; the aphelion, quite close to Jupiter; the inclination, rather small; and the lifetime less than 10^7 years, in order that the orbit not be changed too much by planetary perturbations [539].

It is hard to find sources satisfying such severe restrictions. Periodic comet orbits with aphelia inside Jupiter are neither observed nor theoretically calculated to have a sufficient concentration of perihelia near 1 AU. Perhaps there are instabilities in the Trojan (q 1/1 in Figure 5.8) or Hilda (q 3/2 in Figure 5.8) groups which greatly enhance their probabilities of collision [539].

Dust

In addition to the separately identifiable bodies, it is evident that there are a lot of smaller particles which are loosely categorized as dust. Evidences of this dust are meteors; certain types of comet tails; impact measurements on rockets and space probes; and the *zodiacal light*: a broad, faint band of light symmetrical about the ecliptic and decreasing in intensity rapidly with increasing angular distance from the sun. The zodiacal light is caused by the scattering of solar light from dust particles.

The principal force in addition to gravitation that must be considered is that of radiation pressure. For the pressure p on a surface of reflectivity κ at angle θ to the direction of the sun, assuming diffuse reflection:

$$p = (1 + \kappa) \frac{\mathbf{s} \cdot \mathbf{n}}{c} \cos \theta \tag{5.3.43}$$

where n is the vector normal to the surface; c is the velocity of light; κ varies from 0 for perfect absorption to 1 for perfect reflection; and s is the solar flux:

$$s \approx \frac{1.4 \times 10^6}{r^2} \text{ ergs cm}^{-2} \text{ sec}^{-1} \tag{5.3.44}$$

for r in AU. The effect of the pressure in (5.3.43) is to blow away particles of large enough area-to-mass ratio A/m: that is, particles of less than about 0.5μ diameter. For particles of intermediate size, $1-800 \mu$, the Poynting-Robertson effect is important, causing them to spiral in toward the sun. This effect is most simply considered as an aberration causing a component v/c of the radiation pressure to be directed counter to a particle moving with average transverse velocity v (see problem 5.6) [344].

The Poynting-Robertson effect has long been considered an explanation of the absence of dust from the inner parts of the solar system. However, as knowledge of the interplanetary medium has improved, it appears that not only may simple mechanical drag, (4.2.13), be comparable to the *PR* drag, but also that the particle may acquire sufficient electric charge q that Coulomb drag from interaction with an electrical field $\mathbf{E}$ and Lorentz forces from interaction with the interplanetary magnetic field $\mathbf{B}$ may be significant:

$$\mathbf{F}_{EM} = q(\mathbf{E} + \mathbf{v} \times \mathbf{B}) \tag{5.3.45}$$

Estimates of q in interplanetary space are generally on the order of $+10$ volts, which makes the electromagnetic force of comparable importance to the radiation pressure for particles smaller than about 1μ [29, 308].

Particles coming within the capture radius $\sigma(u, R, M)$, (5.3.36), will collide with the earth. Their masses are estimated from their effects on the atmosphere at entry: from photography, through their brightness; or from radar, through the intensity of ionization [488]. The central portion of the curve in Figure 5.12, the meteors, is observed in this manner. At the lighter end of the meteorite range there is order-of-magnitude corroboration with photometry of the zodiacal light and microphone measurement by satellite. At the heavier end the data roughly corroborate the size distribution obtained from recovered meteorites with appropriate allowance for ablation on passage through the atmosphere (see Section 8.4) [166]. Recent measurements of acoustic waves generated by bodies entering the atmosphere indicate that the amount of ablation of the more fragile types of stony meteorites may have been greatly underestimated in the past [365].

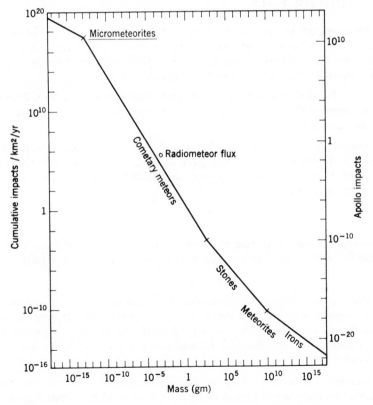

Figure 5.12: Flux of extraterrestrial objects. From Hawkins [166, p. 150].

The data summarized in Figure 5.12 are applicable to the rate of infall of bodies into the moon, and hence to the distribution of craters on the moon. Hence some of the problems associated with this application are summarized in Chapter 7.

In the early 1960's there was evidence of a concentrated dust cloud around the earth (in the sense of gm/cm^3, rather than of flux in $gm\ cm^{-2}\ sec^{-1}$). Such a cloud would require a third force, since two-body capture cannot occur except by collision, with capture radius as given by (5.3.36). The obvious force is radiation pressure. (See problem 5.9.) However, more recent observations indicate no dust concentration. These results are corroborated by theoretical analyses which conclude that nearly all particles coming into the earth from interplanetary space are on collision course, and that there should be no appreciable dust concentration caused by either the instreaming flux or by any sort of a satellite cloud bound in geocentric orbits [310, 359].

PROBLEMS

5.1. Following a procedure similar to (4.2.15–17), calculate the rates of motion of node Ω and perihelion $\tilde{\omega}$ of Mercury due to the other planets, Venus, Earth, Jupiter, etc. How do these calculated rates compare with those given in Table 5.2? Which planet's perturbation is most important?

5.2. Prove Poisson's theorem to second order, that is, that if the force function F_0 has the form of (5.1.9), then the sum of second-order terms giving rise to long periodic variations ΔL is zero.

5.3. Assume that the primordial solar system consisted of many small particles of mass m_i in Keplerian orbits of negligible inclination but appreciable eccentricity, and a distribution of semimajor axes a_i such that the density of the solar system approximated a rule

$$\rho(r) \propto \frac{\rho_0}{r^n}, \qquad n > 0$$

Assume further that each planet of semimajor axis a_p and negligible eccentricity was formed by collision of particles of perihelion distance approximating a_p:

$$a_p \approx a_i(1 - e_i)$$

and that angular momentum is conserved on collision: that is, any excess orbital angular momentum of the particles is transferred to rotational angular momentum of the planet. Is it possible to find an exponent n on the density distribution to approximate both the observed planetary distribution, (5.1.12), and angular momentum density, Figure 5.2?

5.4. Calculate the velocity of escape, that is, the minimum velocity that must be imparted to a particle at the surface of a body of mass M and radius R in order for the particle to go to infinity.

5.5. Derive equation (5.3.39): the distance of closest approach d of a small body to a planet assuming rectilinear paths as in Figure 5.11.

5.6. Derive the Poynting-Robertson effect for a circular orbit assuming that it can be treated as an aberrational effect: that is, using the radiation pressure p as given by (5.3.43) and assuming that it has a component pv/c counter to the motion v of the perihelion, derive a formula for the lifetime of a spherical particle as a function of its initial semimajor axis a, radius s, and density ρ.

5.7. Eight Apollo asteroids of radius $R > 0.5$ km have been discovered in earth-crossing orbits, but none has ever been accidentally rediscovered. Prove that the probability P that the total number of earth-crossing asteroids of $R > 0.5$ km is no greater than S will be:

$$P = \frac{(S-1)!}{S^7(S-8)!}$$

5.8. Derive a modification of equation (5.3.40) for the close-approach velocity $\mathbf{u}$:

$$\mathbf{u}' = \mathbf{u}\,\frac{d^2u^4 - \mu^2}{d^2u^4 + \mu^2} - \mathbf{d}\,\frac{2u^2\mu}{d^2u^4 + \mu^2}$$

where $\mathbf{d} = \{x, y, z\}$, the vector of position of undisturbed closest approach. Using this equation, deduce the limitations on the distribution of velocities $\mathbf{u}$ for any "focusing" effect of the earth on meteorites impacting the moon, mentioned in Section 7.2.

5.9. Estimate the magnitude of force per unit mass and "braking distance" for radiation pressure to be an effective means for interplanetary particles to be trapped into geocentric orbits. What limitation does this estimate make on the size of the particles which can be so trapped? Can there be a significant population of small enough particles?

5.10. What is the capture radius of the sun for a particle of velocity u relative to the sun? (Neglect radiation pressure effects.) Assume that the interstellar matter of density 10^{-25} gm/cm^3 *all* has a velocity u relative to the sun equal to its velocity relative to the galaxy, 30 km/sec. How much mass would the solar system acquire from this interstellar matter in 4.5×10^9 years? (Neglect temperature of the gas.)

REFERENCES

The most useful compilation of data pertaining to the solar system is *Allen* [4]. The 1964 I.A.U. astronomical constants are summarized and discussed by *Wilkins* [441]. More recent results pertaining to some of the parameters listed are from *Anderson* [17], *Ash et al.* [20], and *Vaucouleurs* [413].

In addition to the celestial mechanical texts mentioned in Chapter 4, a useful book is *Brown & Shook* [53]. A collection of recent papers is edited by *Contopoulos* [79]. A simple introduction to most of this chapter is the book by *Blanco & McCusky* [36].

The principal recent calculation of the variations in the planetary orbits over 10^6 years is by *Brouwer & van Woerkom* [50]. Reviews pertaining to planetary motions are given by *Brouwer & Clemence* [48] and *Hagihara* [155]. The Pluto-Neptune problem is explored numerically by *Cohen & Hubbard* [76] and analytically by *Hori & Giacaglia* [182]. *Ter Haar & Cameron* [396] give a summary of dynamical properties of the solar system. The tabulation of commensurabilities is by *Roy & Ovendon* [347].

Papers pertaining to tidal friction in the solar system are *Jeffreys* [198], *MacDonald* [254], *Goldreich* [139, 140], *Goldreich & Soter* [145], and *Allan* [546]. Spin-orbit coupling is investigated by *Colombo & Shapiro* [78], *Goldreich & Peale* [143, 144], *Shapiro* [502], and *Bellomo et al.* [547].

Books on comets are *Lyttleton* [250] and *Richter* [334]. Some of the statistics quoted herein are from *Porter* [321], *Oort* [296], and *Tyror* [404]. The perturbation of comet orbits by the planets and their subsequent evolution is investigated by *van Woerkom* [415], *Whipple* [435, 436], and *Brady* [40]. Other papers pertaining to the origin of comets and comets outside the planetary system are *Oort* [295], *Whipple* [438], *Öpik* [297], and *Lyttleton* [250].

Papers about the dynamics of the asteroid belt and the various commensurabilities and other regularities therein are *Brouwer* [45, 46], *Rabe* [326] (plus several earlier papers), *Schubart* [357], *Message* [276], and *Columbo et al.* [552]. Collision probabilities, lifetimes, and the possibilities of obtaining meteorites from asteroids are investigated by *Öpik* [298, 303], *Arnold* [18], *Wetherill* [432, 539], and *Wetherill & Williams* [433].

The dynamics of interplanetary dust are analyzed by *Robertson* [344], *Parker* [308], and *Belton* [29]. The infall of material to the earth is reviewed by *Hawkins* [166], and *Parkin & Tilles* [557]; acoustic-wave data pertaining thereto are referred to by *Shoemaker* [365]. See also the book by *Öpik* [299] and the reviews by *McIntosh* [488] and *Whipple* [514]. The dynamics of dust near the earth is exhaustively investigated by *Shapiro et al.* [359]; see also *Peale* [310].

In addition to the papers specifically cited, there are several reviews on subjects in this chapter in the volumes edited by *Kuiper & Middlehurst* [232] and *Middlehurst & Kuiper* [279].

Chapter 6

OBSERVATIONS OF PLANETARY SURFACES

To obtain information about any object there must be, of course, a transmission of matter or energy. In this chapter we discuss the deductions that can be made about the planets by purely energy transmissions. Such energy must be transmitted as electromagnetic waves in some part of the spectrum sketched in Figure 6.1.

The disproportionate width assigned to the narrow band "visible" in Figure 6.1 exists because (1) the output of the dominant energy source, the sun, is peaked within this band; (2) the moon and planets reflect a significant portion of this energy; (3) the earth's atmosphere is transparent in this band; and (4) a variety of sensors—the eye, the photoelectric cell, etc.—are sensitive to the visible. The relative importance of different categories of observation is a consequence of the interaction between these four factors of energy source: natural or artificial; planetary reflection, absorption, and reemission characteristics; atmospheric transfer characteristics; and sensors.

Because of the relatively low temperatures of energy sources and absorption by the atmosphere, the electromagnetic spectrum useful for studying the planets is truncated at the short wavelength, or high-frequency end; the ultraviolet and x-ray parts make no contribution. In this chapter we descend the spectrum from the visibile, or optical, for which the most power and detail is available; to the infrared, in which the energy emitted by the planets is

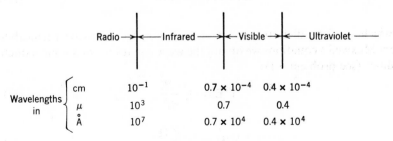

Figure 6.1: The electromagnetic spectrum.

peaked; and to the radio, for which much more sensitive detectors are available, as well as artificial energy sources. In Chapter 7 we return to more elaborate interpretation, in which the bulk of the information, and hence the context for other data, is obtained from the most detailed observations, photographs.

Planetary observations are at best marginal adventures, beset with instrumental, environmental, and interpretational difficulties. Hence, more than in other chapters, observational data should be regarded with skepticism, and theoretical models in most cases should be taken as aids toward interpreting observations rather than as conclusive explanations.

6.1 Optical Observations

Reflection and Refraction

Since light is useful in studying the planets almost entirely because of their reflecting properties, the laws of reflection of electromagnetic waves are pertinent. As with all electromagnetic waves, Maxwell's equations, previously referred to in Section 3.2, apply. Let $\mathbf{E}$ be the electric vector; $\mathbf{B}$ the magnetic vector; ρ, the density of the medium; and $\mathbf{J}$, the current intensity. Then, neglecting displacement currents, Maxwell's equations are, in cgs units [81, 190]:

$$\nabla \cdot \mathbf{D} = 4\pi\rho \tag{6.1.1}$$

$$\nabla \cdot \mathbf{B} = 0 \tag{6.1.2}$$

$$\nabla \times \mathbf{E} + \frac{1}{c}\frac{\partial \mathbf{B}}{\partial t} = 0 \tag{6.1.3}$$

$$\nabla \times \mathbf{H} = \frac{4\pi}{c}\mathbf{J} \tag{6.1.4}$$

where:

$$\mathbf{D} = \epsilon\mathbf{E}, \qquad \mathbf{H} = \frac{\mathbf{B}}{\mu} \tag{6.1.5}$$

in which ϵ is the dielectric constant and μ is the magnetic permeability. From Maxwell's equations we obtain the wave equations for a nonconducting medium (see problem 6.1):

$$\nabla^2\mathbf{E} = \frac{\epsilon\mu}{c^2}\frac{\partial^2\mathbf{E}}{\partial t^2} \tag{6.1.6}$$

$$\nabla^2\mathbf{H} = \frac{\epsilon\mu}{c^2}\frac{\partial^2\mathbf{H}}{\partial t^2} \tag{6.1.7}$$

In free space, both ρ and $\mathbf{J}$ are zero. A plane wave propagating in the z direction can then be represented as:

$$\mathbf{E} = \mathbf{E}(z, t) \tag{6.1.8}$$

whence

$$\frac{\partial \mathbf{E}}{\partial x} = \frac{\partial \mathbf{E}}{\partial y} = 0 \tag{6.1.9}$$

But

$$\nabla \cdot \mathbf{D} = \epsilon_0 \nabla \cdot \mathbf{E} = 0 \tag{6.1.10}$$

results in

$$\frac{\partial \mathbf{E}}{\partial z} = 0, \qquad E_z = 0 \tag{6.1.11}$$

Hence $\mathbf{E}$ has only x- and y-components; it is a transverse wave. Equation (6.1.3) yields:

$$c \frac{\partial E_x}{\partial z} = - \frac{\partial B_y}{\partial t}, \text{ etc.} \tag{6.1.12}$$

So far, the amplitudes of E_x, E_y are independent. The difference between E_x and E_y depends on the *polarization* of the electric wave. We are interested in what happens to components of $\mathbf{E}$, and hence to its polarization, when the wave encounters a surface: that is, an interface at which there is a change in the material properties ρ, ϵ, and μ. Assume an incident plane wave $\mathbf{E}_i$ of sinusoidal form:

$$\mathbf{E}_i = \mathbf{E}_{0i} \exp\left[j(\omega t - k_1 \mathbf{n}_i \cdot \mathbf{r})\right] \tag{6.1.13}$$

where $\mathbf{n}_i$ is the unit vector normal to the wave front, j is $\sqrt{-1}$, and $\mathbf{r}$ is the position vector. The most general forms of the reflected wave $\mathbf{E}_r$ and transmitted wave $\mathbf{E}_t$ for a plane surface will then be:

$$\mathbf{E}_r = \mathbf{E}_{0r} \exp\left[j(\omega_r t - k_1 \mathbf{n}_r \cdot \mathbf{r} + A)\right] \tag{6.1.14}$$

$$\mathbf{E}_t = \mathbf{E}_{0t} \exp\left[j(\omega_t t - k_2 \mathbf{n}_t \cdot \mathbf{r} + B)\right] \tag{6.1.15}$$

The requirement that the tangential components of $\mathbf{E}$ and $\mathbf{H}$ must be continuous across an interface in turn requires that $\mathbf{E}_r$, $\mathbf{E}_t$, $\mathbf{E}_i$ be identical functions of time and position on the interface, and that ω_r and ω_t both equal ω. If we further apply the law that the angle of reflection equals the angle of incidence, we get, taking the z-axis normal to intersection, defining θ_i as the angle of the axis of propagation thereto, and the x-axis as the intersection of the two planes (see Figure 6.2):

$$\mathbf{E}_i = \mathbf{E}_{0i} \exp\{j[\omega t - k_1(\sin \theta_i x - \cos \theta_i z)]\} \tag{6.1.16}$$

$$\mathbf{E}_r = \mathbf{E}_{0r} \exp\{j[\omega t - k_1(\sin \theta_i x + \cos \theta_i z)]\} \tag{6.1.17}$$

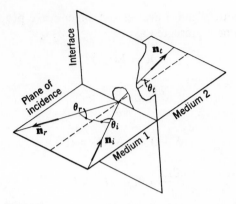

Figure 6.2: Incidence of a plane electromagnetic wave on a plane surface.

$\mathbf{E}_{0i}$, $\mathbf{E}_{0r}$, and $\mathbf{E}_{0t}$ are governed by continuity requirements and Snells' law:

$$\frac{\sin \theta_t}{\sin \theta_i} = \frac{k_1}{k_2}$$

The components normal to plane of incidence are obtained from the continuity requirements for $\mathbf{H}$:

$$\left(\frac{E_{0r}}{E_{0i}}\right)_N = \frac{\sqrt{\dfrac{\epsilon_1}{\mu_1}} \cos \theta_i - \sqrt{\dfrac{\epsilon_2}{\mu_2}} \cos \theta_t}{\sqrt{\dfrac{\epsilon_1}{\mu_1}} \cos \theta_i + \sqrt{\dfrac{\epsilon_2}{\mu_2}} \cos \theta_t} \qquad (6.1.18)$$

and the components parallel to plane of incidence from $\mathbf{E}$ continuity:

$$\left(\frac{E_{0r}}{E_{0i}}\right)_P = \frac{-\sqrt{\dfrac{\epsilon_2}{\mu_2}} \cos \theta_i + \sqrt{\dfrac{\epsilon_1}{\mu_1}} \cos \theta_t}{\sqrt{\dfrac{\epsilon_2}{\mu_2}} \cos \theta_i + \sqrt{\dfrac{\epsilon_1}{\mu_1}} \cos \theta_t} \qquad (6.1.19)$$

Solar Illumination of the Planets

Although in the case of the moon there exist both perceptible natural luminescence on the night side and reflections of artificial signals by lasers, in the category of optical observations we are concerned mainly about the variation in intensity with wavelength of the emanations from the solar source, and about the variation of the intensity of reflection both with wavelength and location on the planet. Measurement of the intensity of reflection is further classified as *photometry*, the intensity integrated over all wavelengths; *colorimetry*, the variation of intensity with wavelength; and *polarization*, the variation of intensity with direction of oscillation. All of these measurements are affected not only by the chemical composition of the surface, but also by the structure of the surface both on a fine scale—crystalline or amorphous, etc.—and on a macroscopic scale—roughness, etc.—and by the atmospheres of the planet and the earth.

The solar visible spectrum is peaked at $0.48\ \mu$. The definition of visible intensity in effect is determined by standard photometric devices with response curves of peaks and half-intensity points given in Table 6.1.

"Intensity" is thus the energy density integrated under one of these response curves. Intensity received from a body is commonly expressed in astronomy by *magnitude* m_V. For energy flux in ergs $cm^{-2}\ sec^{-1}$

$$m_V = \mu_1 - 2.5 \log_{10} E \qquad (6.1.20)$$

A more general form is:

$$m_V = \mu_1 - 2.5 \log_{10} \int E(\lambda)\ d\lambda$$

The energy density $E(\lambda)$ can be used to define the effective magnitude for a particular waveband $\Delta\lambda$.

The constant μ_1 determined by fit to several objects is -11.55 ± 0.05. The received visible flux E_V from the sun at 1.0 AU is 1.40×10^6 ergs cm^{-2} sec^{-1}. Hence, for the sun m_V is -26.8. For the moon, m_V is -12.7 [161, 413].

In defining the effective magnitude m_V of a planet we have phase angle and varying distance problems; see Figure 6.3. It is customary to correct a standard distance from both sun and earth with phase angle corrections by the formula:

$$V = V(1, 0) + 5 \log rd + \Delta m(\alpha) \qquad (6.1.21)$$

where V is the photometrically measured intensity, r and d are defined by Figure 6.3, and $\Delta m(\alpha)$ depends on (1) geometry: a function of the portion k of the visible disc which is illuminated:

$$k = \tfrac{1}{2}(1 + \cos \alpha) \qquad (6.1.22)$$

TABLE 6.1: STANDARD PHOTOMETRIC WAVELENGTHS

	Peak	Half-intensity Points	
U	$0.353\ \mu$	0.33–$0.39\ \mu$	Ultraviolet
B	0.448	0.40–0.50	Blue
V	0.554	0.51–$0.59\ \mu$	Visual
R	0.690		Red
I	$0.820\ \mu$		Infrared

and (2) diffuse reflection by surface and atmosphere. It is customary to express $\Delta m(\alpha)$ as a power series in α, determined experimentally. For α in degrees [161, 413]:

Mars $\Delta m(\alpha) = 1.50(\alpha/100°)$

Mercury: $\Delta m(\alpha) = 3.80(\alpha/100°) - 2.73(\alpha/100°)^2 + 2.00(\alpha/100°)^3$

Venus: $\Delta m(\alpha) = 0.09(\alpha/100°) + 2.39(\alpha/100°)^2 - 0.65(\alpha/100°)^3$ (6.1.23)

Earth: $\Delta m(\alpha) = 1.30(\alpha/100°) + 0.19(\alpha/100°)^2 + 0.48(\alpha/100)^3$

Moon: $\Delta m(\alpha) = 3.05(\alpha/100°) - 1.02(\alpha/100°)^2 + 1.05(\alpha/100°)^3$

The uncertainties in these formulae are appreciable: other data may give values of $\Delta m(\alpha)$ differing by as much as 0.4.

The value of $\Delta m(\alpha)$ given for Mars applies at angles $\alpha \geq 14°$. At smaller angles there is an enhancement in magnitude due to backscattering effect, similar to that described below for the moon, such that the magnitude $V(1, 0)$ is -1.73 for zero phase angle. The value given in Table 6.2 is the one compatible, however, with the $\Delta m(\alpha)$ in (6.1.23) [491]. Several planets have an intrinsic diurnal variation with rotation. In addition, the earth and Mars have annual variations; Jupiter undergoes long-periodic variations in surface features; and Uranus has an 84-year variability associated with its oblateness. Results are summarized in Table 6.2. Most of the values in Table 6.2 have a variation between different determinations on the order of 0.10.

The *color* of a planet is conventionally defined by the difference $B - V$ in magnitude of the standard blue and visual photometric responses defined by Table 6.1. For the sun, $B - V$ is 0.63. The planetary values of $B - V$ are given in Table 6.2. All the planets except Uranus and Neptune have values higher than the sun. Since the magnitude scale m is negative, these higher $B - V$ values mean that most of the planets are redder than the sun.

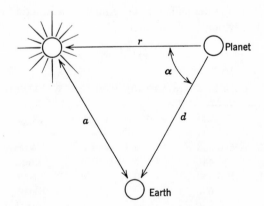

Figure 6.3: Locations defining effective planetary magnitude.

TABLE 6.2: VISIBLE MAGNITUDES AND COLORS OF THE PLANETS
AND PRINCIPAL SATELLITES

Planet	$V(1, 0)$	Diurnal Variation	$B - V$
Mercury	−0.36		0.93
Venus	−4.29	0.00	0.82
Earth	−3.87	irreg.	
Mars	−1.52	±0.15	1.36
Jupiter	−9.4	irreg.	0.83
Saturn	−8.88	0.00	1.04
Uranus	−7.17		0.56
Neptune	−6.87	?	0.41
Pluto	−1.01	±0.11	0.80
Moon	+0.21	±0.08	0.92
Io	−1.90	0.21	1.17
Europa	−1.53	0.34	0.87
Ganymede	−2.16	0.16	0.83
Callisto	−1.20	0.16	0.86
Titan	−1.16		1.30
Triton	−1.16	±0.25	0.77

From Harris [161].

Reflectivity of a Planet

From the visible magnitude of the sun, the magnitude of a planet, (6.1.21), and geometry we can deduce the portion of incident light reflected. The principal measure of reflectivity is the *Bond albedo*, defined as the total flux reflected in all directions divided by the total incident flux. Let σ be the angle subtended by the radius of a planet at distance d

$$\sigma \approx \frac{R}{d}$$

and σ_1 the angle at a distance of 1 AU. Also define $j(\alpha)\sigma_1{}^2$ as the flux per steradian in direction α from the sun. Then for the albedo A

$$A = \frac{2\pi}{\pi R^2 E_s(a/r)^2} \int_0^\pi j(\alpha)\sigma_1{}^2 \sin \alpha \, d\alpha$$

$$= \frac{2j(0)r^2}{E_s a^4} \int_0^\pi \Phi(\alpha) \sin \alpha \, d\alpha$$

$$= pq \qquad (6.1.25)$$

where E_s is the flux received from the sun at 1.0 AU.

p is the *geometrical albedo*:

$$p = \frac{E_0 r^2 d^2}{E_s R^2} = \frac{E_0 r^2}{E_s \sigma_1^2}$$

$$= \frac{10^{0 \cdot 4(m_s - m_p)}}{\sigma^2} \qquad (6.1.26)$$

where m_s and m_p are the magnitudes of the sun and planet respectively. p is the ratio of the average luminance of the planet at full phase ($\alpha = 0$) to that of a perfectly diffusing surface (Lambert surface) at the same distance from the sun and normal to the incident radiation.

q is the *phase integral*:

$$q = 2 \int_0^\pi \Phi(\alpha) \sin \alpha \, d\alpha \qquad (6.1.27)$$

The evaluation of q depends on the reflecting properties of the planet. If the planet were a perfectly diffuse reflector—that is, each element of the planet surface reflected energy uniformly over the hemisphere visible from it—it would obey the Lambert scattering law. In this case the luminance L in direction α is defined by

$$L(\alpha) = \frac{E_s}{\pi} \cos \alpha \qquad (6.1.28)$$

The resulting phase function is:

$$\Phi_0(\alpha) = \frac{1}{\pi} [\sin \alpha + (\pi - \alpha) \cos \alpha] \qquad (6.1.29)$$

whence

$$q_0 = \frac{3}{2} \qquad (6.1.30)$$

No planet is a perfect Lambert scatterer; generally Φ decreases much more rapidly with increase in α in cases where it has been measured. The magnitude phase function $\Delta m(\alpha)$ given in (6.1.23) depends on the solar magnitude and the reflectivity phase function $\Phi(\alpha)$: see problem 6.2. Results for p, q, and albedo A for visual (V) are given in Table 6.3. The estimated probable errors for the albedos of the terrestrial planets are 4 or 5 percent. The phase integrals $q(V)$ given for the four major planets are theoretical rather than observed, and are probably correct within 0.1. The $q(V)$ observed for the moon has been assumed applicable to the other satellites. Where there is an appreciable atmosphere, diffuse reflection allows for multiple scattering, leading to an apparent darkening of the limb: a considerable problem in radiative transfer [161, 413].

TABLE 6.3: PLANETARY ALBEDO

Planet and Satellite	Geometric Albedo $p(V)$	Phase Integral $q(V)$	Albedo $A(V)$
Mercury	0.104	0.560	0.058
Venus	0.650	1.087	0.705
Earth	0.367	1.095	0.36
Mars	0.194	0.88	0.171
Jupiter	0.445	(1.65)	0.73
Saturn	0.461	(1.65)	0.76
Uranus	0.565	(1.65)	0.93
Neptune	0.509	(1.65)	0.84
Pluto	0.130	(1.07)	0.14
Moon	0.115	0.585	0.07
Io	0.92	(0.585)	0.54
Europa	0.83	(0.585)	0.49
Ganymede	0.49	(0.585)	0.29
Callisto	0.26	(0.585)	0.15
Titan	0.21	(0.585)	0.12
Triton	0.36	(0.585)	0.21

From Harris [161], Vaucouleurs [413], and O'Leary [491].

Model of Scattering by the Lunar Surface

The low geometric albedos $p(V)$ and phase integrals $q(V)$ for Mercury and the moon are explicable only as a consequence of a dark material with an intricate surface structure of particles that are very small, but still large compared to the wavelength of light—on the order of 10 μ—and a large proportion of voids, as suggested by Figure 6.4. This "fairy castle" structure

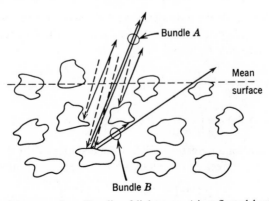

Figure 6.4: Actual lunar surface. Bundle of light rays A is reflected back unattenuated, while Bundle B is partially blocked. From Hapke [158, p. 4574].

will give a return comparable to that of a Lambert scatterer, $1.5p$, only at normal incidence; at other angles shadows cast by the structure will strongly reduce the return, thus making the surface a strong backscatterer. The mathematical model of the lunar surface proposed by Hapke [158] assumes low reflectivity, so only single scattering is important, and random orientation of reflecting objects. The principal parameters of the model are:

$n \equiv$ number of reflecting objects per unit volume.

$\sigma \equiv$ average cross-sectional area of an object.

$\tau \equiv$ mean attenuation length of a beam of light rays in the medium.

$b \equiv$ total reflectivity of an object.

$\sum (\alpha) \equiv$ scattering law of an individual object; the fraction of incident light reflected at an angle α to the incident beam.

For a given angle of incidence with respect to the normal to the mean surface θ and angle of reflection ϵ, the portion of light reflected from an object at depth z below the surface will depend not only on the medium attenuation $\exp(-z/\tau \cos \epsilon)$ but also on the geometrical blocking as indicated in Figure 6.4. The unblocked fraction $F(z, \alpha)$ will be a function of the angle α between the incident and reflected rays as well as the depth z of the reflecting element; it can be calculated for the idealized model, Figure 6.5, as the area of overlap of the two intersecting cylinders of radius y:

$$u = \frac{z \sec \theta \tan \alpha}{2y}$$

$$F(z, \alpha) = \frac{2}{\pi} [\cos^{-1} u - u(1 - u^2)^{1/2}], \qquad 0 \leq u \leq 1 \qquad (6.1.31)$$

$$= 0 \qquad\qquad u < 0, \quad u > 1$$

If the light reflected from a volume element $r^2\, d\omega\, dr$, where r is distance along the reflected ray and $d\omega$ is an element of solid angle, then the reflected intensity I for incident intensity E_0 would be

$$I = E_0 n \sigma b \sum (\alpha) a\, d\omega \int_{r=R}^{\infty} r^{-2} \exp\left(-\frac{z}{\tau}\cos\theta\right) \exp\left(-\frac{z}{\tau}\cos\epsilon\right) r^2\, dr$$

$$= E_0 n \sigma a b \sum (\alpha)\, d\omega \int_{r=R}^{\infty} \exp\left[-(r - R)(1 + \cos\epsilon/\cos\theta)/\tau\right] dr \qquad (6.1.32)$$

where a is the area of a detector and R is the distance of the detector from the mean surface. The effect of the blocking is to replace an attenuating factor

$$\exp\left[-z(\sec\theta + \sec\epsilon)/\tau\right]$$

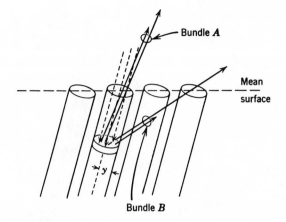

Figure 6.5: Idealized model of situation in Figure 6.4. From Hapke [158, p. 4574].

by

$$F \exp{(-z \sec{\theta}/\tau)} + (1 - F) \exp{[-z(\sec{\theta} + \sec{\epsilon})/\tau]}.$$

For reciprocity of incident and reflected rays, ϵ and θ must be equal—as will be practically the case for strong backscatters. Thence (6.1.32) becomes

$$I = E_0 n\sigma a \, d\omega b \sum(\alpha) \int_{r=R}^{\infty} \left\{ F(r, \alpha) \exp{[-(r - R) \cdot (1 + \cos{\epsilon}/\cos{\theta})/2\tau]} \right.$$

$$\left. + [1 - F(r, a)] \exp{[-(r - R) \cdot (1 + \cos{\epsilon}/\cos{\theta})/\tau]} \right\} dr \quad (6.1.33)$$

If we approximate $F(r, \alpha)$ by $1 - u$, then we get

$$I = E_0 a n^{-1/3} \omega b \left(1 + \frac{\cos{\epsilon}}{\cos{\theta}}\right)^{-1} \sum(\alpha) B(\alpha, g) \quad (6.1.34)$$

where

$$B(\alpha, g) = \begin{cases} 2 - \dfrac{\tan{\alpha} \, (1 - e^{-g/\tan{\alpha}})(3 - e^{-g/\tan{\alpha}})}{2g}, & \alpha \leq \dfrac{\pi}{2} \\ 1, & \alpha \geq \dfrac{\pi}{2} \end{cases} \quad (6.1.35)$$

and

$$g = \frac{2y}{\tau} \quad (6.1.36)$$

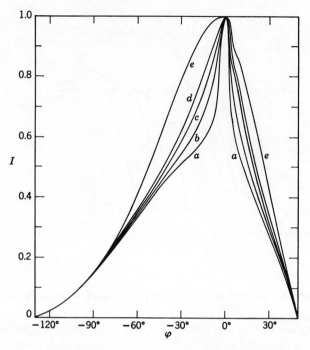

Figure 6.6: Photometric functions for a lunar area on the $\lambda = 40°$ meridian, showing the effect of the compaction parameter g on the shape of the curve: $a, g = 0.2$; $b, g = 0.4$; c, $g = 0.6$; $d, g = 0.8$; $e, g = 2.0$. From Hapke [158, p. 4577].

The principal variable remaining in (6.1.34) is the scattering function $\Sigma(\alpha)$, which depends on the microscopic properties of the reflecting particle. The law that best fits the observations for the moon is

$$\sum(\alpha) = \frac{2}{3\pi} \frac{\sin \alpha + (\pi - \alpha) \cos \alpha}{\pi} \tag{6.1.37}$$

which is the law for a sphere whose surface elements scatter according to Lambert's law—characteristic of opaque particles with fairly rough faces oriented at random.

Figure 6.6 shows the results for the amount of light reflected into a terrestrial detector from a small portion of the surface at position (λ, φ) on the moon at phase angle φ. The value of the compaction parameter g that best fits the data is 0.8.

Experiments indicate that the lunar observations, and this model which is consistent with them, are most similar to the reflecting characteristics of a layer of fine, loosely compacted dust with about 90 percent voids. (However, the porosity determined by the Surveyor landers is considerably less, so the problem must be regarded as unsolved.) At angles of more than 60°, the lunar surface model must be further modified to allow for the shadowing effect of many steep-sided (≥45°) depressions [158, 159].

Polarization

Further information on the fine structure of planetary surfaces is obtained from the polarization P, defined by:

$$P = \frac{E_x^2 - E_y^2}{E_x^2 + E_y^2} \qquad (6.1.38)$$

where E_x and E_y are the amplitudes of the two components as used in (6.1.12–19). As could be obtained by substitution in (6.1.18–19), reflection from a surface will modify the polarization dependent on the angle of incidence, θ.

In addition to the effects of (6.1.12–19), dependent on electromagnetic properties of the surface, a real surface may affect the polarization by shadowing, multiple scattering, and other effects. Hence the study of polarization of sunlight by planetary surfaces has proceeded in an experimental manner, comparing the planetary polarization with that obtained for materials in the laboratory.

The polarizations obtained for the moon, Mercury, and Mars are all rather similar. They are given in Figure 6.7.

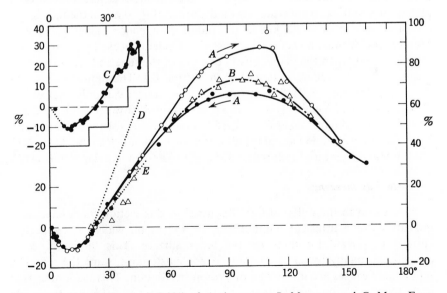

Figure 6.7: Polarization (unit 0.001) of A: the moon; B: Mercury; and C: Mars. From Dollfus [97, p. 368].

The shape of the planetary polarization curve given by Figure 6.7 is fairly well approximated in the laboratory by dark, opaque finely powdered substances, although not as high a maximum is attained. The negative dip at about 12° is apparently the consequence of diffraction or shadowing in a complex structure such as Figure 6.4. The depth of this minimum varies with both albedo and grain size. For an albedo approximating that of the moon, 0.07, the grains should not be more than a fraction of a millimeter to get the minimum of −0.010. Polarization observations are also of value to estimate the amount of atmosphere of a planet [97].

Comparison of all the optical characteristics of the moon—intensity, spectrum, and albedo as well as polarization—with those of rock and meteorite powders in the laboratory obtains a best match with iron-rich basic rocks which have been irradiated by a simulated solar wind. These results agree fairly well with the alpha-scattering results described in Section 9.1 [523].

Planetary Diameters

An optical measurement which is not as simple as it might appear is the apparent diameter of a planet. Turbulence in the earth's atmosphere, distortions of the eye and the telescope, the finite width of the micrometer wire, and darkening of the planet's limb by scattering in its atmosphere lead to uncertainties on the order of ±0.1″ in the apparent semidiameter of a planet—amounting to uncertainties on the order of ±20 km in the radius of a terrestrial planet or ±200 km in the radius of a major planet [413]. For Mercury and Venus, however, there are independent checks by photoelectric measurements when the planet passes in front of the sun, and, very recently, measurements by radar, as described in Section 6.4. The optical radius obtained for Mercury is 2440 ± 10 km, which is almost certainly that of the solid surface. For Venus, 6120 ± 10 km is obtained; however, the probable altitude of the clouds makes 6085 ± 15 km more likely for the solid surface. Mars has a perceptible flattening; allowing for its clouds leads to 3375 ± 15 km for Mars' equatorial radius and 3350 ± 15 km for the polar radius [413].

Lunar Luminescence

In addition to the reflected light discussed in this section there have been indications of a transient luminescence on the moon which recurs preferentially in certain locations on the lunar surface. This luminescence is constituted mainly by some emission bands clustering toward the red. The most likely causes are ultraviolet or proton irradiation. There is a moderate correlation of luminescence with solar activity, but not enough to decide definitely what is the predominant process [490].

6.2   Infrared Observations

Moving down the electromagnetic scale in frequency, we must become more concerned about the planets as absorbers and reemitters than as reflectors. The spectrum of the energy emitted by a body depends on its temperature. Hence we are interested in a standard of comparison for thermal emission: a model that relates temperature to energy radiation. The principal such radiation model is the blackbody, the theory of which is based on the statistical mechanical theory of ideal gases: systems of particles with negligible mutual interaction.

Blackbody Radiation Theory

A gas of identical particles in a volume V in equilibrium at temperature T has associated with it an energy per particle kT, where k is the Boltzmann constant: 1.38044×10^{-16} erg/°K. Let

$$\left. \begin{array}{l} \epsilon_r \equiv \text{energy of one particle} \\ n_r \equiv \text{number of particles} \end{array} \right\} \text{in a quantum state } r$$

$$R \equiv \text{possible quantum states of the whole gas}$$

$$\beta \equiv 1/kT$$

(6.2.1)

By a quantum state of the whole gas we mean a particular specification of the three components of momenta of all particles in the system. Then the relative probability of having the gas in state R will be [331]:

$$\exp\left(-\beta \sum_r n_r \epsilon_r\right) = P_R \tag{6.2.2}$$

The mean number of particles in a particular state s will be from all combinations containing n_s. If we assume that there is no limitation on the number of particles, that is, if we adopt *photon statistics*, then this mean number of particles will be:

$$\bar{n}_s = \frac{\displaystyle\sum_{n_s} n_s\, e^{-\beta n_s \epsilon_s}}{\displaystyle\sum_{n_s} e^{-\beta n_s \epsilon_s}}$$

$$= \frac{1}{e^{\beta \epsilon_s} - 1} \tag{6.2.3}$$

called the *Planck distribution*.

As stated, the radiation is in accord with Maxwell's laws, and hence in a vacuum the electric field must propagate in accordance with the wave equation

(6.1.6) with $\epsilon\mu = 1$. Assume a solution of the form

$$\mathbf{E} = \mathbf{A}\, e^{i(\mathbf{x}\cdot\mathbf{r}-\omega t)} \tag{6.2.4}$$

where ω is a frequency of oscillation and

$$\kappa = |\mathbf{x}| = \frac{\omega}{c} \tag{6.2.5}$$

$\mathbf{x}$ is called the *wave vector*. By the fundamental quantum law, the energy is

$$\epsilon = \hbar\omega = \hbar\kappa c \tag{6.2.6}$$

where $\hbar$ is the Planck constant divided by 2π, $6.62 \times 10^{-27}/2\pi$ erg sec. The total energy for a particle is twice its mean kinetic energy (see Section 4.1), or its momentum times velocity; hence we get for the momentum

$$\mathbf{p} = \hbar\mathbf{x} \tag{6.2.7}$$

As stated after (6.2.1), the definition of a quantum state is a specification of the three components of momentum $\mathbf{p}$. Hence the number of particles n_r or n_s in a particular state can be expressed as a function of the wave vector $\mathbf{x}$, and to obtain the total number of particles n per unit volume we can integrate over the total range of wave vectors $\mathbf{x}$ instead of summing over the total number of states s:

$$n = \int_{\text{wave vector space}} f(\mathbf{x})\, d^3\mathbf{x} = \sum_s n_s \tag{6.2.8}$$

where $f(\mathbf{x})$ is a *frequency density*.

Assuming the volume V to be an arbitrarily large parallelepiped, it can be shown that the increment $f\, d^3\mathbf{x}$ integrated over the volume V must be expressible as a product of integer increments Δn_x, Δn_y, Δn_z:

$$\int_V f\, d^3\mathbf{x}\, dv = \Delta n_x\, \Delta n_y\, \Delta n_z = \frac{Vf}{(2\pi)^3}\, d^3\mathbf{x} \tag{6.2.9}$$

But the mean number of photons per unit volume in a particular state s, or corresponding value of $\mathbf{x}$, is that given by (6.2.3), so, substituting for ϵ_s from (6.2.6),

$$f(\mathbf{x})\, d^3\mathbf{x} = \frac{1}{e^{\beta\hbar\omega} - 1}\frac{d^3\mathbf{x}}{(2\pi)^3} \tag{6.2.10}$$

This number density is related to temperature T through the factor β. For a body to be in equilibrium—that is, to have constant temperature—the flux of photons absorbed and emitted by the body must be equal. Therefore we can calculate the flux emitted by a surface element in the same manner as the flux absorbed by the surface element.

To allow for both directions of polarization of the electromagnetic wave, (6.1.8–15), multiply (6.2.10) by two. To obtain the total number of photons striking a unit of surface area, consider the flux through a solid angle $\sin\theta \, d\theta \, d\varphi$ where θ is the angle to the normal and φ is azimuth about the normal. The rate at which photons of wave vectors $\varkappa$ (or frequency ω) will strike the unit area through this solid angle is then $2cf\cos\theta \, d^3\varkappa$. To obtain an energy rate E, multiply by the energy per particle, $\hbar\omega$:

$$E(\kappa) \, d\omega(\sin\theta \, d\theta \, d\varphi) = 2\hbar\omega f(\kappa) \cos\theta \, d^3\varkappa$$

$$= 2\hbar\omega c f(\kappa) \cos\theta \, \frac{\omega^2}{c^3} \, d\omega \sin\theta \, d\theta \, d\varphi \quad (6.2.11)$$

expressing $d^3\varkappa$ in spherical coordinates and using (6.2.5) for κ.

Integrate over the hemisphere:

$$E(\kappa) \, d\omega = \frac{4\pi\hbar\omega^3}{c^2} f(\varkappa) \, d\omega$$

$$= \frac{\hbar\omega^3}{2\pi^2 c^2} \cdot \frac{d\omega}{e^{\beta\hbar\omega} - 1} \quad (6.2.12)$$

using (6.2.10). Integrate with respect to ω (best done by changing the independent variable to $\eta = \beta\hbar\omega$), and substitute for β from (6.2.1):

$$E = \sigma T^4 \quad (6.2.13)$$

where

$$\sigma = \frac{\pi^2 k^4}{60 c^2 \hbar^3} = 5.670 \times 10^{-5} \text{ erg cm}^{-2} \text{ deg}^{-4} \text{ sec}^{-1} \quad (6.2.14)$$

Equation (6.2.13) is the *Stefan-Boltzmann law*. If a body is a perfect blackbody of temperature T, then substituting in (6.2.13) gives the energy flux emitted in ergs cm^{-2} sec^{-1}. To obtain the distribution of this energy with respect to wavelength $\lambda = 2\pi c/\omega$, return to (6.2.12) and use (6.2.1 and 5) to obtain

$$E_\lambda \, d\lambda = \frac{2hc^2}{\lambda^5} \cdot \frac{1}{e^{hc/kT\lambda} - 1} \, d\lambda \quad (6.2.15)$$

A logarithmic plot of E_λ versus λ is given in Figure 6.8 [331].

The temperature T obtained from a given energy flux E by applying the Stefan-Boltzmann law, (6.2.13), is known as the *brightness temperature*. For

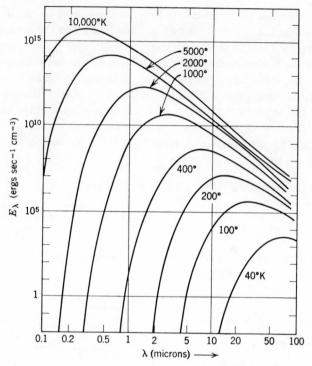

Figure 6.8: Energy spectrum for blackbody radiation. Based on Joos & Freeman [200, p. 623].

example, from the solar constant, (5.3.44), we get at the surface of the sun ($R = 0.00463$ AU):

$$E \approx 6.3 \times 10^{10} \text{ ergs cm}^{-2} \text{ sec}^{-1}$$

$$T \approx 5800°K \tag{6.2.16}$$

Thus according to (6.2.15) and Figure 6.8, the solar radiation has a peak around 0.5 μ in the visible region.

The actual temperature of the photosphere is about 200°C higher than the brightness temperature given by (6.2.16), because scattering leads to darkening of the sun's limb. Allowing for reduction in the energy absorbed due to reflection, as measured by the albedo A (6.1.25), it is also true that the actual temperatures of planetary surfaces are higher than brightness temperatures because of surface roughness, atmospheric absorption (the "greenhouse" effect), energetic particle radiation, etc. However, there is still considerable information not only in the integrated temperature T, but also in the temperature $T(\lambda)$ deduced from the energy received $E_\lambda \, d\lambda$ in a particular frequency band.

Planetary Temperatures and Diurnal Variation

Assuming that all energy not reflected is absorbed and reemitted in accordance with blackbody theory, we get for the mean temperature of a planet

$$T_M = \left(\frac{1}{\sigma} \cdot \frac{\text{energy absorbed}}{\text{surface area}} \right)^{1/4}$$

$$= \left(\frac{1-A}{\sigma} \cdot \frac{E}{a^2} \cdot \frac{\text{cross-section area}}{\text{surface area}} \right)^{1/4}$$

$$= \left(\frac{1-A}{\sigma} \cdot \frac{E}{a^2} \cdot \frac{\pi R^2}{4\pi R^2} \right)^{1/4}$$

$$= \left(\frac{E(1-A)}{4a^2\sigma} \right)^{1/4} \tag{6.2.17}$$

where E is the solar constant, 1.40×10^6 ergs cm^{-2} sec^{-1}; A is the albedo, given in Table 6.3; and a is the semimajor axis in AU. Substituting numbers,

$$T_M = \frac{(1-A)^{1/4}}{a^{1/2}} \cdot 278°\text{K} \tag{6.2.18}$$

Values of the mean temperatures of the planets from (6.2.18), together with those deduced from observations, are given in Table 6.4. Comparing with Figure 6.8 we see that planetary radiations should peak in the infrared, 2–50 μ wavelengths.

TABLE 6.4: INFRARED TEMPERATURES OF THE PLANETS

Planet	Mean T Theoretical (°K)	Observed (°K)	Equatorial ΔT Observed (°K)	Deduced Inertia, $1/\gamma$ (cal deg^{-1} sec$^{-1/2}$ cm^{-2})
Mercury	440	(min. <150°)		<0.01
Venus	229	210*	~10	
Earth	246	290	—	
Moon	273	~205	300	0.0008
Mars	216	~230	>90	0.004
Jupiter	102	150*		

* Cloud top temperatures.

If any energy absorbed was immediately reemitted, then the instantaneous temperature on the night side would be zero and on the daylight side would be for a point at ψ arc distance from the subsolar point:

$$T_D = \left[\frac{E(1 - A)}{a^2\sigma} \cos \psi\right]^{1/4} = \left[\frac{(1 - A)}{a^2} \cos \psi\right]^{1/4} 393°\text{K} \quad (6.2.19)$$

In actuality, of course, temperature variations are considerably milder on planets with atmospheres because of convective transfers of heat. Even in the case of a planet without atmosphere we should expect some modification because of transfer of heat by thermal conduction inward during the day and outward at night. If the variation of surface temperature (6.2.19) is approximated as a diurnal sinusoidal variation, at depth z there is a damping factor $\exp(-\sqrt{\omega/2\kappa}\, z)$ and a phase lag $z\sqrt{2\kappa\omega}$ (see problem 2.14), where κ is the thermal diffusivity (2.4.5). However, a sinusoid is a poor approximation to the fourth root factor in (6.2.19) for the day combined with a zero factor for the night. Instead, we must write an equation summing the energy flux at the planetary surface due to the input from the sun, $E \cos \psi/a^2$; the thermal emission, σT^4; and the thermal conduction, $K\partial T/\partial z$ [228]:

$$0 = K\frac{\partial T}{\partial z} - (1 - A_e)\sigma T^4 + (1 - A_a)\frac{E}{a^2}\cos \psi \quad \text{Day}$$

$$= K\frac{\partial T}{\partial z} - (1 - A_e)\sigma T^4 \quad \text{Night} \quad (6.2.20)$$

and solve it in conjunction with the temperature equation (2.4.4):

$$\frac{\partial T}{\partial t} = \kappa\frac{\partial^2 T}{\partial z^2} \quad (6.2.21)$$

In (6.2.20–21) the positive z-axis is inward, and we have specified separate albedos for emission A_e and absorption A_a because of the differences in the wavelengths of the radiations involved.

The solution of (6.2.20–21) must be done either numerically or iteratively. However, to get a qualitative appreciation of the effect of the material parameters K and κ, we can obtain $\partial^2 T/\partial z^2$ from the "night" part of (6.2.20) and substitute in (6.2.21):

$$\frac{\partial T}{\partial t} = \frac{\kappa}{K^2}(1 - A_e)^2\sigma^2 4T^7 = \frac{4}{K\rho C}(1 - A_e)^2\sigma^2 T^7 \quad (6.2.22)$$

using (2.4.5). Hence the greater $1/K\rho C$, the more extreme will be changes in temperature T with variations in the solar input $E \cos \psi$. The quantity

$$\frac{1}{\gamma} = (K\rho C)^{1/2} \tag{6.2.23}$$

is known as the *thermal inertia*: the smaller the inertia $1/\gamma$, the more resistant is the material to transfers of heat. Figure 6.9 is a plot of solutions of (6.2.20–21) for a point on the moon's equator for various values of γ, assuming A_a and A_e are both 0.07, as given by Table 6.3. Figure 6.9 shows that for smaller values of the inertia $1/\gamma$, not only will the temperature drop lower at night due to inability of the material to conduct heat outward, but also the temperature will rise higher during the day due to less transfer inward—the peak in Figure 6.9 is not perceptibly different from the value given by (6.2.19). The principal defect of the calculations on which Figure 6.9 is based is neglect of the temperature dependence of the conductivity K, proportionate to T^3, as in (2.4.10) [515].

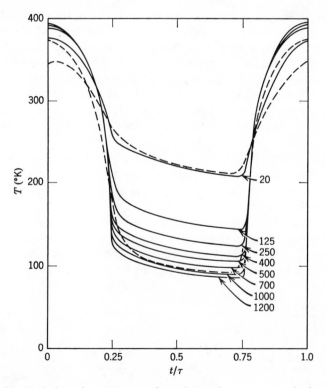

Figure 6.9: Variation of temperature of a point at the equator on the lunar surface for different values of the reciprocal of thermal inertia (in cm² sec$^{1/2}$ °C/Cal). Based on Krotikov & Troitskii [228, p. 845].

In the case of the moon, there also occur eclipses. The much sharper cutoff in illumination causes a more abrupt drop in temperature than for the lunation. Hence the eclipse curves have a more sensitive dependence on the thermal inertia $1/\gamma$ [369].

Results of Observations

The thermal inertias $1/\gamma$ deduced for Mars and the moon are extremely small. From the values given in Section 2.4, we get about 0.07 cal $°C^{-1}$ $sec^{-1/2}$ cm^{-2} as typical for earthly rocks. The lowest for materials occurring naturally on earth is 0.004 for pumice, or volcanic ash. The still lower value of 0.0008 for the moon obtained from both eclipse and lunation indicates an extremely porous material, such as has already been mentioned in Section 6.1 as indicated by the moon's reflective properties.

Infrared observations are made by a variety of techniques. A bolometer measures the increase in electrical resistance when a blackened metal foil is heated by absorbing radiation. A thermocouple measures the current generated by heating the junction of two dissimilar metals. A Golay cell measures the change in pressure caused by the heating of a confined gas. The most accurate technique now is probably the use of semiconductor (e.g., germanium) photoconducting crystals which absorb infrared photons and release a corresponding electric charge. The photoconductor device must be operated at as low a temperature as practicable to minimize "noise" from the surroundings, and should be calibrated frequently against the sky by use of a rotating chopper blade or other device in order to eliminate the background effect [286].

Besides being difficult to make, infrared observations are difficult to interpret because of absorption by both the planetary and earth atmospheres. Carbon dioxide (CO_2), water vapor (H_2O), and ozone (O_3) all have several strong absorption bands in the near infrared. Consequently, infrared observations from the earth must be made through one of the "windows" in the spectrum of atmospheric absorption shown in Figure 6.10. Another complication originating in the planetary atmosphere is limb darkening due to scattering. This effect is most pronounced on Venus, for which it amounts to about 20°C.

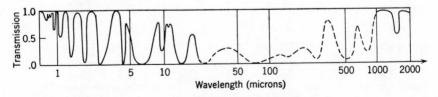

Figure 6.10: Atmospheric transmission. From *Infrared Astronomy* by B. C. Murray and J. A. Westphal. © 1965 by Scientific American, Inc.

Besides the mean temperatures and diurnal variations given in Table 6.4, appreciable variation in detail has been observed in the infrared emissions of both the moon and Venus.

The resolution of lunar observations now corresponds to about 15 km at the lunar surface, sufficient to show several hundred anomalies of more than 20°C magnitude at the time of lunar eclipse. The most striking features are hot spots associated with certain craters, some of them 40°C or more warmer than their surroundings. According to Figure 6.9, these spots must have higher thermal inertia (lower γ) than average. These craters have other evidences of being relatively new, as discussed in Chapter 7. In addition, there are several larger areas—moderate-sized maria—of about 10°C enhancement. Figure 6.11

Figure 6.11: Infrared anomalies during the December 19, 1964, lunar eclipse. Dots indicate "hot spots," lines indicate thermal enhancements. The line spacing is equal to the actual scan separation. From Shorthill & Saari [369, p. 219].

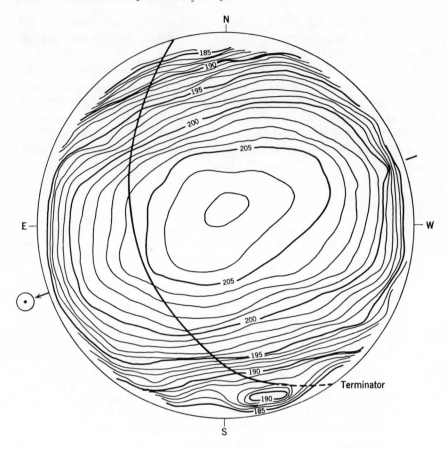

Figure 6.12: Infrared observations of Venus on December 15, 1962. Brightness temperatures in degrees centigrade. From Murray et al. [287].

summarizes the results obtained by Shorthill and Saari [369] from an eclipse in 1964 [500].

Infrared observations of Venus have been made from both the earth and the Mariner II space probe. The earth-based observations of Murray and associates [287] at 8 to 14 μ are shown in Figure 6.12. The variation of temperature with solar angle is quite mild, indicating the dominant effect of the atmosphere. Limb darkening caused by atmospheric scattering or other effects is evident. The principal anomaly, a hot spot of about 6°C near the south pole, is apparently the consequence of an atmospheric storm [287].

The Mariner II observations of Venus were made at two wavelengths: 10.4 μ, which is the middle of a CO_2 absorption band, and hence should measure cloud top temperature; and 8.4 μ, which suffers negligible atmospheric absorption, and hence should measure solid surface temperature. The latter obtained a mean temperature of 210°C.

Infrared observations of Mercury are quite difficult because of its closeness to the sun. It has been determined, however, that the minimum is something less than 150°K [527].

Reflection Spectrophotometry

In addition to the brightness temperature measurements described here, spectroscopic observations are made at infrared frequencies in order to estimate chemical composition. These observations have been principally to determine atmospheric components of Mars and Venus from H_2O, CO_2, CH_4, and N_2O absorption lines at various wavelengths between 0.8 and 5.0 μ. Of more pertinence to the solid planets are attempts to match planetary reflection spectra with those of minerals. The most detailed measurements have been of Mars at wavelengths of 0.5 to 4.5 μ. Some results have obtained a curve of albedo versus wavelength with a maximum near 0.6 μ and a minimum near 0.9 μ, similar to the curve for iron oxides hydrated in varying degrees, $Fe_2O_3 \cdot nH_2O$, called limonite. Other observations do not obtain a curve similar to that for limonite, and permit a wider variety of materials. The observations require considerable care to eliminate atmospheric effects by observing the moon or a star under as similar conditions as Mars as possible, and thus to use it as an indirect standard to compare to the sun [352, 372, 452].

6.3 Radio Emissions from Terrestrial Planets

Theory of Thermal Emission

If longer wavelength radiation is observed, we should expect that more than purely surface properties of the planet may be significant. In this case, we must consider the radiation emitted by an internal element of volume, which necessitates taking into account the absorption by the material between this element and the surface. Let the absorption per unit volume be α; then if I_0 is the initial intensity of radiation in energy rate per unit area per steradian, the intensity I after a distance x will be [315]:

$$I = I_0 \, e^{-\alpha x} \tag{6.3.1}$$

To obtain the attenuation factor α, replace the current $\mathbf{J}$ in the last of Maxwell's equations, (6.1.4), by Ohm's law:

$$\mathbf{J} = \sigma \mathbf{E} \tag{6.3.2}$$

where σ is the conductivity (not the Stefan-Boltzmann constant), and replace the sinusoidal assumption, (6.1.13), by a damped sinusoidal solution:

$$\mathbf{E} = \mathbf{E}_0 \exp(-\alpha \mathbf{n} \cdot \mathbf{x}) \exp[j(\omega t - k\mathbf{n} \cdot \mathbf{x})] \tag{6.3.3}$$

where $\mathbf{n}$ is the direction cosine of the wave.

The result for a poor conductor ($\sigma \ll \omega\epsilon/4\pi$) is [190]:

$$\alpha \approx \frac{2\pi}{c}\sqrt{\frac{\mu}{\epsilon}}\,\sigma = \frac{\sqrt{\mu\epsilon}}{c}\,\omega \tan\varphi \tag{6.3.4}$$

where φ is the loss angle, $\tan^{-1}\alpha/k$. Such proportionality of attenuation to frequency ω is observed in experiments on terrestrial rocks.

Consider the radiation in an elemental solid angle $d\Omega$ at angle θ to the normal emerging through an element of planetary surface area da, as shown in Figure 6.13. Define an element of volume by the intersection of the plane $x, x + dx$ with the solid angle $d\Omega$. The contribution of this element of volume to the radiation emitted through da will be

$$K\,dx(x\sec\theta)^2 \sec\theta\,d\Omega\,d\zeta \exp\left(-\int_0^x \alpha\sec\theta\,dx\right) \tag{6.3.5}$$

where K is the radiation per unit volume per unit solid angle within the relevant frequency limits, and $d\zeta$ is the solid angle subtended by da at the volume element:

$$d\zeta = \frac{da\cos\theta}{(x\sec\theta)^2} \tag{6.3.6}$$

Substituting (6.3.6) in (6.3.5) and integrating with respect to x obtains for the total intensity through da in direction θ:

$$I = d\Omega\,da \int_0^\infty K \exp(-\alpha x \sec\theta)\,dx \tag{6.3.7}$$

To obtain the radiation K, we can take advantage of the fact that the radio frequencies ω are small enough that in (6.2.12) $\exp(\beta\hbar\omega)$ can be replaced by $1 + \beta\hbar\omega$. Thence, using (6.2.1), we get

$$E_\omega\,d\omega = \frac{k\omega^2\,d\omega}{2\pi^2 c^2}\,T$$

$$= 2\pi q(\omega)\,d\omega T \tag{6.3.8}$$

known as the *Rayleigh-Jeans law*. (In Figure 6.8, we are off to the right of the graph, where all the lines are straight.) Now E_ω was the energy emitted by a blackbody into a vacuum, in which there is no attenuation. In thermodynamic equilibrium, the energy received is equal to the energy emitted. But the energy received by the volume element in Figure 6.13 from like adjacent

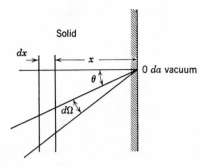

Figure 6.13: Electromagnetic radiation from within a body.

volume elements is reduced by the attenuation per unit volume factor α, so the same must apply to the emitted energy per interval of frequency $d\omega$, K:

$$K = \alpha q T \tag{6.3.9}$$

(the 2π in (6.3.8) has disappeared because E_ω was for a hemisphere rather than for a unit solid angle). So (6.3.7) becomes

$$I = d\Omega \, da\alpha q \int_0^\infty T(x) \exp\left(-\alpha x \sec\theta\right) dx \tag{6.3.10}$$

If $T(x)$ were a constant T_B, then (6.3.10) would integrate to the radiation of a blackbody, in which the attenuation α cancels out:

$$I_B = d\Omega \, daq T_B \cos\theta \tag{6.3.11}$$

Following convention, instead of intensity I use the corresponding apparent brightness temperature T_ω, adding the subscript ω to emphasize that it is dependent through the attenuation α on frequency [315]:

$$T_\omega = \frac{T_B}{I_B} I = \alpha \sec\theta \int_0^\infty T(x) \exp\left(-\alpha x \sec\theta\right) dx \tag{6.3.12}$$

Penetration of Diurnal Variation

The actual temperature $T(0)$ at the surface is given by the solution of (6.2.20–21), and will be a curve such as one of those given in Figure 6.9. This curve can be represented by a Fourier series:

$$T(0) = T_0 + \sum_{n=1}^\infty T_n \cos n\omega_s t \tag{6.3.13}$$

where ω_s is the rate of rotation of the planet with respect to the mean sun.

Then for $T(x)$, making a solution similar to problem 2.14,

$$T(x) = T_0 + \sum_{n=1}^{\infty} T_n \exp\left(-\beta_n x\right) \cos\left(n\omega_s t - \beta_n x\right) \qquad (6.3.14)$$

where, using (2.4.5) and (6.2.23),

$$\beta_n = \sqrt{\frac{n\omega_s}{2\kappa}} = \sqrt{\frac{n\omega_s}{2}}\frac{1}{K\gamma} \qquad (6.3.15)$$

κ is the diffusivity, (2.4.5). Let $T(x)$ be represented by only the $n = 0$ and 1 terms, and substitute in (6.3.12):

$$T_\omega = \alpha \sec\theta \int_0^\infty \left[T_0 + T_1 e^{-\beta x} \cos\left(\omega_s t - \beta x\right)\right] e^{-\alpha x \sec\theta}\, dx \qquad (6.3.16)$$

which may be integrated (problem 6.9) to:

$$T_\omega = T_0 + \frac{T_1}{(1 + 2\delta + 2\delta^2)^{1/2}} \cos\left(\omega_s t - \Phi\right) \qquad (6.3.17)$$

where

$$\delta = \frac{\beta}{\alpha}\cos\theta \qquad (6.3.18)$$

and

$$\tan\Phi = \frac{\delta}{1 + \delta} \qquad (6.3.19)$$

The parameter δ depends on the ratio of thermal attenuation β to electromagnetic attenuation α. It can also be expressed as the ratio of the electromagnetic penetration depth l_e to the thermal penetration depth l_t; using (6.3.4),

$$\delta = \frac{l_e}{l_t} \propto \omega^{-1} \propto \lambda \qquad (6.3.20)$$

Hence for increasing wavelength λ we should expect a decrease in the amplitude of the diurnal oscillation of the apparent brightness temperature T_ω, from (6.3.17), and an increase in its phase lag, from (6.3.19). Further, if the sole source of heat is the sun and if the albedo A_e in (6.2.20) is constant, we should expect the same mean temperature T_0 at all wavelengths.

The body for which the most detailed observational data is available is, of course, the moon. As has been indicated both by the backscattering of light and the great amplitude of the monthly variation of infrared temperatures, the moon apparently is covered by a layer of such high porosity that it is unlikely to be very thick. Hence the foregoing treatment should be modified to take into account the additional layer. Furthermore, the porosity of the layer makes it likely that the albedo A_e—or rather the reflectivity R, in radio terminology—will differ from that for the visible. The resulting modification of (6.3.17):

$$T_\omega = (1 - R)\left[T_0 + \frac{T_1}{(1 + 2\delta_s + 2\delta_s^2)^{1/2}(1 + 2\delta + 2\delta^2)^{1/2}}\cos(\omega_s t - \Phi - \Phi_s)\right]$$

$$(6.3.21)$$

where the s-subscripted quantities refer to the surface layer. The normal reflectivity R is related to the dielectric constant by (6.3.22), which is derived from (6.1.18–19), with unit permeability μ:

$$\dot{R} = \left(\frac{\sqrt{\epsilon} - 1}{\sqrt{\epsilon} + 1}\right)^2 \qquad (6.3.22)$$

The dielectric constant ϵ of porous material of density ρ is related to the constant ϵ_0 of the solid material (of density ρ_0) by:

$$\epsilon = \epsilon_0\left[1 - \frac{3p}{[(2\epsilon_0 + 1)/(\epsilon_0 - 1)] + p}\right] \qquad (6.3.23)$$

where porosity $p = 1 - (\rho/\rho_0)$ [228, 401].

Results of Observations of the Moon

The principal results from observations of the moon are summarized in Table 6.5. The values given in the table are those in (6.3.24) for a point on the lunar equator, to which actual observations can be reduced using the θ dependence expressed by (6.3.18):

$$T_e = T_{e0} + T_{e1}\cos(\omega_s t - \Phi_e) \qquad (6.3.24)$$

The measurement errors in Table 6.5 are those given by several observers. Since measurements at such low power levels are difficult and subject to systematic error, it is not surprising that the discrepancies are greater than would be expected from the quoted uncertainties. The principal difficulty is obtaining an adequate calibration for the lunar emission as contrasted to that of the sky background (which exceeds that of the moon for wavelengths more than 100 cm). Some of the inferences which have been drawn from the data follow [101, 410].

1. The amplitude T_{e1} and phase lag Φ_e of the monthly variation observed at wavelengths up to 30 cm are consistent with a porous surface layer of thickness 6($\pm$3) meters and a thermal inertia $1/\gamma$ of $1/600(\pm200)$. The density of this layer is about 1.0 gm/cm³. In the outermost 4 cm or so the density

TABLE 6.5: OBSERVED LUNAR RADIO EMISSION

λ (cm)	T_{e0} (°K)	T_{e1} (°K)	Φ_e (deg)	Measurement Error ($\pm\%$)
0.13	219	120	16	15
0.30	206	61	22	5
0.40	204	56	23	4
0.80	211	40	30	15
0.86	180	35	35	15
1.25	215	36	45	10
1.63	207	32	10	3
2.00	190	20	40	7.5
3.15	195	12	44	15
3.2	216	16	15	3
9.4	220	5.5	5	5
9.6	218	7	40	2.5
10.3	207			15
11.0	214			12
14.2	221			3.5
21	250	≤ 5		15
23	254	≤ 6.5		15
35	236			4
36	237			3
50	240			5
70.16	217			8
168	233			4

Based on Troitskii [410, p. 379] and Drake [101, p. 281].

appears to decrease to 0.6 gm/cm³ and γ correspondingly increase to 1000. Other indicators of the properties in the outer few centimeters are the magnitude of higher terms than T_{e1} in the Fourier spectrum at wavelengths of 3.2 cm or less. Figure 6.14 shows the variation in T_e observed at 0.30 cm; although the curve has considerably less amplitude than surface temperatures, such as those shown in Figure 6.9, it still has a sharp rise in temperature at dawn. Observations of the change in radio emission at lunar eclipses also lead to a high value around 1000 of the thermal parameter γ.

2. The reflectivity R of the moon is even lower at radio frequencies than in the visible, as deduced from polarization measuements as well as the constant component, monthly variation, and variation over the disc of the radio temperature. Up to 12-cm wavelength, the reflectivity is only about 0.02. At longer wavelengths there is a moderate increase to 0.04 for $\lambda > 33$ cm. The corresponding dielectric constants ϵ are 1.7 and 2.25 respectively. The

variations of reflectivity with location on the disc appear to have some correlation with the variations of infrared temperature.

3. The mean temperatures T_{e0} in Table 6.5 appear to show an increase with wavelength λ on the order of $0.6°K/cm$. Such an effect could very likely be caused by calibration errors, but if the rise is real, then it can be explained only as a consequence of an increase in temperature with depth, since it is too large and of the wrong sign to attribute to variation of reflectivity with wavelength. So

$$\frac{dT}{dz} \approx \frac{dT_{e0}/d\lambda}{dl_e/d\lambda}$$

$$= \frac{dT_{e0}/d\lambda}{l_t m} \tag{6.3.25}$$

using (6.3.20) with

$$m = \frac{\delta}{\lambda} \tag{6.3.26}$$

To deduce l_t, or $1/\beta_1$, from (6.3.15), we need an estimate of the diffusivity κ, or of the conductivity K, since κ is $K^2\gamma^2$. The one quantity that seems reasonable to extrapolate from terrestrial data is the heat capacity, whence using 600 for γ, 1.0 for ρ, and (Section 2.4) 0.25 for C,

$$K = \frac{1}{\gamma^2 \rho c} \approx 10^{-5} \text{ cal cm}^{-1} \text{ °C}^{-1} \text{ sec}^{-1} \tag{6.3.27}$$

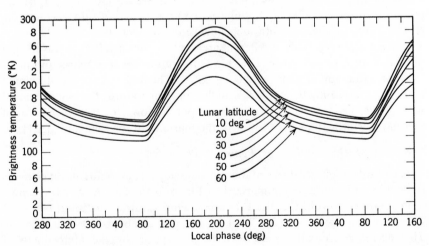

Figure 6.14: Observations of lunar equator brightness temperature at 0.30-cm wavelength over 50 days. From Drake [101, p. 282].

and

$$l_t = \frac{1}{\beta_1} = \sqrt{\frac{2}{\omega_s}} \, K\gamma \approx 10 \text{ cm} \qquad (6.3.28)$$

The value of m deduced from the data in Table 6.5 is about 2 cm^{-1}, whence from (6.3.25)

$$\frac{dT}{dz} \approx \frac{1}{20} \frac{dT_0}{d\lambda} \approx 0.03°\text{C/cm} \qquad (6.3.29)$$

From (2.4.1) the mean heat flow, using (6.3.15 and 25)

$$q = K \frac{dT_0}{dz}$$

$$= \sqrt{\frac{\omega_s}{2}} \frac{l_t}{\gamma} \cdot \frac{1}{l_t m} \frac{dT_0}{d\lambda}$$

$$= \sqrt{\frac{\omega_s}{2}} \frac{1}{\gamma m} \frac{dT_0}{d\lambda} \approx 10^{-6} \frac{dT_0}{d\lambda}$$

$$\approx 0.6 \times 10^{-6} \text{ cal cm}^{-2} \text{ sec}^{-1} \qquad (6.3.30)$$

This heat flow is about two-fifths of that observed on earth. However, since on the moon the ratio of surface area to mass, $4\pi R^2/M$, is about six times as much, the heat flow expected should be only one-sixth of the earth's. It is obvious that a more accurate value of $dT_0/d\lambda$ is needed [101, 401]. Furthermore, the foregoing theory should be reexamined taking into account the temperature, and hence depth, dependence of conductivity.

4. Recent observations of different areas on the moon at 0.3 cm wavelength obtain an average difference $\Delta T(\varphi)$ in temperature between maria and highlands as a function of phase of 2.6° ± 0.2°K. The difference in albedo would make the maria only 0.8° ± 0.3°K higher in temperature; the balance could be explained by a dielectric constant ϵ about 0.2 lower or by a reciprocal of thermal inertia γ 16 percent lower in the maria than the highlands [521].

Results of Observations of Venus

The results of observations of thermal emissions from Venus at wavelengths from 0.13 to 68 cm are summarized in Figure 6.15. The most marked phenomenon is a drop in the disc brightness temperature from about 600°K at 2 cm wavelength to about 350°K at 0.8 cm, and to about 300°K at 0.13 cm. This decrease generally is ascribed to absorption by the atmosphere of radiation from the solid surface: most likely by dust particles or cloud particles (ice crystals or water droplets). Absorption by water vapor is ruled out by the absence of any pronounced dip in the brightness temperature

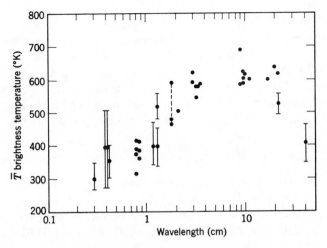

Figure 6.15: Observed mean brightness temperatures of Venus. From Barrett [24, p. 1568].

near 1.35 cm wavelength, where a resonance would be expected. Observations at 1.9 cm by Mariner II (of validity questioned by some) indicate a strong limb darkening which makes cloud particles the most likely absorbers. The strongest evidence that the emission is from the solid surface, rather than from an ionosphere, is its very slight polarization, only 0.008 ± 0.005 estimated at 10.6 cm (6.1.31). The estimated dielectric constant ϵ is 2.2 ± 0.2, indicating some porosity of the surface. Phase effects in the brightness temperature of Venus are given by:

$$\bar{T}_B(0.8 \text{ cm}) = 427°\text{K} + 41 \cos (\Phi - 21°)°\text{K}$$

$$\bar{T}_B(3.15 \text{ cm}) = 621(\pm 7)°\text{K} + 73(\pm 9) \cos [\Phi - 11.7°(\pm 33°)]°\text{K} \quad (6.3.31)$$

$$\bar{T}_B(10 \text{ cm}) = 622(\pm 6)°\text{K} + 41(\pm 12) \cos [\Phi - 21°(\pm 9°)]°\text{K}$$

An analysis of the 3.15 and 10 cm observations similar to that which has been applied to the moon, (6.3.12–20), shows that the surface properties of Venus are similar to those of the moon, and that the periodic variations are consistent with the slow retrograde rotation. The estimated surface temperatures are thus: mean disc, 700°K; mean darkside, 600°K; mean brightside, 800°K; subsolar point, 1000°K; antisolar point, 610°K; pole, 470°K [319]. These calculations are confirmed by interferometric observations at 10.6 cm wavelength, which indicate that the poles are about 25 percent cooler than the equator [516].

Not well explained is the apparent decrease in temperature from 10 to 70 cm wavelength; an internal interface between materials of differing dielectric, causing reflection of some radiation, has been suggested.

Observations of Other Planets

Observations of the temperature of Mars do not yet yield any information beyond that the mean temperature is about the blackbody value of 216°K given in Table 6.4, as expected for such a rapidly rotating object: see Table 6.6.

Observations of Mercury are difficult because its closeness to the sun does not permit measurements near 0° or 180° plase angle. Measurements at 3.4 mm obtain a brightness temperature I_B varying with solar phase angle Φ of:

$$\bar{T}_B(0.34 \text{ cm}) = 277(\pm 12)°\text{K} + 97(\pm 17)\cos[\Phi + 29°(\pm 10°)]°\text{K} \quad (6.3.32)$$

However, measurements at 1.9 cm give a diurnal amplitude of 75°K, too great to reconcile with a simple model such as in (6.3.1–19), despite the complications introduced by the long days (174 earth days) and orbital eccentricity [24, 210, 319, 467]. A thermal inertia of about 0.002 cal °C^{-1} cm^{-2} sec$^{-1/2}$ is inferred [526].

Observations of Jupiter

The most spectacular planetary emission is that of Jupiter. But the marked properties of Jupiter's radiation are definitely a consequence of its source being energetic particle interactions in the magnetosphere rather than thermal emission from the surface. The radio emission from Jupiter has two distinct parts: (1) At wavelengths of 1–150 cm, the radiation is steady, of predominantly linear polarization, from a source several times more extended than the planet. The source generally is believed to be electrons gyrating in Jupiter's magnetic field. (2) At wavelengths more than about 7 meters, the radiation is sporadic, elliptically polarized, and often very intense. This

TABLE 6.6: OBSERVED MARTIAN RADIO EMISSION

Wavelength, λ (cm)	Mean Brightness, T (°K)
0.8	225 ± 10
3.14	211 ± 20
3.75	185 ± 15
6.0	192 ± 26
10.0	177 ± 17
11.0	162 ± 18
12.5	225 ± 39
21.0	190 + 41

Based on Barrett [24] and Kellerman [210].

emission has a pronounced peak at 15 meters, but there are other peaks. It has variations correlated with the rotation of Jupiter and the orbital revolution of Io. The size of the source of this long wave radiation is rather limited in magnitude: less than 5″ angle, or on the order of a tenth of Jupiter's radius. The nature of the source is still poorly understood: a coherent emission, either from a large number of energetic particles in the ionosphere or some sort of interaction between nonelectromagnetic waves that produces electromagnetic waves.

Because planetary emissions constitute a rather minor portion of the interesting fields of study opened up by the great development of radio astronomy in recent years, the refinement and detailing of their observation as well as their interpretation is in a considerable state of flux at present.

6.4 Radar

Signal Transmission and Reflection

Provided sufficient power is available, it should be expected that different information would be obtained by generating a radio signal artificially rather than depending on natural emission. A transmitter sending a power P_t into an antenna will generate a flux density F_t at distance r of:

$$F_t = \frac{P_t G}{4\pi r^2} \tag{6.4.1}$$

where G is the *gain* of the antenna over isotropic radiation. For an antenna with aperture of area A and wavelength of radiation λ,

$$G = p \frac{4\pi A}{\lambda^2} \tag{6.4.2}$$

where p is an efficiency factor: 0.50 to 0.65 for a parabolic antenna.

The total power P_p reflected by a planet of radius a at distance r then will be:

$$P_p = \frac{P_t G}{4\pi r^2} R\pi a^2 \tag{6.4.3}$$

where R is the reflectivity at normal incidence, related to the dielectric constant ϵ by (6.3.22). The flux F_r received at the earth then will be:

$$F_r = \frac{P_t G g}{(4\pi r^2)^2} R\pi a^2 \tag{6.4.4}$$

where g is a directivity factor dependent on the reflective properties of the planet. The flux (6.4.4) is integrated over the same antenna area A as for the transmission to obtain the power received P_r; substituting for G from (6.4.2)

$$P_r = \frac{P_t A^2 R g a^2}{4\lambda^2 r^4}$$ (6.4.5)

This received power must exceed a noise power P_n:

$$P_n = [(n-1)T_0 + T_a]kb$$ (6.4.6)

where T_0 is the instrumental temperature; n is a receiver noise factor; T_a is the brightness temperature of the background sky; k is Boltzmann's constant; and b is the energy bandwidth of the receiver. The sky brightness T_a is a function of wavelength λ approximately according to the empirical rule:

$$\log T_a \approx (2.5 \log \lambda - 2.7 \pm 0.6)$$ (6.4.7)

for λ in centimeters and T_a in degrees Kelvin. The energy bandwidth b is defined as the range of frequencies admitted by the filters of the receiver. The practical limitation on reducing the bandwidth is that it can be done only by lengthening the radar pulse, which in turn reduces the radiated power P_t.

Furthermore, if the planet is rotating there is a frequency broadening due to the difference in rate of motion relative to the earth of opposite sides of the planet. For a radar beam wider than the planet, the bandwidth is:

$$b = \frac{4\omega_s R}{\lambda}$$ (6.4.8)

where ω_s is the planet's rotation rate. This frequency broadening is in addition to the Doppler frequency shift due to the orbital motion of the planet and the earth's rotation.

If the planet were a specularly reflecting sphere, only the closest point would reflect a signal. In actuality, a signal will be received at later times from other parts of the planetary surface because (1) it will be, to some extent, a diffuse reflector; and (2) it will be imperfectly spherical, so that at a given arc distance φ from the nearest point an enhanced signal will be received from areas with slopes of about φ with respect to the horizontal from the closest point. The summation of these effects is the directivity factor g in (6.4.4–5); in practice, of course, as much detail as possible of the wavetrain is analyzed. Finally, the polarization of the signal will be affected by reflection in accordance with (6.1.18–19).

All the aforedescribed effects—directly factor g, reflectivity R, Doppler frequency shift, rotational frequency broadening, polarization, etc.—are useful to deduce information about the planet, particularly if frequency dependent. Furthermore, the range in combination with the rotational contribution to the Doppler shift can be used to map particular features on the surface [580].

Theory of Backscattering by a Planetary Surface

The principal theoretical difficulty involving planetary properties is accounting for the backscattering at specified angles to the incident ray and the normal as a function of both dielectric and geometrical properties of the surface. The basis of most approaches to the problem is the Kirchhoff (or Helmholtz) diffraction integral. Let E be some quantity that satisfies the wave equation [26]:

$$\nabla^2 E + k^2 E = 0 \tag{6.4.9}$$

and let

$$\psi = \frac{e^{ikr}}{r} \tag{6.4.10}$$

where r is distance from an arbitrarily selected point P. Surround the point P by a small sphere S_1 of radius R. Let S be any other closed surface completely bounding S_1. Then, in the volume bounded by S and S_1, ψ as well as E will satisfy the wave equation (6.4.9), and hence the left side of Green's second theorem (see problem 6.11) will vanish. Thus, from the right side,

$$\int_S \left(E \frac{\partial}{\partial n} \frac{e^{ikr}}{r} - \frac{e^{ikr}}{r} \frac{\partial E}{\partial n} \right) d\sigma + \int_{S_1} \left(E \frac{\partial}{\partial n} \frac{e^{ikr}}{r} - \frac{e^{ikr}}{c} \frac{\partial E}{\partial n} \right) d\sigma = 0 \tag{6.4.11}$$

where $\partial/\partial n$ is the derivative normal to the surface. Calculate the second integral:

$$\int_S (\cdots) \, d\sigma = 4\pi R \, e^{ikR} \int_{S_1} \left[\left(ik - \frac{1}{R} \right) E - \frac{\partial E}{\partial n} \right] d\sigma \tag{6.4.12}$$

whence

$$\lim_{R \to 0} \int_{S1} (\cdots) \, d\sigma = -4\pi E(P) \tag{6.4.13}$$

and

$$E(P) = \frac{1}{4\pi} \int_S \left(E \frac{\partial}{\partial n} \cdot \frac{e^{ikr}}{r} - \frac{e^{ikr}}{r} \cdot \frac{\partial E}{\partial n} \right) d\sigma \tag{6.4.14}$$

Since the point P was arbitrarily selected, (6.4.14) will give the solution of the wave equation (6.4.9) at any point interior to a surface S over which the function and its normal derivative are known.

The Kirchhoff integral is easily extended to surfaces that are not closed, by considering them as being "closed" by another surface of zero reflection coefficient, or so distant as to be of negligible influence in the vicinity of the part of interest. Thus the backscattered radiation E_R at any point can be calculated if the field and its normal derivative are specified on the surface. If the surface is approximately plane—that is, if the radius of curvature of the surface is large compared to the wavelength—then the plane reflection formulas, (6.1.18–19) apply. The field on S will be a combination of the incident and reflected fields:

$$E_S = (1 + Q)E_i \qquad (6.4.15)$$

whence:

$$\left(\frac{\partial E}{\partial n}\right)_S = (1 - Q)E_i \mathbf{k}_i \cdot \mathbf{n} \qquad (6.4.16)$$

where Q is the reflectivity of the field, E_i is the incident field, $\mathbf{k}_i$ is its wave vector, and $\mathbf{n}$ the local normal vector, as shown in Figure 6.16. To minimize geometrical complications, we consider a one-dimensional model. Let $\mathbf{k}_r$ be the wave vector of the reflected ray; then the distance r in (6.4.14) to the observation point P can be written [153]

$$k_r r = k_r r_0 - \mathbf{k}_r \cdot \mathbf{r}' \qquad (6.4.17)$$

where $\mathbf{r}'$ is the vector from the origin to the reflection point. Then if $r \gg r'$, we can write:

$$\psi = \frac{e^{ik_r r}}{r} = \frac{e^{ik_r r_0}}{r_0} e^{-i\mathbf{k}_r \cdot \mathbf{r}'} \qquad (6.4.18)$$

Substitute (6.4.15, 16, and 18) in (6.4.14) (and set $\mathbf{r} = 0$ in the integrand):

$$E_R(\varphi, r_0) = \frac{e^{ik_r r_0}}{4\pi r_0} \int_S E_i[Q(\mathbf{k}_i - \mathbf{k}_r) - (\mathbf{k}_i + \mathbf{k}_r)] \cdot \mathbf{n}\, e^{-i\mathbf{k}_r \cdot \mathbf{r}'}\, ds \qquad (6.4.19)$$

Assuming E_i to have the sinusoidal form, (6.1.13), gives in the coordinate system of Figure 6.16 at the reflection point:

$$E_i = E_0 \exp(i\mathbf{k}_i \cdot \mathbf{r}') = E_0 \exp[ik_i(h \cos\varphi - x \sin\varphi)] \qquad (6.4.20)$$

Since the receiver is at the same location as the source, we can write:

$$\mathbf{k}_i = -\mathbf{k}_r = \mathbf{k} \qquad (6.4.21)$$

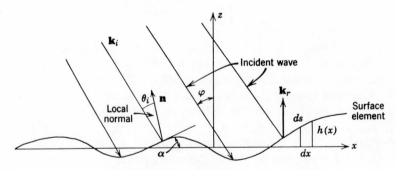

Figure 6.16: Geometry of radiation incident on an undulating surface. From Hagfors [153, p. 3780].

Substitute (6.4.21) into (6.4.20) and both into (6.4.19)

$$E_R(\varphi, r_0) = \frac{E_0 e^{-ikr_0}}{2\pi r_0} \int_S Q(\theta_i) \cos \theta_i \exp[-2ik(x \sin \varphi - h \cos \varphi)] \, ds \quad (6.4.22)$$

The signal received from a point at angle φ from the closest point will depend on the slope (tan α in Figure 6.16), of the terrain at angle φ. We therefore wish to replace the locally referred incident angle θ_i by φ and the slope $t = \tan \alpha$. From the figure and cosine sum identity:

$$\cos \theta_i = \cos (\varphi - \alpha) = \frac{\cos \varphi + t \sin \varphi}{\sqrt{1 + t^2}} \quad (6.4.23)$$

We can also replace the locally referred element ds:

$$ds = \frac{du}{\cos \alpha} = \sqrt{1 + t^2} \, dx \quad (6.4.24)$$

So, replacing the factor outside the integral by C,

$$E_R(\varphi, r_0) = C(r_0) \int Q(t)(\cos \varphi + t \sin \varphi)$$
$$\times \exp[-2ik(x \sin \varphi - h \cos \varphi)] \, dx \quad (6.4.25)$$

If there were a dominant topographic feature, located by the combination of range r_0 and Doppler shift, then the enhancement of the signal over the general level as the feature rotated across the disc could be used to deduce the height h using (6.4.25). To define "general level," however, we need some statistical measure of the heights h, slopes t, and reflectivity $Q(t)$ of the planetary surface. The simplest measure of statistical properties of a function of a one-dimensional continuum is the autocovariance function $K(\Delta x)$, the mean product of values a distance Δx apart. In this case, we have

$$K(\Delta x) = \langle Q(t)Q^*(t')(\cos \varphi + t \sin \varphi)(\cos \varphi + t' \sin \varphi)$$
$$\times \exp[2ik \cos \varphi(h - h')]\rangle, \quad \Delta x = x - x' \quad (6.4.26)$$

where the angle brackets $\langle \ \rangle$ denote averaging. Then for the average power

$$\langle |E_R|^2 \rangle = |C|^2 \iint K(\Delta x) \exp(-2ik \, \Delta x \sin \varphi) \, d(\Delta x) \, dx \quad (6.4.27)$$

In the covariance function $K(\Delta x)$ of (6.4.26), if the reflectivity Q is close to specular, then reflections for slopes yielding almost normal incidence, or $t = \tan \varphi$, will dominate in the integral. The considering the reflection function in (6.4.26)

$$F(t, t') = Q(t)Q^*(t')(\cos \varphi + t \sin \varphi)(\cos \varphi + t' \sin \varphi) \quad (6.4.28)$$

as a Taylor series expansion about this slope tan φ, the evaluation of $K(\Delta x)$

can be carried out as the integration of a joint probability distribution of height differences Δh and end-point slopes t, t' for an interval Δx:

$$\langle |E_R|^2 \rangle = \frac{E_0^2}{r_0^2 \lambda^2 \cos^2 \varphi} |Q_0|^2 \iint \exp\{-(2kh_m \cos \varphi)^2(1 - \rho(\Delta x)]\}$$
$$\times \exp(-2ik \, \Delta x \sin \varphi) \, d(\Delta x) \, dx \quad (6.4.29)$$

where $\rho(\Delta x)$ is the autocorrelation of h over distance Δx; h_m is the rms height; the radiation, (6.4.27), has been converted to radiation per unit wavelength by multiplying by the wave vector $k = 2\pi/\lambda$; and $|Q_0|^2$ is the power reflectivity at normal incidence, R, given by (6.3.22).

For application the solution (6.4.29) must be extended to two dimensions. If the distribution of heights is assumed to be Gaussian, with a scale length of covariance l,

$$\rho(\Delta x) = \exp\left[\frac{-(\Delta x)}{l^2}\right]^2 \quad (6.4.30)$$

the average power as a function of angle of incidence φ is:

$$\bar{P}(\varphi) = \cos^{-4} \varphi \exp\left(\frac{-l^2 \tan \varphi}{4h_m^2}\right) \quad (6.4.31)$$

The gain g in (6.4.4–5) is:

$$g = 1 + 2\left(\frac{h_m}{l}\right)^2 + \cdots \quad (6.4.32)$$

Observed Reflection by the Moon

This "quasispecular" model is only valid for a smooth surface, that is, one that has no irregularities comparable to the wavelength of the radar, λ. Furthermore, the effect of shadowing—significant near the limb—is neglected. If the model is applied, then we should expect a rapid dropoff from the maximum reflection at the closest point. In actuality, the radar reflection does not continue to follow the law (6.4.31) closely beyond an angle φ of about $40°$–$60°$, but instead diminishes more slowly as if it were a combination of (6.4.31) and a law [113, 114, 115]

$$\bar{P}(\varphi) \propto \cos^{3/2} \varphi \quad (6.4.33)$$

The proportionality (6.4.33) is intermediate between two models of diffuse reflection; the Lambert:

$$\bar{P}(\varphi) \propto \cos^2 \varphi \quad (6.4.34)$$

and the Lommel-Seeliger:

$$\bar{P}(\varphi) \propto \cos \varphi \quad (6.4.35)$$

Beyond $\varphi \approx 80°$, the law (6.4.35) appears to apply.

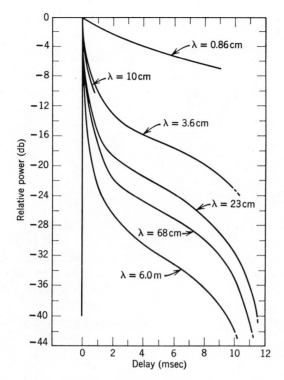

Figure 6.17: Average echo power reflected by moon $\bar{P}(t)$ as a function of delay. From Evans & Hagfors [114, p. 4880].

The obvious suggestion is that the moon is partly a quasispecular and partly a diffuse reflector. If this were true, we should expect that the diffuse portion would vary inversely with wavelength—since a higher proportion of objects would be large enough to cause scattering for shorter wavelengths—and that the degree of polarization should depend on the diffuse portion. Both of these effects in fact are observed.

Figure 6.17 shows the variation of power reflected with wavelength.

A summary of the results obtained from radar observations of the moon since 1960 is given in Table 6.7. The high values for the cross-section factor at the long wavelengths may arise from systematic errors introduced by ionospheric effects.

The variation of the dielectric constant ϵ with wavelength in Table 6.7 may be caused by a layered structure in the moon: the longer wavelengths reach deeper, more compacted material. Separate evidence of such layering has been obtained by examining the difference in return power of the two components of polarization as a function of the angle of incidence, in accordance

TABLE 6.7: RADAR OBSERVATIONS OF THE MOON

Wavelength, λ (cm)	Cross-section Factor, gR	Diffuse Portion of Power	Diffuse Portion of Surface	Average Slope, α	Dielectric Constant, ϵ
0.86	0.07	0.85	0.68		2.13
3.6	0.04	0.35	0.17	15°	2.72
23.0	0.065	0.25	0.11	10°	
68.0	0.064	0.20	0.08	10°	2.79
1130–1920	0.13–0.19				

From Evans [113] and Evans & Hagfors [114].

with (6.1.18–19). The results obtained are summarized in Figure 6.18: they indicate a definitely lower dielectric constant of 1.7–1.8, in better agreement with the values from thermal emission observations. The fitting of a two-layer model with an ϵ of 1.8 for the upper layer to the data then obtains several tens of centimeters for the layer thickness and a dielectric constant of 4 or 5 for the lower layer. This higher value then to some extent explains, through (6.3.22), the higher cross-section factor gR for the long wavelength radar [154].

Radar Mapping of the Moon

The operation since 1964 of the 1000-ft radar of the Arecibo Ionospheric Observatory, at 70-cm wavelength, has enabled mapping of features on the moon with a resolution of about 2 km. This mapping shows localized enhancements reflectivity by factors as much as 20, suggesting areas of rough, exposed, and compacted rock. These localized enhancements are strongly correlated with high optical albedo and with the hot spots found by infrared observations during an eclipse. A prominent example, the crater Tycho, is

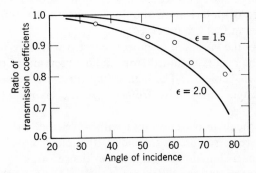

Figure 6.18: Ratio of radar transmission coefficients for the moon as a function of angle of incidence. Circles indicate observed values. From Hagfors *et al.* [154, p. 1155].

shown in Figure 6.19. Such features show many evidences of being relatively new, as discussed in Section 7.2. On a broader scale, the enhancements shown by highland areas over maria are about $1\frac{1}{2}$ to 2 [137, 397].

Recently radar observations of similar detail have been made at 3.8 cm wavelength by the MIT Lincoln Laboratory Haystack radar. At this shorter wavelength the enhancement of features such as Tycho is much less, as if there were a few centimeters of low reflectivity material over the high reflectivity surface [462].

Radar Observations of the Planets

Observations have been made of Venus at wavelengths from 3.6 to 780 cm· The reflectivity gR varies from 0.12 to 0.20 except at 3.6 cm, where it is only 0.009: apparently a consequence of atmospheric absorption. Venus has a power curve similar to the moon's in Figure 6.17, except that it rises to a peak about 5 db higher at the closest point—indicating that Venus is somewhat smoother than the moon. A smoother surface is also indicated by a lower amount of depolarization. The mean slope deduced for Venus is also less than the moon's, about 8°. The dielectric constant, ϵ, is about 4, comparable to about the lowest observed for terrestrial silicates. Some considerable local enhancements on Venus have been observed and mapped in fair detail near the equator. The period of rotation -243.1 days in Table 5.1 also, of course, was derived from radar, by the motion of reflection prominences across the radar Doppler spectra [102, 144, 314].

Mercury thus far appears to be very similar to the moon, with a cross-section factor of 0.06–0.07. The rotation period of 59 ± 3 days was deduced by radar.

Observations of Mars indicate that it is smoother than Venus. Mars appears to have considerable variations in reflectivity—from 0.03 to 0.13 in gR. A resolution of about 6°, or 350 km, of features on Mars has been attained. Areas of high radar reflectivity appear to be correlated with areas that are dark optically. Sometimes, however, the high radar reflectivity area is offset in longitude from the optically dark area in a direction toward the point closest to the earth. This direction of offset suggests that the dark areas are elevations, rather than depressions. The amount of offset α will be the slope of the elevation; from the slope α and the length in longitude $\Delta\theta$ of the feature, its height can be estimated as

$$h_{\max} \leq R\alpha\Delta\theta \tag{6.4.36}$$

Heights ranging from 4 to 16 km have been deduced in this manner for several dark areas on Mars [355].

As mentioned in Chapter 5, the radar data in conjunction with optical data and orbital theory have been used to improve significantly the numerical

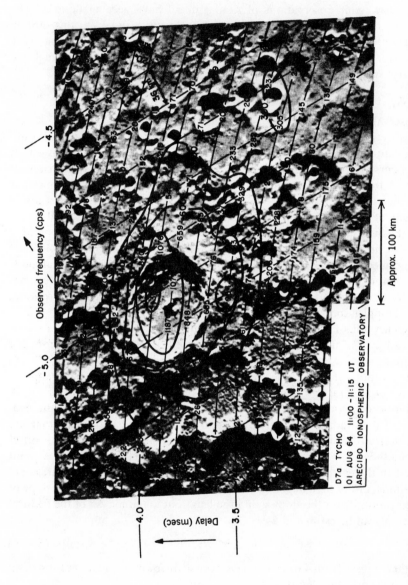

Figure 6.19: Contours of scattering enhancements of the crater Tycho. From Thompson [397]. Photo by Arecibo Ionospheric Observatory.

values for several parameters of the solar system. Among these are radii for Mercury: 2434 ± 2 km, and Venus: 6056 ± 1 km, which are much better than the values based on optical measurements [20].

PROBLEMS

6.1. Derive the electromagnetic wave equations, (6.1.6 and 7), from Maxwell's equations (6.1.1–4).

6.2. Derive the relationship between the magnitude phase function $\Delta m(\alpha)$, (6.1.23), and the reflectivity phase function Φ used in (6.1.27).

6.3. Derive the polarized reflection equations, (6.1.18 and 19), from the expressions for the electric wave (6.1.16 and 17) and the continuity requirements of the interface. Why is continuity of tangential, rather than normal components specified?

6.4. Derive the reflectivity at normal incidence,

$$ R = \left(\frac{\sqrt{\epsilon} - 1}{\sqrt{\epsilon} + 1} \right)^2 $$

(6.3.22) for unit permeability μ from the reflection equations (6.1.18 and 19).

6.5. A nuclear fission explosion produces a temperature on the order of $10^6\,°K$. Assuming this to be true over a sphere 10 cm in diameter, calculate approximately:
    (a) the total rate of electromagnetic radiation from the surface of this sphere;
    (b) the radiation flux (power incident per unit area) at a distance of 1 km;
    (c) the wavelength corresponding to the maximum in the radiated power spectrum.

6.6. Derive a formula to give the lifetime of a sphere of ice in a circular orbit as a function of its initial radius and distance from sun. What is the lifetime obtained for a radius of 100 meters and a distance from the sun of 1 AU?

6.7. Derive equation (6.3.4) for the attenuation factor α of electromagnetic waves in a poor conductor.

6.8. The *surface brightness* $2K_\omega\, d\omega$ is defined as the amount of energy within the frequency internal $d\omega$ radiated perpendicularly from an element of surface, per second per square centimeter, within a unit solid angle. Derive "Kirchhoff's law," which states that the surface brightness is equal to the ratio of rate of energy emission by a body to the absorptive power:

$$ K_\omega = \frac{E_\omega}{1 - A} $$

What relation does Kirchhoff's law have to the energy emission from a volume element within a planet, (6.3.9)?

6.9. Integrate the equation for diurnal temperature variation, T_ω, (6.3.16), to obtain the result given by equations (6.3.17–19).

6.10. Assume a planet to be 2 AU from the sun, and to have a visual albedo of 0.15.

The averaged infrared brightness temperature is observed to be 189°K. Is this temperature consistent with the planet being a blackbody? What assumptions must be made to answer this question?

What do you estimate will be the maximum and minimum temperatures on the planet's surface if it rotates once every 24 hours and if it has thermal properties like (a) those deduced for the moon; (b) those of average igneous rocks on earth?

The variation in temperature at the equator T_1, in the 24-hour period is $\pm 5°$. What do you deduce about the thermal inertia, $(K\rho c)^{-1/2}$?

The mean temperatures from 1 cm and 10 cm microwave emissions are 190°K and 200°K respectively. Using the above derived thermal inertia, what do you estimate to be the heat flow from the planet's interior?

6.11. Make an estimated calculation of the mean equatorial temperature T_{0e} and diurnal variation T_{1e} at the surface of Mercury, assuming it to have the same thermal inertia γ as the moon.

6.12. Applying the divergence theorem—used, e.g., on page 105—to the vector $\mathbf{A}$ defined by:

$$\mathbf{A} = E\nabla\psi$$

derive Green's first theorem:

$$\int_V \nabla E \cdot \nabla\psi \, dv = \int_S E\frac{\partial\psi}{\partial n} \, ds - \int_V E\,\nabla^2\psi \, dv$$

where $\partial/\partial n$ denotes the derivative normal to the bounding surface, and Green's second theorem:

$$\int_V (E\,\nabla^2\psi - \psi\,\nabla^2 E)\,dv = \int_S \left(E\frac{\partial\psi}{\partial n} - \psi\frac{dE}{dn}\right)dS$$

6.13. Derive (6.4.16), the normal derivative of a component of a field, from (6.4.15)

6.14. Write an expression to convert signal time delay t, as given in Figure 6.17, to angle φ from closest point.

6.15. Discuss qualitatively the technique for deducing the average terrain slopes and percent roughness of the moon from radar reflections.

REFERENCES

The basic physics applicable in this chapter include both electromagnetism, *Jackson* [190], *Corson & Lorrain* [81]; and thermodynamics, *Reif* [331]. Collections of papers about observations of the planets are *Kuiper & Middlehurst* [232] and *Brown et al.* [55]; of the moon in particular, *Kopal* [217] and *Hess et al.* [175].

The principal reference used for the photometry was *Harris* [161] and for polarization, *Dollfus* [97]. The optical scattering theory is that of *Hapke* [158, 159], who also utilizes polarization data to infer lunar surface composition [523]. *Vaucouleurs* [413] reviews all types of optical measurements of the planets; new results for Mars have been obtained by *O'Leary* [491]. Discussions of lunar luminescence are by *Ney* [490] and *Kopal* [220]. Papers on reflection spectrophotometry are *Sagan et al.* [352], *Younkin* [452] *Sinton* [372], and *Pollack & Sagan* [530].

Reviews of infrared observations are by *Murray & Westphal* [286] and *Petit* [312]. Important results pertaining to Venus are given in *Murray et al.* [287]; to the moon, in *Shorthill & Saari* [369, 500]. Recent observations of Mercury are by *Murray* [527].

The thermal emission theory given here is principally that of *Piddington & Minett* [315] and *Krotikov & Troitskii* [228]. Another detailed development is by *Pollack & Sagan* [319]. Results for the moon are reviewed by *Drake* [101] and *Troitskii* [401]; for the planets, by *Barrett* [24], *Kellerman* [210], and *Kuz'min* [483]. Recent observations of Mercury are discussed by *Gary* [467]. Important recent observations of Venus are by *Clark & Kuz'min* [516]; of the moon, by *Gary* [521].

The development of radar scattering theory is based on *Hagfors* [153]; a textbook on the subject is *Beckmann & Spizzichino* [26]. Radar observations of the moon are reviewed by *Evans* [113]; important papers are *Evans & Pettengill* [115], *Rea et al.* [329], *Hagfors et al.* [154], and *Evans & Hagfors* [114]. Radar mapping of the moon by the Arecibo facility is described by *Thompson* [397] and *Gold* [137]. Radar observations of the planets are reviewed by *Pettengill* [313], *Muhleman* [284], and *Eshelman* [462]; recent results are given by *Pettengill et al.* [314] and *Dyce et al.* [102]. The radar measurement of topography on Mars is by *Sagan et al.* [335]. The most advanced use of radar data for solar system parameters is by *Ash et al.* [20]. The radar determination of planetary rotations is analyzed by *Shaprio* [580].

In addition to the papers specifically referenced, there are several more in the issue No. 12, Vol. 690, of *Journal of Research, National Bureau of Standards: Radio Science*, 1965.

Chapter 7

GEOLOGY OF THE MOON AND MARS

If a planet is not shrouded by clouds, then the application of the physical observations described in Chapter 6 will be in a context provided by photographs, which acquire considerably more detail and whose value is further enhanced by being the medium of observation closest to that of humans, and hence more readily interpreted.

If a planet is readily observable by photography, it normally will have very little atmosphere, such as the moon, Mercury, or Mars. If it has very little atmosphere then it is subject to bombardment by meteorites, and we should expect such a planet to have meteorite craters as one of its leading characteristics. Other considerations that would lead us to expect meteorite impact and the associated cratering and fragmentation to be more important on a smaller planet are: first, that a planet of higher area/mass ratio will be a more efficient radiator of heat and hence will have a lower temperature gradient upon going into the interior, thus leading to less igneous activity; second, it will have had a lower initial temperature since there was less gravitational energy to convert into heat; and third, it is less likely to have oceans or appreciable amounts of water sufficient to cause significant erosion and sedimentation. The lower level of igneous activity makes likely a lesser degree of differentiation in the smaller bodies. Hence we should expect that the geology of smaller bodies such as the moon, Mars, and Mercury will be appreciably different from that of the earth, and we should expect that the relative importance of types of structures will be greatly altered as well as there being a considerable difference in interpretation. As for Venus, it may well be similar to the earth, but its geology at present is very much in the mist.

The plan of the chapter therefore is first to first examine meteoritic impact as a geologic phenomenon, and to extract such information as can be obtained from terrestrial experience; then to discuss lunar geology, because it has much the greater detail of photography available; and finally, to examine Mars primarily in terms of the significant differences it might have from the moon.

7.1 Impact Cratering

In Section 5.3, the rate of infall of small bodies into the earth was discussed, the principal results being summarized in Figure 5.12. In this section we wish to explore the implications of these observations: their consequences on earth, and the extrapolations that can be made to the moon and to Mars. The questions to be investigated are:

1. The mechanics of impact: what happens when a small body strikes the solid surface of a planet; the size and shape of the crater formed, as a function of the surface material, and of the mass, velocity, and impact angle of the body; the amount of material thrown out, both to escape and to fall back on the planet; the degree of melting and fragmentation of material.

2. Terrestrial evidence pertinent: laboratory experimentation, artificial explosions, natural craters, and shock phenomena, taking into account the modifying effect of the atmosphere.

3. Problems of extrapolation: modifications with the size of the planet; the effect of the proximity of the earth in the case of the moon and of the proximity of the asteroid belt in the case of Mars.

Hypervelocity Impact

Experiments with impacts at high velocities (in excess of about 2.5 km/sec) indicate that the response of both the impacting projectile and the target material is essentially fluid. At an early stage of the impact, the stresses set up are much greater than the mechanical strength of either projectile or target. Hence the material behaves as though it had virtually no strength—that is, as a fluid.

As the front of the projectile moves into the target, a spray of fine particles squirts out to the side. Next a shock wave radiates from the impact point, compressing and accelerating the material of the target. Another shock wave backs into the projectile, decelerating it. These waves may generate heat enough to cause melting. Next the target material flows radially from the impact point, opening up a crater. The projectile material also flows radially, and some of the material moves around the crater edge and is ejected in a sheath-like jet. As the crater grows, the angle of the jet steepens, and the velocity of ejection decreases. Meanwhile, the front of the shock wave moves ahead with the expanding crater following close behind. Between the two is a hemispherical shell of hot matter. The shock wave weakens as its volume of action increases, and it is overtaken by tension waves connecting free surfaces with the material moving away underneath. At length the strength of the target material takes over [72].

The foregoing description applies primarily to projectile and target of ductile metal; in the case of rock, which is more brittle, the process is less perfect, with considerable irregularity due to fragmentation. In all cases, however, hypervelocity impact is best described by hydrodynamic equations, plus equations of state to take into account the change in density of the

material with pressure, as discussed in Section 2.5. These equations are [34]:
(1) the equation of motion (c.f. (2.4.14)) in Eulerian form, neglecting viscosity, elasticity, etc.:

$$\rho\dot{\mathbf{v}} + \nabla p + \rho\nabla V = 0 \qquad (7.1.1)$$

(2) conservation of mass:

$$\rho\nabla \cdot \mathbf{v} + \dot{\rho} = 0 \qquad (7.1.2)$$

(3) internal energy, applying the adiabatic approximation (i.e., dq zero in (1.2.5)):

$$\dot{E} - \frac{p\dot{\rho}}{\rho^2} = 0 \qquad (7.1.3)$$

and (4) the equation of state:

$$p = p(\rho, E) \qquad (7.1.4)$$

Equations (7.1.1–4), together with the potential function V and appropriate boundary and initial conditions, completely specify the motion. The form of the equation of state (7.1.4) may be (at lower pressures) the Birch form (2.5.19), or it may be one obtained from shock experiments, (1.2.3) and Figure 1.16, extrapolated by approximate nuclear theories used for stellar interiors.

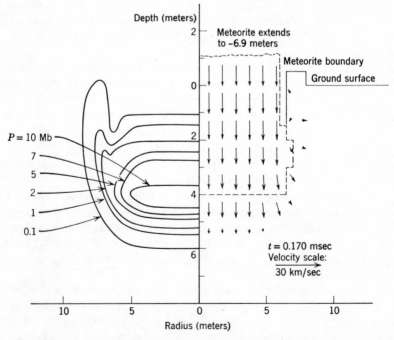

Figure 7.1: Pressure and velocity field at 0.17 msec; 30 km/sec, 12,000-ton iron projectile in tuff target. From Bjork [33, p. 3380].

Calculation of a Hypervelocity Impact

Attempts to solve equations (7.1.1–4) for the meteor impact problem approximately taking into account momentum and energy conservation considerations have obtained results erroneous by order-of-magnitude. Hence the most precise integrations have been numerical, in which the matter of the projectile and target is represented by many particles which carry with them the appropriate mass, momentum, internal energy, and kinetic energy through a fixed spatial grid. The pressures and velocities of such a calculation are shown in Figures 7.1–3, which apply to a 12,000-ton projectile of iron density (7.85 gm/cm^{-3}) striking tuff (density 1.7) at a velocity of 30 km/sec. Note in Figure 7.2 that a zero velocity stagnation point first develops about 12 meters deep, above which material is thrown out, and below which it is

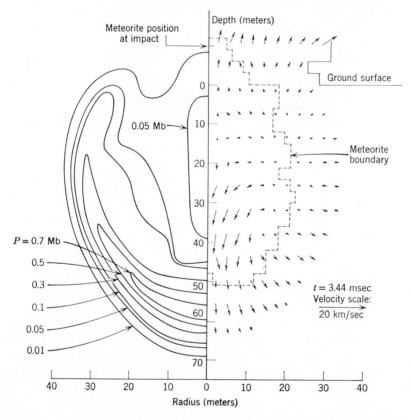

Figure 7.2: Pressure and velocity field at 3.44 msec; 30 km/sec, 12,000-ton iron projectile in tuff target. From Bjork [33, p. 3383]

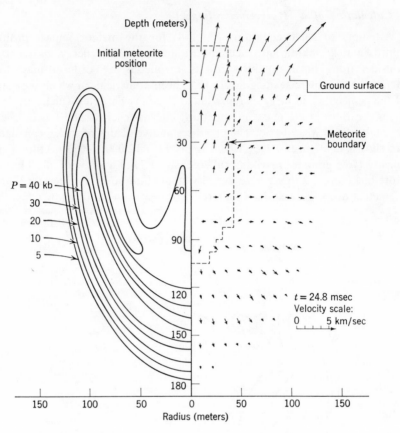

Figure 7.3: Pressure and velocity field at 24.8 msec; 30 km/sec, 12,000-ton iron projectile in tuff target. From Bjork [33, p. 3386].

being driven deeper. By Figure 7.3, about 20 msec later, the stagnation point has penetrated to about 80 meters deep. The maximum pressure has also dropped by a factor of 250 from the initial 10 Mb to 40 kb [33].

The velocities of the upward thrown material can be used to carry forward the integration of paths in the gravity field and thence to determine the size of the crater that will remain and the distribution of material about the crater. The final crater in the case diagrammed is estimated to attain a radius of 500 meters and a depth of 150 meters [33].

Terrestrial Meteorite Craters

Hypervelocity impacts have been reproduced on a small scale in the laboratory [129, 131]. To test the impact calculations on a large scale, as

Figure 7.4: The Great Meteor Crater of Arizona. Note circularity, depth/diameter ratio, raised rim, hummocky throwout. Photo by John Shelton, Claremont, Calif.

described above, as well as to get some statistics on frequency of occurrence to corroborate Figure 5.12 and extend it to the right, meteorite craters on earth are used. Since a meteorite must be quite large not to have its velocity reduced below that for hypervelocity impact—say, much more than 200 tons (see problem 7.1)—the craters that have been identified are all at least 20 meters in diameter. Figure 7.4 is a photograph of the best known, the Great Meteor Crater in Arizona. The radius of the Arizona Meteor Crater is 600 meters. By calculations such as those described, this radius requires a meteorite mass of about 72,000 tons for a 30 km/sec impact velocity, or about 190,000 tons for the minimum velocity of 11.2 km/sec (the earth's escape velocity). Figure 7.5 is a simplified cross section of the crater. The lens

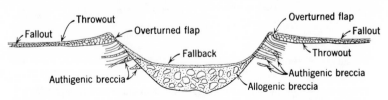

Figure 7.5: Cross section of meteorite crater. From Short [367, p. 590].

of breccia—rock fractured by the pressure waves—below the crater is almost as large as the crater itself. In the material thrown out around the crater, the sequence of different rock types is the reverse of the strata in the area: that is, the material first thrown out is the first to fall. The diameter/depth ratio is usually about 3 [362, 367].

Use of Nuclear Explosion Cratering

All the meteorite craters are circular in shape, without indication of any direction of motion of the meteorite. This circularity is a consequence of the explosive nature of the hypervelocity impact, the energy being the kinetic energy $Mv^2/2$ of the meteorite. The rapidity and low gas generation of hypervelocity impact cratering suggest that it should be similar to cratering by nuclear explosion, rather than the slower chemical explosion. Figure 7.6 is an example of a nuclear explosion crater with a relatively shallow shot point [367].

Although there are some differences in detail, the similarity is sufficient that considerable data on nuclear craters can be used for empirical rules applicable to meteor craters. The diameter of nuclear explosion craters varies systematically with the depth of burst scaled for the energy of the explosion. The effective depth of burst of an impact crater in turn depends mainly on the velocity of the meteorite and the relative density of the meteorite and the target rocks. If the energy conversion was of the same efficiency for all sizes of cratering explosions, we would expect that both the depth and the diameter would vary proportionally to the $\frac{1}{3}$ power of the energy released. Nuclear experiments indicate that the larger the explosion, the less efficient, so that the appropriate exponent is to the $\frac{1}{3}$ power of the energy released. For a given size explosion in kilotons TNT equivalent, we should expect that the diameter of the crater would also vary with the depth of the explosion and that using the $\frac{1}{3}$ power rule we could, from an explosion of a given energy, extrapolate results to other energies with depths scaled proportionate to the $\frac{1}{3}$ power of the energy [422]. In the case of meteorites we should expect that if we assume their velocities to be all comparable, say 15 km/sec at impact, there would be one particular scaling law; this would also depend on the densities and

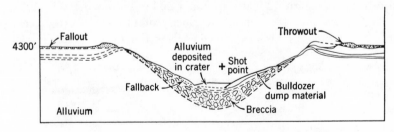

Figure 7.6: Cross section of Jangle U nuclear explosion crater. From Short [367, p. 590].

strengths of the meteorite and target material, but for typical value this scaling depth is about 4.6 m/(kt TNT)$^{1/3}$. For this depth-scaling law the diameter of a crater in meters obtained from experiments in nuclear explosions is:

$$D = 77\,W^{1/3} \qquad (7.1.5)$$

where W is the energy released in kilotons TNT equivalent. One kt TNT equivalent is 10^{12} cal or 4.2×10^{19} ergs. Then the energy released by the impact of a meteorite is, for M in grams and V in kilometers per second:

$$W = \frac{\frac{1}{2}MV^2}{4.2 \times 10^9} \qquad (7.1.6)$$

Combining (7.1.5) and (7.1.6),

$$2R = D = 0.332\,M^{1/3}\,V^{2/3} \qquad (7.1.7)$$

which obtains 367 meters for a radius in the example described by Figures 7.1–3, compared to about 500 meters from the numerical integration [366].

Throwout Calculations

The calculation of the amount of material thrown out of an impact crater is of interest in two different respects: first, to determine the characteristic pattern of material around a crater; and second, in the case of the moon and Mars, to estimate how much material is ejected at greater than escape velocity to contribute to the meteorite population.

The principal rule applying to crater throwout, Schröter's rule, was actually deduced from lunar craters. Schröter's rule states that the volume of the rim equals the volume of the crater depression. However, more recent experience with nuclear explosion craters as well as measurements of smaller lunar craters indicate that the ratios of rim to crater volume fall between 0.4 and 0.8. The discrepancy appears to be due partly to the ejection of much material beyond the edge of the exterior crater rim slope and partly to the vertical and lateral displacement of bed rock adjacent to the crater depression [316].

The results of actual measurements of several nuclear explosion craters from bursts ranging in energy from 0.02 to 100 kt TNT equivalent are summarized in Figure 7.7, which gives the ratio of the ejected mass M_i within distance r to the total ejected mass M_e for a crater of radius R. Thus, for example, on the average 50 percent of the ejected mass falls within a distance of 2.2 crater radii. The same experiments also showed that for the outer parts of the throwout there is considerable variation with direction of ejecta density, as summarized in Figure 7.8 for a crater of 100 kt TNT equivalent energy and 183 meters radius. Such rayed patterns of ejecta appear characteristic of all explosion craters, impact as well as nuclear [66].

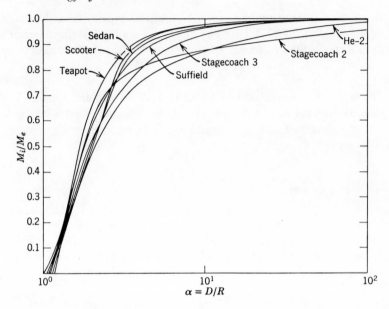

Figure 7.7: Mass distribution of ejecta from nuclear explosion craters. From Carlson & Jones [66, p. 1909].

Scaling from Earth to Moon

The true size and shape of an explosive crater and the extent of its associated brecciation should depend mainly on the energy of the explosion and the properties of the material in which it takes place: that is, the gravitational term ∇V is relatively unimportant in the governing equations (7.1.1–4). Also the distribution of ejection velocities should be dependent mainly on energy and material properties. But the distribution of ejecta location will depend mainly on the gravitational acceleration, as indicated by the ordinary ballistic equation

$$r = \frac{v^2 \sin 2\alpha}{g} \tag{7.1.8}$$

(see problem 7.2). Hence on a smaller planet a given energy will produce roughly the same size crater, but the ejecta will be more widespread. The effect of a smaller g also will be to allow less material to fall back into the crater, so that the apparent size of the depression will be increased.

Experimental Data on Ejecta

Experiments with hypervelocity impacts in a vacuum at velocities up to 7 km/sec indicate that the amount of material ejected will be 10^3 to 10^4 times

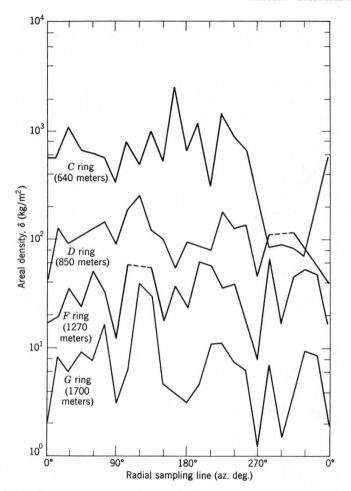

Figure 7.8: Distribution of ejecta with azimuth for a 100-kt nuclear explosion crater. From Carlson & Jones [66, p. 1905].

the mass of the impacting meteorite. This amount is very little affected by the porosity of the surface material, unless it has a high bonding strength, such as pumice. On the moon such a large "cloud" of ejecta would have a considerable erosive effect. Furthermore, about 1 percent of the ejecta will be at velocities exceeding the lunar escape velocity of 2.4 km/sec [129, 131].

Experiments with impacts in a vacuum at velocities on the order of 1 km/sec result in craters whose size and shape will be considerably affected by the target strength and angle of impact. For impact angles less than 60° from the horizontal, the arc over which ejecta are thrown is less than 180°. The shape of the crater may be elongated to as much as a 5:3 ratio, depending on the nature of the material. The entry side of the crater generally will be the steeper for low-angle impacts [130].

Shock Metamorphism

Additional indicators of pressures and temperatures attained in impact craters, and hence of the energy of the impacting body, are mineralogical shock effects, or shock metamorphism. These effects include: (1) multiple sets of closely spaced planar microstructures; (2) in the case of quartz and plagioclase, transformation to glass; (3) high-pressure polymorphs, such as coesite and stishovite; (4) nickel-iron spherules; (5) droplets of certain minerals requiring temperatures in excess of 1500° C; (6) dense glass of bulk rock composition, with dissolved iron oxide particles; and (7) shatter cones, nested conical structures with grooved surfaces, ranging from millimeters to meters in length [69, 368].

Calculated Cratering Rates

To estimate the frequency of infall of meteorites on the moon and Mars, we start with Figure 5.12, which gives as the frequency of infall of meteorites of mass greater than M in grams, roughly:

$$\text{Earth:} f = \begin{cases} 10^{15} \, M^{-1.0}, & M < 10^{10} \text{ gm} \\ 10^{11} \, M^{-0.6}, & M > 10^{10} \text{ gm} \end{cases} \tag{7.1.9}$$

where f is the number per 10^6 km^2 per 10^9 years. Combining equations (7.1.7 and 9), we get for a frequency/10^6 km^2/Æ of impact craters of diameter larger than D:

$$\text{Earth:} f = \begin{cases} 0.377 \times 10^{11} \, V^2 D^{-3.0}, & M < 10^{10} \text{ gm} \\ 0.218 \times 10^9 \, V^{1.2} D^{-1.8}, & M > 10^{10} \text{ gm} \end{cases} \tag{7.1.10}$$

for V in kilometers per second and D in meters. Setting the velocity as 15 km/sec we get:

$$\text{Earth:} \log_{10} f = \begin{cases} 12.93 - 3.0 \, \log_{10} D, & D < 425 \text{ meters} \\ 9.75 - 1.8 \, \log_{10} D, & D > 425 \text{ meters} \end{cases} \tag{7.1.11}$$

Thus, for example, (7.1.11) gives about one impact crater larger than 1 km in diameter for an area the size of the North American continent (24.3×10^6 km^2) about every 2000 years. This rate seems high relative to the number which have been found in all North America, but not relative to the number found in areas favorable to discovery, such as the Canadian shield.

7.2 The Surface of the Moon

Estimated Crater Frequency

Taking into account the different capture cross sections and surface areas, the frequency for the moon should be 0.474 times as great as for the earth for an approach velocity of 10 km/sec (5.3.36). Because of the lower escape velocity, the diameter for the mass of 10^{10} gm will be less (see problem 7.3):

$$\text{Moon: } \log_{10} f = \begin{cases} 12.28 - 3.0 \ \log_{10} D, & D < 340 \text{ meters} \\ 9.23 - 1.8 \ \log_{10} D, & D > 340 \text{ meters} \end{cases} \tag{7.2.1}$$

If we assume the moon has the same age as that estimated for the earth, 4.55×10^9 years, then we obtain:

$$\text{Moon: } \log_{10} F = \begin{cases} 12.94 - 3.0 \ \log_{10} D, & D < 340 \text{ meters} \\ 9.89 - 1.8 \ \log_{10} D, & D > 340 \text{ meters} \end{cases} \tag{7.2.2}$$

It is sometimes contended that there should be a greater crater frequency on the side toward the earth because of a gravitational "focusing" effect; see problem 5.8 [25, 366, 439].

Observed Crater Frequencies

The moon's surface has been customarily divided into two distinct areas:

1. The uplands, generally (but not always) of higher elevation, characterized by higher albedo, greater irregularity at a kilometer scale, and many more craters observable from the earth.

2. The maria, darker in color, relatively flat, and much fewer large craters.

The crater frequency for diameters D greater than 1 km is approximated by [366]:

$$\text{Moon: } \begin{cases} \text{Uplands: } \log_{10} F = 11.05 - 2.12 \log_{10} D \\ \text{Maria: } \quad \log_{10} F = \quad 8.12 - 1.71 \log_{10} D \end{cases} \tag{7.2.3}$$

where F is the frequency in number per 10^6 km^2 and D is the diameter in meters. These frequencies are plotted on Figure 7.9, to compare with those extrapolated from the earth, by (7.2.2). Also plotted on Figure 7.9 are counts based on Ranger VII photographs and earth-based photographs of the Mare Cognitum, in which the Ranger VII impacted (see Figure 7.10 for locations on the moon of places referred to). For craters smaller than about a kilometer, the frequency counts are considerably complicated by secondary and non-impact craters and the effects of obliteration of smaller craters by subsequent impacts [163, 551].

Crater frequency counts indicate that the ages of different maria, the large dark open areas, vary appreciably. In a sample of eight large maria, the craters per 10^6 km² more than one mile, or 1.6 km, in diameter, vary from 242 up to 540, compared to the average of 426 given by the second part of (7.2.3). This variation in crater frequency is utilized as part of an attempt to obtain a sequencing of geological events on the moon analogous to that on the earth, as described below.

The most recent information about crater frequencies is from Lunar Orbiter satellite photos. These photos confirm the frequencies of small craters in maria obtained from Ranger VII photos. However, the frequencies of small craters in upland areas are surprisingly less: if the "uplands,

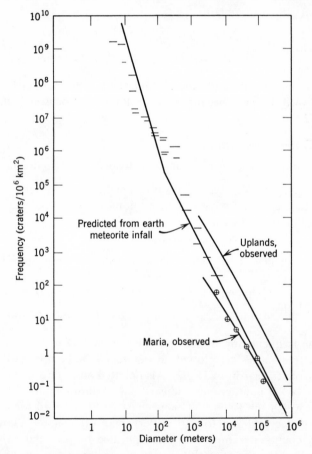

Figure 7.9: Cumulative frequency of craters on the moon. From Hartmann [163, p. 210], Shoemaker *et al.* [366], and equation (7.2.2).

Figure 7.10: Index map of locations on the moon. R7, R8, R9: Ranger impact locations; S1, S3, S5, S6, S7: Surveyor landing locations.

observed" line in Figure 7.9, were extended to the left, it would fall below the maria counts between 10^2 and 10^3 meters.

Types of Features

We discuss lunar features classified into five somewhat arbitrary types:

1. Craters.
2. Rilles.
3. Protrusions.
4. Faults.
5. Plains, or maria.

Primary Impact Craters

The photos of the moon often seen are taken with the sun at a considerable angle to the normal in order to obtain detail. Thus there is the illusion that the lunar terrain is rather steep. Actually, it is fairly gentle. Figure 7.19 gives a good impression of lunar relief, including a shallow old crater (Marius) about 40 km in diameter and 1500 meters deep. In many cases an observer standing at the center of a large crater would be unable to see the rims because of the curvature of the moon. There are five craters that are larger than 200 km.

Craters may be further classified according to:

1. Impact craters.
   (a) Primary.
   (b) Secondary.
2. Volcanic craters.
3. Collapse features.

Primary impact craters are nearly circular, they have a smooth floor, they sometimes have a central peak (but not always), and the floor is lower than the surrounding plain. The larger craters, those on the order of tens of kilometers across, have a series of terraces on the inner wall, apparently caused by slumping. Immediately outside the rim the terrain is extremely hummocky from throwout. Further out, these hummocks and depressions become more distinct ridges and valleys, but they never attain the distinctiveness of a terrestrial terrain dissected by erosion. An example of a large impact crater 90 km in diameter, Copernicus, is shown in Figures 7.11 and 7.12. As can be seen in Figure 7.12, the central peak is quite irregular.

Large impact craters on the moon are appreciably shallower than impact craters on earth; the ratio of rim volume to depression volume may be as high as 1:1, and the diameter:depth ratio may be 10:1 or more. A general empirical relationship between depth d and diameter D of Baldwin [22] for craters up to 30 km diameter is:

$$\log_{10} D = 0.0256 \, (\log_{10} d)^2 + 1.027 \log_{10} d + 0.896 \qquad (7.2.4)$$

for d and D in meters. Explanations suggested for the shallowness of the large craters have been (1) some sort of isostatic compensation; (2) impact-triggered volcanism; and (3) slumping of material from the crater wall. The last phenomenon has obviously occurred in the case of Copernicus.

An important subcategory of primary craters are the rayed craters. These are characterized by long bright streaks, called *rays*, extending in some cases a hundred or more kilometers from the crater. They appear prominently on the photo of Copernicus, Figure 7.11. Other examples of rayed craters are Tycho (86 km), Aristarchus (46 km), and Kepler (34 km). Rayed craters are often correlated with strong radar returns (see Figure 6.20) and with a high albedo and a less rapid than average drop in temperature after passing into

Figure 7.11: Copernicus region, lat. 10°N, long. 20°W. Note irregular throwout, secondary craters, bright rays around new primary crater; superposition of these features on older features. Photo by F. Pearce, Mount Wilson Observatory, 1929.

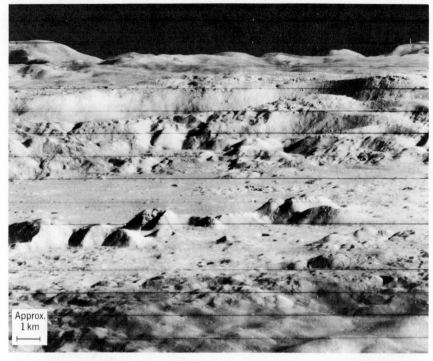

Approx.
1 km

Figure 7.12: Copernicus crater, lat. 10°N, long. 20°W. Note irregular central peak, flat crater floor, slumping and terracing of far crater wall, hummocky terrain in front of near crater wall. Photo by NASA, Lunar Orbiter II.

the darkness, as if the insulating layer that prevails over most of the moon were thin or lacking [218, 361].

Lunar Orbiter satellite photos indicate some modification of the afore-described geometry for the smaller craters. Terracing does not occur in craters less than about 70 meters in diameter. Craters in the intermediate range of about 35–70 meters have a flat floor, while the smaller craters are quite bowl-shaped. Variations in these crater characteristics among different areas have been used to deduce variations in the depth of the fragmented surface layer from 3 to 10 meters.

It also appears that the rate of infall of meteorites is such that an area will become "saturated" with craters below a certain size: that is, the frequency remains constant because the number being obliterated is equal to the number being formed. This saturation time follows roughly the law

$$T \approx 0.033 D^{3/2} \qquad (7.2.5)$$

for diameter D in meters and time T in 10^6 years [468].

Secondary Impact Craters

Secondary craters are myriads of small, closely spaced craters extending outward from the major primary craters like a series of gouges. They generally are elongated along an axis at a small angle to the direction from some primary crater. The secondary craters tend to be shallower in comparison to their diameter than the primary craters. They are sometimes correlated in location with rays extending from the same primary crater. By using the principal of superposition, the secondary craters also form a means of dating the sequence of events on the moon. The rays mentioned in connection with certain primary craters are possibly material splashed out of the secondaries. The rays are highly reflective and extend outward five or six diameters from relatively new craters like Copernicus or Tycho. The distribution of sizes of particles apparently thrown out from major craters is difficult to explain: the amount of energy released in a major meteoritic impact would be expected to cause a good deal more shattering and pulverizing of the material. An explanation which has been suggested is that some of the major craters are due to comets that have a gas cloud: the gas would give a certain uplift, or carry, to the particles; it also would result in a sorting out of particles by size, such as appears to be the case in the relative locations of rays (presumably small particles) and secondary craters, caused by large particles. The gas also would enable acceleration of the larger objects which form the secondary craters, without their being shattered by the explosion. Apparent fading of rays with age also can be used to put craters into a chronological sequence. Examples of secondary craters appear in Figure 7.11, as well as, on a larger scale, in Figures 7.13, 7.20, and 7.22 [361, 363, 364].

Volcanic Craters

The noncircularity and close proximity to each other or proximity to the features to be described later, called rilles, of some craters leads to the idea that some of the craters are of volcanic origin. Volcanoes on earth are two main types: the *explosive volcano*, which is the spewing out of material from a vent—the spalling off of material from the walls of the vent is what forms the crater in this case; and *the caldera*, which may be either violent, such as Krakatoa, or quiescent (subsiding) such as some in Hawaii. The caldera is formed by the collapse of the roof over a chamber from which material has been withdrawn by lava flow or by pyroclastic eruption and ash flow [503]. The lunar craters have a character inconsistent with calderas in that their floor is lower than the surrounding terrain, whereas calderas, being formed by the collapse of the summit of a preexisting volcanic pile, commonly have a floor higher than the surrounding terrain. The hummocky ring of material outside the rim of lunar craters also is not characteristic of calderas.

Figure 7.13: Southeast part of Mare Nubium, including Straight Wall and Deslandres. Approximately 25°S, 10°W. Note Straight Wall fault, chain of craters at lower center, volcano-like cone near right edge. Photo by Mount Wilson Observatory and Lunar & Planetary Laboratory, University of Arizona.

Hence those craters on the moon which would be volcanic are believed to be of the explosive type, in particular a type known as *maars*. Maars are caused by piecemeal spalling and slumping of walls of a volcanic vent and hence often have an irregular shape and look quite different from a meteoritic crater. They also may have a floor somewhat lower than their surroundings. The rim of a maar is formed of ejecta. The maximum slope of this rim is usually about 30°. The volume of the rim is less than that of a crater and the rim is characterized by distinct bedding corresponding to different stages of outspewing. Usually there is no central cone. A factor important in the formation of a maar is steam, an excellent agent to cause spalling of rock. If there are maars on the moon we should expect to see also evidence of outgassing. Another feature of maars that might make them associated with the moon is that they tend to lie in chains or rows and often have no connecting geological feature at the surface. Examples of chains of small craters not explainable as secondary craters of large primary impacts are (1) across the center of Deslandres (formerly Hell plain), a series of craters about 4 km across spaced 1 to 10 km apart over a stretch of 100 km: see Figure 7.13; (2) northeast of Stadius between Copernicus and Eratosthenes several craters 3 to 5 km across, most of them adjacent to other craters or merging in with them, and at the north end passing into a rille (see Figure 7.11); (3) the rilles on the north side of the crater Alphonsus, several small overlapping craters: see Figure 7.14. Some craters in Alphonsus are surrounded by diffuse dark halos at a radius of 4 to 5 km, possibly the consequence of volcanic ash throwout: see Figure 7.14.

Occasionally there are also features that look more like earthly volcanoes, with dome-shaped or symmetrical hills with small craters at their peak. A number of them are across the rise from Oceanus Procellarum near the northern edge just north of Hortensius. Also a good example just midway between Hortensius and Copernicus is a symmetrical hill 5 or 6 km across, several hundred meters high with a 1 km crater in the summit (see Figure 7.11) [361].

As mentioned in the introduction to this chapter, however, it is sometimes difficult to accept the idea of volcanism in a small body such as the moon. In carrying out the calculations of thermal models, as discussed in Sections 2.4 and 9.2, the depth of close approach to melting is much greater. Hence an alternative hypothesis which has been proposed is that some of the crater-like features which are difficult to attribute to meteorites but which are thought to be of internal origin are collapse features associated with the gradual withdrawal of water due to outgassing [231]. However, various protrusions which have appeared on Lunar Orbiter photographs suggest igneous activity more strongly than ever, as discussed below.

A listing of the features expected in impact craters and volcanic craters is

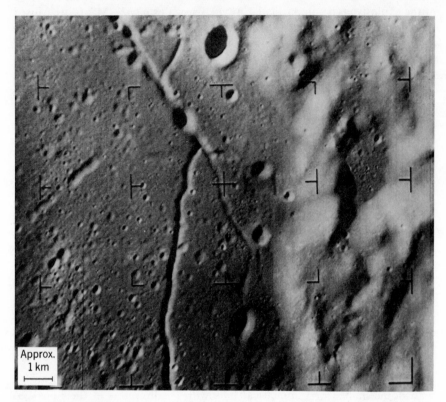

Figure 7.14: Northeast part of crater Alphonsus, lat. 13°S, long. 3°W. Note rilles overlapped by craters, secondary crater chains, relatively smooth uplands. Photo by NASA, Ranger IX.

given in Table 7.1. In general, the impact craters should have more the appearance of violent circumstances of formation. Perhaps the most important thing to emphasize is that the appearance of the two categories of craters is distinct only in underlying structure, which is, of course, inaccessible at the moment for lunar features. Furthermore, for the largest impact craters the situation may be further confused by the impact being a trigger for considerable volcanism.

Lunar Chronology

In certain areas of the moon the combination of crater counts and superposition of craters and thrown-out material can be used to construct somewhat of a history. The most marked example occurs in the northwest part of

TABLE 7.1: CHARACTERISTICS OF LUNAR CRATERS

| Property | Impact | | Volcanic | |
	Primary	Secondary	Maars	Caldera
Maximum size	No limit	Dependent on ejecta, and hence size, of associated primary	5 km	Several km—say <20 km
Shape	Circular	Elongated	Usually circular, sometimes elongated along chains	Somewhat irregular, but never elongated
Underlying structure	Lens of breccia, intense pressure effects	Moderate pressure effects	Funnel-shaped vent, filled with mixture of volcanic and local material	Larger vent: more volcanic material than maars
Surrounding rock	Highly deformed		Truncated	
Ejecta	No particular size limit	Relatively little—very irregular distribution	Always <3 m. Typically small high trajectory and hence symmetric distribution	Similar to maars
Outer slopes	Hummocky	Hummocky	Smooth	Smooth
Central cone	Rare	None—unless containing ejecta	Rare	Sometimes
Slumping of walls, terracing	Common	Common	Common	Common

the moon: the newest large feature in the area is the crater Copernicus: in its total area of the crater and ejecta rim, 50,000 km², there appear to be only two recognizable impact craters more than 1 km across, which implies, using (7.2.1), an age of about 0.1 Æ. In contrast, Eratosthenes, just to the north-east, has so many craters that the age is probably more than 0.4 Æ. There are pronounced rays emanating from Copernicus, whereas there is virtually no evidence of rays at Eratosthenes. Furthermore, the pattern of throwout

Approx.
100 km

Figure 7.15: Mare Imbrium and surroundings, approximately 30°N, 10°W. Note super-position of features suggesting chronological sequence Apennines, Archimedes, Imbrium, Eratosthenes, Copernicus. Photo by Mount Wilson Observatory, 1919.

material is much more markedly associated with Copernicus than with Eratosthenes, much of it being superimposed upon the latter crater. Eratosthenes itself, however, appears to be newer than the Mare Imbrium to the north of it, since craters which have the appearance of secondaries of Eratosthenes are imposed upon the Mare Imbrium. In contrast, the crater Archimedes, farther to the northeast, does not have such a pattern of secondaries around it: see Figure 7.15. On the contrary, it has the appearance of having been flooded by the material of the Mare Imbrium. However, to the southeast of Archimedes, there are appreciable patterns of what would appear to be secondary craters associated with Archimedes in the mountainous area called the Apennines. In this manner Shoemaker and his colleagues at the U.S. Geological Survey have constructed a sequence of lunar geological periods, starting with the Apennines and followed in turn by Archimedes, Mare Imbrium, Eratosthenes, and finally Copernicus. This sequence, however, lacks an absolute time scale such as we have on the earth with geochronology; there is just the approximate time obtained by the combination of meteorite infall rate to the earth and the assumption of uniformity of this rate. As indicated in Figure 7.9, the excess of upland cratering over that predicted suggests that the infall rates in the past may have been higher than the present by a factor between 3 and 10. Higher rates also are indicated by the far side of the moon, which appears to be much more "uplands" and less "maria" in character than the near side; see Figure 7.16 [361, 363].

Rilles

The second type of lunar terrain feature, the rille, is one that may not have any close terrestrial counterpart. The nearest type of feature we have on earth that runs across many other features are the wrench-type faults, such as the San Andreas. However, there is no evidence found yet on the moon of any such horizontal displacement of features on opposite sides of a rille comparable to that which occurs on the San Andreas fault or the Mendocino fault. Instead, the rilles just cut across other features without any perceptible significant displacement laterally on opposite sides as if they were the consequence of simple fractures due to tension resulting from some sort of expansion of the moon.

The two terrestrial analogs that offer the closest parallels are: (1) the *graben*, a trench formed by two parallel normal faults, the result of tension; and (2) less likely, the *diatreme*, a funnel-shaped volcanic vent often elongated and usually filled with sediments. Diatremes fit some of the patterns of volcanic craters mentioned previously. Indeed, there is considerable association between rilles and series of noncircular craters, possibly volcanic. An

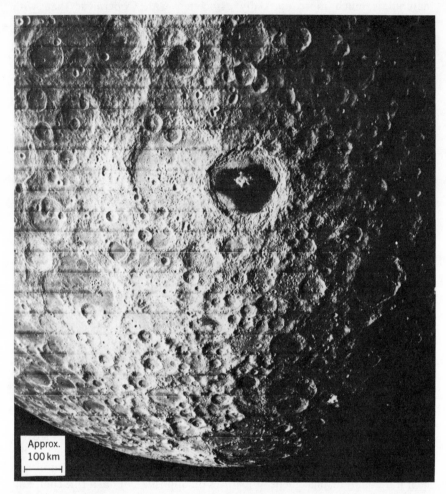

Figure 7.16: Far side of the moon: southern hemisphere, centering on about 125°E long. Note high crater density; large crater (Tsolkovsky) about 240 km diameter with terracing, smooth floor, irregular central peak. Photo by NASA, Lunar Orbiter III.

example occurs in the crater Alphonsus, Figure 7.14. The most spectacular rilles on the moon are Ariadaeus and Hyginus, near the center of the visible face. Both of these rilles are a hundred kilometers or more in length: see Figure 7.17. There are also occasional sinuous rilles, although none as prominent as the large straight rilles. The best example is known as Schröter's rille, near the crater Aristarchus: see Figure 7.18. The sinuous rilles look as though they have been worn by erosion, like a stream. Alternative hypotheses are that the erosion was by a stream of water [536, 570], or by a stream of ash [291].

Some of the sinuous rilles show evidence of being rather new; hence difficulties of the water erosion hypothesis are first, a source of water, and second, a means of preventing its rapid complete evaporation. The association of craters 1–10 km in diameter with the heads of rilles suggests that a large meteorite is required to break through a permafrost layer to release trapped water. The depth of this water must vary from place to place, since most craters do not give rise to rilles. To prevent evaporation, there have been suggested an atmosphere generated by a very large comet [536] or, more plausibly, ice created by the drain of heat of vaporization for some evaporating water [570].

Lunar Orbiter satellite photography has revealed several small rilles, both straight and sinuous, 100 or more meters in width and several kilometers in length. One sinuous rille runs down the center of the Alpine Valley, a great graben-like cleft. In other places, the rilles form a gridiron-like pattern, usually associated with volcanic-like craters. Their explanation must be considered still much in doubt.

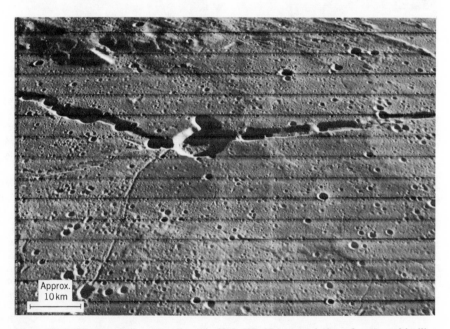

Figure 7.17: Hyginus Rille, approximately 8°N, 6°E. Note association of craters with rille, wrinkle ridges. Central crater is 10 km in diameter, 800 meters deep. Photo by NASA, Lunar Orbiter III.

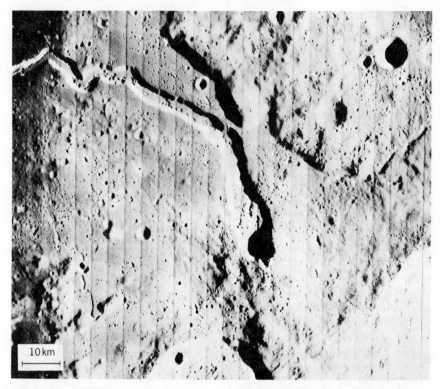

Figure 7.18: Schröter's Rille and Cobra Head. Approximately 25°N, 49°W. Note "source" of rille in mound, sinuosity and parallelism of sides of rille. Photo by NASA, Lunar Orbiter V.

Figure 7.19: Oceanus Procellarum and crater Marius, approximately 10°N, 50°W. Note wrinkle ridges, domes, sinuous rilles, shallowness of crater Marius, gentleness of relief. Photo by NASA, Lunar Orbiter II.

326

Protrusions

The third category of lunar features includes protrusions, hills, domes, peaks, and the like. In several places there are some domes that look as though they were due to some sort of igneous intrusion. Several such domes appear in Figure 7.19. The domes are 3 to 15 km in diameter and 300 to 500 meters high; several are quite rough and show cracks and pits near their summits. Such structures could be caused by a magma thrusting up into a crust. The existence of features having a definitely volcanic character is relatively rare. One of the most marked is in Regiomontanus, immediately to the northeast of Deslandres (see Figure 7.13). The crater Alphonsus has a definite central peak of some 3500 feet, shown in Figure 7.20. Alphonsus is also the site of suspected gas emissions.

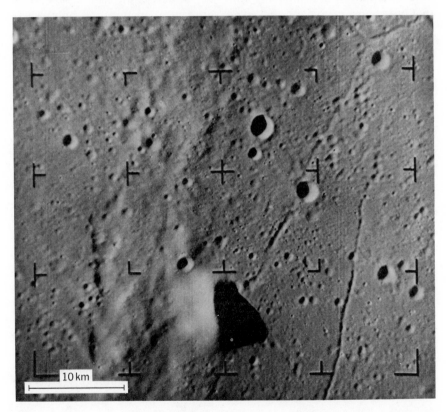

Figure 7.20: Crater Alphonsus central peak, 13°S, 2°W. Note volcanic appearance of peak, rilles with associated craters, smoother texture of terrain to west of peak. Photo by NASA, Ranger IX.

The third type of protrusion, ridges, is very common on the earth but rare on the moon. There are a few features on the moon with a ridge-like character, which look like dikes that had intruded into fissures opened by tension. Many maria show extensive wrinkle-like ridges, such as show prominently in Figure 7.19; see also Figures 7.13 and 7.22. On a much smaller scale, in some Ranger photos are detected wrinkles passing through craters, suggesting an internal origin [411].

Lineaments

Some investigators detect general patterns of lineaments on the moon which underlie the terrain [118]. In most cases these lineaments radiate from a major feature such as Mare Imbrium. An example is in the area just to the north of and including the crater Alphonsus; it appears in Figure 7.20 as a marked difference in texture, in a band 1 km wide just west of the central peak, from that of the area east of the peak. There are several areas on the moon where there is a noticeable ridge-and-trough pattern in the surface texture not markedly related to the topography, as if it were controlled by some sub-surface structure.

There is also a marked change in texture on the east side of Alphonsus (see Figure 7.14), associated with the abrupt rise of uplands which have an appearance like bread dough. A more localized example of an upland with a sharp boundary is shown in Figure 7.21. This "bread dough" appearance suggests high viscosity, which in turn would be characteristic of acidic rocks [293].

Associated with the "tree-bark" texture of uplands such as those in Figures 7.14 and 7.21 is the scarcity of small craters previously mentioned. It appears as though both phenomena are the consequence of transfer of frag-mented material. However, the texture and lack of craters occur even in some rather level uplands, which makes it difficult to hypothesize a mechanism which would not also act in the maria.

Faults

Of the fourth category of feature, faults, the only type found on earth which is also found on the moon is the normal fault as defined in Section 1.4. The best example of a normal fault is known as the Straight Wall, located on the east side of Mare Nubium just north of Deslandres (see Figure 7.13). The Straight Wall is almost 100 km long and about 250 meters high. As mentioned, no wrench or strike-slip faults have been found yet on the moon [291, 361].

Maria

The final feature, the largest and the most prominent on the moon other than the craters, includes the plains or maria. The most marked characteristic

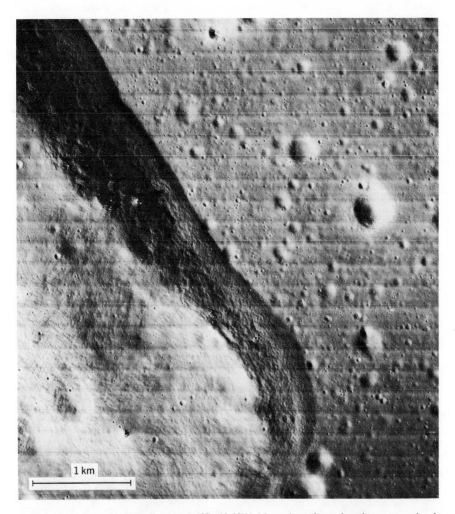

Figure 7.21: Oceanus Procellarum, 2.4°S, 42.8°W. Note sharp boundary between uplands on left and mare on right, higher crater density on mare, "tree bark" texture of uplands. Photo by NASA, Lunar Orbiter III.

of the maria is that they are much darker. This darkness on the earth, of course, is generally associated with more basic materials; the obvious suggestion from their color is that the maria are due to lava flows. If this is true, then the lava on the moon must be much more fluid than lava on the earth, because nowhere on the moon are there scarps such as are found on terrestrial lava flows, on the order of 5 to 10 meters high. If the lava on the moon possessed viscosity and freezing rate similar to those of lava on the earth, there would be marked irregular cliffs of this sort. Furthermore, the maria are extraordinarily level: domes having a slope of only 1 to 2 degrees are clearly distinguishable by their shadows [291].

Two alternatives to lava flows are suggested to account for the maria. The first is ash flows: a volcanic emission which is a combination of gas and fine solid particles will spread a surprising distance, despite the absence of an atmosphere, and will result in quite a level surface [291]. The second alternative is that the maria are deposits of fragments created by the impacting of many particles of all sizes on the moon. Again, there is a problem in the means of transport of such fragments; electrostatic effects on dust particles have been suggested, as discussed below [137].

An interesting feature the maria sometimes evidence is a downward settling. In some cases craters which have been "flooded" by maria material show an erasure of the crater pattern on the side toward the center of the maria, but not on the side away from the maria. Also there are some cases

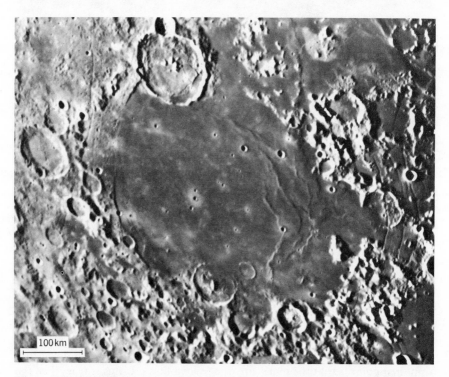

Figure 7.22: Mare Humorum, approximately 25°S, 40°W. Note concentric rille system, wrinkle ridges, crater rims "drowned" on side toward mare, white haloes around new craters. Photo by Catalina Observatory and Lunar & Planetary Laboratory, University of Arizona.

of concentric rille systems around the centers of the maria. A good example of these features are found in Mare Humorum in the southwest part of the visible face of the moon, shown in Figure 7.22. If there is indeed any isostatic adjustment as was suggested in connection with the shallowness of large craters, then the maria must be composed of heavier material than the surroundings [291, 363].

The Lunar Surface Layer

Regardless of the large-scale nature of lunar features, the Luna, Ranger, Surveyor, and Lunar Orbiter photos have generally been held to confirm that the lunar surface layer is the consequence of a long and thorough process of fragmentation and refragmentation. The outlines of craters generally are quite rounded, except for evidently very recent craters. A good example is shown in Figure 7.23. The major feature is a new primary crater about 150 meters in diameter. Evident in the photo are the sharp edge of the new crater, despite some slumping on the inside wall; many boulders thrown out in a pattern which becomes quite irregular more than two radii from the center; and some secondary craters. All other craters of more than 25 meters diameter have rounded outlines. But there are many smaller craters with sharp edges, suggesting an ample source of small fragments to round off the contours of larger craters. An alternative hypothesis to a layer fragmented by meteorite impact is a layer of ash.

A continual fragmentation together with the welding which occurs in a very high vacuum would result in a layer of porous, low-density material. The smoothness to the radar coupled with the strong backscattering of visible light, discussed in Chapter 6, suggest that the moon is covered with such a structure, roughly on the scale of 10 μ to 1 mm.

Since the maximum grain size in this sort of structure is determined by the ratio of the weight of a grain to forces between the grains, we should expect that there would be some sort of limit on grain size. The Surveyor digger experiments indicate that the surface layer is weakly cohesive (like fine damp sand) and with most grains less than 60 μ in diameter, an appreciable fraction less than 10 μ. The Surveyors also found somewhat higher densities than inferred from radio emission and radar: 0.7 to 1.2 gm/cm^3 for the upper few millimeters, and 1.6 gm/cm^3 at a depth of several centimeters. The corresponding porosities vary from 0.8 to 0.5. The thermal inertia $1/\gamma$ found from temperature variations was somewhat higher: 1/500 [511, 525, 533, 562].

Since most slopes on the moon are rather gentle, the smooth uniformity of distribution of the small material seems difficult to attain, particularly the sharp intersection of level areas with rises, as in Figure 7.21. Such sharpness of intersection occurs on quite a small scale, as evidenced by Surveyor photos: see Figure 7.24. The transport mechanism must be one that

Figure 7.23: Oceanus Procellarum, 2°N, 42°S. Note sharp edge and slumping inside new crater, pattern of boulders thrown out, secondary craters, more rounded edges on older craters. Photo by NASA, Lunar Orbiter III.

operates on quite a small, almost centimeter, scale. Gold has suggested electrostatic effects [137]. There must be an appreciable potential gradient close to the surface; if a small particle is knocked loose by a meteorite, then it will have a charge relative to its surroundings, and will be buoyed further than if it were neutral. Such a mechanism would operate to smooth out slopes until they were negligible. But, again, Surveyor III raises a problem: the same smooth, fine-grained surface sharply intersecting protruding rocks occurs on slopes of more than 10° [511].

By comparing the degree of rounding of the rims of old craters with

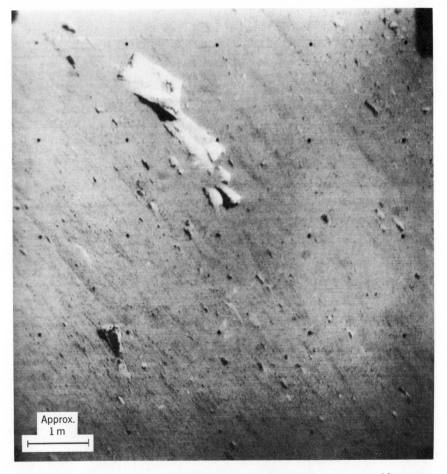

Approx.
1 m

Figure 7.24: Area in vicinity of Surveyor I, covering about 50 square meters. Note angularity of blocks, whiteness of blocks compared to fine surface material. Photo by NASA, Surveyor I.

laboratory craters covered with varying thicknesses of sand, it has been deduced that the layer of granular material on the moon varies in thickness from 1 to 10 meters [192, 562]. The bearing capacity of this layer has been estimated in at least three different ways: (1) from the maximum slopes which the material can maintain, at least 2×10^4 dynes/cm^2 [193]; (2) from the size of rocks, and their distance from their originating crater, sustained by the material, 2 to 4×10^5 dynes/cm^2 [169]; (3) from the touchdown dynamics of Surveyor landers, about 6×10^5 dynes/cm^2 [194, 562].

A final puzzle provided by the Surveyor is the color of the surface material: an extremely thin surface layer of light dust, over a darker layer of fragmented material about 2 meters thick, over a much brighter compacted material. Evidence of the brightness of this lower layer is the albedo of the rocks thrown out of craters penetrating more than 2 meters [511]. Lower layer material may be the source of the bright rays associated with large new craters. An alternative hypothesis is that the ray brightness results from the recent fine pulverization of throwout material.

Summary

In summary, the moon is largely characterized by having a considerably quiter geology than the earth. The small likelihood of reaching high temperatures at shallow depth we should expect would result in much less igneous activity. The external stimuli provided by meteorites in at least recent geological times is much less than that provided by erosion and sedimentation on the earth. Consequently, the moon is much nearer equilibrium condition than the earth; the relief on the moon averages a good deal less than six times as high as that on the earth, as we might expect from equal-strength considerations. However, the more information obtained about the moon, the more evidence is found of activity that is generated internally: for example, the alpha-scattering experiment on Surveyors 5, 6, and 7 indicates that the surface chemical composition is similar to basalt, a differentiated material (see Table 9.1). It is still a matter of debate, however, as to the exact nature of the internal response of the moon, and even as to whether the stimulus to this internal response of the moon is mainly that of meteorites themselves or whether it is generated by outgassing, igneous activity, or other internal sources.

7.3 The Surface of Mars

Cratering Frequency Estimates

If we go through the same extrapolation exercise (7.1.11 to 7.2.1) for Mars as for the moon to obtain an estimate of impact rates, we must take account of:

1. Higher frequencies of meteorite approach because of closer proximity to the asteroid belt.

2. Lower approach velocities, in proportion to the circumsolar Kepler velocity $\sqrt{GM_\odot/a}$.

3. Different capture cross section, due to different mass and radius.

4. Different escape velocity, due to different mass and radius.

Of these points, 2 through 4 are all straightforward and only 1 is a speculative matter. The combination of 2 and 4, using Tables 5.1 and 5.3, results in a typical impact velocity on Mars being 9.5 km/sec (corresponding to 15 km/sec for the earth). The combination of 2, 3, and 4 results in a frequency of impact per unit area for a given mass of meteorite on Mars 0.62 times that on earth, and a formula for Mars corresponding to (7.1.11):

Mars, assuming same meteorite flux as earth:

$$\log_{10} f = \begin{cases} 12.32 - 3.0 \ \log_{10} D, & D < 327 \text{ meters} \\ 9.30 - 1.8 \ \log_{10} D, & D > 327 \text{ meters} \end{cases}$$

(7.3.1)

where f is per 10^6 km²/Æ.

Concerning point 1, calculations which assume that meteorites come from asteroids obtain about 25 for the Mars/earth ratio of meteorite fluxes [18]. However, as discussed in Section 5.3, such calculations may not be too meaningful because of the difficulty of reconciling the results with meteorite age distributions, indicating the possibility of another source such as comets [303, 433]. Applying the 25 ratio we get:

Mars, assuming a meteorite flux 25 times the earth's:

$$\log_{10} f = \begin{cases} 13.52 - 3.0 \ \log_{10} D, & D < 327 \text{ meters} \\ 10.70 - 1.8 \ \log_{10} D, & D > 327 \text{ meters} \end{cases}$$

(7.3.2)

Applying the lifetime factor of 4.55×10^9 years, analogous to (7.2.2),

Mars, assuming a meteorite flux 25 times the earth's:

$$\log_{10} F = \begin{cases} 14.18 - 3.0 \ \log_{10} D, & D < 327 \text{ meters} \\ 11.36 - 1.8 \ \log_{10} D, & D > 327 \text{ meters} \end{cases}$$

(7.3.3)

The crater density on Mars obtained from the Mariner IV photos of Mars (Figure 7.27) for diameters greater than 20 km approximates the formula

$$\text{Mars: } \log_{10} F = 8.85 - 1.71 \log_{10} D \tag{7.3.4}$$

For diameters below 20 km, there is an apparent decrease in the slope, as indicated in Figure 7.25, where the observed crater density falls short of the predicted by a factor of about 2.4, suggesting an age of 2.0×10^9 years for the

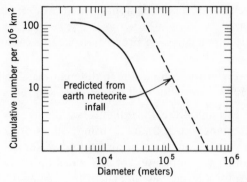

Figure 7.25: Integral distribution of crater diameters on Mars. From Leighton *et al.* [244].

surface of Mars. These results are probably about as good as can be expected until a better understanding of the sources of meteorites is attained [30, 164, 302].

Visual Observations of Mars

Most of the interesting information about Mars observed from the earth is visual because much of the information is from its color, and the length of the time exposure required for photography coupled with atmospheric shimmer results in loss of considerable detail. The best resolution attainable with visual observation of Mars is about 0.2″, which is equivalent to about 60 km on the surface of Mars at closest approach. Figure 7.26 is an example of the detail obtained by a careful observer.

The surface of Mars is divided into three main types of areas on the basis of color. About 70 percent is orange-yellow or reddish, called *continentes*. About 27 percent is actually a reddish-brown shade, called *maria*, but looks greenish or bluish compared with the continentes. The maria often tend to be

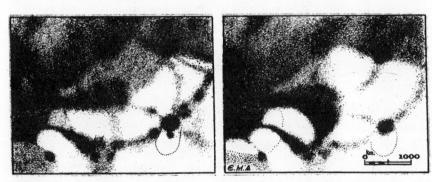

Figure 7.26: Drawings of the Solis Lacus region. *Left:* 1924; *right:* 1926. The dotted region in the lower right corner was obscured by clouds. From Antoniadi [459, p. 141].

located in a succession of broad rounded features on the order of 150 km wide, similar to the lower half of Figure 7.26. Under poor visual conditions these successions tend to appear linear, and hence are the origin of the idea of canals. The remaining 3 percent of the surface is white and located at the polar caps.

The inclination of the Martian equator to the ecliptic is 24°. Consequently there are appreciable seasonal variations in temperature. Seasonal variations in coloring are observed. The polar caps almost disappear during the Martian summer and then grow appreciably with the onset of winter. In the spring, as they decline, considerable irregularities appear at the edge of the polar caps. These irregularities appear in the same locations year after year, as if they were associated with topographic features. The maria have some seasonal variation; there is in general a pole-to-equator progression of a darkening each spring which fades away in the autumn. However, there is considerable erratic variation in the darkness in the maria, and also superimposed on the seasonal changes are some considerable secular or long periodic variations, sometimes covering areas of several hundred kilometers. The changes between the two drawings in Figure 7.26 are typical of such secular variation.

In addition to the aforedescribed features, which apparently pertain to the solid surface of Mars, there are more evanescent phenomena:

1. White clouds, often in large formations extending several hundred kilometers and remaining for several days or even weeks and sometimes moving at velocities up to 30 km/hr.

2. Dust storms, sometimes seasonal, but usually occurring suddenly and erratically and often again covering hundreds or thousands of kilometers of the Martian surface. Occasional dust storms will take several weeks or a couple of months to die away.

3. Blue haze, best observed near the limb, which is a progressive loss of detail in shorter wavelengths. It may be either an atmospheric effect or an intrinsic loss of surface contrast.

The Mariner IV experiment obtained an upper limit of only 7.0 mb for the Martian atmospheric surface pressure; this rareness of the atmosphere, coupled with the low temperature of $230 \pm 50°K$ (Table 6.4) places severe limitations on the ways in which the seasonal and erratic variations in the appearance on Mars can be explained. In particular, it is difficult to find a capability of such an atmosphere holding enough water vapor to be a source and a sink for the polar caps. It therefore has been suggested that the caps are CO_2 instead [243]. The rareness of the atmosphere also indicates that the dust particles in the storms must be quite small, a few microns in diameter, to take so long to settle down on the Martian surface again. The dust storm suggests that most of the Martian surface is covered with a loose layer; such a layer would be consistent with the low thermal inertia, $1/\gamma$, of 0.004 (Table 6.4). A pecularity of the maria, however, is that they do not become permanently covered by the dust from storms: they always show through again after the dust settles. Some observers therefore believe that they may be some form of vegetation. Objections to this hypothesis are (1) the low temperature (below freezing) and consequent lack of water, and (2) the infrared spectra of maria shows no resemblance to that of chlorophyll [98, 302].

Mariner IV Photography

In recent years, there have been two important new types of data pertaining to the topography of Mars. One was the Mariner IV photography, the best of which is shown as Figure 7.27.

The decrease in slope of the frequency curve in Figure 7.25 for diameters

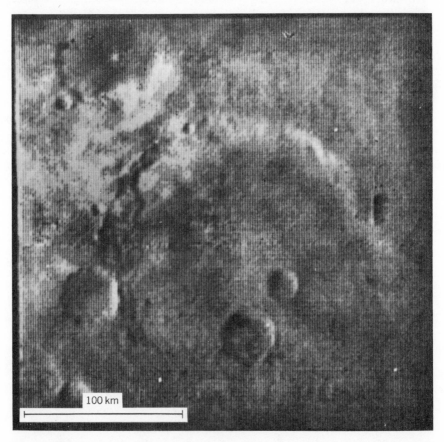

100 km

Figure 7.27: Surface of Mars. Note several large, rather shallow-appearing craters. Photo by NASA, Mariner IV.

below 20 km suggests that erosion has been operating on the Martian surface. Also suggestive of erosion is the relative shallowness of Martian craters: they appear to have a depth-to-diameter ratio of only about 0.025, compared to about 0.10 on the moon (this "shallowness" may be a consequence of fogging of the pictures) [242]. The break in the crater size at 20 km has been interpreted by Öpik [302] as indicating an erosion rate about 0.03 times that in a terrestrial desert, but 70 times that due to micrometeorites on the moon. The Mariner IV photos covered too small a portion of the surface of Mars to show any significant differences between continentes and maria [242, 244, 302].

Radar Observations

The second type of significant new information about Mars is the determination of variations in elevations by radar. As discussed in Section 6.4, the dark areas appear to be highlands of about 6 km elevation above the bright areas for features of limited extent, and 10–20 km for the extensive maria. Such elevations do not imply any greater departures from hydrostatic equilibrium than exist in the earth. The slopes are all rather gentle, 4° or less. Particularly shallow slopes (1 to 2°) were found for features showing secular change, such as those in Figure 7.26, suggesting that the change is caused by the wind-borne deposit and removal of dust. The identification of dark areas as highlands leads to the interpretation of the "canals" as ridges. The very slight atmosphere on Mars indicates that there should be insignificant temperature differences in the elevation differences of 10–20 km or less [353, 354].

Summary

In summary, it appears that Mars is geologically much more alive than the moon but definitely moribund compared to the earth. This is still much more than we can say about Venus or Mercury.

PROBLEMS

7.1. Calculate the minimum mass of a spherical meteorite that can penetrate the earth's atmosphere without losing more than, say half its momentum, for densities of 3.5 and 7.8 gm/cm^3.

7.2. Derive the ballistic equation (7.1.8) to get the range r for a projectile departing with initial velocity v and angle α to the horizontal.

7.3. Calculate the frequency of impact of meteorites of approach velocity 10 km/sec for the moon, (7.2.1), from that given for the earth, (7.1.11), neglecting "focusing" effects.

7.4. How deep a hole would a meteorite of density 3.3 gm/cm^3 and diameter 10 meters with an impact velocity of 10 km/sec make on the moon? On Mars? (Assume surface with same density.)

7.5. Discuss the relative merits of the dust and the lava hypotheses for the lunar maria.

7.6. Discuss the possible causes of the dark area on Mars and their variations.

7.7. How many craters will we see on "Mariner" type photos of Mercury?

REFERENCES

Charters [72] gives a general discussion of hypervelocity impact. The numerical integration of hypervelocity impact is described by *Bjork* [33] and *Bjork & Brooks* [34]; its application to the Arizona Meteor Crater, by *Shoemaker* [362]. References for empirical rules based on nuclear explosions and their application to impact cratering are *Violet* [422], *Shoemaker et al.* [366], and *Short* [367]. The distribution of ejecta is analyzed by *Carlson & Jones* [66], *Pike* [316], *Gault et al.* [131], and *Gault et al.* [129]. *Gault et al.* [130] discuss low-velocity impact applicable to secondary cratering. Descriptions of meteor craters on the earth's surface are given by *Krinov* [227] and *Baldwin* [21]. Shock effects are reviewed by *Short* [368] and *Chao* [69]. The text on meteor flight through the atmosphere is by *Öpik* [299]. Extrapolation of terrestrial meteor infall rates to the moon is described by *Shoemaker et al.* [366] and *Whipple* [439].

Recent books on the moon are *Baldwin* [21] and *Fielder* [118]; collections of articles are *Kuiper & Middlehurst* [232], *Kopal* [217], *Hess et al.* [175], and *Brown et al.* [55]. The summary of lunar geology in Section 7.2 is based mainly on reviews by *Shoemaker* [361, 363], *O'Keefe* [291], and *Kopal* [218]; also *Smith* [503]. Important aids to study of the moon are collections of photographs edited by *Kuiper* [230] and *Kopal* [219].

Results of space probe experiments are described in detail in compilations by *Heacock et al.* [168, 169] *Jaffe et al.* [194, 562], and *Vreblanovich et al.* [511].

Various interpretations of the photographs referred to herein are by *Kuiper* [231], *Urey* [411], *Shoemaker* [364], *Quaide et al.* [325], *Gault et al.* [468], *O'Keefe et al.* [293], and *Lingenfelter et al.* [570]. Crater counts are by *Hartmann* [163] and *Chapman* [551]. Papers on the nature of the lunar surface layer are *Gold* [137], *Jaffe* [192, 193], *Ryan* [499], *Hapke* [160], *Scott* [533], and *O'Keefe & Scott* [528]; others are in a volume edited by *Salisbury & Glaser* [356]. *Ross* [579] calculates erosion rates.

The principal English language text solely on Mars is *Vaucouleurs* [412]. The description in Section 7.3 is based mainly on *Dollfus* [98] and *Öpik* [302]; other recent reviews are by *Loomis* [248] and *Rea* [328]. There have been three waves of papers on Martian cratering rates since Mariner IV, each energetically correcting the previous wave; the latest wave comprises the papers of *Öpik* [302], *Binder* [30], and *Hartman* [164]. The Mariner IV photography is described by *Leighton et al.* [244] and *Leighton* [242]. The interpretation of elevation differences deduced from radar is found in *Sagan & Pollack* [353, 354] and *Pollack & Sagan* [320]. The behavior of carbon dioxide on Mars and its pertinence to the ice caps is the subject of the paper by *Leighton & Murray* [243].

Chapter 8

METEORITES AND TEKTITES

The only samples of solid matter we have from outside the earth are the objects known as meteorites. They are universally considered to have come from outside the earth because:

1. They are shaped—ablated, and sometimes fragmented—as if they had passed rapidly through the atmosphere, but are not associated with any volcanic activity.
2. In many cases, the meteorite is observed to fall, often in association with a detonation or a fireball.
3. They virtually always contain free nickel and iron which are rarely found in terrestrial rocks.
4. The free iron and nickel has a banded crystalline structure, called a Widmanstätten pattern (see Figure 8.5) which is never found in artificial iron-nickel objects.

Meteorites occur in three very distinct classes according to iron and nickel content. The total Fe + Ni proportion (oxides and sulfides as well as free) of *iron* meteorites is always more than 0.94; of *stony-iron* meteorites, always between 0.40 and 0.60; and of *stony* meteorites, always less than 0.35, and usually more than 0.20. If the identification of "meteorite" is limited to item 1 of the foregoing list, then there is a fourth class of objects: natural glasses called *tektites*, which always have a Fe + Ni proportion less than 0.05. It is a matter of debate whether tektites are of extraterrestrial origin, because of their chemical similarity to the earth's crust as well as the lack of observed falls. Hence we shall follow the customary practice of discussing the tektites quite separately from the "proper" meteorites.

8.1 General Properties and Classification

Statistics of Meteorites

Meteorite occurrences are classified as *falls* if they are observed to fall, and as *finds* if not observed prior to finding. Table 8.1 lists falls and finds by class. A single "occurrence" often results in many separate pieces. There are

TABLE 8.1: CLASSIFICATION OF METEORITE OCCURRENCES

Meteorite	Falls	Finds
Irons	43	551
Stony irons	12	58
Stones	723	404
Tektites	0	10
Total	778	1023

Based on Hey [475, pp. xv–xxx].

probably more than 1,000,000 specimens of the proper meteorites—irons, stony irons, and stones—and about 650,000 of the tektites. Table 8.1 is biased in favor of the iron meteorites because they are much easier to distinguish from terrestrial rocks than are stone meteorites. Hence the proportion of stone meteorites coming to earth from space is probably more than the 0.92 deduced from the "falls" column in Table 8.1. Another bias is that many more meteorite falls are observed in densely populated areas. In Japan, of which the area is 0.382×10^6 km², 30 meteorite falls have been recovered in 90 years. If the same rate applied to the entire earth (510×10^6 km²), then there would be an average of about 450 recovered meteorite falls per year.

The size of meteorite specimens ranges from 60 tons down to 0.3 mg, or even smaller, if we include meteorite dust: magnetic iron spherules less than 0.2 mm in diameter usually found in deep-sea sediments. There are several iron meteorites that weigh more than a ton, but the largest stone meteorite only approaches one ton. The fall rates given by Figure 5.12 are based on the assumptions that 90 percent of a stone meteorite and 80 percent of an iron meteorite are ablated passing through the atmosphere (see Section 8.4). Adjusting for these ablation percentages, we get for the frequency of fall f of a meteorite of mass greater than m striking the earth's solid surface [166]:

$$\log_{10} f = 0.27 - \log_{10} m \qquad (8.1.1)$$

for stony meteorites, and:

$$\log_{10} f = -2.81 - 0.7 \log_{10} m \qquad (8.1.2)$$

for iron meteorites, for f in km^{-2} year^{-1} and m in grams. The difference in slopes of equations of (8.1.1) and (8.1.2) is consistent with the iron meteorites having a greater crushing strength, and thus a greater resistance to breaking up upon collision. Recent acoustic wave data on infalling bodies indicate that there probably are even greater biases because of considerable differences in fragility [365].

Meteorite falls show no significant correlation with other astronomical phenomena; in particular, they are not correlated with the meteor showers, which are correlated with some comets [263].

Of the minerals described in Section 1.1, those that are more basic—low O:M ratio—are more common in meteorites. A distinction in pyroxenes which is sometimes important is between a rectangular (orthorhombic) and skewed (monoclinic) structure. The orthorhombic pyroxenes important in meteorites are enstatite (mole ratio $Fe/(Fe + Mg) < 0.10$), bronzite ($0.10 < Fe/(Fe + Mg) < 0.20$), and hypersthene ($0.20 < Fe/(Fe + Mg)$). (These ratios distinguishing among pyroxenes are meteoriticists' definitions, and differ from those used by mineralogists.) The important monoclinic pyroxenes usually contain calcium: diopside ($CaMgSi_2O_6$) and pigeonite ($CaFeSi_2O_6$ or $CaFeSiAlO_6$).

The less common monoclinic form appears to be a consequence of mechanical deformation of the orthorhombic form. The relative proportions of magnesium and iron in the orthorhombic pyroxene is the principal means of naming important categories of chondritic meteorities: enstatite, bronzite, and hypersthene.

Of the feldspar series shown in Figure 1.3, the plagioclase is most common in meteorites, usually in the oligoclase range.

The principal mineral forms of the free iron and nickel that distinguish meteorites from terrestrial rocks are *kamacite*, body-centered cubic α-iron with less than 7 percent nickel, and *taenite*, face-centered cubic γ-iron with more than 27 percent nickel. (See Figure 8.1.)

In addition, meteorites contain lesser quantities of several minerals containing chalcophile or volatile elements which are rarely or never found on earth: troilite, FeS; cohenite, Fe_3C; schreibersite, $(Fe, Ni)_3P$; oldhamite, CaS; daubreelite, $FeCr_2S_4$; lawrencite, $FeCl_2$; and pentlandite, $(Fe, Ni)_9S_8$.

Beyond the iron content already mentioned, meteorites are classified according to the extent to which the iron is oxidized; according to their mineralogy; and according to their crystal structure: that is, the principal properties that might pertain to their history. The classification now used almost universally is essentially that instituted by Prior in 1920 with some subsequent refinements. Table 8.2 gives all types of meteorites in this

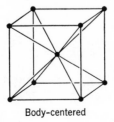

Body-centered

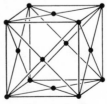

Face-centered

Figure 8.1: Cubic lattices.

TABLE 8.2: CLASSIFICATION OF METEORITES

Class	Portion of Classified Falls	FeO/(FeO + MgO)	Principal Content*	Structure
Stones				
Chondrites	(0.837)			
Carbonaceous, or C		0.33 to 1.00	Ol, Ka, Ta, Tr, Se, C	
Unclassified	0.003			
Type I, or C1	0.007		No Ol, mostly Se	1
Type II, or C2	0.019		Equal Ol and Se	2
Type III, or olivine-pigeonite or ornansite, or C3	0.022		Mostly Ol	3, 4
LL, amphoterite, or soko-banjite	0.056	0.44	Hy, Ol, Pl, Tr; Fe, 0.19–0.22	3, 4, 5, 6
Ordinary			Ol, Hy, Br, Ka, Ta, Tr, Pl, Cl	
L, or hypersthene	0.392	0.20 to 0.33	Fe, 0.20–0.23	3, 4, 5, 6
H, or bronzite	0.323	0.10 to 0.20	Fe, 0.27–0.30	3, 4, 5, 6
Enstatite, or E			En, Pl, Ka, Ta, Tr	
Type I, or HH	0.004	0.00 to 0.05	Fe, 0.32–0.35; high S	3, 4
Type II	0.016	0.00 to 0.10	Fe, 0.24–0.30; low S	4, 5, 6
Achondrites	(0.085)		CaO, 0.05–0.25	
Calcium-rich, or basaltic		0.48 to 0.66	Cl, Pl	
Eucrites	0.037		Cl, Pl	Like terrestrial igneous rock
Howardites	0.017	~0.55	Hy, Cl, Pl	Brecciated

Structure column note: Petrological types (see p. 352); most common underlined.

Calcium poor			CaO < 0.03	
Diogenites	0.011	0.22 to 0.33	Hy, Cl	Brecciated
Ureilites	0.003	0.16 to 0.20	Ol, Cl, Ka	Silicate grains in black carbonaceous matrix
Aubrites	0.010 (0.017)	0.00 to 0.07	En, Cl	Normally brecciated
Stony Irons				
Pallasites	0.006	~0.25	Ka, Ta, Ol, Tr; Ni-Fe, 0.25–0.63	Large Ol crystals in Ni-Fe matrix
Mesosiderites	0.010	~0.50	Hy, Pl, Ol, Ka, Ta, Tr; Ni-Fe, 0.40–0.70	Fine grained, complex
Irons				
Octahedrites, or O	(0.062) 0.050		Ka, Ta, Tr, Sc	Ka, Ta bands parallel to octahedral planes
Extremely coarse (Oge)			Ni, 0.055–0.065	Ka bands >4 mm
Coarsest (Ogg)			Ni, 0.06–0.07	Ka bands, 2–4 mm
Coarse (Og)			Ni, 0.07–0.09	Ka bands, 1–2 mm
Medium (Om)			Ni, 0.075–0.09	Ka bands, 0.5–1.0 mm
Fine (Of)			Ni, 0.08–0.10	Ka bands, 0.25–0.5 mm
Finest (Off)			Ni, 0.10–0.14	Ka bands, <0.25 mm
Hexahedrites, or H	0.010		Ka, Sc, Tr; Ni, 0.04–0.06 Ta, Ka	Large Ka crystals
Ataxites, or D			Ni, 0.12–0.38	Finely granular, structureless aggregate
Nickel-rich	0.001			
Nickel-poor	0.001			

* Abbreviations: Br = bronzite; C = carbon; Cl = clinopyroxene; En = enstatite; Fe = iron; Hy = hypersthene; Ka = kamacite; Ol = olivine; Or = orthopyroxene; Pl = plagioclase; S = sulfur; Sc = schreibersite; Se = serpentine; Ta = taenite; Tr = troilite.

Based on Mason [263, p. 52], Wood [446, p. 340], Anders [12], Hey [475], and Van Schmus & Wood [414].

classification for which there have been 2 or more observed falls (plus ataxites, of which there is only one fall but many finds). The index of oxidation iron of in Table 8.2 is the ratio $FeO/(FeO + MgO)$. Items in the table which some investigators might classify differently are (1) LL (or amphoterite) is sometimes considered a subclass of the L (or hypersthene); (2) the enstatite type I and II classes are widely regarded as rather arbitrary divisions of a continuum of characteristics; and (3) the carbonaceous type III, or olivine-pigeonite, includes or omits different meteorites according to whether the classification is based on carbon on pigeonite content. Because of these types of uncertainties, the portions of falls in Table 8.2 should be regarded as approximate.

8.2 Chemistry and Structure of Chondrites

The name of the chondrites derives from the fact that most of them contain chondrules: spheroidal bodies 1 mm in diameter (see Figure 8.2). However, a more fundamental distinction from the other stony meteorites, the

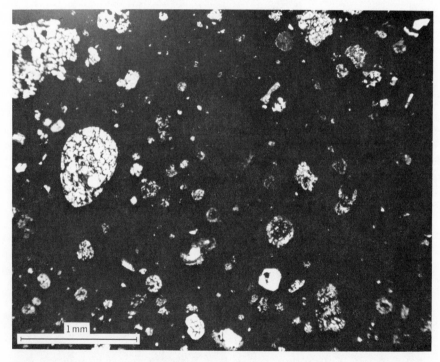

Figure 8.2*a*: Cross section of a petrological type 2 chondritic meteorite (Murray, a carbonaceous II chondrite, C2). Note opaque amorphous ground mass, evidencing no heating or crystallization, associated with hydrocarbon content; relatively few and irregular chondrules. From Wood [446, Pl. 6a]. Photo by American Natural History Museum, New York.

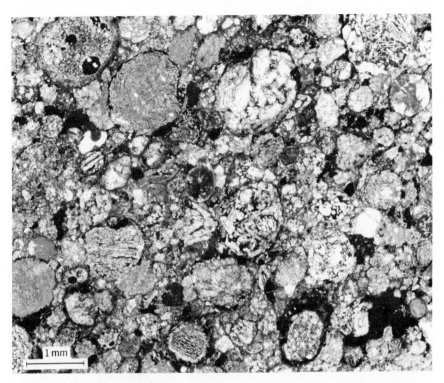

Figure 8.2*b*: Cross section of a petrological type 4 chondritic meteorite (Cynthiana, a hypersthene chondrite, L4). Note well-defined chondrules, some with microcrystalline, others with barred, structure; moderate recrystallization; uniform olivine and pyroxene structure; small amounts of black troilite. From Van Schmus & Wood [414, Fig. 8].

achondrites, is the texture of the chondrites: most chondrites apparently have not experienced as severe heating processes as have the achondrites.

The chondrites are the most studied class of meteorites because (1) they are by far the most common falls, as indicated by Table 8.2; (2) they have a chemical composition close to that of the sun, lacking mainly the volatiles H, He, Ne, C, N, O, and S; and (3) their textures, with the metals and silicates mixed together, imply that they have never been subjected to any severe pressures or temperatures, and hence are probably much closer to the primitive nonvolatile chemical composition of the solar system than the severely differentiated crust of the earth.

Iron Content and Oxidation

The main bases of chemical classification of the chondrites are primarily the extent to which their iron content is oxidized; and secondarily, the total iron content. These bases are shown in Figure 8.3. The division of the chondrites into six distinct classes according to degree of oxidation is obvious in the figure. Less obvious is a division according to total iron content, but it is significantly present. If all classes had the same total iron, they would all lie on the same line of 45° slope. In actuality, the classes appear to lie on at least four such 45° tracks, as indicated on the figure, corresponding to total iron contents of about 21, 25, 28.5, and 33 percent respectively. Of the chemically active common elements—H, O, C, Si, Mg, S, and Fe—iron, the heaviest, is the least affected by changes in pressure and temperature. Hence if we wished to explain the iron oxidations and contents as consequences of different histories since an original uniform chemical mix, the reduction-oxidation variation would depend mainly on the loss of volatiles, while the total iron content would depend mainly on the loss of silicates. Both of these

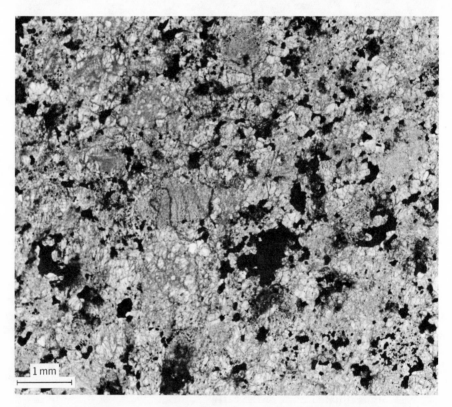

Figure 8.2c: Cross section of a petrological type 6 chondritic meteorite (Peace River, a hypersthene chondrite, L6). Note extensive recrystallization; almost complete obliteration of chondrules; appreciable development of plagioclase: white grains about 0.1 mm in diameter. From Van Schmus & Wood [414, Fig. 11].

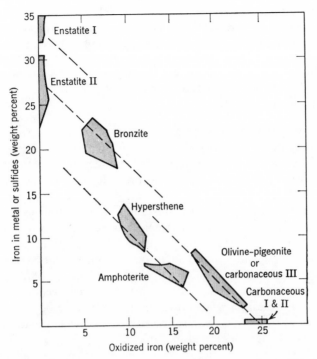

Figure 8.3: Relationship between oxidized iron and iron as metal or sulfide in chondritic meteorites. Dashed lines are lines of constant total iron content. Based on Mason [263, p. 78] and Craig [460].

losses are more likely to occur upon increase in temperature, so a simple model based on temperature would lead to negative correlation between total iron content and iron oxidation. This correlation is true for the series amphoterite-hypersthene-bronzite-enstatite, but is reversed by the carbonaceous chondrites, which have the highest content of volatiles and hence presumably would be the closest to any primeval chemical mix. Hence, even for this simplest chemical distinction, at least a dual-mechanism hypothesis is required, such as mixes in different ratios of two primitive fractions.

Other Chemical Properties

The SiO_2/MgO ratio also discriminates sharply between different chondrite classes. For enstatite (E) chondrites, the ratio is 1.75 to 2.05; for ordinary (H, L, LL) chondrites, 1.53 to 1.64; and for carbonaceous (C) chondrites, 1.37 to 1.47 [455].

Connected with these variations in iron and magnesium content are two properties of chondritic meteorites known as Prior's rules, which relate the iron content to the two chemically similar metals magnesium (Mg), which has a stronger affinity to oxygen than does iron (Fe), and nickel (Ni), which has a weaker affinity. Prior's rules, originally stated in 1916, are:

1. The Ni/Fe ratio is negatively correlated with the metal content.
2. The FeO/(MgO + FeO) ratio (given in Table 8.2) is negatively correlated with the metal content.

Prior's rules originally were applied to all chondrites as a group. The rule does apply roughly between classes. With the refinement of chemical analyses, however, it has become less clear to what extent they apply between different meteorites within the same class, such as bronzite or hypersthene or amphoterite. Although the variations between meteorites within the same class are small, they are not consistent with an equilibrium oxidation-reduction state. In general, however, as the oxygen:metal ratio increases, more of the iron is transferred from the reduced to the oxidized state, thus increasing the FeO/(FeO + MgO) ratio and increasing the Ni/Fe ratio. The varying FeO/(FeO + MgO) ratio also is reflected in the names of the chondrite classes: hypersthene, bronzite, and enstatite being pyroxenes of increasing proportion of magnesium relative to iron. In the mineralogy of chondrites, the pyroxene/olivine ratio is also negatively correlated with the FeO/(FeO + MgO) ratio, as indicated in Table 8.3.

The development of the electron microprobe, which can analyze single grains as small as a few microns in size, enables the determination of the Fe and Mg content separately for each mineral. The consequence of such more refined analyses is an even more distinct separation into classes than that in Figure 8.3. Thus all bronzite chondrites have a Fe/(Fe + Mg) mole ratio ranging 0.161–0.194 in the olivine, and 0.147–0.172 in the pyroxene, while all hypersthene chondrites have an olivine range 0.216–0.244 and (with one exception) a pyroxene range 0.193–0.217. The amphoterites are also more sharply distinguished: an olivine range 0.263–0.290 and a pyroxene range 0.222–0.246. In all these classes, the olivine/pyroxene iron content ratio is around 1.1 [209].

Chondrite Structure

The structure of chondritic meteorites is closely correlated with the chemical classification. The chondrules appear in all types of chondrites except the carbonaceous type I, which contains the most volatiles. This is in accord with the structure of the chondrules being one that requires rapid melting and cooling: extremely fine-grain structure, very little chemical differentiation of nonvolatiles, and droplet shape. The actual process by which this rapid melting and cooling occurs—volcanic activity or meteoritic impact or shock

TABLE 8.3: PRINCIPAL MINERAL CONTENTS OF CHONDRITES (≥ 5 PERCENT), BY WEIGHT

Meteorite Class	Portion of									
	Org*	Eps	Mag	Se	Pl	Ol	Cl + Or	Tr	Ka + Ta
Carbonaceous I	0.06	0.18	0.20	0.54	—	—	—	—	—
Carbonaceous II	0.05	0.02	0.02	0.46	—	0.45	—	—	—
Carbonaceous III	0.02	0.02	0.05	0.05	0.05–0.10	0.70–0.65	0.05	0.05	0.00–0.05
Amphoterite	—	—	—	—	0.05–0.10	0.60–0.55	0.25–0.30	0.05	0.01–0.04
Hypersthene	—	—	—	—	0.05–0.10	0.55–0.35	0.25–0.35	0.05	0.05–0.10
Bronzite	—	—	—	—	0.05–0.10	0.40–0.25	0.20–0.35	0.05	0.16–0.21
Enstatite II	—	—	—	—	0.05–0.10	0.00	0.50–0.60	0.07–0.10	0.20–0.23
Enstatite I	—	—	—	—	0.05	0.00	0.50	0.12–0.15	0.25–0.28

* Abbreviations: Org = hydrocarbons and carbon; Eps = epsomite, $MgSO_4 \cdot 7H_2O$; Mag = magnetite, Fe_3O_4 or other magnetic spinel; others as in Table 8.2.
Based on Mason [263, p. 80] and Anders [12].

351

wave in a primeval gas and dust cloud—is still a matter of considerable debate: see Section 8.5.

In addition to the chondrules which suggest rapid heating, most chondritic meteorites evidence to varying degrees mild metamorphism, blurring of the chondrule-matrix boundaries, and a crystallization of the metal grains, all of which suggest a slow "cooling" at temperatures of 400°–700° for times on the order of 10^7–10^8 years. The carbonaceous chondrites are much more fragile than the ordinary; they lack a crust formed by ablation, and appear to have been broken up into many fragments. After fall, carbonaceous chondrites weather quickly, and hence are always falls rather than finds. Therefore the proportion entering the atmosphere may be many times that indicated in Table 8.2.

Other interesting structural properties of chondrites are frequent brecciation, suggestive of shock, and alignment of elongated metal grains, suggestive of formation in a magnetic field which has been found in some ordinary chondrites, but not carbonaceous chondrites [12].

The structural variations of chondritic meteorites recently have been systematically classified and related to chemical variations by Van Schmus and Wood [414]. They divide the chondrites into petrological types on the bases of (1) homogeneity of silicate composition, indicative of degree of thermochemical equilibration; (2) the ratio of monoclinic to orthorhombic pyroxene, positively correlated with rapid quenching, and negatively with the extent of slow recrystallization; (3) plagioclase content, dependent on degree of metamorphism; (4) igneous glass content, negatively correlated with recrystallization; (5) the taenite/kamacite ratio, correlated with the degree of metamorphism; (6) the amount of Ni-rich sulfide minerals, inversely correlated with metamorphism; (7) the extent to which the chondrules have merged with the matrix; and (8) the abundance of the volatiles C and H_2O.

These criteria were used to establish six petrological types:

Type 1: Lack of chondrules, high volatile contents, fine-grained material. This type is coincident with type I carbonaceous chondrites.

Type 2: Inhomogeneity of olivines and pyroxenes; high clinopyroxene/orthopyroxene ratio; presence of igneous glass, Ni-rich sulfides, and some C and H_2O. This type is coincident with type II carbonaceous chondrites (see Figure 8.2*a*).

Type 3: Large variability of olivine and pyroxene composition; high clinopyroxene/orthopyroxene ratio; presence of igneous glass and minor amounts of carbon; absence of nickel from sulfides. Some enstatite, ordinary, and type III carbonaceous chondrite specimens all fall in this type.

Type 4: Generally a transitional category between types 3 and 5; the most distinct indicator is that about 20 percent of the pyroxene is clinopyroxene.

Most specimens of this type are bronzites (H), but there are some of all other classes (see Figure 8.2*b*).

Type 5: Uniformity of olivine and pyroxene composition, very little clinopyroxene; chondrules discernible but not clearly delineated; well-developed plagioclase of predominantly microcrystalline material. Meteorites of this type are about 60 percent bronzites (H) and 35 percent hypersthenes (L), plus a few amphoterites (LL) and enstatites.

Type 6: The most recrystallized of chondrites, some with virtually complete obliteration of primary textures, and considerable development of plagioclase. The great majority of specimens of this type are hypersthenes (L); it also comprises most enstatites (E) and amphoterites (LL), plus several bronzites (H) (see Figure 8.2*c*).

The six petrological types form a progression from unequilibrated to fully equilibrated systems. Meteorites of the same type but of different chemical classes are not necessarily related genetically, but they have been subjected to similar conditions of pressure and temperature [414].

Volatile and Minor Element Abundances

Certain elements are of particular interest because their volatility, or the volatility of their compounds, makes them sensitive indicators of the thermal history of the meteorite. The more important of these elements are given in Table 8.4. There is considerable variation of content of some elements among meteorites, or even among different parts of the same meteorite. This variability is compounded by experimental difficulties for the scarcer elements. Hence it is dubious whether meaningful averages can be obtained for each class of meteorite. General practice has been followed in Table 8.4 in giving such averages for all classes except the enstatites, where the range of recent determinations is given in a direction coinciding with the division into class II (low Fe, S; metamorphosed) and I (high Fe, S; unmetamorphosed).

Also shown in Table 8.4 as a standard of comparison are "cosmic" abundances which are based on solar and stellar, as well as meteoritic, determinations plus semiempirical rules of nucleosynthesis, as discussed in Section 9.1.

The abundances of the volatile elements in Table 8.4 are generally correlated with the degree of oxidation with the striking exception of the enstatite I chondrites. Despite these enstatites being the most highly reduced, they show little loss of volatiles relative to the "cosmic" values, and are closer to the type I carbonaceous chondrites than any other. Apparently these enstatites have suffered relatively little heating since the initial conditions that caused formation of the chondrules and loss of oxygen. Their petrological type—3 or 4—also indicates little disturbance.

TABLE 8.4: ABUNDANCES OF VOLATILE AND TRACE ELEMENTS IN CHONDRITIC METEORITES

(ratio to 10^6 for Si)

Element	"Cosmic"	Carbonaceous Type			Ordinary	II ←——— Enstatite ———→ I	
		I	II	III		II	I
F	1 600	2 560	2 400	1 700	1 000	1 200	2 340
S	375 000	500 000	230 000	120 000	110 000	124 000	345 000
Cl	8 850	2 000	1 200	1 200	700	910	4 300
Zn	500	700	500	300	130	35	1 800
Ga	11.4	51	31	23	12	—	35
Ge	360	143	53	32	22	—	94
Cd	0.9	2.1	1.5	0.8	3	0.06	4.7
Te	4.7	6.8	3.1	1.6	0.6	0.4	3.5
I	0.8	0.5	0.8		0.05	0.1	0.4
Hg	0.3	29	4.4	2.8	0.1	0.15	1.3
Tl	0.1	0.2	0.1		0.0007		0.1
Bi	0.1	0.2	0.2		0.002		0.1
Pb	0.5	3.8	1.5		0.15		3

Based (more or less) on Anders [12, pp. 635, 638], Ringwood [339, p. 124], Mason [266, pp. 31, 33–34], Greenland [145], Greenland & Lovering [472], Reed & Allen [493], Ehmann & Lovering [108], Suess & Urey [382].

A systematic examination of the abundances of 27 volatile elements has recently been made by Larimer and Anders [568]. Besides the great variations in depletion of volatiles between chondrite types indicated by Table 8.4, they find appreciable differences in the same meteorites between the matrix on the one hand and the metallic grains and the chondrules on the other, as though the latter had been subjected to higher temperatures. Taking into account the thermochemical relationships discussed below, they infer accretion temperatures less than 400°K for carbonaceous chondrites; 400–480°K for enstatite I chondrites; less than 530°K for petrological type 3 ordinary chondrites; and 530–650°K for other ordinary and enstatite II chondrites.

In addition, there are certain trace elements which show marked variation from one group of meteorites to another without being particularly volatile. As discussed in Sections 8.3 and 8.5, such variations may be clues to common genesis. The most extensively measured of such elements, gallium and germanium, are given in Table 8.4.

Hydrocarbons in Chondrites

A subject of considerable recent investigation and discussion has been the organic content of carbonaceous chondrites, the hydrocarbons that form about 5 percent of the content of type I and type II. These compounds are of interest not only because of possible biogenic implications, but also because they impose the most severe restrictions on the temperatures which the meteorites could have experienced. Some of the hydrocarbons could not exist at temperatures more than 300°K at negligible pressures, or more than 500°K at a pressure of one atmosphere. Furthermore the creation of some carbon compounds by equilibrium processes requires a reduction of the amount of hydrogen present to values much closer to that in the planets than in the sun. The latter condition has led to the general hypothesis that hydrocarbons were formed by high-energy, nonequilibrium processes, resulting from ultraviolet or charged particle irradiation, in a reducing atmosphere (i.e., largely CH_4, NH_3, and H_2O).

A large portion of the organic compounds in the carbonaceous chondrites—mostly nonvolatile and insoluble polymers—have not been identified, and hence much of the argumentation has used indirect indicators such as the geometric organization perceived under the microscope or the infrared spectra of extracts dissolved in carbon tetrachloride. These spectra have a considerable resemblance to infrared spectra of petroleum and sediments, being closest to those of ancient sediments. Volatile compounds, such as CH_4, C_4H_8, C_6H_6, have been identified by applying mass spectrometry to the gases evolving from a sample in an evacuated chamber.

The suspicion of terrestrial contamination has always persisted, of course. However, the best examinations have been careful to keep the specimen in a sterile environment and to use samples from different parts of the interior of the specimen [264, 378, 410, 473].

Thermodynamic Implications

This section has necessarily been somewhat descriptive and classificatory. In the subsequent analytic stage, explanation of the chemical content of a meteorite—or differences of content between meteorites—is logically first attempted by an appeal to equilibrium processes under the mildest possible conditions. Equilibrium processes are the reactions that take place in a closed system of a given composition well mixed at a specified temperature and pressure in an indefinitely long duration. The thermodynamics discussed in Section 1.2 is applicable to such processes. Probably the most pertinent to chondritic meteorites is that relating free iron to pyroxene and olivine [283]

$$\overset{\text{pyroxene}}{2 \text{ MgSiO}_3} + \overset{\text{metal}}{2 \text{ Fe}} + \overset{\text{gas}}{\text{O}_2} \rightleftarrows \overset{\text{olivine}}{\text{Fe}_2\text{SiO}_4} + \overset{\text{olivine}}{\text{Mg}_2\text{SiO}_4} \qquad (8.2.1)$$

According to the law of mass action, the rate of a reaction in either direction is proportionate to the concentrations of the reactants, that is, the substances on the side *from* which the reaction is proceeding. Equilibrium is then obviously the case where the two opposing rates are equal. Denoting the proportion of a substance A by $[A]$, the state of equilibrium for a given temperature T and pressure P must be expressible by a particular value of the quantity K, defined by:

$$K = \frac{[\text{Fe}_2\text{SiO}_4][\text{Mg}_2\text{SiO}_4]}{[\text{MgSiO}_3]^2[\text{Fe}]^2[\text{O}_2]} \qquad (8.2.2)$$

We wish to relate the *equilibrium constant K* to the thermodynamic variables discussed in Section 1.2. The quantity that related the energy to the pressure and temperature conditions P, T was the Gibbs free energy G, defined by equation (1.2.11); it in turn was related to the number of moles of each component, n_i, by equation (1.2.18). The free energy change ΔG in a chemical reaction is defined as [281, 466]:

$$\Delta G = G(\text{products}) - G(\text{reactants}) \qquad (8.2.3)$$

If ΔG is zero, there is no net work by any change at constant temperature and pressure, and hence equilibrium prevails. If ΔG is positive, the reaction (8.2.1) will proceed from right to left, and if negative, in the reverse direction.

To evaluate K, we need experimental data for ΔG at one combination of pressure and temperature, at least. Conventionally taken as the *standard* state are a pressure of one atmosphere and a temperature of 25°C. The free energy for the standard state is symbolized as G^0.

For a gas, such as O_2, there applies the ideal gas law:

$$PV = RT \qquad (8.2.4)$$

where R is the gas constant, $1.98717 \, cal° \, K^{-1} \, mole^{-1}$. Then, for constant temperature T, from (1.2.8) and (1.2.11),

$$dG = V \, dP = RT \, d \ln P \qquad (8.2.5)$$

Integrating

$$G - G^0 = RT \ln P \qquad (8.2.6)$$

for P in atmospheres, since P^0 is 1 atmosphere. If the system were comprised completely of ideal gases of n_i moles and P_i partial pressure each,

$$n_i(G_i - G_i^0) = RTn_i \ln P_i \qquad (8.2.7)$$

Writing the general expression for a chemical reaction such as (8.2.1) as:

$$\sum v_i A_i = 0 \qquad (8.2.8)$$

where A_i is a substance, $v_i > 0$ for a product, and $v_i < 0$ for a reactant, and using (8.2.3), we get:

$$\Delta G - \Delta G^0 = RT \sum v_i \ln P_i \qquad (8.2.9)$$

For equilibrium ΔG is 0. If

$$K = \frac{\prod\limits_{\text{products}} P_i^{v_i}}{\prod\limits_{\text{reactants}} P_i^{v_i}} \qquad (8.2.10)$$

Then at equilibrium:

$$K = \exp\left(\frac{-\Delta G^0}{RT}\right) \qquad (8.2.11)$$

If the total pressure P is unchanged by the reaction, then the partial pressure is proportionate to the mole fraction X_i (Henry's law), and in (8.2.10) P_i can be replaced by X_i—so that K becomes the *equilibrium constant*. For a solution that includes nonideal fluids, such as a melt represented by (8.2.1), the partial pressure must be replaced by a quantity called the *fugacity*, f_i, which is identical with the partial pressure for an ideal gas. Hence in an integration such as (8.2.6), a ratio f/f^0 must replace P, since f^0 is not necessarily unity. The fugacity is a measure of the escaping tendency of a component in solution: for the nonvolatiles in (8.2.1), this would only exist if there were other compounds present of affinity for the constituents of (8.2.1), such as nickel for the iron. Otherwise, we can proceed to replace the nonvolatiles in (8.2.2) by their fractional components:

$$K = \frac{[1 - X(\text{Mg, Ol})]^2 [X(\text{Mg, Ol})]^2}{[X(\text{Mg, Px})]^2 P_{O_2}} \qquad (8.2.12)$$

where $X(\text{Mg, Ol})$ is the atomic ratio $\text{Mg}/(\text{Mg} + \text{Fe})$ in the olivine, $X(\text{Mg, Px})$ is the same ratio in the pyroxene, and P_{O_2} is the pressure of the oxygen gas in atmospheres *provided that* the pressure of the standard state is 1 atmosphere.

So, if the free energies of formation G^0 of the various constituents at standard temperature and pressure are determined in the laboratory, then the equilibrium constant K at any temperature T can be calculated by equation (8.2.11), and for a specified oxygen pressure P_{O_2} the division into olivine and pyroxene can be calculated by equation (8.2.12). The required data are given in Table 9.7.

The ΔG^0 obtained is $-122{,}823$ cal. Hence at ordinary temperatures the reaction (8.2.1) would go to the right. At higher temperatures there would be a shift toward the left: that is, the portion of pyroxene and free iron would increase at the expense of the olivine, which would correspond to a leftward shift in Figure 8.3.

Other reactions that should be taken into account are:

$$\tfrac{1}{2}\text{Mg}_2\text{SiO}_4 + \text{FeSiO}_3 \rightleftarrows \tfrac{1}{2}\text{Fe}_2\text{SiO}_4 + \text{MgSiO}_3 \qquad (8.2.13)$$

and

$$\text{FeSiO}_3 + \text{Fe} + \tfrac{1}{2}\text{O}_2 \rightleftarrows \text{Fe}_2\text{SiO}_4 \qquad (8.2.14)$$

Although these thermodynamic considerations are important and unavoidable for an understanding of chondritic chemistry, the degree to which chondritic meteorites approach equilibrium varies greatly, as was discussed in connection with the petrological types. The less equilibrated chondrites appear never to have been very long at elevated temperatures, and also evidence appreciable mechanical mixing, loss of volatiles, etc., not to mention shock—rapid transitional events—in such phenomena as the chondrules. Thus it is appropriate to postpone the discussion of the origin of the chondrites until after examination of the other types of meteorites, which may come from other parts of the same systems, and of properties which are more physical than chemical—isotopic composition, gas content, etc.—and hence providing additional boundary conditions on past environments [283, 485, 575].

8.3   Chemistry and Structure of Other Meteorites

The remaining types of meteorites in Table 8.2, comprising 15 percent of falls, all differ from the chondrites in that they have compositions and structures indicating significant periods of high temperatures and pressures in the past.

Achondritic Meteorites

The achondritic meteorites are the most similar to terrestrial igneous rocks. As implied by their name, they do not contain chondrules. They are highly differentiated, and have the appearance of being produced by partial melting and fractional crystallization in a gravitational field. Like terrestrial rocks, achondrites are deficient in metals and sulfides relative to ordinary chondrites. Achondrites are classified as calcium-rich and calcium-poor. The calcium content is positively correlated with the degree of oxidation of iron, as indicated by Figure 8.4.

The mineralogy of the calcium-poor achondrites is rather simple, being almost entirely coarse-grained pyroxene. The aubrites are very similar in composition to the enstatite chondrites *less* most of their nickel-iron and troilite. The pyroxene in aubrites is virtually iron-free, hence they are sometimes called enstatite achondrites. The diogenites consist mainly of hypersthene. Both these types of meteorites are characterized by a brecciated structure, with large angular fragments on the order of 40 mm across in a matrix of smaller particles. The ureilites have a composition similar to the hypersthene chondrites, less troilite and some nickel-iron plus some carbon.

The calcium-rich achondrites are mostly pyroxene—mainly hypersthene in the howardites, pigeonite in the eucrites—plus considerable plagioclase. The structure of many eucrites is coarse-grained, similar to diabase or gabbro, with orientations of their crystal structure suggesting formation by solidification from a magma. Some eucrites contain the form of SiO_2 called tridymite, which apparently cannot exist at pressures above 3 kb, but which may be a decomposition product of a high-pressure phase. The howardites are more brecciated than the eucrites [12].

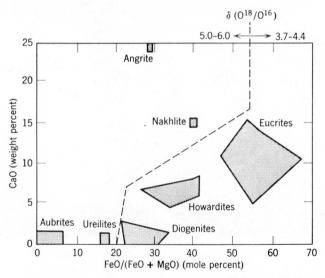

Figure 8.4: Relationship between calcium content and iron oxidation of achondritic meteorites. Based on Mason [263, p. 107]. Also division between oxygen-isotope ratio groups.

Stony-Iron Meteorites

The two principal classes of stony irons are quite distinct in both composition and structure. The stony part of the pallasites is largely olivine, which occurs in grains on the order of 10 mm in a nickel-iron matrix. It is generally thought that the pallasites are pieces of a disturbed core-mantle boundary of a small parent body. The stony part of the mesosiderites is mainly pyroxene and plagioclase, similar to the calcium-rich achondrites. The mesosiderites have a finer-grained structure than the pallasites [12].

Iron Meteorites: Structure and Nickel-Iron Relationships

The iron meteorites are remarkable for the drastic degree to which the lithophile elements—silicates, etc.—have been removed. Their composition is 94 to 99.5 percent iron-nickel, most being close to the upper figure. Most of the remainder is usually troilite, occurring in spherical nodules centimeters

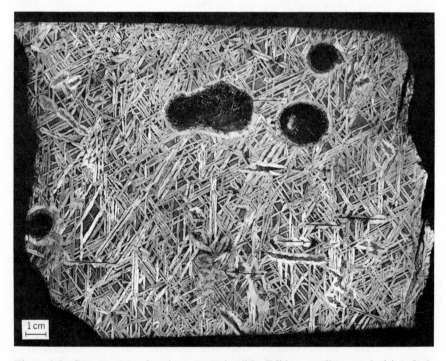

Figure 8.5: Cross section of an iron meteorite (Mt. Edith, a medium octahedrite, Om), showing Widmanstätten pattern. Note white bands about 1 mm wide: kamacite; thin (0.1 mm) lines bounding kamacite: taenite; dull gray background: plessite; large (3 cm) black nodules: troilite; shiny gray lamelae and rims around troilite: schreibersite. Photo by Smithsonian Institution, Washington, D.C.

in diameter. Schreibersite can be fairly abundant, up to about 2 percent. About 0.3–0.5 percent cobalt is present in solid solution in the iron-nickel. Consequently the principal basis of classification of iron meteorites is their nickel concentration, which in turn is correlated with their minerology: their division into kamacite (less than 0.07 Ni), taenite (more than 0.27 Ni), and plessite, an intergrowth of the two.

The irons of lowest nickel content, the *hexahedrites*, include 44 finds and 6 falls which cluster closely about an average composition of 0.935 Fe, 0.055 Ni, 0.005 Co, and the remainder P, S, Cr, and C. Hexahedrites are made of large cubic crystals of kamacite. Etching on a polished surface usually shows fine lines called Neumann bands, which are lamellae of twinned metal, apparently the result of strong mechanical deformation at low temperatures: evidence of violent impact or explosion.

The commonest class of irons is the *octahedrites*, of which there are over 400 finds in addition to 36 falls. Octahedrites are characterized by the *Widmanstätten* structure, an example of which is shown in Figure 8.5. This structure contains four systems of parallel plates or lamellae, up to 3 cm thick, of kamacite. These four systems parallel the faces of an octahedron. The polyhedral spaces between lamellae are filled with plessite. A narrow layer of pure taenite usually separates the kamacite plates from the plessite polyhedra. As indicated in Table 8.2, the width of the kamacite bands is related to the nickel content.

An electron microprobe traverse across a Widmanstätten pattern is shown in Figure 8.6. The nickel content in the kamacite is quite constant at 5–7 percent, except sometimes for a dip of 1 percent or so on the boundary of the taenite. In the narrow taenite layer the nickel content rises sharply to 35–80 percent. The dropoff on the plessite side is more gradual, to roughly constant content between 10 and 25 percent.

The Widmanstätten structure is generally explained as the result of cooling of the iron-nickel alloy from temperatures above 900°C. A nickel-iron phase diagram for a pressure of 1 atmosphere is given in Figure 8.7. At temperatures above the line ABC, the taenite structures is stable. If an iron-nickel alloy cools to a point such as B, kamacite of composition B' separates out of the taenite. If the cooling is slow enough, this kamacite will precipitate in lamellae parallel to one of the planes of the taenite lattice. As the cooling continues, the composition of equilibrium taenite migrates along BC, and the composition of equilibrium kamacite along $B'C'$. The total amount of nickel is constant, but both minerals are tending to increase their nickel content—hence the low-nickel kamacite must increase faster and faster with respect to the high-nickel taenite, and the widths of the kamacite bands must increase. Furthermore, to maintain equilibrium compositions, there must be a migration of nickel atoms from the phase boundaries.

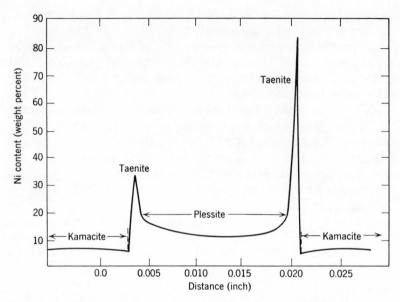

Figure 8.6: Variation in nickel content across an iron meteorite. From Wood [446, p. 378].

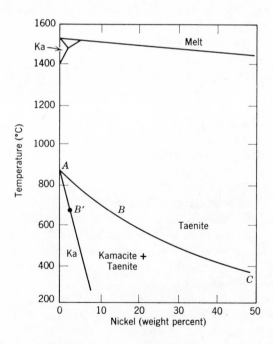

Figure 8.7: Fe-Ni diagram at 1 atm pressure. From Wood [446, p. 379].

The migration of nickel atoms in the foregoing processes is, like any diffusion, very much temperature dependent. Hence measurements of nickel-content gradients by electron microprobe have been used to infer cooling rates. About two-thirds of the rates lie between $1°C/10^6$ yr and $10°C/10^6$ yr, although the total variation in cooling rates is 0.4 to $500°C/10^6$ yr. If thermal history calculations similar to those described in Section 2.4 are carried out with plausible contents of radiogenic materials, then to obtain cooling rates of $1°C/10^6$ yr planets only 130–260 km in radius are required; for $10°C/10^6$ yr, 50–90 km (see Figure 8.8) [12, 471].

Iron meteorites characterized by an essentially plessite structure, without any kamacite bands, are known as *ataxites*. Most ataxites have a high nickel content, greater than 14 percent, and are classified as nickel-rich ataxites. Only one ataxite fall has been observed, but there have been 36 finds. The absence of kamacite bands has been interpreted as due to formation at a high pressure of several kilobars. There are also some ataxites of low nickel content, apparently the product of very rapid cooling [446].

Iron Meteorites: Trace Elements

Aside from nickel-iron relationships, the chemistry of iron meteorites must necessarily be trace chemistry. The most fruitful of these trace analyses have been for gallium (Ga) and germanium (Ge). The contents of these elements have a strong positive correlation with each other. They also have some correlation with nickel and iridium content and with meteorite class. These data suggest division of the iron meteorites into six rather tight groups, I, II, IIIa, IIIb, IVa, and IVb, plus a scattering of others, as shown in Figure 8.9. It has been suggested that each of these Ga-Ge groups belongs to a different parent body, each body with a different cooling rate evidenced by the different ranges of nickel content. Chondrites and pallasites also vary appreciably in their Ga and Ge content (though not as much), and hence there is the further possibility that these elements may indicate a genetic relationship, as discussed in Section 8.5 [12, 149, 428, 471, 512].

Diamonds in Meteorites

An indication of the minimum size for the parent body of a meteorite might be a mineral content which is thermodynamically stable only at high pressures. The best known such mineral is the diamond, which requires pressures of 16 kb at 25°C and 41 kb at 1000°C. Hydrostatic pressures of these magnitudes require bodies of more than 1000 km radius.

Diamonds definitely have been found in three achondrite falls and in one iron meteorite find. The three achondrites, all ureilites, evidence shock, while the iron "find," known as Canyon Diablo, is constituted by several thousand fragments found around Meteor Crater in northern Arizona. There is thus

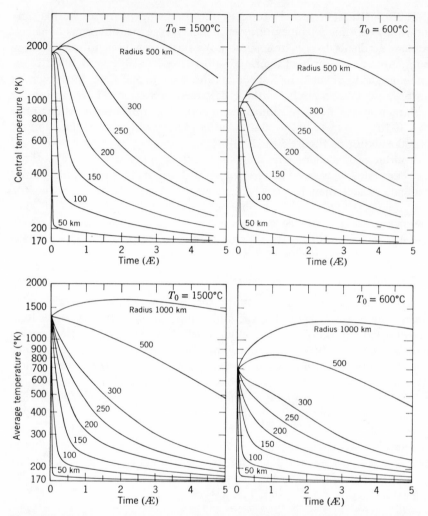

Figure 8.8: Cooling curves of asteroids for initial central temperatures sufficient for melting (1500°C) and intense thermometamorphism (600°C). Surface temperatures: 170°K; heat capacity: $0.198 + 0.98 \times 10^{-4}T$ cal gm^{-1} deg^{-1}, thermal conductivity: 0.005 cal sec^{-1} cm^{-1} deg^{-1}; radioactive content: U = 0.011 ppm, Th = 0.040 ppm, K^{40} = 0.101 ppm. By J. A. Wood in Anders [12, p. 596].

suggested the alternative hypothesis that the diamonds were created by shock, which has been done in the laboratory at pressures of more than 300 kb. Meteor Crater is estimated to have been created by a meteorite of about 100,000 tons (see Section 7.1), sufficient to generate such pressures on impact. The diamond-bearing fragments show an extraordinary correlation with location with respect to the crater: diamonds were found in 122 of 1212 specimens from the crater rim, but only in 1 to 233 specimens from the plains around the crater. Hence it is generally considered that the Canyon Diablo diamonds were created on impact.

However, the three diamond-bearing ureilites were all less than 3 kg in mass, and thus too small not to be decelerated by the atmosphere to a velocity too low to generate the required pressure on impact. The requisite shocks could only have occurred in some prior collisions, such as on the breakup of the parent body. There thus still exist some differences of opinion as to the origin of the diamonds, arising from differences of interpretation of the relationship of the diamonds to the surrounding graphite and the degree of deformation of the surrounding silicates. Hence the possibility of a parent

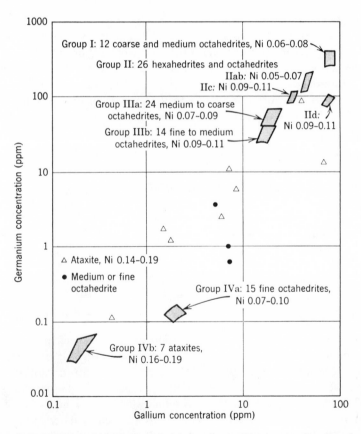

Figure 8.9: Gallium, germanium, and nickel contents of iron meteorites. Based on Wasson [428] and Wasson & Kimberlin [512].

body of more than 1000 km radius depends more on other considerations discussed in Section 8.5 [13, 67].

8.4 Isotopic Composition, Gas Content, and Dating

The chemical compositions of meteorites discussed in the previous sections depends on a great variety of causes, both chemical reactions and physical processes. However, isotopic ratios and inert gas contents depend only on physical processes—nucleosynthesis, irradiation, fusion, melting, diffusion, etc. Hence the measurement of such properties may offer more discriminating information as to the past history of the meteorite. Furthermore, the experimental sensitivity that can be attained by physical techniques such as mass spectrometry of gas isotopes is orders-of-magnitude better than chemical analysis because of the great reduction in contamination difficulties.

History of a Meteorite

The physical history of any meteorite can be summarized by eight or ten principal events. At each of these events there were created or retained certain elements whose present amounts can be used to determine the date or duration or temperature or location of certain conditions. The events can be roughly divided into three categories according to the manner of production of the elements which are now found in the meteorite.

1. *Primordial*:
     Nucleosynthesis
     Spallation
     Turbulence, heating, etc. in solar nebula
2. *Radiogenic*:
     Planetary condensation
     Solidification, after melting
     Gas retention
     Planetary breakup
3. *Cosmogenic*:
     Time in orbit
     Time on ground

The "primordial" events entail the creation or sorting of elements under extreme conditions, such as could have existed only in a star or the solar nebula: nucleosynthesis, the creation of elements by neutron capture and other processes which require extraordinary temperatures, as described in Section 9.1; spallation, the creation of lighter elements by high-energy irradiation, such as may have been produced by the sun in its creation; and finally, the distribution of materials in the violent events of the solar nebula which presumably existed prior to formation of the planets.

The "radiogenic" events entail the fixing in the same vicinity of radioactive elements and their radiogenic products. If "vicinity" is defined as the entire body, this fixing takes place for nonvolatiles upon condensation of the planet. A much more localized fixing will take place for gaseous radiogenic products, such as xenon or neon or helium, on cooling past the temperature of diffusion for the particular gas and solid matrix. Conversely, the shock associated with the breakup of the parent body may drive off the gaseous products.

The "cosmogenic" events depend on high-energy cosmic rays which produce isotopes, many of them short-lived, in the meteorite. If the meteorite was buried more than a meter or so in its parent body, the production of cosmogenic isotopes would not start until the body was broken up. After falling to earth, if the meteorite lay upon the ground a while, the screening of the cosmic rays would result in the decay of some radioactive cosmogenic products, which can be used to date the time on the ground.

We shall discuss these three categories of processes in reverse order of chronology, and thus in an order of increasing speculativeness.

Cosmogenic Contents

The cosmic rays near the earth are mainly high-energy protons, with some alpha particles and a small fraction of heavy nuclei. Their sources are believed to be mainly within the galaxy: supernovae, contact binaries, red flare stars, etc. Taking the unit of energy E as the Gev (10^9 electron volts = 1.6×10^{-3} erg), the distribution of particle energies above 1 Gev is well represented by a law of the form $(1 + E)^{-2.5}$. The mean kinetic energy per nucleon is about 4 Gev. In space, the total flux over all directions amounts to about five nucleons per square centimeter per second.

The mean absorption thickness—the amount of matter that can be penetrated before stopping—of the primary cosmic flux is about 150 gm/cm². However, the primary cosmic flux produces a lot of lower-energy secondary flux, such that there is actually an increase in the total particle flux in the first few centimeters of a body, before there is an eventual decrease.

If the product of a cosmic-ray irradiation is a radioactive substance, then eventually there will be attained for unstable products a situation in which the rate of nuclei decay is equal to the rate of new nuclei formation: this state is known as secular equilibrium. If it is assumed that the cosmic-ray flux has been constant for a time comparable to the half-life of the product, then the decay rate measured at the time the meteorite falls will give the production rate prior to fall. To transform this production rate rigorously into a flux rate, we need the depth of the sample in the meteorite, the geometry of the meteorite surface, the energy spectrum of the bombarding flux, and the reaction cross section of the target material as a function of energy. Cross sections are obtained experimentally by bombarding a material similar to the meteorite in a high-energy accelerator. The results of such experiments indicate that the combination of the aforementioned circumstances for a given target material of mass number A_t can be summed up by an empirical formula:

$$Q(A_p) = k(A_t - A_p)^{-k_2} \qquad (8.4.1)$$

where $Q(A_p)$ is the rate of formulation of products of mass number A_p, k is proportional to the flux intensity, and k_2 is dependent on both the size of the body and the depth below the surface. For iron as the target, k_2 varies from 2.1 at the surface of a small meteorite (radius 15 cm) to 2.7 at the center of a large meteorite (radius 50 cm). For iron meteorites, results from decay products with different half-lives have indicated a constancy of the flux rate within 40 percent.

If the product A_p is stable, then the total amount $C(A_p)$ in a bombardment time T can be written:

$$C(A_p) = Tk'(A_t - A_p)^{-k'_2} \qquad (8.4.2)$$

Variation of k' from the k in (8.4.1) would indicate change in the cosmic-flux intensity, while a difference of k_2' from k_2 would indicate change of the geometry of the meteorite in space, due either to further breakups on collision or to erosion of the surface. Small iron meteorites, which would have the greatest changes of k_2, indicate that there is very little erosion of irons in space. However, for the more friable, and more complicated, stony meteorites to which the simple model (8.4.1–2) is of more dubious application, the possibility of significant space erosion remains, as discussed below [11, 12, 181].

In addition to the apparently negligible—or, in any case, presumably gradual—space erosion, there is the very abrupt loss by ablation upon entering the atmosphere, which will result in variations with depth of different products differing from (8.4.1). From this inconsistency, the original depths of the samples can be reconstituted and the total amount ablated can be calculated. Estimates of the final ablation rate are also obtainable by thermomagnetic or metallographic examination of the heat-affected zone near the surface of the meteorite. Such data are the bases for the ablation percentages used in constructing the lower end of Figure 5.12. Some examples are summarized in Table 8.5 [11].

The principal target materials in a meteorite are essentially the most abundant isotopes: Fe^{56} and Ni^{58} in irons; O^{16}, Mg^{24}, and Si^{28} in stones are also important. Most radioactive products are so short-lived that they are present only in trace amounts, and measurable only by counting the gamma particles or other indicators of their decay. In these cases, the exposure age of the meteorite can be deduced from the ratio of the radioactive parent either to its stable daughter: e.g., Cl^{36}/Ar^{36}, Al^{26}/Ne^{21}, etc; or to another isotope of the same element: e.g., K^{40}/K^{41}. In other cases, the cosmic-ray exposure age

TABLE 8.5: EXAMPLES OF IRON METEORITE ABLATIONS DEDUCED FROM RADIOGENIC CONTENT

Postatmospheric Mass (kg)	Ablation Loss (%) by				
	He^3/He^4	He/Ne	He^3	Metallog.	Thermomagnet.
450	92	78			
1550	86				
480	73		45	20–48	
6.75	99				
14		78			
75.75					27
0.2					60

Based on Anders [11, p. 424].

is derived from the ratio of a stable product to another isotope, which can be done with sufficient accuracy only for inert gases: e.g., $Ne^{21}/Ne^{20}/Ne^{22}$, Ar^{36}/Ar^{38}, and He^3/He^4. The use of this technique to determine ages depends on a production rate which is usually assumed constant within a class. The principal nuclides which have been used in determining cosmic-ray exposure ages are summarized in Table 8.6.

Cosmic-ray exposure ages of iron meteorites deduced from K^{40}/K^{41} ratios are summarized in Figure 8.10. The ages obtained by other ratios involving shorter half-lives—Cl^{36}/Ne^{21}, Cl^{36}/Ar^{36}, Ar^{39}/Ar^{38}, Al^{26}/Ne^{21}—are nearly always less, which might indicate either an increase in cosmic-ray flux or secondary breakups of some meteorites; the significance of the discrepancies is obscured by the determinations being made by different workers.

TABLE 8.6: PRINCIPAL ISOTOPES USED IN COSMIC-RAY EXPOSURE AGE DETERMINATIONS

		Radiation Products		Decay Products		
		Typical Concentrations in Falls (disintegrations $min^{-1} kg^{-1}$)			Typical Concentrations ($cm^3/gm \times 10^{-8}$)	
Isotope	Half-life (yr)	Irons	Stones	Isotope	Irons	Stones
H^3	12.3	35–100	260–310	He^4	160–1100	4–220
C^{14}	5.6×10^3	1.7–1.8	40–60	Ne^{21}	2.1–15.2	0.4–63
Na^{22}	2.6		60–90	Ar^{38}	10.5–69	0.7–2.6
Al^{26}	7.4×10^5	3.6	45–70			
Cl^{36}	3.1×10^5	9–22	7–8			
Ar^{39}	2.7×10^2	7–13	7.5–11.5			
K^{40}	12.7×10^8	(0.13–0.82×10^{-9} g/g)				

Based on Honda & Arnold [181, pp. 206–208].

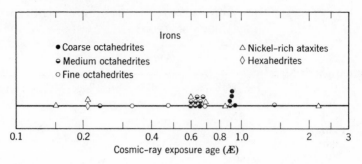

Figure 8.10: Cosmic-ray exposure ages of iron meteorites. From Anders [12, p. 667].

It is estimated that if the mass of meteorites of age around 0.63 Æ all came from the same parent body in the asteroidal belt, it would have to be of at least 5 km radius [12].

Cosmic-ray exposure ages of stony meteorites deduced from He^3, Ne^{21}, and Ar^{38} contents are summarized in Figure 8.11. These ages are dependent on a

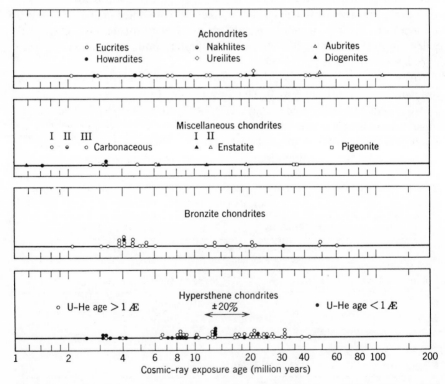

Figure 8.11: Cosmic-ray exposure ages of stony meteorites. From Anders [12, p. 671].

He^3 production rate of 1.96×10^{-8} cm^3 gm^{-1} $(10^6$ yr$)^{-1}$ at 20°C, and rates for Ne^{21} and Ar^{38} estimated from the average He^3/Ne^{21} and Ne^{21}/Ar^{38} ratios.

The remarkable fact about Figures 8.10 and 8.11 is that all 125 (plus one that fell off the left of the logarithmic scale of Figure 8.11) of the stony meteorites have ages less than all of the 25 iron meteorites, most of them by an order-of-magnitude. Hence if we want to explain the iron and stony meteorites as originating in different parts of the same parental body, some different orbital history of the stony meteorites must be hypothesized. The obvious suggestion is space erosion. If k in equation (8.4.1) has the form $k_0 e^{-aR}$, where k_0 and a are constants and R is the depth of the sample in the meteorite, then the cosmogenic production rate of a nuclide X is [120]:

$$\frac{dX}{dt} = A\, e^{-aR} \tag{8.4.3}$$

where A is a constant. The total content of a stable nuclide is then:

$$X = A \int_0^T e^{-a(r+Et)} dt \tag{8.4.4}$$

where T is the true age, r is the depth in the meteorite upon entry into the earth's atmosphere, and E is the surface erosion rate. The measured radiation age T' will then be:

$$T' = \frac{X}{A\, e^{-ar}}$$
$$\approx \frac{1 - e^{-aET}}{aE} \tag{8.4.5}$$

Then for $T \gg T'$, there will be a cutoff age T'':

$$T'' \approx \frac{1}{aE} \tag{8.4.6}$$

If the cluster of bronzite ages around 0.004–0.006 Æ is disregarded, a good fit to the data of Figure 8.11 by the model of equation (8.4.5) with $a = \frac{1}{45}$ cm^{-1} is obtained by:

$$E \approx 0.5 \times 10^{-6} \text{ cm/yr} \tag{8.4.7}$$

Whether or not this erosion rate is plausible depends not only on the amount of dust, but also on the size of the dust particles relative to the size of the grains in the stony meteorites between which the cohesion is distinctly weaker than in the irons—on the order of millimeters. Some models of the asteroid belt do contain more than sufficient dust of this size, but there is still left the question of the dust distribution between the belt and the earth. In any case, even an exponentially increasing erosion rate fails to fit the 0.004–0.006 Æ bronzite age cluster in the same model with the other data in Figure 8.11 [120].

Another exposure-age technique which is applicable to short durations is that of fission tracks. Protons striking a radioactive element, primarily U or Th, in a meteorite will induce a fission, the product of which causes a track of destruction in the crystal structure which is detectable on etching and optical telescope examination. Induced fission is distinguishable from spontaneous fission by a characteristic V track caused by acceleration of the struck nucleus prior to fission. In this manner, an average exposure age of less than 300 years for tektites has been deduced. In meteorites, fission tracks have been found to be caused mainly by heavy-element cosmic rays, and have been used to infer preatmospheric size and space erosion [122, 123].

Radiogenic Dating

The decay systems used for radiogenic dating of meteorites are the same as those used in geochronology listed in Table 1.5, with the addition of occasional use of Re^{187}-Os^{186} (half-life 43 Æ). The deduction of ages from Re^{187}-Os^{186} decay is similar to that from Rb^{87}-Sr^{86}, owing to the existence of nonradiogenic Os^{186}. The index used, analogous to Sr^{87}, is Os^{187}. The equation corresponding to (1.3.5) is:

$$\frac{Os^{187}}{O^{186}} = 0.83 + \frac{Re^{187}}{Os^{186}} [\exp(T\lambda) - 1] \qquad (8.4.8)$$

The time T deduced from several iron meteorites is 4.0 ± 0.8 Æ. This time dates a fixing of the Re/Os ratio, but the events—other than solidification—associated with the fixing are uncertain, since neither the absolute amounts nor the ratio of rhenium and osmium correlate with other properties of iron meteorites described in Section 8.3.

Also used for dating solidification of meteorites are the Rb^{87}/Sr^{87} and Pb^{207}/Pb^{206} ratios, as described in Section 1.3. Some calcium-rich achondrites have virtually zero Rb^{87}, and a Sr^{87}/Sr^{86} ratio of about 0.70, very close to that of terrestrial rocks. Chondrites have considerably more Rb^{87}, and an appreciably higher Sr^{87}/Sr^{86} ratio. All these meteorites fit very closely a straight line corresponding to $T = 4.37 \pm 0.2$ Æ.

The Pb^{207}/Pb^{208} age, (1.3.4), deduced for several meteorites, both stones and irons, is 4.6 ± 0.2 Æ. Some irons seem to have lost a lot of uranium [12].

Radiogenic dating of meteorites differs from the geochronology discussed in Section 1.3 in its emphasis on the use of gaseous products of decay, since they presumably measure the cooling of the meteorite to a temperature at which gaseous diffusion is negligible. Because diffusion depends on grain size, concentration gradients, mineral type, etc. as well as temperature, this "gas retention" temperature is difficult to define precisely, and it is more realistic to speak of a gas-retention temperature range of 160°C or so.

The decay systems used to determine gas-retention ages are U^{235}, U^{238}, Th^{232}-He^4 and K^{40}-A^{40}. The retention of helium is negligible above 200°C, and essentially complete below 40°C. The comparable gas-retention temperature range for argon is 320°C–160°C. Hence if the cooling of the meteorite body from, say, 300°C to 50°C (575°K–325°K) took more than a few times 0.1 Æ, then there should be a perceptible discrepancy between the U, Th-He^4 and K^{40}-A^{40} ages. Looking at Figure 8.8, we see that such slow cooling through the range 575°K–325°K would occur for any body of more than 150–200 km radius.

The observed results of U, Th-He^4, and K^{40}-A^{40} ages are summarized in Figure 8.12. They are consistent with the idea that in any discordance between the ages, the helium age should be less. We can group the results into four classes:

1. *Concordant long ages* of more than 3.0 Æ require rapid cooling in a body small enough to permit such cooling (i.e., less than 150–200 km radius), but sufficient to protect the meteorite against cosmic-ray irradiation until the breakup time indicated by Figure 8.11 (unless, as mentioned, the low exposure ages are due to erosion in space).

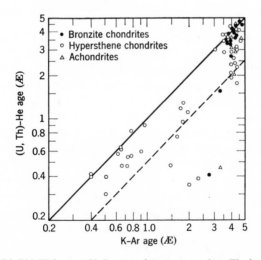

Figure 8.12: (U, Th)-He^4 versus K-Ar ages of stony meteorites. The broken line corresponds to a discrepancy of a factor of two. From Anders [11, p. 494; 12, p. 658] and Heymann [176, p. 211].

2. *Discordant long ages* imply cooling in a larger body, but even the maximum discrepancy of 3 Æ in Figure 8.12 would not permit a radius much more than 300 km, since the radiogenic content—particularly K^{40}—is enough to cause appreciable heating of a larger body before cooling to 600°K.

3. *Concordant short ages*, such as the hypersthenes of less than 1 Æ in Figure 8.12, indicate some type of shock which caused loss of all gas followed by rapid cooling, such as might occur on the breakup of a parent body.

4. *Discordant short ages* indicate a partial outgassing, such as might occur due to milder shock on collision, or to heating by the sun at a perihelion closer than the earth (although meteorites indicating loss of cosmogenic gases from such heating have been excluded from Figure 8.12).

The most striking phenomenon deduced from gas retention ages is that many, perhaps most, hypersthene chondrites were shocked about 520 ± 60 million years ago. About 30–40 hypersthene chondrites have U, Th-He outgassing dates around 0.5 Æ. The K-Ar ages range from concordance, 0.5 Æ, to 2.7 Æ. These meteorites also show other shock characteristics, such as recrystallization of their olivine. The obvious hypothesis is breakup of a parent body 0.5 Æ ago. However, the much shorter cosmic-ray exposure ages indicate subsequent additional breakups [176].

The uranium, thorium, and potassium contents of iron meteorites are too small to make (U, Th)-He^4 or K^{40}-A^{40} dating practicable [11, 12, 176, 370].

Xenology

Another inert gas measured in meteorites which could be a radiogenic product is xenon. Xe^{129} is known to be produced by the decay of I^{129} with a half-life of 16.9×10^6 years. The formation of I^{129} in perceptible quantities is calculated in nucleosynthesis theories: for example, a model assuming steady-state galactic synthesis over a duration of 20 Æ yields an $(I^{129}/I^{127})_0$ ratio of 0.00125 (see problem 8.9). Hence if the parent body of a meteorite cooled below the gas-retention temperature for xenon (about 310°C) before the I^{129} had, essentially, decayed completely, then there should be an excess content of Xe^{129}.

To determine how much of the Xe^{129} measured in a meteorite was produced by radioactive decay of I^{129}, we need a technique that discriminates between xenon associated with iodine sites in the meteorite, and xenon associated with other sites. The solution to this problem takes advantage of the fact that neutron irradiation of I^{127} produces Xe^{128}. If a meteorite is irradiated in an atomic pile enough to assure that its artificial Xe^{128} content is much greater than its natural Xe^{128} content, then upon heating of the meteorite in steps to various temperatures, the amounts of Xe^{128} driven off at different temperatures will measure the Xe gas retentivity of different iodine sites. At sites of low retentivity, the gas is less tightly bound, and hence can be driven off at lower temperatures. In addition some of the natural xenon at these sites will have been lost, and hence it will be deficient in comparison to the irradiation-produced Xe^{128}. At higher temperatures, the gas driven off will be from sites where it is tightly bound enough to be held ever since the decay that produced it. This binding applies to both the artificial Xe^{128} and the natural Xe^{129}. Thus, above a certain temperature, the amounts driven off at different temperatures should have constant ratios Xe^{128}/I^{127} and Xe^{129}/I^{129}, and hence constant Xe^{129}/Xe^{128}.

The aforestated relationships are expressible by the equation [332]:

$$\frac{Xe^{129}}{Xe^{132}} = \underbrace{\left(\frac{Xe^{129}}{Xe^{132}}\right)}_{\text{primord.}} + \underbrace{\left(\frac{Xe^{129}}{I^{127}}\right)}_{\text{radiogen.}} \underbrace{\left(\frac{I^{127}}{Xe^{128}}\right)\frac{Xe^{128}}{Xe^{132}}}_{\text{irrad.}} \qquad (8.4.9)$$

The isotope Xe^{132} is customarily used as a standard because it is the commonest in terrestrial xenon. Figure 8.13 is an example of an iodine-xenon correlation plot for a neutron-irradiated chondritic meteorite. Above 900°C, the points on Figure 8.13 fit a slope of 2.90 $\pm$ 0.10 very closely. The I^{127}/Xe^{128} ratio measured for a potassium iodide monitor placed in the atomic pile with

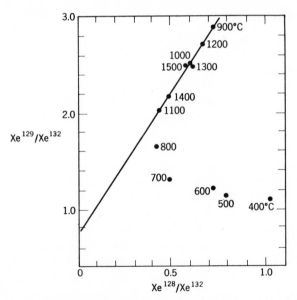

Figure 8.13: Xenon driven off from the Bjurböle hypersthene chondrite at 100°C temperature increments. From Turner [403, p. 5436].

the meteorite was 2.75×10^4. We thus deduce a Xe^{129}/I^{127} ratio of $2.90/2.75 \times 10^4 = 1.05 \times 10^{-4}$, which in turn will equal the I^{129}/I^{127} ratio at the time the meteorite began to retain xenon.

If we use the primordial ratio $(I^{129}/I^{127})_0$ of 1.25×10^{-3}, and the half-life of 16.9×10^6 years in equations (1.3.1–2), then an age of $60 \pm 2 \times 10^6$ years is obtained for the meteorite. Other xenon-retention ages which have been obtained by this iodine-correlation technique are 53.0×10^6 years for an enstatite and a bronzite; 68.0×10^6 years for the dark fraction and 60×10^6 years for the light fraction of a gas-rich bronzite (see below); and 68.0×10^6 years for Renazzo, a type II carbonaceous chondrite of unusual disequilibrium between its chondrules and matrix. The greatest discordance from these ages is 35×10^6 years for Bruderheim, a hypersthene that evidences shock. A chondrule removed from Bruderheim yields, however, a retention age of 58×10^6 years.

Despite uncertainties in the proper primordial iodine ratio $(I^{129}/I^{127})_0$, the Xe^{129} technique does definitely fix the xenon-retention time after I^{129} formation as relatively brief compared to the 5.0 Æ time scale of the solar system. Much more dubious is the manner of I^{129} formation. The short time is much easier to reconcile with spallation of Te^{128}, as described in Section 9.1, than it is with nucleosynthesis in some super star [121, 273, 332, 403].

Primordial Rare Gases

Full consideration of the radiogenic xenon content of meteorites cannot be separated from the general problem of the primordial rare gases of meteorites. By *primordial*, we mean associated with the formation and cooling to gas retention of meteorites, as distinguished from *primeval*, associated with formation of the solar system as a whole. Primordial gases are sometimes referred to as *trapped* gases, to indicate nonradiogenic or nonfission origin. Compared to the standards of (a) "cosmic" abundances estimated from several sources plus semiempirical rules of nucleosynthesis, and (b) the abundances observed in the earth's atmosphere, meteorites show considerable anomalous variations in their inert gas content with respect to (1) the absolute abundances; (2) the relative abundances of isotopes; and, even, (3) the relative abundances of different parts of the same meteorites.

Figure 8.14 summarizes the relative abundances of the inert gases in meteorites, the earth, and the original cosmic mix estimated from the sun and nucleosynthetic theories. All gases are depleted with respect to solar abundances, markedly as a function of atomic mass. This depletion varies from nine to four orders-of-magnitude for the carbonaceous chondrites, which appear to be the least disturbed class in this respect as they were in others. The extra light gases for the seven meteorites classified as gas-rich have a peculiar explanation. These meteorites, whose abundances are connected

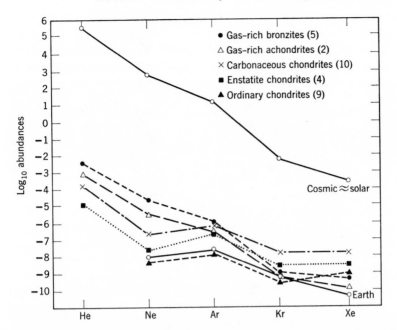

Figure 8.14: Abundances of rare gases. The abundances for meteorites are in cubic centimeters per gram, which roughly equals atomic abundances normalized to $\log_{10}$ (Si) = 2.0. Based on Signer & Suess [370, p. 245], Pepin & Signer [311, p. 255], and Anders [12, p. 675].

by dashed lines in the figure, are remarkable in that they are highly differentiated with excess He, Ne, and Ar concentrated in only part of the meteorite. The gas-rich meteorites are characterized by a structure of light-colored inclusions a few millimeters in diameter in a dark matrix. The helium concentration in the dark matrix is often greater than 10^{-2} cm³/gm³, while in the light inclusions it is normally less than 10^{-5} cm³/gm³. The hypothesis most generally accepted is that the extra gases were acquired by particle irradiation of the dark matrix material by a solar wind when it was in the form of a dust [311].

As was noted to be the case for other rare elements, the enstatite chondrites, despite their more reduced chemistry, have abundances intermediate between those of the carbonaceous and ordinary chondrites. The ordinary chondrites, like the earth, are the most severely depleted. This depletion generally is considered to be one of the strongest evidences that the earth lost its primeval atmosphere.

It is interesting that the abundances for the ordinary chondrites and the earth's atmosphere follow each other so closely, except for the xenon. An obvious suggestion is that the parent body of the chondrites condensed

TABLE 8.7: XENON ISOTOPE RATIOS

Material	$\dfrac{Xe^{124}}{Xe^{132}}$	$\dfrac{Xe^{126}}{Xe^{132}}$	$\dfrac{Xe^{128}}{Xe^{132}}$	$\dfrac{Xe^{129}}{Xe^{132}}$	$\dfrac{Xe^{130}}{Xe^{132}}$	$\dfrac{Xe^{131}}{Xe^{132}}$	$\dfrac{Xe^{134}}{Xe^{132}}$	$\dfrac{Xe^{136}}{Xe^{132}}$
Chondrites								
Carbonaceous (3)	0.0048	0.0043	0.083	1.055	0.1604	0.816	0.379	0.320
Enstatite (3)	0.0044	0.0037	—	2.98	0.161	0.806	0.384	0.322
Ordinary (2)	0.0051	0.0048	0.084	1.31	0.159	0.812	0.390	0.330
Achondrite (1)	0.077	0.0097	0.081	0.92	0.145	0.768	0.459	0.413
Earth	0.0036	0.0033	0.071	0.98	0.151	0.788	0.388	0.330

Based on Anders [11, p. 461] and Hohenberg et al. [477].

earlier than the earth, and hence acquired more Xe^{129} through I^{129} decay. However, since several processes may affect isotope ratios, it is worthwhile to examine all xenon-isotope contents.

It thus appears from Table 8.7 that although the chondritic meteorites have had an enrichment in Xe^{129} relative to the other isotopes, this mechanism is far from being able to account for the orders-of-magnitude differences shown in Figure 8.14. A trend that does appear distinctly in Table 8.7 is that Xe^{M}/Xe^{132} ratios for $M < 132$ are higher in the meteorites than in the earth's atmosphere. This effect is believed to be due to neutron or proton irradiation in an early active stage of the sun, perhaps when the chondritic material was dust in the solar nebula. Such irradiation would create Xe^{128} from I^{128} or Xe^{131} from Te^{130}, for example. The heavier isotopes of xenon generally are held to be produced by fission: of plutonium-244, which has a 75×10^{6} year half-life, or of uranium, both spontaneous and thermal-neutron induced. Experiments measuring the amounts of different isotopes driven off at different temperatures, similar to those described pertaining to Xe^{129}, show a definite positive correlation of the Xe^{134} and Xe^{136} fractions as a function of temperature, but little or none for Xe^{130} and Xe^{131}. This suggests that more than one type of xenon is present, and that the Xe^{134} and Xe^{136} are produced in a similar way.

The lighter krypton isotopes also show an enhancement in meteorites relative to the earth, which is also believed to be caused by irradiation. There are no likely fission or radiogenic products among the krypton isotopes.

The isotope ratios of the lighter gases do not show such distinct patterns, apparently because they are subjected to a considerably greater variety of effects. An additional mechanism which has been tentatively identified is diffusion, which for isotopes of a given element would have rates inversely proportionate to the square root of mass. Diffusion is thought to account for the much lower Ne^{20}/Ne^{22} ratio of meteorites as compared to the earth [11, 12, 311, 381].

Oxygen Isotope Ratios

A final category of gas-isotope analysis which only recently has been applied intensively to meteorites is determination of O^{18}/O^{16} ratios, which previously have been used in studying temperature and water-content dependence of igneous and metamorphic processes. Oxygen-isotope ratios are usually expressed in a mil difference from a standard:

$$\delta = \left[\frac{(O^{18}/O^{16})\text{sample}}{(O^{18}/O^{16})\text{standard}} - 1 \right] 1000 \qquad (8.4.10)$$

where the standard is standard mean ocean water. The value of δ is normally negatively correlated with the temperature of formation, T_F: thus sandstone may have a δ of 15, while the pyroxenes in terrestrial igneous rocks range from 5.5 to 6.6. The results for meteorites are best related to the iron-oxidation graphs. For chondrites, Figure 8.3:

1. Enstatite, bronzite, and hypersthene chondrites have pyroxene δ values of 5.4 to 6.3, suggesting T_F comparable to terrestrial ultrabasic igneous rocks.

2. Carbonaceous I and II chondrites have whole-rock δ values of 8.4 to 12.2, suggesting low T_F.

3. Carbonaceous III chondrites have whole-rock δ values of -0.8 to 5.5, suggesting high T_F.

An O^{18}/O^{16} analysis of achondritic meteorites divides them into two groups, falling on either side of a straight line on Figure 8.4 running from [FeO/(FeO + MgO), 20 percent; CaO, 0 percent] to [FeO/(FeO + MgO), 50 percent; CaO, 20 percent]. The meteorites to the left of this line—aubrites, ureilites, nakhlites, and angrites—have high δ's, 5.0 to 6.0; the meteorites to the right of this line—diogenites, howardites, and eucrites—have low δ's, 3.7 to 4.4 (except one 5.3, which happens also to have an unusual structure) The stony-iron mesosiderites also fall in this low-δ group.

Probably the most impressive result of the O^{18}/O^{16} analyses is the tightness of the group comprising the enstatite and ordinary chondrites, and of the group comprising the diogenites, howardites, and eucrites, suggesting two distinct genetic classes [391].

8.5 Origin of Meteorites

We wish, of course, to relate all the multifarious facts about meteorites described in the preceding four sections in as simple a history as possible. At this point, it might be helpful to list some of the more salient properties as a checklist in discussing their causes:

1. The meteorites divide into three distinct classes by iron content (Table 8.2).

2. By far the largest number of observed falls are chondrites (Table 8.1).

3. Iron meteorites are generally larger than stone meteorites.

4. By far the largest proportion of chondrites are bronzites and hypersthenes (Table 8.2).

5. Chondrites are generally fragile and all have a structure of unusual heterogeneity compared to terrestrial rocks; all except carbonaceous type I contain chondrules. Carbonaceous chondrites are more fragile than ordinary.

6. Chondrites divide into six or seven distinct groups by reduced versus oxidized iron content (Figure 8.3).

7. Chondrites have a less distinct division into three or four groups by total iron content (Figure 8.3).

8. Chondrites of all classes (except carbonaceous I and II) evidence greatly varying degrees of thermochemical equilibrium, as expressed by the petrological types, of little correlation with chemical content.

9. The four carbonaceous I chondrites are the closest of all meteorites to solar and cosmic abundances (Table 8.4).

10. Certain enstatite chondrites, high in iron and sulfur content, are the closest to carbonaceous in retention of minor elements and rare gases (Table 8.4 and Figure 8.14).

11. Carbonaceous I and II chondrites contain hydrocarbons unstable at temperatures above 200°C.

12. Magnetic anistropy has been found in all ordinary chondrites in which it has been sought, but not in any carbonaceous chondrite.

13. All chondrites have cosmic-ray exposure ages less than 60 million years and the ages show clusters to which it is impossible to fit a uniform production and space erosion model (Figure 8.11).

14. Solidification ages of all meteorites are 4.0 to 4.6 Æ.

15. Gas retention ages of most chondrites are 4.0 to 5.0 Æ (Figure 8.12).

16. Discordances between long (>3.0 Æ) helium and argon retention ages are small enough to indicate a cooling rate as fast as a planet of less than 300 km radius (Figures 8.8, 8.12).

17. Some chondrites—nearly all hypersthenes—have gas-retention ages, both concordant and discordant, indicating complete or partial outgassing 0.4 to 2.0 Æ ago (Figure 8.12).

18. The Xe^{129} content of six chondrites indicates an interval between I^{129} formation and xenon retention (about 310°C) of 35 to 68 million years.

19. Five bronzite chondrites and two achondrite meteorites have a dark matrix of about ten times as great light rare-gas content as the lighter inclusions.

20. Chondritic meteorites show an excess of light xenon isotopes relative to terrestrial xenon.

21. Chondritic meteorites show a deficiency of heavy xenon isotopes relative to terrestrial xenon.

22. The O^{18}/O^{16} ratios of enstatite and ordinary chondrites from a very tight group close to the values for ultrabasic rocks (δ 5.4 to 6.3).

23. The O^{18}/O^{16} ratios of carbonaceous I and II chondrites are similar to those of granitic rocks (δ 8.4 to 12.2).

24. Achondritic meteorites have a much more differentiated structure than chondrites, sometimes similar to igneous rocks.

25. Achondritic meteorites divided into two classes of CaO content—less than 3 percent and more than 5 percent—positively correlated with the degree of iron oxidation (Figure 8.4).

26. Some eucrites contain tridymite, which is unstable at pressures above 3 kb.

27. Two ureilites contain diamonds, and were too small to create sufficient pressures to form diamonds at impact on earth.

28. Aubrites have a composition similar to enstatite chondrites, less some nickel-iron and troilite; ureilites have a composition similar to hypersthene chondrites less some nickel-iron and troilite.

29. All achondrites have cosmic-ray exposure ages less than 120 million years; less than 45 million years for the calcium-rich.

30. Of the five common classes of achondrites, those of low iron oxidation (aubrites, ureilites) have O^{18}/O^{16} ratios similar to the enstatite and ordinary chondrites (δ 5.0 to 6.0), while those of higher oxidation (diogenites, howardites, eucrites), plus the stony-iron mesosiderites, have extremely low O^{18}/O^{16} ratios (δ 3.7 to 4.4).

31. Stony-iron pallasites have a structure—large silicate inclusions in a nickel-iron matrix—suggesting a core-mantle boundary in a small planet.

32. Iron meteorites are mainly very pure metal, 93 percent or more nickel-iron, with troilite impurities concentrated in large nodules and appreciable amounts of schreibersite.

33. The Widmanstätten structure of irons and associated gradients of nickel content indicate two groups of cooling rates, clustering around 1°C/million years (corresponding to 130–260 km planet radius) and 10°C/million years (corresponding to 50–90 km planet radius) (Figure 8.8).

34. The gallium, germanium, and nickel contents of irons can be used to designate at least six distinct classes (Figure 8.9).

35. Diamonds have been found in one major iron meteorite, but in specimens whose locations are highly correlated with the events of its terrestrial impact.

36. The cosmic-ray exposure ages of iron meteorites range from 0.15 to 2.3 Æ, with clusters around 0.63 and 0.9 Æ (Figure 8.10).

Despite the impressive number of pertinent "facts" in this list, it would be surprising indeed if a complete history of the meteorites could be deduced entirely separate from the history of other parts of the solar system. The idea of an "origin" of a meteorite distinct from the origin of other parts of the solar system only has meaning if it is defined as the differentiation of the meteorite from other material. Obviously there could have been more than one such differentiation, and hence a rather complex history. Probably the best we can hope to do is to establish limits on the conditions which have been experienced by the meteorites, which in turn will limit the circumstances of origin and evolution of the terrestrial planets—the subject of this book—and of the rest of the solar system.

We have implicitly assumed in this chapter, and in Chapter 1, that the heavy radioactive elements, uranium and thorium, were never created in the sites in which they have been used for radiogenic dating, and hence that they were created somewhere else a finite time ago. Some assertions which at this point we shall take as given by nuclear physics and astronomy, both galactic and extragalactic, are (1) the age of the universe is considerably more than the upper limit of 5 Æ or so that the Pb^{207}/Pb^{206} ratios, etc., in the earth and meteorites indicate; (2) the pressures and temperatures required to create the heavier elements—beyond Fe^{56}—are greater than those in the sun; (3) there exist stars within our galaxy big enough to create such temperatures and pressures; (4) such stars, "supernovae," sometimes blow up most catastrophically. Thus the solar system must have been created out of the remnants of such a blowup, by condensation of a gas and dust cloud.

The earliest possible "origin" of meteorites is therefore differentiation from such a primeval cloud, the solar nebula, and the simplest history we could hypothesize would be direct condensation from the cloud some 4–5 Æ ago of the meteorites in their present form. Such a history would be attractive in several ways for the largest class of meteorites, the chondrites: it would account for their fragile and heterogeneous structure; their appearance of experiencing only mild conditions except for occasional transient events; and such properties as the rapid melting and quenching of the chondrules, the irradiation of the gas-rich meteorites, and the evidences of spallation products such as some of the rare gas isotopes. The variations in iron oxidation and chemical content could be accounted for by variations in the cloud, while the sorting of these variations into distinct groups instead of a continuum could perhaps be explained by the sweeping out of segments of this continuum by the planets.

The principal objection to such a simple history for the chondrites is their short cosmic-ray exposure ages, which cannot be explained by any erosion; they must have been stored in some parent body throughout most of their history. Given that a parent body is required, the next question is how large it must be; furthermore, there are the questions of how many immediate parent bodies and whether there has been more than one generation of parent bodies. The existence of more than one parent body is a more satisfying explanation of the compositional groupings of the chondrites, as well as their similarity in some respects to other classes of meteorite, such as in O^{18}/O^{16} ratios or trace element content. It is desirable to keep the parent bodies of chondrites as small as possible, since it is not understood how to break up a large body of more than a few tens of kilometers radius without vaporizing all the material. Also limiting the size of the parent bodies are the rapid cooling rates indicated by the consistency of Ar^{40} and He^4 retention dates, the relatively short I^{129}-Xe^{129} ages, and the low temperature requirements of carbonaceous chondrites. Perhaps one of the strongest indicators of a sizable parent body for ordinary chondrites is the existence of magnetic moments in those ordinary chondrites in which it has been measured.

The origin of the chondrules has had several explanations. The most favored is that they were formed by a rapid heating and cooling, within minutes, in a primeval dust cloud by a shock wave [447] or lightning discharge [585]. The principal objection to this hypothesis is their somewhat complex mineralogy. Alternative explanations are that they were splashed out by volcanic eruption or meteorite impact, which requires an earlier generation of parent bodies, in view of the apparent radiogenic Xe^{129} content of chondrules; and that they were formed in place by diffusion, which contradicts their negative correlation with other evidences of metamorphism.

The carbonaceous type I chondrites are of special interest, of course, because they have the composition closest to solar and cosmic. However, attempts to explain all chondritic compositions as derived from the carbonaceous type I have considerable difficulties because of the lack of correlation of varying degrees of depletion with volatility or fugacity for many lesser elements as well as for oxygen and silicates, as previously mentioned in connection with Figure 8.3. Usually attempts to establish genetic relationships conclude that there are four or five such sequences taking the different groups of chondritic meteorites as starting points. However, at present there is no genetic classification satisfactorily accounting for all the meteorite data listed at the beginning of this section.

The genesis of the more differentiated meteorites—achondrites, stony irons, and irons—generally indicates larger parent bodies, in order to provide higher temperatures. In order to produce enough heat to melt iron and enough pressure to create diamonds, some theories have required lunar-sized original parent bodies. However, there is still the great difficulty of how to break up a moon, as well as the apparent lack of all but 3 percent of the remains of such a body in the solar system. There have been two alternative suggestions for the heat source. 1. The short-lived radioactive isotope Al^{26}, which has a 0.74×10^6 years half-life. If there was sufficient energetic radiation emitted to create by spallation the I^{129} indicated by the Xe^{129} content, it would have created more than enough Al^{26} by the same process [555]. 2. Resistive losses from electrical currents induced in the planet by the strong magnetic field of the early sun [581].

An alternative hypothesis for the pressure source creating diamonds, other than shock, is a massive primordial atmosphere which was later blasted away [406].

As has been mentioned, nickel-content gradients associated with the Widmanstätten patterns of iron meteorites indicate relatively rapid cooling rates and hence small parent bodies, while six or more close Ga-Ge-Ni groups suggest as many separate parent planets. These Ga-Ge-Ni groups are also correlated with cooling-rate groupings [512].

The location of the immediate parent bodies of the meteorites generally has been held to be in the asteroid belt. Most of the eleven or so meteorite trajectories which have been estimated from actual observation have had aphelia in, or approaching, the asteroid belt. The collision frequency deduced from the observed density of the asteroid belt, plus probabilistic calculations as described in Section 5.3, obtain times from collision in the main belt to impact on earth consistent with the 0.15–2.3 Æ cosmic-ray exposure ages of iron meteorites. However, the short exposure ages, times-of-day of falls, and other considerations discussed in Sec. 5.3 make it difficult to find satisfactory immediate parent bodies for the stone meteorites. The main asteroid belt and Mars-crossers lead to overlong exposure ages, and there are too few Apollo asteroids. The moon has a surface composition similar to calcium-rich achondrites (see Table 9.1), but leads to ages much too short, unless a very few large impacts are postulated. Comets thus seem the most likely source at the moment [18, 303, 433, 539].

Several coherent theories of the origin of meteorites have been formulated, varying widely in several aspects. The most fundamental variable is probably the size of the primordial parent body required, from small asteroidal, which has the weakness of attributing too many processes to the environment of a remote and little understood primeval nebula, to lunar, which has the weakness of requiring the breakup of a large body. In order of the increasing size required, the principal theories are those of Wood [447, 448, 450], Anders [12, 555, 568] Levin [245], Ringwood [239], Suess [380], and Urey [409]. The important undisputable fact about meteorites, however, is that they come from inside the solar system. Hence they constitute an important segment of chemical information pertaining to the origin of the solar system [12, 65, 339, 381, 405, 409, 447, 450, 555, 568].

8.6 Tektites

Description and Classification

Tektites are glassy stones usually between 0.5 and 10 centimeters in diameter. The glass usually looks black, or olive-green in thinner or more translucent sections. There are three main structural types [292]:

1. *Muong Nong* tektites are irregular chunks of broken glass, whose breakage evidences a pronounced interior pattern of parallel layers. Muong Nong tektites also have strain patterns indicating that they originated as fragments of a much larger body, and are generally found in clusters aggregating some tens of kilograms weight (Figure 8.15a).

2. *Splash-form* tektites have shapes approximating fluid bodies, usually under some distorting effect such as rotation: spheres, ellipsoids, teardrops, saucers, etc. Most tektites are in this class. The surface is marked by pits, grooves, notches, and long tracks. Splash-form tektites have a strain pattern indicating that they cooled as separate bodies (Figure 8.15b). Also includable in this class are oceanic *microtektites*, glassy objects less than 1 mm in diameter found in some ocean cores in a layer near the sediments showing the geomagnetic reversal 0.7×10^6 years ago [136].

3. *Australites* also have the form of a cooled liquid, but have had the glass removed systematically from one side, called the anterior side. This removal

Figure 8.15a: Muong Nong tektite. Soil in grooves brings out layered structure. From O'Keefe [292, p. 175]. Photo by John A. O'Keefe, NASA Goddard Space Flight Center.

Figure 8.15*b*: Splash-form indochinite from Thailand. Pits indicate internal fluid structure. From O'Keefe [292, p. 175]. Photo by John A. O'Keefe, NASA Goddard Space Flight Center.

has the appearance of aerodynamic ablation or thermal spalling, and in some cases the glass has flowed from the anterior side to form a flange, which gives the australite a button-shape (Figure 8.15*c*).

The ten tektite "finds" in Table 8.1 vary greatly in the number of specimens and the geographic extent covered by them, as summarized in Table 8.8.

The three types of glasses listed at the end of Table 8.8 generally are not considered to be tektites, mainly on the basis of a chemical content characterized by a much higher proportion of silica.

The ages, obtained principally by K^{40}-Ar^{40} dating, indicate very strongly that the tektites are the products of only four events, despite the gaps in geographic distribution, and, in the case of the 700,000-year group extending from South China to Tasmania, great differences in structural type. This grouping is borne out by mineralogical differences, particularly in the relative amounts of different types of feldspar (Figure 1.3). Thus all North American tektites analyzed have markedly less lime (i.e., less CaO) than all other tektites analyzed; moldavites have less soda (Na_2O) than all others; only Ivory Coast tektites have more soda than potash (K_2O), in which they are deficient with respect to all other tektites except some North American. On the other hand, all the Australasian tektites form a tight group, except for some deficiency of the indochinites in lime with respect to the others.

Figure 8.15c: Australite, 2.3 centimeters diameter, rear view. From O'Keefe [292, p. 176]. Photo by Roy C. Clarke, Smithsonian Institution.

Table 8.9 compares the chemical contents of tektites with various types of terrestrial rocks and the most similar meteorites, carbonaceous chondrites. The nonvolatile chemical similarity of tektites to highly differentiated crustal rocks, not only for the major components listed in Table 8.9 but also for many trace elements, is the principal argument in favor of terrestrial origin for tektites [395]. One possible exception is the O^{18}/O^{16} ratio: all of those measured (except some Ivory Coast) fall between 8.9 and 10.8 in δ value: comparable to granite, and appreciably lower than sediments [392]. One of the most remarkable properties of tektites is a water content of only 10^{-5} to 10^{-4}.

TABLE 8.8: TEKTITES AND SIMILAR BODIES

Name and Location	Extent (km × km)	No. Specimens (approx.)	Type	Age (10^6 yr)
Bediasites: E. Texas, U.S.A.	250 × 20	2,000	Splash	34.0
Central Georgia, U.S.A.	300 × 150	100	Splash	34.0
Martha's Vineyard, U.S.A.	0 × 0	1	Splash	34.0
Moldavites: Czechoslovakia	400 × 150	55,000	Splash	14.6
Ivory Coast, West Africa	100 × 100	200	Splash-Australite	1.0
Indochinites: Thailand, Indochina, and South China	1000 × 1000	40,000	Muong Nong and splash	0.7
Billitonites and malaysianites: N. East Indies and Malaya	1200 × 800	7,500	Splash	0.7
Philippinites (rizalites): Philippines	1000 × 300	500,000	Splash	0.7
Javanites: Java	100 × 100	7,000	Splash-Australite	0.7
Australites: S. $\frac{3}{4}$ Australia and Tasmania	3500 × 2500	40,000	Australite	0.7
Oceanic microtektites: triangle Ryukyus-Australia-W. Indian Ocean	6000 × 6000	Many 1000's	Splash	0.7
Darwin glass: W. Tasmania	10 × 2		Like Muong Nong	∼0.6
Aouelloul glass: Mauritania	1 × $\frac{1}{2}$		Like Muong Nong	∼0.3
Libyan Desert glass: N.W. Egypt	80 × 25		Like Muong Nong	∼34.0

Based on Mason [263, pp. 202–204], O'Keefe [292], Baker [23, pp. 11–34], and Glass [136].

Tektites are also severely lacking in other volatiles, so that they must have formed under high vacuum conditions [292].

Terrestrial Impact Origin

Therefore, if the tektites were formed on earth, it must have been by the impact of a body large enough to have blasted the atmosphere entirely away in the impact area. Furthermore, the atmosphere must have been removed in order to enable the driving of such small bodies over areas as wide as Australia. The occurrence of such an event should be evidenced by both the earth's surface and the structure of the tektites, and should be deducible by theoretical consideration of meteorite or comet impact on earth. Some of the pertinent properties of tektites [292] (particularly australites):

1. They appear to have been already rigid glass upon entering the atmosphere on final descent.

2. They appear to have been twice melted, first during primary formation and second by aerodynamic heating on atmospheric entry.

3. The abundance of round or nearly round shapes of australites indicates that solidification took place in the absence of significant aerodynamic forces.

4. Some tektites have been found to contain small amounts of the nickel-iron, troilite, and schreibersite common in meteorites.

5. Some Muong Nong tektites contain coesite, the phase of silica requiring pressures above 16 kb and no subsequent melting.

TABLE 8.9: COMPARISON OF CHEMICAL CONTENTS OF TEKTITES

(portion by weight)

Chemical	Carbonaceous Chondrites	Peridotite	Basalt	Granite	Sandstone	Shale	Bediasites	Moldavites	Austra-lites	Indo-chinites	Darwin Glass
SiO_2	0.28	0.43	0.48	0.69	0.78	0.58	0.76	0.80	0.73	0.74	0.86
Al_2O_3	0.02	0.02	0.15	0.14	0.048	0.15	0.14	0.11	0.12	0.13	0.07
FeO	0.27	0.099	0.081	0.022	0.003	0.038	0.038	0.025	0.040	0.040	0.017
MgO	0.19	0.37	0.086	0.011	0.012	0.035	0.007	0.014	0.020	0.024	0.010
CaO	0.016	0.030	0.107	0.026	0.055	0.051	0.007	0.013	0.035	0.018	0.001
Na_2O	0.006	0.004	0.023	0.039	0.004	0.038	0.015	0.005	0.012	0.013	0.001
K_2O	0.001	0.001	0.007	0.038	0.013	0.031	0.020	0.029	0.023	0.024	0.018

Based on O'Keefe [292, p. 180], Taylor & Sachs [395, p. 243], Mason [263, p. 74], and Ahrens [2, p. 28].

6. The cosmic-ray exposure age of tektites is less than 300 years by the fission-track technique.

7. The drastic degree to which both crystal structure and volatiles are absent from tektities, compared to industrial glasses, would be difficult to attain in the brief interval of an impact—which implies that the parent material of the tektites was glass even before impact.

8. The angular character of the few voids that appear in tektites would be difficult to attain by fusion of a crystalline material.

9. Laboratory simulations require entry velocities on the order of escape velocity, 11.2 km/sec, in order to attain the same degree of aerodynamic shaping as australites (some variation is allowable, dependent on the angle of entry).

10. Rare gases found in tektite voids have terrestrial isotope ratios.

If the impacting body is to remove the atmosphere sufficiently to permit transcontinental transport of tektites as well as evacuation of volatiles, then the energy provided by the impacting body must be at least the potential energy of the atmosphere blasted out—roughly, the amount of atmosphere above the tangential plane, as in Figure 8.16:

$$E = \int_0^\infty \rho_0\, e^{-z/h_0} g_0\, \frac{z_0^{\,2}}{(z_0 + z)^2}\, 2\pi(z_0 + z)^2\, z\, dz$$

$$= 2\pi \rho_0 g_0 z_0^{\,2} h_0^{\,2} \tag{8.6.1}$$

$$\approx 2 \times 10^{30}\, \text{ergs} \approx 5 \times 10^{10}\, \text{kt TNT equivalent}$$

where ρ_0 is sea-level air density, 1.2×10^{-3} gm/cm³; g_0 is sea-level gravity, 980 cm/sec²; z_0 is the earth's radius, 6.4×10^8 cm; and h_0 is the scale height of the atmosphere, 8×10^5 cm. Assuming impact velocity on the order of 10 km/sec, such energy requires a body of about 10^{18} gm. Extrapolating from

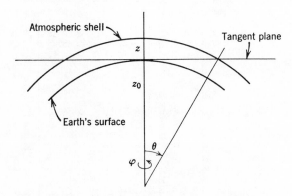

Figure 8.16: Geometry of impact for energy calculation.

Section 7.1, we see that if the body had a density comparable to that of the earth's crust, a crater on the order of 100 km diameter would have been formed. About 200 km from the European field is a 25 km crater of similar age, the Ries Kessel, and at about the same distance from the Ivory Coast field is a 13 km crater of similar age, Bosumtwi [501]. The North American field is so old (34×10^6 yr) that its crater may have been obliterated, but there is no known crater associated with the young Australasian field. The absence of big craters suggests impacting bodies of much less density, that is, comets. But there are still the problems of why the tektites are found in only one particular direction from the Ries Kessel: none has ever been picked up in the populous areas of France and Germany; and of the location of the Australasian impact: the size progression from australite to Muong Nong suggests Antarctica or the Southern Ocean, which moves the energy calculations to new orders-of-magnitude entailing vaporization of ice or water [246]. Possibly further determination of the distribution of oceanic microtektites will elucidate the Australian origin problem.

Lunar Origin

More detailed trajectory calculations make it difficult to reconcile the high velocities and variations in impact angle indicated by aerodynamic shaping with terrestrial origin [70]. However, even given a vacuum created by impact, probably the greatest problem of the terrestrial-origin hypothesis is removing virtually all crystal structure and water in such a short time [292].

The brief cosmic-ray exposure age of tektites indicates that the only possible extraterrestrial source is the moon. Further it is generally agreed that, if the origin is lunar, the meteorite minerals, the coesite, the absence of water, and the need to attain the escape velocity of 2.4 km/sec all indicate meteorite impact rather than volcanic eruption. Differences of opinion exist, however, as to whether the tektites came from the moon to the earth as separate bodies or in one large body [70, 292].

If the tektites came as separate bodies, then they all must have come from the same limited portion of the throwout cone of the lunar impact in order for the strewn field not to be scattered over the entire earth. This limitation is difficult to accept for the Australasian field in view of the considerable difference in both apparent degree of initial melting and in ablation on atmospheric entry over the range from Muong Nong to australite tektites. Furthermore at least a few sporadic tektites with perceptible cosmic-ray exposure ages would be expected.

Transit of a single body from the moon terminating in grazing incidence at the earth's atmosphere is more effective in explaining the limited distribution of the strewn fields. It also explains the north-south variations in the characteristics of the Australasian field as the consequence of successive passage through perigee in which the effect on the body proceeds from the wrenching off of solid chunks to ablative melting. Such effects have been observed in the reentry of artificial satellites. Although such a grazing incidence may seem forbiddingly improbable for a natural object, one occurrence of grazing incidence of a meteor has actually been observed in the Cyrillid shower of 1913, which extended from Canada to Brazil [292].

The difficulty in the single-body theory is at the lunar end: how to wrench such a large chunk off the moon without breaking loose many smaller pieces. About the best suggestion is that the initial effect of a large impact on the moon is to generate a cloud of gas or dust which traps all but the largest masses. The rayed character of relatively new large lunar craters may also be due to this effect.

The principal present chemical evidence regarding the moon's surface is unfavorable to the lunar hypothesis of tektite origin: the alpha-scattering observations by Surveyors 5-7 indicate oxygen, magnesium, aluminum, silicon, and iron contents much closer to basalt than to tektites; see Table 9.1 [508, 583].

The tektites constitute a fascinating problem which is still unsolved, mainly because of imperfect understanding of the complex dynamics of great impacts.

PROBLEMS

8.1. Calculate the standard free energy of formation ΔG^0 of $-122,823$ cal/mole specified for the reaction (8.2.1).

8.2. Discuss the significance of the environment in applying the thermodynamic theory at the end of Section 8.2 to the problem of chondrite formation: that is, what would occur in a closed environment from which the gases could not escape? What would occur in an open environment? What should be considered the independent variables in each case?

8.3. Given Stokes' law for the velocity of rise v of a bubble of density ρ' in a medium of density ρ,

$$v = \frac{2}{9} r_b{}^2 \frac{(\rho' - \rho)g}{\eta}$$

where g is gravitational acceleration, r_b is the radius of the bubble, and η is viscosity, speculate as to the conditions under which the pallasites could have been pieces of a core-mantle boundary of a parent body.

8.4. An iron meteorite has an 8 percent nickel content. In what subclass does it fall? What is the expected width of the kamacite bands? At what temperature did the kamacite probably first separate from the taenite? What would have been the effect of high pressures on the phase diagram Figure 8.7, and hence on the meteorite structure?

8.5. It is reported that the 0.15×10^{-4} cm aluminum skin on an artificial satellite is being destroyed at a rate less than 1 percent a year. Discuss whether this figure is consistent with the 0.5×10^{-6} cm/yr of equation (8.4.7) inferred from chondrite (mainly hypersthene) cosmic-ray exposure ages.

8.6. What solidification age is indicated by the following ruthenium-osmium ratios in a meteorite:

	Os^{187}/Os^{106}	Re^{187}/Os^{186}
Mineral A	0.842	0.200
Mineral B	0.854	0.400

8.7. In a xenon analysis by the neutron-irradiation technique, an I^{127}/Xe^{128} ratio of 2.75×10^4 was obtained from an iodide monitor. At higher temperatures, the Xe^{129} and Xe^{128} driven off fit closely the equation

$$\frac{Xe^{129}}{Xe^{132}} = 2.5 + 2.1 \frac{Xe^{128}}{Xe^{132}}$$

What is the inferred interval between I^{129} formation and Xe^{129} retention?

8.8. The O^{18}/O^{16} ratios of carbonaceous I and II chondrites and of tektites are very similar. Discuss the possibilities of common origin.

8.9. In theories of nucleosynthesis, the iodine isotopes I^{127} and I^{129} have about the same formation rate K. As stated in the text, I^{129} decays with a half-life of 16.9×10^6 years. Assume a steady state of I^{129} in the galaxy—i.e., decay equal to formation—for a duration T. What will be the I^{129}/I^{127} ratio for a duration T of 2×10^{10} years? 2×10^9 years? What effect will this time T have on the I^{129} formation—Xe retention interval deduced from a Xe^{129} excess?

8.10. Calculate the energy requirements for creation of the australites by a body hitting in the Antarctic Ocean; and for a body hitting the Antarctic ice sheet. What other evidences of such an event might still remain?

REFERENCES

The study of meteorites and tektites is largely an application of physical chemistry, for which texts such as *Moore* [281] and *Daniels & Alberty* [87] are appropriate. The principal textbooks on meteorites are those of *Mason* [263] and *Krinov* [226]. However, the pace of development in meteorites has been such that this chapter has drawn more on the lengthy review of *Anders* [12], supplemented by other reviews by *Wood* [446, 450] on chemistry and structure; *Anders* [11] on gases and dating; *Urey* [409] and *Ringwood* [339] on chondrites; *Mason* [266] on enstatite chondrites; *Honda & Arnold* [181] on cosmic-ray effects; *Pepin & Signer* [311] on rare gases; *Suess* [381] on implications as to origin; *Reynolds* [332] on xenon isotopes; and *Hayes* [473] and *Mason* [264] on organic contents of chondrites. *Van Schmus & Wood* [414] analyze chondrite classification.

The principal journals for work on meteorites are *Geochimica et Cosmochimica*

Acta and the *Journal of Geophysical Research*; some papers also appear in *Icarus*. Collections in which articles on meteorites appear are *Craig et al.* [84] and *Geiss & Goldberg* [132]. Papers referred to in this chapter include *Keil & Fredericksson* [209] on electron-microprobe analyses of chondrites; *Larimer* [485] and *Mueller* [283, 575] on the thermodynamics of chondrites; *Fisher* [120] on space erosion; *Fleischer et al.* [122, 123] on fission-track dating; *Turner* [403], *Merrihue* [273], and *Fisher* [121] on xenon isotope analyses; *Signer & Suess* [370] on rare-gas content; *Wood* [449] and *Goldstein & Short* [471] on cooling rates of iron meteorites; *Wasson* [427, 428], *Wasson & Kimberlin* [512], and *Greenland* [149] on gallium-germanium contents; *Taylor et al.* [391] on oxygen isotope ratios; and *Heyman* [176] on gas contents and shock effects of hypersthenes. The contending points of view on diamonds in meteorites are given in *Carter & Kennedy* [67] and *Anders & Lipshutz* [13], while differing opinions on the organic contents of carbonaceous chondrites are given by *Studier et al.* [378] and *Urey* [410]. Various theories pertaining to the origin of meteorites are given in *Wood* [447, 448, 450], *Anders* [12], *Levin* [245], *Ringwood* [339], *Suess* [380], *Urey* [409], *Fish et al.* [555], and *Larimer & Anders* [568].

The most extensive text on tektites is by *Baker* [23]. A collection of informative papers is that edited by *O'Keefe* [290]. The section on tektites in this book is based principally on the review by *O'Keefe* [292]. Various aspects of tektite entry and impact problems are explored by *Hawkins* [165], *Lin* [246], and *Chapman & Larson* [70]; the oxygen isotope data are by *Taylor & Epstein* [392]; the finding of tektites in ocean sediments is reported by *Glass* [136]; and the trace-element abundances by *Taylor* [394] and *Taylor & Sachs* [395].

Chapter 9

CONSTITUTION AND ORIGIN
OF THE TERRESTRIAL PLANETS

In the first eight chapters a great deal of information pertinent to the constitution of the planets has been discussed. In this chapter we wish to correlate this information plus such additional data as may be pertinent toward the goal of inferring the structure of the terrestrial planets, and thence their history. The task is somewhat similar to that carried out for the earth in Chapters 1 and 2. First we seek chemical boundary conditions from the terrestrial data in Chapter 1 and the meteorite data in Chapter 8, plus inferences drawn from the solar spectrum, cosmic rays, and so on, and the element and isotope ratios indicated by nuclear experiment and theory. Then we review the limitations, such as density, rotation rate, and so on, imposed by the physical observations and theory discussed in Chapters 2–7. The two sorts of data are then combined to deduce the most likely internal structures of the moon and planets. The final section uses the same information to attempt to discuss the origin and subsequent history of the planets.

9.1 Chemical Evidences

In addition to the geochemical data described in Chapter 1, the observations of planetary surfaces described in Chapter 6, and the meteorite data described in Chapter 8, possible sources of information pertinent to the past and present chemical constitution of the terrestrial planets include:

1. Spectroscopic observations (x-ray, ultraviolet, visible, infrared) of: the sun, stars and nebulae, comets, and planetary atmospheres.
2. Energetic particle fluxes from: cosmic rays, the sun, and the moon.
3. Elemental abundance ratios predicted by nuclear theory based on high-energy accelerator experiments and observations of certain stars.

Spectroscopy

As described in Section 6.2, a blackbody of temperature T will radiate energy proportionate to T^4 with a wavelength distribution also temperature dependent, as shown in Figure 6.8. The observed spectra of the sun and planets differ from the smooth curves of Figure 6.8 not only because of the absorption by the earth's atmosphere, but also because of the absorption and emission characteristics of the radiating bodies. Since these character-istics depend on the chemical structure of their surfaces and atmospheres, we should expect that departures from the blackbody curve will furnish evidence as to chemical composition.

The quantum theory of the atom states that its electrons may occupy only discrete energy states. On a shift of energy ΔE from one state to another, there will be emitted or absorbed radiation of frequency v, where:

$$v = \frac{\Delta E}{h} \tag{9.1.1}$$

in which h is the Planck constant, 6.6252×10^{-27} erg sec. In the simplest model of an atom, the Bohr orbital model of one proton of mass M and one electron of mass m revolving at an angular rate ω about the center of mass, the angular momentum will be:

$$2\pi(mr^2 + MR^2)\omega = nh \tag{9.1.2}$$

where n is an integer and r, R are the respective distances from the center of mass:

$$mr = MR \tag{9.1.3}$$

Equate centripetal acceleration and electromagnetic attraction:

$$m\omega^2 r = \frac{e^2}{(r + R)^2} \tag{9.1.4}$$

where e is the charge on each body (gravitational attraction being negligible). The total energy of the atom:

$$
\begin{aligned}
E &= T + V \\
&= \tfrac{1}{2}mr^2\omega^2 + \tfrac{1}{2}MR^2\omega^2 - \frac{e^2}{r + R} \\
&= -\frac{2\pi^2 me^4}{n^2 h^2\left(1 + \dfrac{m}{M}\right)}
\end{aligned}
\tag{9.1.5}
$$

using (9.1.2–4) to eliminate ω, r, and R. Then for the frequency v of radiation generated by a transition from a level of integer n_i to one of integer n_f, from (9.1.1) and (9.1.5):

$$v = \frac{2\pi^2 me^4}{h^3\left(1 + \dfrac{m}{M}\right)}\left(\frac{1}{n_f{}^2} - \frac{1}{n_i{}^2}\right) \tag{9.1.6}$$

For the hydrogen atom, the series $n_f = 1$, $n_i = 2, 3, \ldots, \infty$ is the *Lyman series*; $n_f = 2$, $n_i = 3, 4, \ldots, \infty$ is the *Balmer series*; $n_f = 3$, $n_i = 4, 5, \ldots, \infty$ is the *Paschen series*, etc. Using the cgs values of 4.8029×10^{-10} for e, 9.108×10^{-28} for m, and 1836.12 for M/m, there are obtained wavelengths c/ν of 0.1216 to $0.0192\,\mu$ (ultraviolet) for the Lyman; 0.6563 to $0.3650\,\mu$ (visible) for the Balmer; and 1.876 to $0.822\,\mu$ (infrared) for the Paschen series.

In addition to the spectral series caused by the changes in energy level, there are other series arising from the quantization of the other action variables p_i of the orbit, such as the G and H defined by equations (4.1.40–42):

$$\oint p_i \, dq_i = n_i h \qquad (9.1.7)$$

The quantum mechanics of the atom differs from classical mechanics, however, in that the electron has an angular momentum and magnetic moment about its own axis which interacts with the field of the nucleus. The components of this electron spin can take only the discrete values $\pm \frac{1}{2} h / 2\pi$. The effect of this spin-orbit interaction on the spectra is to cause a fine line splitting. (In addition there is a nuclear spin which gives rise to a splitting too fine to be observed in spectra.)

The refinement of the theory of the atom by the application of the Schrödinger equation yields solutions which confirm equation (9.1.5) in that there is a discrete set of permissible energy levels so long as the energy is negative. However, the same theory predicts a continuum of energy levels for positive energy. In the case of the hydrogen atom, the most obvious way to attain a positive energy level would be to attach another electron. Such an association would break up very quickly; however, given neutral hydrogen plus a sufficient supply of electrons, we should expect this "negative ionization" of hydrogen and the reverse process of electron detachment to result in a continuous spectrum rising to a maximum intensity near $0.85\,\mu$ wavelength.

For atoms more complicated than hydrogen, the spectral series depend on the degree of ionization, the shell structure of the atom, and on exclusion rules as to the allowable states of the electrons within a shell. For a particular element and ionization, the minimum energy, or "ground" state, corresponds to certain specified energy levels, called subshells, for each shell. The allowable one-jump transitions in energy level are only between different adjacent shells; however, under special excitation, such as may occur in a rarefied gas, certain "forbidden" transitions occur.

The calculation of the energy jumps, and hence frequencies of radiation, of the more complex atoms is of considerably greater difficulty because of the noncentral mutual interactions between electrons. In addition, there are complexities arising from interactions between electron spins and from spin-orbit couplings. Hence the identification of spectral lines, and their explanation, has proceeded by a combination of experiment, empirical rules, and theoretical derivation [6, 241].

Solar Abundances

The use of spectroscopy to determine abundances we should expect to depend not only on the identification of spectral frequencies, or wavelengths, but also on some measure of intensity. Since various effects result in no spectral line being perfectly "sharp," the measure of intensity most generally used is the *equivalent width*, which is essentially the energy-flux excess or deficiency integrated over the frequency bandwidth in which the emission or absorption is perceptible. For an absorption centering at wavelength λ:

$$W_\lambda = \frac{c}{v_0{}^2} \int_0^\infty \left(1 - \frac{I_v}{I_c}\right) dv \qquad (9.1.8)$$

where c is the velocity of light, v_0 is the frequency at the center of the line, I_v is the intensity at frequency v in the line profile, and I_c is the intensity in the continuum. The equivalent width is very much dependent on the environment in which the excitation generating the spectrum occurs. The environment of most concern here is the sun.

The visible zones of the sun are, from the innermost outward [6, 43]:

1. The *photosphere*, about 350 km thick. Nearly all of the sun's radiation comes from this layer. The density varies from about 2.5×10^{-8} gm/cm³ at the base to about 4×10^{-10} gm/cm³ at the top, while the temperature varies from about 7500°K to 4500°K.

2. The *chromosphere*, a transition zone about 10,000 km thick. The structure is very inhomogeneous, with strata of differing density and temperature varying from about 4000°K to 20,000°K.

3. The *corona* has a density of 10^9 particles per cubic centimeter at its base, but no clearly defined upper boundary. The temperature is higher than 2×10^{6}°K in parts.

The principal difference of solar radiation from blackbody radiation arises from the continuous absorption by negatively ionized hydrogen. The main source of solar-abundance estimates is line absorption by the photosphere in the visible frequencies. These estimates are believed to be fairly good estimates of overall solar abundances relative to hydrogen because the outer part of the sun is in vigorous convection.

An optimum spectral analysis of the sun utilizes a model atmosphere to take into account the variation in radiation and absorption with altitude. However, since values of the parameters for an atmospheric model depend on the spectrum, this analysis must be an iterative process. The starting point is to assume that the absorption all takes place in a single layer of atomic number density N, known as the *Schuster-Schwarzschild approximation*. Equation (9.1.8) becomes:

$$W_\lambda = \frac{c}{v_0^2} \int_0^\infty \frac{N\alpha_v}{1 + N\alpha_v} \, dv \qquad (9.1.9)$$

where α_v is an absorption coefficient dependent primarily on the probability of the transition (such as the n_i to n_f in equation (9.1.6)), and secondarily on lifetimes at the respective levels (radiation damping), collisional damping, and Doppler broadening arising from both thermal and turbulent motion [6, 454]:

$$\alpha_v = f_{n'n} \cdot \frac{e^2}{mc} \cdot \frac{\lambda}{V} \frac{a}{\sqrt{\pi}} \int_{-\infty}^\infty \frac{e^{-s^2}}{a^2 + (v - s)^2} \, ds \qquad (9.1.10)$$

$$v = \frac{\Delta\lambda}{\lambda} \frac{V}{c} \qquad (9.1.11)$$

$$a = \frac{\lambda}{V} \frac{\Gamma}{4\pi} \qquad (9.1.12)$$

where $f_{n'n}$, the *Ladenberg oscillator strength*, is an atomic constant that expresses the probability of the transition between levels n' and n; V is the combination of the gas kinetic and turbulent velocities; and Γ is the sum of the radiation and collisional damping.

To correlate different lines obtained from different transitions of the same element, a plot of $\log W/\lambda$ against $\log Nf\lambda$, known as a *curve of growth*, is made. Further elaborations of such plots are made to determine the temperature T and electron pressure P_e for an atmospheric model which in turn is used for more refined analyses. (See p. 100 in Aller [5] for a numerical example.)

Spectroscopically determined abundances of elements in the sun are summarized in Table 9.2. The principal weakness in estimation of solar abundances is determination of the f values, or transition probabilities. Calculation of the f values is feasible only for the simplest atoms; most of them require difficult experimental determinations. Other difficulties are the great spreading of strong lines versus the faintness of weak lines. Some very common gaseous elements—He, Ne, F, Cl, A—have not been satisfactorily determined by observations of the sun from earth because their strong lines all fall in the ultraviolet [6, 454]. A possible objection to Table 9.2 is the use of silicon as a standard because of the relative weakness of the determination of its solar abundance; solar and stellar spectroscopists in fact use hydrogen as a standard.

Ultraviolet observations from artificial satellites have been used to make new determinations of the abundances of some of the commonest elements, mainly from emissions in the corona at wavelengths between 0.03 and 0.16 μ. Some of the levels of ionization indicated are considerable—e.g., removal of 15 electrons from Fe—and require temperatures well in excess of $10^{6\circ}$K. Because they pertain to a different part of the solar atmosphere and because they are relatively new, these determinations are shown in a different column of Table 9.2.

Other Spectral Abundances

Among other stars, those that are somewhat larger than the sun are of greatest interest because the burning rate is roughly proportional to the mass squared. Consequently the larger stars observable are rather new, and hence are likely to be better samples of the interstellar medium. Included in Table 9.2 are the abundances determined from type B stars, which have surface temperatures of 18,000° to 24,000°K, compared to the 5780°K of the sun. The main conclusion is that the sun is not appreciably different in composition from the interstellar medium.

Abundances pertinent to the constitutions and origin of the terrestrial planets are, if they could be determined, those of the planetary atmospheres and surfaces and of the comets. The comets are particularly interesting because they are the presently existing objects whose structure is most likely to be similar to that of the original condensations from the solar nebula. Because of their low temperature, however, comets have molecular spectra, that is, emissions arising from fluorescence, electron collision, proton collision, etc., of molecules such as NH, CN, C_3, CH, C_2, and NH_2. Such spectra are considerably more complex, and hence the interpretation of cometary spectra is more concerned with identification of the molecules involved, physical conditions in the comet, excitation mechanisms, etc., than with the refinement of abundance determination. In any case, comets appear to have abundances of the common volatiles closer to those of the sun and the major planet atmospheres than to those of the terrestrial planet atmospheres [43]. This fact suggests that the comets were formed and have spent most of their existence far from influence of solar radiation, well beyond Jupiter.

Constituents spectroscopically identified in the atmosphere of Venus are CO_2, CO, HF, and HCl [517]; in the atmosphere of Mars, CO_2 plus traces of reduced gases such as CH_4 [518].

CO_2 in the atmsophere of Mars is about 10 percent, and the total atmosphere, as estimated from the Mariner IV occultation experiment, is about 2 percent of the earth's. The balance of the atmosphere is presumed to be the inert gas N_2 [548].

The U.S.S.R. Venus probe determined an atmospheric pressure of 15 to 22 atmospheres at altitudes of 16–26 km. The content of the atmosphere was more than 90 percent CO_2, 0.4 percent oxygen, and not more than 1.6 percent water and oxygen together. Nitrogen, for which the threshold sensitivity was 7 percent, was not detected [534].

The predominance of carbon dioxide in the atmosphere of Venus is an unsolved problem. There are three hypotheses suggested. (1) Water was originally present in large quantities, but has been photodissociated in the upper atmosphere, resulting in loss of the hydrogen to space and fixing of the oxygen in the crust [520]. (2) The hydrogen was lost during formation by the material forming the solid planet, and hence CO_2 has been outgassed instead of H_2O [379]. (3) Venus captured, or retained, its atmosphere from the solar nebula. Hence, the contents of the Venusian atmosphere may constitute significant boundary conditions on origin [548].

Spectroscopic observations of Jupiter in the red and near infrared (0.6 to 0.9 μ) obtain CH_4 and H_2 abundances consistent with a C/H ratio of 0.63 $\times$ 10^{-3}, not significantly different from the sun. Observations in the ultraviolet (0.2 to 0.3 μ) indicate deficiencies with respect to the sun for N (as NH_3) and S(as H_2S). The former is explicable as a consequence of clouds, but not the latter; possibly H_2S is unstable. In addition, there are absorptions apparently due to some more complex hydrocarbons. For the present, the observations are not inconsistent with a solar composition for Jupiter [556].

Cosmic Rays

By emulsion and counter measurements in high-altitude balloons, a very small fraction of cosmic rays have been identified as particles more massive than protons. Suggested abundances based on these results are given as galactic cosmic-ray abundances in Table 9.2. Their differences from other abundances in the table—particularly the greater amounts of Li, Be, B—are believed to be the consequence of spallation interactions in the interstellar medium between the supernovae at which the cosmic rays originated and the earth. It is estimated that only a few grams per square centimeter over the entire path are required to produce such a modification [306].

Abundances also have been estimated for the flux of particles received from the sun upon the occurrences of flares. These are listed in Table 9.2 as solar cosmic-ray abundances.

Radiation from the Moon's Surface

Recently measurements have been made of the natural gamma radiation from the moon by the U.S.S.R. satellite Luna 10 and of induced alpha and proton radiation by the U.S.A. lunar landers Surveyor V, VI, and VII.

The Luna 10 carried a 32-channel scintillation gamma spectrometer. The greater part of the radiation detected is induced by cosmic rays, both through prompt reactions and decay of short-lived radio isotopes. Assuming that the spectra of cosmic-ray-induced γ radiation in the satellite vehicle and the lunar surface have the same form and differ only in intensity enables subtracting out of the induced spectrum, leaving about 10 percent to be ascribed to natural radioactivity from K, U, Th. The spectrum thus obtained indicated a level of activity not greater than that of basic rocks such as basalt [421].

The Surveyors carried a source of alpha particles consisting of 100 mc of curium-242, which emits alpha radiation over a very narrow energy spectrum. The effect of this radiation on another element is to induce alpha and proton

TABLE 9.1 : ABUNDANCES OF ELEMENTS BY ALPHA SCATTERING

Element	Dunite	Basalt	Granite	Mare	Moon Mare	Uplands	Tek-tite	Ca-Rich Achon-drite	Hyper-sthene Chon-drite
C	0.00	0.00	0.01	<0.03	<0.02	<0.02	0.00	0.00	0.00
O	0.58	0.59	0.62	0.58	0.57	0.58	0.60	0.59	0.53
Na	0.00	0.02	0.02	0.02	0.02	0.03	0.01	0.01	0.01
Mg	0.19	0.04	0.01	0.03	0.03	0.04	0.01	0.05	0.14
Al	0.00	0.07	0.06	0.065	0.065	0.08	0.04	0.05	0.01
Si	0.15	0.18	0.24	0.185	0.22	0.18	0.26	0.18	0.15
$15 < Z < 21$	0.02	0.05	0.04	0.13	0.06	0.06	0.03	0.05	0.03
$22 < Z < 30$	0.02	0.03	<0.01		0.05	0.02	0.02	0.05	0.10

Based on Turkevich et al. [508, 583].

emission over a range of energies up to a maximum cutoff characteristic of the particular element. The detector consisted of 128 energetic particle counters each corresponding to a particular energy band. After accumulating counts over a duration on the order of a day, the excess of the observed spectrum over background was least-squares fitted by a combination of spectra from eight elements or combinations thereof: C, O, Na, Mg, Al, Si, $28 < A < 45$, and $45 < A < 65$, where A is atomic mass.

The results from the alpha-scattering experiment are given in Table 9.1, as well as 9.2. The agreement with basaltic rock and the "basaltic" Ca-rich achondrite is closer than with either the more basic dunite or hypersthene chondrite on the one hand, or the more acidic granite or tektite on the other. The high aluminum and low iron abundances found in the uplands by Surveyor VII are somewhat puzzling. In any case, it seems that the lunar surface material is the result of a differentiation similar to that of the basalts [508, 583].

Summary of Abundances

Table 9.2 includes all elements whose $\log_{10}$ (abundance) is greater than 3.2. It therefore includes all data pertinent to the main question of the bulk

TABLE 9.2: ABUNDANCES OF COMMON ELEMENTS

No. Z	Symbol	B Star	Galactic Cos. Ray	Solar Cos. Ray	Sun UV	Sun Photosph.	Chond. Carb. I	Chond. Ord.	Chond. Enst.	Moon's Surface	Earth's Crust	Suess-Urey "Cosmic"
						($\log_{10}$ atomic abundances normalized to 10^6 for Si)						
1	H	10.55	8.60	9.51	10.00	10.70	6.7				4.56	10.60
2	He	9.76	6.40		9.30		0.0					9.46
3	Li		6.82	<5.8		−0.5	1.7	1.7			2.47	2.00
4	Be					0.0		−0.2	−0.4		1.49	1.30
5	B					<1.7		0.8			1.98	1.38
6	C	6.85	7.18	7.25	6.78	7.7	5.91			5.1	3.20	6.54
7	N	6.73	<6.8	6.76	5.78	6.7	4.70				2.14	6.82
8	O	7.33	6.92	7.48	6.64	7.7	6.98	2.8	3.2	6.5	6.45	7.33
9	F	5.10	<5.9	<6.0			3.6				3.53	3.20
10	Ne	7.27	6.40	6.60	5.70	8.2	−2.5	−5.0	−4.0			6.93
11	Na		6.20			4.1?	4.81	4.58	4.51	5.1	5.03	4.64
12	Mg	6.49	6.43	6.12	5.96	6.10	6.02	5.97	5.93	5.2	4.91	5.96
13	Al	4.77	5.70			4.90	4.93	4.76	4.74	5.6	5.50	4.98
14	Si					6.00	6.00	6.00	6.00	←	6.00	6.00
15	P	4.03			3.90	4.04	4.04	3.84	5.4		3.54	4.00
16	S	6.03	6.03	6.24	5.15	6.00	5.70	5.0	4.5		2.92	5.57
17	Cl	4.77					3.35	3.8	3.7		2.57	3.95
18	A	5.46					−3.3	−5.4	−3.7	5.5		5.18
19	K			<5.8		3.4?	3.55	3.75	3.71		4.74	3.50
20	Ca				4.48	4.74	4.87	4.74	4.68		5.01	4.69
21	Sc					1.50	1.5	1.5	1.4		1.71	1.45
22	Ti					3.38	3.64	3.44	3.36		4.18	3.39
23	V					2.82	2.47	2.29		5.3	2.43	2.34
24	Cr					3.60	4.08	4.04	3.96		2.29	3.89
25	Mn					3.50	3.95	3.86	2.76		3.25	3.84
26	Fe		6.37	<5.8	5.70	5.29	5.95	5.94	5.91		5.01	5.78
27	Co					3.40	3.37	3.30	3.50		1.64	3.25
28	Ni					4.61	4.69	4.63	4.67	→	2.10	4.44

Based on: Aller [5, p. 115; 7, p. 22], Palmeira & Peiper [306, p. 419], Pottasch [322, p. 838], Ringwood [339, pp. 119, 124], Urey [409, pp. 10–11], Mason [265, p. 45], Suess & Urey [382, p. 56], Turkevich et al. [508, 583], Bernas et al. [540, pp. 461–465], O'Mara [543]. and Conti [553].

chemical composition of the terrestrial planets. Of most of the heavier elements, accurate determinations exist only for the earth's crust and meteorites; estimates for about 20 have been made by solar spectroscopy. Some of these scarcer elements are nonetheless of interest for one or more of several reasons:

1. Indicators of conditions of separation: fractionation in the gas phase, separation of gas from condensed matter, or differentiation in condensed phases. Particular groups of interest in this category are the rare gases and, roughly, the group of elements classified as chalcophile in Table 1.4.

The heavy rare gases were discussed in Section 8.4 (see Figure 8.14). Unfortunately, they are not observable in the solar spectrum. The heaviest gas measureable in the hot *B*-star spectrum, argon, has a much higher stellar abundance than predicted by empirical rules for relative abundances of nearby elements.

The chalcophile elements, especially Hg, Cd, Zn, and to a lesser extent As, S, Se, Te, are highly volatile in the presence of hydrogen, and thus abundance variations sould be suggestive of origin conditions. Of these, two are determined in the solar spectrum (see Table 9.3). The corresponding values for the earth's crust are somewhat less than those given for most chondritic meteorites in Table 8.4.

2. Indicators of differentiation without indicating conditions. Fairly pronounced differences of abundances between different classes of meteorites

TABLE 9.3: ABUNDANCES OF SOME RARER HEAVY ELEMENTS

No. Z	Symbol	($\log_{10}$ atomic abundances normalized to 10^6 for Si)				
		Sun Photosphere	Chond. Carb. I	Chond. Ord.	Chond. Enst.	Earth's Crust
29	Cu	2.20	3.00	2.35	2.69	1.95
30	Zn	2.50	3.18	2.46	3.24	2.04
31	Ga	1.45	1.71	1.48	1.86	1.35
32	Ge	1.19	2.13	1.34	1.95	0.33
48	Cd	0.36	0.32	0.48	0.87	−0.26
49	In	0.15	0.20	−2.95		−1.11
53	I		−0.33	−0.62	−0.03	−0.44
80	Hg		1.06	−0.22	−1.70	−1.38
81	Tl		−0.74	−2.70	−0.22	−0.60
82	Pb	0.34	0.58	−0.05	1.23	0.80
83	Bi		−0.77	−1.70	−0.30	−1.00
90	Th		−1.15	−1.47		0.60
92	U		−1.58	−1.63	−1.70	0.30

Based on: Mason [265, pp. 45–46], Urey [409, pp. 9–11], Ringwood [339, pp. 124–125], and Aller [7, p. 22].

have been found without any clear explanation indicated. Such differences of abundance are of value, however, in indicating differences of location of origin. Among these abundances are those for the elements Ga, Ge, In, Tl, Pb, and Bi. See Table 9.3.

3. Heat sources. As discussed in Section 2.4, the only ones significant over an appreciable period of time are potassium, thorium, and uranium, all of which have considerable enrichments in the crust relative to meteorites indicated in Tables 9.2 and 9.3. The heat source possibly significant in the early stages of the solar system, Al^{26}, decays by positron (β^+) emission, but the product Mg^{26} could have been produced in other ways. Hence there is only the indirect Xe^{129} evidence discussed in Section 8.4 of possible significant Al^{26} heating.

4. Indicators of nuclear processes. The determinations of elemental abundances in Tables 9.2 and 9.3 are much affected by various chemical differentiations, as well as observational difficulties. Hence patterns indicative of the nuclear processes by which the elements were created are obscured. For this reason some of the more inert heavier elements are of interest: in particular, the rare earths (atomic numbers 57–71), which have chemical properties very similar to each other, most markedly exhibit relative abundances arising from nucleosynthetic processes.

In addition, as discussed in Section 8.4, abundance ratios for isotopes of the same element should be more reliable indicators of primeval conditions. The firmest evidence for assuming that the solar system started from a cloud of rather uniform material composition is the similarity of isotope ratios in the earth, meteorites, and the sun (other than the cases discussed in Section 8.4 attributable to radiogenic and cosmogenic causes).

Abundance Tables

The optimum combination of abundances from different determinations to constitute a "cosmic" model depends on the purpose for which the model is used. A model designed to study the chemical evolution of the galaxy, in which the sun would be a specimen of a middle-aged G star, would emphasize the solar abundances, and avoid obscuring any differences from B stars or nebulae. A model designed to test theories of nucleosynthesis would utilize as much of the data as possible in order to bring out any systematic patterns. Finally, a model designed to explain the origin and evolution of the solar system would in addition try to utilize the nucleosynthetic theory itself in arriving at the most probable abundances.

The principal abundance table constructed in recent years is that of Suess and Urey [382]. They used principally chondritic meteorite averages for nonvolatiles and solar and stellar averages for volatiles, modified by simple empirical rules for the relative abundances of similar elements. Cameron [62] modified the Suess-Urey table by using some additional nucleogenesis-based criteria, and made some other isolated changes. Twenty-one abundances were changed by a factor of 2 or more, but only one (lead) by a factor of more than 5. Aller [5] gave more weight to solar and stellar determinations, and obtained abundances closer to the Suess-Urey for most light elements and closer to the Cameron for most heavy elements.

Although considerable new work has been done, particularly in meteorite analysis, since 1956, and greater emphasis has been placed on carbonaceous chondrites relative to other meteorites, the differences from the Suess-Urey abundances are quite moderate. In particular, determinations of heavy-element abundances remain closer to the empirical values than to the nucleo-synthesis theoretical predictions. These Suess-Urey abundances are given in Table 9.1 and Figure 9.1.

The empirical rules used by Suess and Urey [382] relate to the atomic number Z, equal to the number of protons in the nucleus; the number of neutrons, N; and the mass number A:

$$A = Z + N \tag{9.1.13}$$

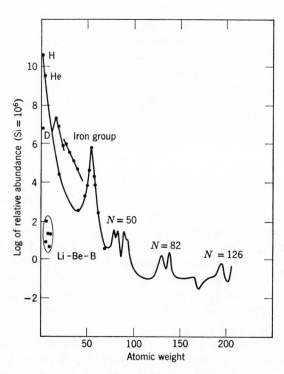

Figure 9.1: Schematic curve of atomic abundances as a function of atomic weight based on data of Suess & Urey [382]. From Burbidge *et al.* [59].

These rules are:

1. Except for hydrogen, elements of even Z are *several times as abundant* as are elements of adjacent odd Z (*Harkin's rule*). (This effect is not shown in Figure 9.1.)

2. Odd A, $A > 50$: the abundances change steadily with A. If isobars (i.e., $Z_1 \neq Z_2$, $A_1 = A_2$) occur, the sum of the abundances of the isobars must be used instead of the individual abundances.

3. Even A:

(a) $A > 90$: the sums of abundances of the isobars change steadily with A.

(b) $A < 90$: the abundances of nuclear species with equal $(N - Z)$ change steadily with A.

4. $A_1 = A_2$ and $Z_1 < Z_2$:

(a) $A < 70$: the nuclide Z_1 is less abundant than the nuclide Z_2.

(b) $A > 70$: the nuclide Z_1 is more abundant than the nuclide Z_2.

5. The abundances according to the foregoing rules are considerably exceeded at mass numbers A where the number of neutrons $N = 2, 8, 20, 28, 50, 82, 126, \ldots$: "magic numbers" corresponding to complete nuclear shells.

We should expect the abundance of a nuclide, once created, to be affected by its stability against spontaneous decay. This stability is a function of the *binding energy* of the nucleus, expressed rather accurately by the quasi-empirical Weizsäcker formula [241]:

$$E_B = \alpha A - \beta A^{2/3} - f(A)(N - Z)^2$$

$$- \gamma Z(Z - 1)A^{-1/3} + \frac{\delta(A)[1 + (-1)^A](-1)^Z}{2} \quad (9.1.14)$$

in which the experimentally determined parameters are:

Volume effect: $\alpha = 15.7$ MeV

Surface effect: $\beta = 17.8$ MeV

Isotope effect: $f = (23.6/A)$ MeV

Coulomb effect: $\gamma = 0.712$ MeV

Odd-even effect: $\delta = (132.0/A)$ MeV

This binding energy is related to the rest mass $M(Z, A)$ by:

$$M(Z, A) = ZM_H + NM_n - E_B \quad (9.1.15)$$

where:

Mass of neutral atomic H^1: $M_H = 1.008142$ amu

Mass of a neutron n^1: $M_n = 1.008983$ amu

The most general condition for stability is: if the rest mass of a given atom is smaller than, or equal to, the total rest mass of any combination of components into which it may be (conceptually) divided, the atom should be stable; if not, it should be unstable with respect to decay into such combinations as have smaller total rest mass. For example, there should occur:

(1) Proton emission,   if $M(Z, A) > M(Z - 1, A - 1) + M_H$
(2) Neutron emission, if $M(Z, A) > M(Z, A - 1) + M_n$
(3) Alpha emission,   if $M(Z, A) > M(Z - 2, A - 4) + M_{He}$
(4) Beta emission,   if $M(Z, A) > M(Z + 1, A)$
(5) Electron capture, if $M(Z, A) > M(Z - 1, A)$
(6) Positron emission, if $M(Z, A) > M(Z - 1, A) + 2m_e$

where m_e is the electron mass, 0.000548763 amu.

Equations (9.1.14–15) and the general stability condition are in fairly good accord with the odd-even effect (empirical rule 1) and the relative abundances of isobars (empirical rule 4). They also predict an abundance peak at iron, $Z = 26$, because it has the maximum binding energy per particle, E_B/A. However, they do not predict the magic number peaks. Furthermore, when the stability criterion is close to being an equality, a decay may not occur because of barriers or selection rules, and, more generally, the stability criterion has only a rough correlation with the decay constant λ.

Nucleosynthesis Processes in Stars

The passive stability rules can account only for the details of relative abundances in a given vicinity. To account for the general sweep of the abundance curve as given in Figure 9.1, as well as the trends expressed by Suess-Urey rules 2 and 3, more active processes are required. Such processes in turn require temperatures in excess of 2×10^7 °K. Some stars have enough mass to attain the energy necessary for these temperatures by gravitational contraction. When a star has contracted sufficiently to raise its central temperature above 10^7 °K, hydrogen atoms H^1 start interacting with each other to initiate a chain of interactions which has as a stable product helium, He^4. The hydrogen burning develops internal pressures which halt gravitational contraction and the star attains a stable "main sequence" state with a burning rate roughly proportionate to the square of its mass.

Because the energy release of hydrogen burning is so great, most stars spend about 90 percent of their lifetime at this stage. When exhaustion of hydrogen is imminent, further gravitational contraction occurs. If the star is sufficiently massive, this contraction raises the temperature above that required for helium burning, about 2×10^8 °K. In this cycle, the principal reactions are summarized as:

$$3He^4 \rightarrow C^{12} + \gamma$$
$$C^{12}(\alpha, \gamma)O^{16}$$

(9.1.16)

where the symbol (α, γ) denotes the absorption of an α particle and emission of a γ particle.

The hydrogen-burning phase of stellar evolution was first worked out by Bethe, von Weizsäcker, and others starting about 1939, and the helium-burning by Salpeter in 1952. These reactions have been fairly well confirmed experimentally: for example, the rate of the $3He^4 \rightarrow C^{12}$ reaction is known within 50 percent. However, the stages following helium burning summarized in Table 9.3 are considerably more complicated because of the larger size of the nuclides, the greater number of possible reactions, the increased temperature sensitivity, and uncertainties as to resonances, capture constants, decay rates, etc.

The principal work on nucleosynthesis beyond O^{16} was by Burbridge et al. [59], who developed the models of process 4 through 8 in Table 9.4 to explain the Suess-Urey abundance curve. Process 3, carbon burning, was subsequently pointed out by Cameron [62] and others as a more likely producer of Ne^{20} than $O^{16}(\alpha, \gamma)Ne^{20}$ as part of helium burning. In addition, oxygen and neon burning may be of significance comparable to the α process, although requiring temperatures 10–30 per cent higher.

Principal features of the abundance curve which the nucleosynthesis model explains are:

1. The greater abundances, relative to adjacent values, at $A = 24, 28, 32, 36, 40,$ and 44 (α process).
2. The peak around the stability maximum $A = 56$ (e process).
3. The peaks at $N = 50, 82, 126$, which have complete outer neutron shells, and hence small capture cross sections and long beta decay times:
   (a) a left peak, of high $N - Z$ (r process),
   (b) a right peak, of low $N - Z$ (s process).

As indicated by the requirement of the s process for both lower-temperature and longer time scale on the one hand, and iron peak nuclei produced by the rapid high-temperature e process on the other, either a star must be able to be in different stages of nucleosynthesis at the same time and subsequently to mix the products, or there must be more than one generation of stars. The latter seems more likely: the type II supernova stars required to attain the temperatures required for the e process are very short-lived: on the order of 2×10^7 years. In turn, the red giants and super giants with sufficient temperature for the s process are continually ejecting material into space.

TABLE 9.4: NUCLEAR PROCESSES IN STARS IMPORTANT FOR NUCLEOSYNTHESIS

No.	Name	Main Reactions	Main Products	Temperature (°K)	Time Scale (years)
1.	Hydrogen burning	$4H^1 \rightarrow He^4$	He^4	2×10^7	10^7–10^{10}
2.	Helium burning	$3He^4 \rightarrow C^{12}$, $C^{12}(\alpha, \gamma)O^{16}$	C^{12}, O^{16}	2×10^8	10^6–10^8
3.	Carbon burning	$2C^{12} \rightarrow Ne^{20} + He^4$, $Na^{23} + H^1$	O^{16}, Ne^{20}, Mg^{24}	5×10^8	10^3–10^6
4.	α process	$Ne^{20}(\gamma, \alpha)O^{16}$ $Ne^{20} + He^4 \rightarrow Mg^{24} + \gamma$, $x^n + He^4 \rightarrow y^{n+4}$, etc.	Mg^{24}, Si^{28}, S^{32}, A^{36}, Ca^{40}, Ca^{44}, Ti^{48}	10^9	10^2–10^4
5.	e process	Statistical equilibrium between nuclei and free protons and neutrons by $(\gamma, -)$, $(-, \gamma)$, etc.	Cr^{52}, Fe^{56}, Ni^{62} and other nuclei of $50 \leq A \leq 62$	4×10^9	10^{-6}–10^{-5}
6.	s process	H, He, C, or O burning or (α, n) reactions produce neutrons captured by nuclides of $A \geq 56$ at a rate slow compared to β decay	Nuclei of $60 \leq A \leq 200$, moderate $(N - Z)$	10^8–10^9	10^2–10^7
7.	r process	Neutrons produced at a catastrophic stage are captured at a rate rapid compared to β decay	Nuclei of $60 \leq A \leq 270$, high $(N - Z)$	1–4×10^9	10^{-6}–10^2
8.	p process	Proton (p, γ) capture by nuclei created by r and s processes; also (γ, n) reactions	Nuclei of $70 \leq A \leq 200$, low $(N - Z)$	2–3×10^9	10^{-6}–10^{-5}

The principal observational confirmation of the s process is the detection of technetium Tc^{99} with a half-life of 2×10^5 years, in the spectrum of a red giant. The principal observational evidence of the r process is decay of the light curves of a type I supernovae with a half-life near 55 days, the half-life of the principal radioactive product of the r process, Cf^{254}. It thus seems plausible that the synthesis of the elements took place in an environment similar to some which exist currently: the interiors of large stars. Hence there also exists the likelihood of further observational evidence [59, 124, 125].

The most evident inadequacy of the stellar synthesis model is that it produces much lower abundances than observed of the light elements H^2, He^4, Li^6, Be^9, B^{10}, and B^{11}. All of these elements *except* He^4 are rapidly destroyed in hydrogen burning in stellar interiors. He^4 is difficult to destroy in a star, but the amount of hydrogen burning indicated by the present overall luminosity of the galaxy is insufficient to account for more than a tenth of the observed abundance of helium. Hence the two inadequacies require environments differing from a stellar interior in opposite directions: the D Li Be B (D standing for deuterium, H^2) production requires an appreciably lower temperature, while the He production requires higher temperatures—or, at least, a stage at which virtually all of the galactic material was concentrated in big O and B-type stars.

Spallation Processes

At temperatures lower than those associated with hydrogen burning—a few 10^6 °K or less—the principal process by which elements can be created is spallation, which is the bombardment of nuclei by high-energy particles to produce nuclei of lower mass and particles of lower-energy. Spallation has already been discussed in Section 8.4 in connection with the effects of cosmic rays on meteorites. However, if spallation is to produce significant abundances of elements, the flux must be several orders-of-magnitude greater than observed in cosmic rays. Such a particle flux is consistent with current models of formation of stars like the sun, which in the final stage of contraction undergo intensive convection in their outer layers, which in turn would result in greatly enhanced radiation, ejection of matter, and atmospheric activity. These phenomena are observed in *T Tauri stars*, whose luminosity versus spectral type and frequent closeness to interstellar dust and short-lived giant stars indicate that they are very young. T Tauri stars also have a very high lithium abundance, 80 to 400 times solar [524, 558].

A flux of sufficient energy will be dominated by protons. Experimental proton bombardment of the elements just above D Li Be B in mass, C N O Ne, obtains Li, Be, B as spallation products with isotope abundance ratios that vary relatively little for likely C N O Ne abundances and proton energy spectra [540]:

$$Li^7/Li^6 = 2.5 \pm 1.0$$
$$B^{11}/B^{10} = 2 \pm 2.5$$
$$Li/Be = 25 \pm 10$$
$$B/Be = 45 \pm 30$$

(9.1.17)

Ratios observed in the sun are:

$$Li^7/Li^6 \approx 10 \pm 5$$
$$Li/Be = 0.16$$

(9.1.18)

and ratios observed in meteorites are:

$$Li^7/Li^6 = 12.5 \pm 0.25$$
$$B^{11}/B^{10} = 4.0 \pm 0.2$$
$$Li/Be \approx 50$$
$$B/Be \approx 10$$

(9.1.19)

In the earth's crust, the isotope ratios Li^7/Li^6 and B^{11}/B^{10} agree with those in meteorites, but the two ratios to Be abundance are lower by a factor of 5 or so. A final ratio which is rather constant in both earth and meteorites is

$$D^2/H^1 = 1.5 \times 10^{-4}$$

(9.1.20)

A model of D Li Be B formation should therefore include, in addition to spallation, explanations for:

1. The increase in the Li^7/Li^6 ratio over spallation in the meteorites and earth as well as the sun, while the B^{11}/B^{10} ratio is relatively unchanged.
2. The great reduction of the Li/Be ratio in the sun only.
3. The virtual constancy of the isotope ratios in the earth and meteorites.
4. The D^2/H^1 ratio.

Two principal models have been proposed. In one, the target material is condensed into planetesimal bodies in the solar nebula. In the other, the target material is in the sun's atmosphere.

Planetesimal Model

Fowler et al. [126] suggested that the proton-induced isotope ratios (9.1.17) were subsequently modified by neutron irradiation. Spallation also produces neutrons; among the possible interactions of neutrons with lithium and boron, $Li^6(n, \alpha)H^3$ and $B^{10}(n, \alpha)Li^7$ have the highest probability of occurring, providing the neutrons have been "thermalized"—that is, reduced sufficiently in energy so that they may be captured. The most efficient thermalizing agent is hydrogen. But if hydrogen is present, then the secondary neutron flux will also produce deuterium, by $H^1(n, \gamma)H^2$.

If all the hydrogen were as equally exposed to the neutron flux as the lithium and boron created by spallation, then the D/H^1 ratio would be about 3×10^{-3}. The observed ratio of 1.5×10^{-4} suggests that most of the hydrogen was shielded from the energetic particle flux. The simplest way to shield hydrogen from flux is to combine it into lumps of ice, H_2O. This combination also makes O^{16} more likely to be the principal target for spallation, since the oxygen will combine with the hydrogen more readily than will the carbon. Temperatures low enough to allow ice to freeze are not unlikely even at a distance of 1 AU from the primeval sun because of the opacity of the surrounding dust cloud. An alternative possibility allowing higher temperatures is incorporation of the water in hydrated silicates.

The "shielding ratio" $1.5 \times 10^{-4}/3 \times 10^{-3}$ of observed to calculated H^2/H^1 ratio was estimated by Fowler et al. [126] to be attainable by condensation of the ice into planetesimals of about 10 meters radius. In order that the hydrogen not absorb all the neutrons, it is also necessary that the hydrogen content be reduced greatly from solar to about $H/Si = 1:1$, that is, a lot more than the ratio for the earth's crust (see Table 9.1), but fairly close to the ratio for carbonaceous I chondrites.

The planetesimal model was proposed partly on the basis of older data indicating Li^7/Li^6 and B^{11}/B^{10} ratios much lower than (9.1.17). However, its main difficulty is the constancy of the isotope ratios in the earth and meteorites. The intensity of irradiation would depend on the distance of the planetesimal from the sun and the depth of the target material in the body. Hence to attain uniformity of isotope ratios the planetesimals would have to be broken up and thoroughly mixed before the earth and meteorite parent bodies were formed.

Solar Atmosphere Model

Since the planetesimal model was proposed, much better determinations of both the laboratory (9.1.17) and natural (9.1.18–19) isotope ratios have been obtained. The absence of variation in B^{11}/B^{10} now becomes, in fact, an argument against any neutron irradiation. Bernas et al. [540] therefore proposed that the proton irradiation of C N O Ne occurred in the sun's atmosphere during its contraction, perhaps even before it became luminous. Prior to separation of the planetary material the Li^7/Li^6 ratio was reduced by (p, α) reactions at temperatures between 2 and $4 \times 10^6\,°K$ at the bottom of the surface convective zone of the young sun, a process which would not have altered the B^{11}/B^{10} ratio. Since the separation of the planetary material, the Li/Be ratio in the sun has been further reduced by (p, α) reactions. This process is evidenced by an observed inverse correlation of Li abundance and age in stars [553].

In this solar atmosphere model, the deuterium will be destroyed at the 10^6 °K temperatures of the convective zone. Hence the D/H ratio of 1.25 × 10^{-4} observed in meteorites must be created by a separate process, such as proton irradiation of helium in the preplanetary gaseous nebula:

$$p + He^4 \rightarrow He^3 + D \qquad (9.1.21)$$

The proton flux required to produce D Li Be B will produce other isotopes of interest. C^{13} will result from spallation on O^{16}: the C^{13}/C^{12} ratio in the earth and meteorites is about ten times the ratio obtained from the solar spectrum. This abundance is compatible with a reduction of the C^{12}/Si ratio from solar by a factor of about 2 × 10^{-4}. Al^{26} will result from spallation on Si^{28} (plus possibly Mg^{26} and Al^{27}) in sufficient abundance to constitute an appreciable heat source in any body of kilometer or greater dimension forming within a few 10^7 years after the spallation. Finally, the I^{129} formation indicated by the Xe^{129} content of meteorites is plausible either from spallation of barium or from neturon capture by Te^{128}.

Cosmological Element Production

The principal explanation for the helium abundance is that it is the consequence of an initial fireball stage of an expanding universe. The evidences for an expanding universe (red shift, darkness of the night sky, density of visible matter, 3°K microwave background radiation) are consistent with a range of model universes which pass through temperatures on the order of 10^9 °K at densities and expansion rates which cause the formation of the required amount of He^4, plus significant abundances of D, He^3, and Li^7. However, these models do not create sufficient Li^6, Be, or B to account for the observed abundances. At present, the greatest difficulty of these models is explaining the anomalously low concentration of helium in some old stars [423].

Summary

In summary, the chemical mix of the solar nebula from which the planets formed appears to be attainable by processes all partially observable in stars today, except for the helium abundance. This mix is intermediate between the sun and the earth's crust in composition, closer to the type I carbonaceous chondrites than anything else known to exist today.

9.2   Planetary Models

Central Models of the Terrestrial Planets

From the masses in Section 5.1 and the radii in Section 6.1, we can calculate the mean densities of the planets. These densities evidently differ appreciably from each other. However, to make significant comparisions and to deduce possible compositions, we need to correct the densities to what they would be if all the material were at the same pressure [197]. This correction in turn depends upon the structure of the planet: that is, the degree to which the iron-nickel (zero-pressure density about 7.9 gm/cm³) has separated from the silicates (zero-pressure density about 3.3 gm/cm³) between the one extreme of homogeneity and the other of a silicate mantle and iron-nickel core. If the mean moment-of-inertia I is known for the planet, then there is an additional integral condition on this separation. However, as discussed in Sections 4.1–2, the measurable quantities are $\Delta I/MR^2$ and $\Delta I/I$, where ΔI is the difference of polar and equatorial moments of inertia. To obtain $\Delta I/MR^2$ requires perturbations of an orbiting body; $\Delta I/I$, observable responses of the planet to torque. Among the terrestrial planets, the former is available only for the earth, the moon, and Mars; the latter, for the earth and moon. But Mars is rotating rapidly enough that we should be able to get a fair estimate of the moment of inertia by assuming hydrostatic equilibrium: that is, using equations (2.1.40) and (2.1.65).

Assuming that each planet is composed of a mixture of olivine-pyroxene (such as the "pyrolite" used in Section 2.5) and iron-nickel, then if M, R, and I are all known, we could solve for both (1) the percent iron-nickel content and (2) the extent to which this iron-nickel has separated into a core. This solution could be made by numerically integrating equation (2.1.47) to obtain pressure and using Figure 1.16 to obtain densities as functions of pressure. If only M and R are known, however, an assumption must be made for one of the unknowns, such as, for (1) the same overall content as the earth, or for (2) either homogeneity or complete separation of the iron-nickel into a core.

Table 9.5 gives a set of solutions based on the assumption that all the iron-nickel has separated into a core.

TABLE 9.5: MEAN DENSITIES OF TERRESTRIAL PLANETS AT 10 KB

Planet	Mean Density (gm/cm³)	Mean Density* (10 kb, gm/cm³)	Portion Iron–Nickel Phase
Mercury	5.44	5.31	0.65
Venus	5.16	3.9	0.265
Earth	5.51	4.03	0.315
Moon	3.34	3.41	0.06
Mars	4.03	3.7	0.19
Chondritic	2.20–3.7	2.45–3.95	0.00–0.30

* Using densities of 3.3 gm/cm³ for silicates and 7.9 gm/cm³ for iron nickel at 10 kb. Based on Ringwood [338, p. 46].

The effect of distributing some of the iron-nickel through a mantle instead of concentrating it all in a core is to increase the portion of iron-nickel, because of its greater compressibility times density. In the case of Mars, a small core is indicated by the relatively large ratio 0.383 for I/MR^2 deduced from the oblateness J_2 and the assumption of hydrostatic equilibrium (see problem 9.1). If the radius of Mars is reduced from 3367 km to 3310 km (see Section 6.1), the density is further increased so that the iron-nickel content for a nearly homogeneous Mars is about equal to the earth's.

The discussion thus far has neglected the effect of temperature on density through thermal expansion and contraction. As discussed in Section 2.4, the thermal state of a planet depends on its temperature of formation, the amount and distribution of radiogenic heat sources, and its size. In general a smaller planet is more effective in getting rid of its heat because of its larger area-to-mass ratio. On the other hand, the lower pressures result in lower melting temperatures. The consequence of these two effects is that the depth at which melting of silicates is most likely to occur is inversely correlated with the size of the planet. The same chondritic-conductive heat models which obtain the highest temperature relative to silicate melting at depths of about 150 km (pressure 50 kb) in earth models attain it at about 1000 km (pressure 40 kb) in moon models and about 500 km (pressure 65 kb) in Mars models. These figures suggest that pressure is the independent variable most appropriate for extrapolation from conditions in the earth's interior to those in other terrestrial planets. The densities obtained in the moon from such an extrapolation are shown in Figure 9.2, together with those from a theoretical model of the thermal regime and compression in the moon [16, 223].

These homogeneous chondritic models of the moon and Mars are self-contradictory, however, in that the melting point of iron is appreciably exceeded, so that the formation of a core would be expected. In any case, it appears that Mercury has much more iron than the earth; Venus, about the same; and Mars, probably less than the earth. Both Venus and Mars could easily have total iron contents in the middle of the range for chondritic meteorites. There remains the possibility of some error in the equations of state from shock compression (Figure 1.16). Also there have been attempts to explain core formation as the consequence of a silicate phase transition [567], but the idea has not yet had any experimental substantiation.

The moon is small enough, and hence possibly of low enough initial temperature, that its low density may be due to retention of volatiles rather than loss of iron. This fact is manifestly true for the parent bodies of the carbonaceous chondrites, which were apparently small enough to radiate most radiogenic heat. But for the same process to apply to the moon it would have had to form while volatiles were still prevalent but after significant heating by Al^{26} or solar-wind induced currents was possible, and with preferably a low

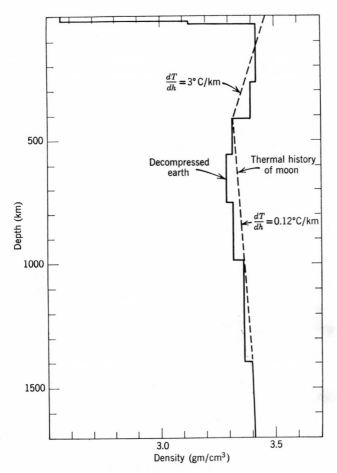

Figure 9.2: Density versus depth in the moon. From Anderson & Kovach [16, p. 88].

K, U, Th content. This hypothesis of volatile retention is also difficult to reconcile with the differentiated surface composition found by the Surveyors (Table 9.1).

Departures from Equilibrium

Also of interest in the planets are any indicators of departures from hydro-static equilibrium: either variations of the external surface or of the gravita-tional field. The essential limitation on the magnitude of these variations is the shearing stresses they necessarily entail. These stresses arise from the attraction of the rest of the planet for the density variations implied by the variations in the external field or form. Thus, if the stress state is comparable, we should expect the absolute magnitude of departures from equilibrium to be inversely proportional to g, the gravitational acceleration. For example, the mountains on the moon should be about six times as high as those on the earth. If we compare dimensionless parameters, such as the gravitational coefficients C_{lm}, S_{lm} in equation (2.1.17), there should be an inverse proportionality to g^2.

By this equal-stress implication rule both the gravitational field and the topographic irregularities indicate that the moon is appreciably closer to hydrostatic equilibrium than is the earth. This is perhaps to be expected from the thermal considerations discussed above: the approach to melting temperature, and hence any zone of minimum strength and maximum convective activity, etc., is probably somewhat deeper in the moon.

For Mercury and Venus, the sole present indicators of departures from hydrostatic equilibrium are their states of synchronous rotation (see Section 5.2), which require certain minimum moment-of-inertia differences $\Delta I/I$ to be stable. These synchronizations require a relatively small $\Delta I/I$ for Mercury, by the g^2 rule, but an unreasonably large $\Delta I/I$ for Venus. It is hoped that the mapping of the topography by radar will yield further information on the nonhydrostatic properties of these planets.

For Mars, the principal indicator of nonhydrostaticity is the discrepancy between the dynamic flattening, 1/194, obtained from the motions of Phobos and Deimos, and the geometric flattening, 1/135, obtained from measurements of photos of Mars. If there is no error in either of these determinations, then the part of the geometric bulge that is in excess of the dynamic bulge must be compensated by some mass deficiency below it. This excess is considerably larger in its stress implication than any that exist on earth; perhaps the measurements may be biased by localized lowlands at the poles or a ring of highlands around the equator. Some further information on the external form of Mars has been deduced recently from radar reflections [354, 355]. These topographic variations are not extraordinarily great in their stress implications.

Summary

In summary, it can be said that the terrestrial planets show pronounced differences in the zero-order property of mean density. These differences indicate different ratios of iron-nickel to silicates (except perhaps the moon), which must be explained in any hypothesis of planet origin. The situation is less clear for the first-order properties of moment of inertia and departures from hydrostatic equilibrium, which bear on the questions of thermal regime and radial differentiation. The principal unknown quantity is the content of heat sources, the radioactive elements K, U, Th. The moon is clearly closer to hydrostatic equilibrium than the earth, but is by no means quiescent. Mars has a high moment of inertia and a magnetic field too weak to be detected by

Mariner IV, both indicating a relatively small core. However, the absence of any significant magnetic field for Venus indicates that the lack of precessional torques may be a more significant factor. The surface features of Mars—meteorite craters, slight atmosphere, no oceans—indicate a lower level of activity than the earth. However, the excess bulge in the geometric surface shape is too big to be supported statically. Venus would be expected to be more active than the earth, since it appears to have about the same bulk composition plus a higher surface temperature. For Mercury, there is no first-order information other than the weak lower bound on the moment of inertia difference ΔI from the synchronous rotation.

The Major Planets

The densities and masses of the major planets given in Table 5.1 immediately suggest *two* additional classes of planets: (1) high mass, low density (Jupiter, Saturn); and (2) moderate mass, moderate density (Uranus, Neptune). Within each class, there is the expected correlation of density with pressure. These planetary classes, together with the terrestrial planets, in turn suggest a three-part classification of chemical substances according to volatility [54]:

1. High: H_2, He
2. Intermediate: H_2O, NH_3, CH_4
3. Low: Fe, MgO, SiO_2, etc.

The principal problem in constructing models of the major planets is the equation of state of the materials: their change of density with pressure. The equation for hydrogen is well enough understood, however, that models of Jupiter and Saturn can be calculated which show they have retained essentially a solar abundance of the high-volatility class of elements, H and He. On the other hand, Uranus and Neptune must be predominantly composed of class 2 substances [480, 578]. Hence a theory of solar system origin must explain the loss of H_2 and He from the outer parts as well as the loss of nearly all volatiles from the inner parts.

9.3 Theories of Origin and Evolution

The difficulty in deducing the origin of the terrestrial planets per se is that it evidently was a process secondary to the formation of the sun and the major planets. To limit the possible circumstances of formation, then, it is desirable to outline the principal ideas of the origin of the solar system as a whole. The main steps in this origin process were:

1. Contraction from an interstellar gas cloud.
2. Formation of the solar nebula.
3. Formation of the sun.
4. Condensation in the solar nebula.

5. Formation of the planets.
6. Dissipation of the excess gas of the solar nebula.

All of these steps necessarily took place, although it is possible that there was no distinct dividing line between 4 and 5, or that step 6 took place before step 5.

Starting Conditions

As with nucleosynthesis, the theories of formation that are most persuasive are those that are to the greatest extent corroborated by observations of processes taking place now. The most important observations are of clusters of stars (see, e.g., Figure 9.3) which have a distribution of luminosity versus color indicating recent formation: large stars (mass $>10M_\odot$) whose total life is less than 50 million years—a few already past the "main-sequence" hydrogen-burning stage; medium-sized stars ($1 - 10M_\odot$) on or just entering the main sequence; and a dearth of small stars ($M < M_\odot$), indicating that they have not yet contracted to the main sequence. These clusters are characterized by a great amount of interstellar gas ($1000M_\odot$ or more), which is luminous because of ionization of the hydrogen by the ultraviolet radiation of the giant O-type stars in the cluster. The density of this gas near the center is on the order of 10^{-21} gm/cm^3, fading out to the 10^{-25} gm/cm^3 average for interstellar (and intercloud) space. There are also considerable localized intensifications of gas density by a factor of 10 or more. Evidence for these intensifications is discrepancies of optical spectrum "forbidden" line intensities (dependent on collisions) from radio intensities (dependent only on ionization).

There are many clouds of interstellar matter of density on the order of 10^{-23} gm/cm^3. For such a cloud to be in equilibrium, there must be a balance between thermal expansion and gravitational contraction; magnetic pressure (3.2.17) is also significant. An instability tending toward contraction will occur if a part of the cloud is of less than average temperature or greater than average density. Calculations based on a typical temperature of about 100°K indicate that the mass required for an instability to lead to star formation is rather large. However, once sufficient mass (about $40M_\odot$) has contracted to form an O star, then the resultant heating of the gas to ionization temperature of 10^4 °K will disrupt the cloud, causing an overall expansion, but also possibly triggering the collapse of many other "protostars" as a consequence of nonuniform heating, etc. It is not clear whether a star such as the sun would be formed as a subcondensation from a larger mass in the initial contraction phase, or as a collapse triggered at the subsequent heating stage. Furthermore, calculations taking into account turbulence and irregularities of the magnetic field may appreciably reduce the mass required for star formation [492].

Approx. 10^{13} km

Figure 9.3: The Orion nebula. Interstellar gas and dust is illuminated by bright young giant stars. Photo by Mount Wilson and Palomar Observatories.

Contraction from Gas Cloud

In any case, we can take the sun as starting from a much more massive concentration of gas colder than the surrounding cloud. This cooler concentration would have a mean density of about 10^{-21} gm/cm^3. Two other important properties are the angular momentum and the magnetic-field intensity. Both of these can be estimated from galactic properties: the cloud should have a rotation rate on the order of the galactic average, 10^{-15} sec^{-1} (although the correlation in direction of stellar and galactic rotation is low [185]) while the magnetic intensity should be a little less than 10^{-3} gauss, allowing for an increase with density from the interstellar average of about 2×10^{-6} gauss.

As discussed in Section 3.2, the effect of a magnetic field is to inhibit instability, that is, to make the motion more laminar, or more connected, and less turbulent. In the problem of star formation this effect operates to increase the size of the critical mass for instability. It also operates on a contracting mass to increase the size of subfragments that may coalesce, and, as first pointed out by Alfven, to transfer angular momentum from the more dense to the less dense parts: the denser inner parts carry along the field lines with them; the less dense outer parts resist the motion of the field lines across them, hence a torque is developed and angular momentum transferred [277].

For a magnetic field to interact with matter, the matter must have an electric charge. In the dispersed interstellar medium, starlight causes sufficient ionization to create this charge. Because of collisions between ions and neutral particles, the degree of ionization necessary to effectively fix the magnetic field in the material medium is rather low. However, one of the most significant differences between various theories has been the density of the protosolar cloud at the time the ionization dropped low enough to permit material to slip easily across field lines; or, alternatively, the magnetic and thermal pressures or turbulent mixing became great enough to break off magnetic lines between the more dense and less dense material. Thus Mestel and Spitzer [278] and Hoyle [184] hypothesized that the ionization became low enough to permit the slipping when the density was still quite low: on the order of 10^{-18} gm/cm^3. This effective elimination of the magnetic field permitted fragmentation of the cloud so that the protosun itself could separate. On the other hand, Cameron [63] maintained that, because of internal sources of ionization such as K^{40} radioactive decay, the magnetic field never separated from the cloud. Hence the original field had to be extremely weak, and the development of a central condensation was prevented until the cloud had contracted to about the size of the present solar system.

If the initial cloud is nonspherical, the gravitational acceleration parallel to the minor axis of the cloud will be more than at right angles thereto. Hence the cloud will tend to become more and more elliptical. Conservation of angular momentum and the existence of a magnetic field parallel to the minor axis will further enhance this tendency of a cloud to flatten. Finally, if considerable contraction has taken place without loss of angular momentum then instability (i.e., the attainment of Keplerian orbit velocity) will first occur at the equator. Thus the nearly coplanar character of motions in the solar system is probably the consequence of a disc-like form of the solar nebula.

The Solar Nebula

The gravitational energy lost during contraction is converted into thermal energy. However, during most of the process the cloud is quite transparent so that the energy is radiated away and the contraction is isothermal. When the cloud has contracted to the size of the solar system, or less, it becomes sufficiently opaque for the temperature to rise. This opacity is a consequence mainly of solid grains, which constitute about 1 percent of the mass of interstellar matter, plus probably molecular absorption. The density at which the temperature starts to rise is variously estimated from 10^{-8} to 10^{-12} gm/cm^3.

When the temperature rises, the ionization rises, so that the magnetic field is once again attached to the matter, and the outward transfer of angular momentum again becomes possible. At this stage, the size of the solar nebula is significant. Estimates of the amount of matter in the nebula outside the sun vary from $0.01 M_\odot$ to $1.0 M_\odot$.

A nebula mass of $0.01 M_\odot$ is the minimum necessary to make up the volatiles missing in the planets compared to solar composition. Such a small nebula has the advantage of minimizing the problem of dissipating the excess gas. On the other hand, it requires the hydromagnetic transfer of angular momentum to be very efficient, and makes condensation and planet formation more difficult both in the sense of low probability of collision and of insufficient opacity to reduce the temperature enough to form ice [184].

A nebula mass of $1.0 M_\odot$ reduces the needs for off-and-on ionization in the contracting cloud, as mentioned, and provides greater opacity and probability of collision for condensation. It also enables the attainment by the means of gaseous accumulations of the pressures and temperatures for the formation of iron meteorites, differentiation of achondrites, etc. Collisions of such gas spheres also may help to blow off the excess material. However, the overriding difficulty of a massive nebula is finding a mechanism of disposing of the excess gas. Furthermore, the considerably greater complications of other processes make the massive nebula an hypothesis to be adopted only if the sparse nebula is demonstrated to be inadequate [63].

In any case, we have as the likely model of the solar system as a primeval separate entity an appreciably flattened nebula of mass 2 to 4×10^{33} gm (1 to $2M_\odot$), radius 4 to 8×10^{14} cm (Neptune orbit to Pluto aphelion), angular momentum 4 to 16×10^{51} gm cm^{-2} sec^{-1} (present plus that of material to be ejected), and principal moment of inertia 10^{62} to 10^{63} gm/cm^2 (very little central densification as yet), and magnetic-field intensity 10^{-5} (interstellar) to 10^{-1} gauss (10^{-4} conserved on contraction from 10^{-24} to 10^{-12} gm/cm^3).

The nebula contracts as long as the magnetic and thermal pressure do not overcome the gravitational attraction (equation (3.2.2)). From 40 to 0.5 AU radius this contraction is rapid, taking only about half a year. Both the magnetic-field intensity and the angular velocity will increase at a rate inversely proportionate to the radius squared. Eventually a gravitational instability (i.e., angular velocity equal to Kepler orbit velocity) develops at the equator and material is shed. If the nebula contracts further, the magnetic field will transfer angular momentum outward from the central cloud to the shed material, causing the latter to move out farther. In the sparse nebula model of Hoyle [184], this instability occurs at a radius of about 3×10^{12} cm, or 0.2 AU, half the radius of Mercury's orbit at which the Keplerian angular motion approximately equals the present rotation rate of the sun. In the massive nebula model of Cameron [63], it occurs almost at the onset.

Formation of the Sun

At a radius of about 0.5 AU (or 100 $R_\odot$), heat and pressure build up enough that the sun becomes luminous. The luminosity is about 100 times that of the present sun, and the surface temperature about 3500°K, as a consequence of convective transfer. The source of energy is still gravitational, and hence there is further collapse at a rate supplying gravitational energy ($\sim GM_\odot{}^2/R$) sufficient to equal that radiated ($\sim \sigma T^4 R^2$). The duration of the collapse in the stage where significant instability occurs in the Hoyle model is about 5×10^3 years [167, 560].

The observational evidence which is most important for any model of solar formation to satisfy is that of *T Tauri* stars, previously mentioned in connection with DLiBeB formation. *T Tauri* stars are defined by a spectrum which contains strong emission lines, indicating an extremely active chromosphere. They are always located in regions of high nebulosity and obscurity, indicating dust, such as the Orion nebula. They undergo considerable oscillations in brightness. Lines in their absorption spectra have Doppler shifts and broadening indicating outward velocities on the order of 100 km/sec. The intensity of this absorption times the surface area of the star and the velocity implies mass loss at the rate of about 10^{-7} $M_\odot$/year [524, 558].

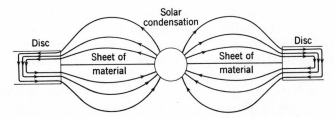

Figure 9.4: Schematic side view of solar condensation and inner edge of disc after Hoyle [184].

Angular-Momentum Transfer

The convection in the contracting sun is important in connection with the hydromagnetic transfer of angular momentum, because the entangling of the magnetic-field lines by the convection will attach them more securely to the sun. Hoyle's diagram of his model is given in Figures 9.4–5. The magnetic field will also be wound up in the planetary disc. Ionization enough for the conductivity to maintain the magnetic field is not a problem; however, there must be a sheet of material between the solar condensation and the disc to resist the pressure of the magnetic field normal to the equatorial plane.

The ability of the magnetic field to exert a torque depends on the field lines

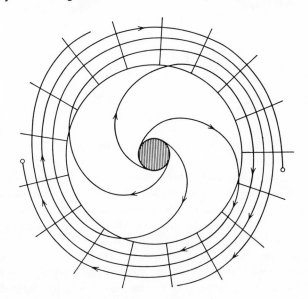

Figure 9.5: Schematic plan view of upper half of Figure 9.4. The lines of force eventually cross the equator and return inward along similar paths.

in Figure 9.5 being twisted to an appreciable angle, say 45°. Then, since stress is $B^2/4\pi\mu$ from (3.2.16), the torque exerted at a radius R will be on the order of $4\pi R^2(B^2/4\pi\mu)R$, or R^3B^2. The angular momentum transferred in a time t will be R^3B^2t. Using 2×10^{12} cm for R, we obtain that a field strength on the order of 100Γ is required to transfer 4×10^{51} gm cm^{-2} sec^{-1} angular momentum in 5000 years [510]. As was the case in the tidal friction of the earth-moon system (Section 4.5), when angular momentum is transferred from rotation of a primary to an orbit revolution of a much smaller secondary, nearly all the energy of the rotation is left in the primary in a form dependent on the manner of exerting torque. In the present case, this form initially would be magnetic: an intensification of the field intensity, which would be effected by a "winding up" of the field around the sun. Taking the starting moment of inertia as $MR^2/10$—that is, a considerable degree of central densification—the total energy to be lost is:

$$\Delta E = \Delta(\tfrac{1}{2}I\omega^2) = \Delta\left(\frac{MR^2\omega^2}{20}\right)$$

$$= \frac{2 \times 10^{33}}{20}[(3 \times 10^{12} \times 2.23 \times 10^{-6})^2 - (7 \times 10^{10} \times 2.7 \times 10^{-6})^2]$$

$$= 5 \times 10^{45} \text{ ergs} \tag{9.3.1}$$

Of which only

$$\Delta E_{\text{disc}} \lesssim \frac{GM_\odot \times 0.01M_\odot}{2R}$$

$$\approx \frac{6.67 \times 10^{-8} \times 10^{-2}(2 \times 10^{33})^2}{2 \times 3 \times 10^{12}} = 0.5 \times 10^{45} \text{ ergs} \tag{9.3.2}$$

goes to the orbiting matter. The remaining energy will severely distort the outer convecting zone of the sun, leading to sporadic outbursts of radiation and energetic particles, and thereby providing mechanisms for spallation effects, chondrule formation, heating the excess gas to escape velocity, etc.

A problem is obtaining low enough temperatures to permit condensation at the distances of the terrestrial planets. The generally accepted contracting solar model of Hayashi et al. [167] has a surface temperature of about 3500°K when the radius is 3×10^{12} cm. However, more than half the 3×10^6-year contraction time is spent when the solar radius is less than $1.5R_\odot$. If most of the severe wrapping-up of the magnetic field which provides the torque to drive out the major planet material occurred at this later stage, then there could be sufficient solids left in the inner parts of the solar system to constitute a smoke providing the necessary opacity.

Condensation in the Nebula

Given time and density enough for sufficient encounters to occur, the process of condensation is still imperfectly understood. If there were considerable inhomogeneities in the gas density—a possibility inhibited by the intense magnetic field—then supersaturation could occur and material would crystallize from the cloud. If the condensation is started by collision of solid particles, then the presence of water or ice would still help them a lot to stick to each other. The structure and apparent chemical composition of comets suggest ice is important for condensation.

Once centers of agglomeration of about 100 km had formed, then gravitational attraction would become significant—that is, the capture velocity $[2(GM/R)]^{1/2}$ of the bodies would be greater than a statistically perceptible fraction of the relative velocities. Another critical size of agglomeration is the minimum body that would resist being swept away with the excess gas that has manifestly been lost from the inner parts of the solar system. For such sweeping along to occur, the gas would have to be dense enough that the effect is expressible as viscous drag, using Stokes' formula for the acceleration A on the body:

$$A_B = \frac{3\pi\eta R}{2m} v \qquad (9.3.3)$$

where η is the viscosity of the gas, R and m are the radius and mass of the body (assumed spherical), and v is the relative velocity. Hoyle [184] applied (9.3.3) taking v to be the increment in velocity acquired in a single revolution due to the acceleration of the gas by energy transferred from the sun. If the outward rate of motion is da/dt then the resulting along-track acceleration, and hence the velocity increment, can be calculated by differentiating Kepler's law (4.1.21):

$$v = A_G P = A_G \frac{2\pi}{n} = A_G \frac{2\pi a^{3/2}}{(GM)^{1/2}} \qquad (9.3.4)$$

Then for $A_B \ll A_G$,

$$\frac{3\pi\eta R}{2m} \frac{2\pi a^{3/2}}{(GM)^{1/2}} \ll 1 \qquad (9.3.5)$$

or

$$R \gg \left(\frac{9\pi\eta}{4\rho}\right)^{1/2} \left(\frac{a^3}{GM}\right)^{1/4} \approx 15 \text{ cm} \qquad (9.3.6)$$

substituting 8.7×10^{-5} gm cm^{-1} sec^{-1} for η, the viscosity of hydrogen; 3 gm/cm^3 for ρ, the density; 6×10^{12} cm, the orbital radius of Mercury, for a; and 2×10^{33} gm for M.

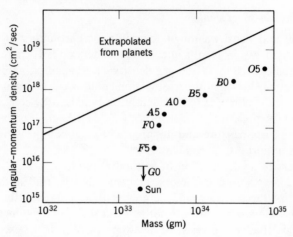

Figure 9.6: Angular-momentum density of stars by spectral type. Based on Allen [4, p. 204].

Stellar Rotation

Some mild corroboration that formation of a nebula, and hence possibly of a planetary system, is characteristic of stars like the sun is furnished by their rotation rates, observed by Doppler broadening of spectral lines. If the graph of angular-momentum density, Figure 5.2, is extended to heavier bodies, the sun falls much farther below the line extrapolated from the planets than do the more massive stars, as indicated in Figure 9.6. The most obvious property relevant is the strong convection of the outer zones of the less massive stars in their contracting stage, which would increase the torque transmittable by the magnetic field. Exceptions to the general rule of slow rotation are binary stars, which are much closer together than are the planets to the sun: suggestive of an agglomeration of the disc into a second star at an early stage of the shedding of the nebula and a consequent breakdown of hydromagnetic angular-momentum transfer. About a third of star systems observed near the sun are double, triple, or quadruple. In addition, there are seven stars observed to have periodic motions indicating an invisible companion of mass less than $0.02 M_\odot$ [54].

Resistive Heating of Protoplanets

A consequence of a rapidly rotating sun with a strong magnetic field may be the generation of appreciable electrical currents in a conducting planet with no insulating atmosphere, through the cutting of the body by the magnetic lines of force. These currents would have resistive losses which would generate heat, in turn affecting the conductivity. Numerical calculations have obtained several 100°C temperature increase in 10^6 years [581].

Interim Summary

The ideas of solar system origin outlined here—essentially those of Hoyle [184] and Cameron [63]—are generally accepted nowadays as satisfying the *necessary* characteristic of hydromagnetic transfer of angular momentum from the central condensation to the outer parts; and having the *desirable* characteristics of making the solar nebula a subfragment of the much larger cloud which has a higher probability of formation from the interstellar medium; of not requiring the extremely improbable (even in a cluster) events of close approach of two stars, or explosion of one member of a binary system; of keeping the ionization at the low levels needed for maintenance of a sufficient magnetic field, and hence making it easier to obtain temperatures low enough to permit condensation; and of not requiring the sun to acquire material from the interstellar medium after it has already formed.

There are several other theories of solar system formation which do not meet one or more of these desiderata; see Jastrow and Cameron [195, pp. 4–37].

Problems of Planetary Formation

The balance of a theory of solar-system formation taking into account the main features is concerned, first, with the differing densities of the major planets, and the related question of loss of hydrogen and helium by the solar system; second, with the large satellite systems of Jupiter, Saturn, and Uranus; third, with the direct rotation of nearly all the major bodies; and fourth, with the asteroid belt.

As mentioned, model calculations indicate that Jupiter and Saturn are of virtually solar composition, but that Uranus and Neptune evidently lost most of the hydrogen and helium [91]. Although sufficient energy was available from the early sun to push these gases out of the solar system, the detailed process by which this "blowing off" took place is unsure.

The extensive satellite systems have a somewhat smaller portion of mass in the secondaries than does the solar system, but drastically less of angular momentum, as shown in Table 9.6 (despite transfers by tidal friction). The

TABLE 9.6: COMPARISON OF PLANETARY AND SATELLITE SYSTEMS

Primary	Total Mass (gm)	Portion in Secondaries	Angular Momentum $(gm \cdot cm^{-2} sec^{-1})$	Portion in Secondaries
Sun	1.94×10^{33}	0.0013	3.21×10^{50}	0.9947
Jupiter	1.90×10^{30}	0.00019	4.43×10^{45}	0.0096
Saturn	0.57×10^{30}	0.00025	0.79×10^{45}	0.0123
Uranus	0.087×10^{30}	0.000096	0.019×10^{45}	0.0075

formation of the major planet satellite systems thus appears to have been the consequence of a similar instability in the primary, but lacking in sufficient magnetic field to cause any significant hydromagnetic transfer of angular momentum.

The direct rotation of the planets follows as a consequence of angular-momentum conservation (problem 5.3), but the actual mechanism of the momentum transfer takes some attention to arrive at the same conclusion: see problem 9.5 [19].

The existence of the asteroid belt in place of a planet suggests that Jupiter had already formed and exerted a disruptive effect inhibiting condensation in the belt, similar to the effect of Saturn's satellites on the rings. As discussed in Chapter 5, the asteroid belt is still undergoing significant evolution.

Formation of the Terrestrial Planets

For the main subject of this book, the terrestrial planets, we thus can start from an inner solar system in which the sun contracting onto the main sequence was surrounded by a well-mixed gas and dust cloud which is in large part at a temperature below 300°K. The mixing is evidenced by the uniformity of primeval isotope ratios in the meteorites and the earth's crust. The low temperature appears essential not only to provide the ice to facilitate condensation and to permit the formation of hydrocarbons in the carbonaceous chondrites, but also to account for the considerable degree of oxidation of metals in all the planets (except Mercury) and in most chondritic meteorites. As first emphasized by Latimer [237], for the cosmic-abundance ratio of oxygen to hydrogen,

$$K = \frac{H_2O}{H_2} \approx 0.002 \qquad (9.3.7)$$

the reaction

$$\tfrac{1}{4}Fe_3O_4 + H_2 = \tfrac{3}{4}Fe + H_2O \qquad (9.3.8)$$

goes completely to the left below 390°K, and completely to the right above 1120°K. Similarly,

$$FeO + H_2 \rightleftharpoons Fe + H_2O \qquad (9.3.9)$$

goes completely to the left below 590°K.

A low temperature also generally is held necessary for the formation of the earth in order to account for the extent to which active volatiles—C, N, O, F, Na, Cl, Hg, etc.—have been retained in the earth, as well as to avoid extensive melting in the subsequent thermal evolution.

The essential features of any theory of the origin of the terrestrial planets are the hypotheses as to the conditions affecting reactions involving the common *active* elements H, C, N, O, Mg, Si, S, and Fe [381]. The important conditions are:

1. The temperature, which depends primarily on the luminosity of the sun, secondarily on the opacity of the nebula, thirdly on the gravitational energy from the contraction of the planet, plus possibly short-lived radioactivity or induced current dissipation.

2. The pressure, any significant variation of which requires an appreciable degree of local condensation.

3. The abundance of hydrogen, which is the element by far the most sensitive to any process expelling gas from the solar system.

To calculate the equilibrium proportions of different compounds given these three conditions, we further require:

4. The elemental abundances, given in Table 9.2.

5. The compounds that might conceivably exist.

6. For each of these compounds, either the free energy $\Delta G°$ or the equilibrium constant K for formation from its constituent elements as a function of temperature.

In Table 9.7 are given the *free energies of formation* $\Delta G°$ at 1 atm pressure and several temperatures for the 28 substances which are most likely to form from the eight elements. An alternative representation is in the form of polynomial coefficients [566]. By free energy of formation of a substance of the form $X_l Y_m Z_n$, we mean the free energy change as defined by (8.2.3) for a reaction of the form

$$\frac{l}{i} X_i + \frac{m}{j} Y_j + \frac{n}{k} Z_k \rightleftharpoons X_l Y_m Z_n \tag{9.3.10}$$

where i, j, k are the number of atoms per molecule in the reference state: usually 1 for solids and 2 for gases.

All but one line of Table 9.7 is experimental data, although for iron compounds the free energy must be calculated rather awkwardly as

$$\Delta G_T{}^0 = \Delta H^0_{298.15} + (H_T{}^0 - H^0_{298.15}) - T\Bigg[(S_T{}^0 - S^0_{298.15})$$

$$+ S^0_{298.15} - \sum_{\text{reactants}} \left(\frac{G_T{}^0 - H^0_{298.15}}{T}\right)\Bigg] \tag{9.3.11}$$

in order to utilize the data as published [564]. The quantity $(G_T{}^0 - H^0_{298.15})/T$, called the *free energy function*, or *fef*, is used because it varies slowly with temperature. The free energies in Table 9.7 for $FeSiO_3$ (which is virtually nonexistent in nature) were calculated on the assumptions that up to 1400°K it has a virtually constant $\Delta(\text{fef})$, like $MgSiO_3$ and Fe_2SiO_4, and above 1400°K, a moderately increasing $\Delta(\text{fef})$, like $MgSiO_3$.

For a given temperature T, the pressure P dependence of the free energy ΔG of a gas is given accurately by (8.2.6); the free energy of a solid can be

TABLE 9.7: THERMOCHEMICAL DATA FOR COMPOUNDS OF COMMON ELEMENTS

(Pressure = 1 atmosphere)

References states and their transition temperatures: C(graphite); Fe(α-1184°K-γ-1165°K-δ-1809°K-l); H$_2$(g); Mg(s-922°K-l); N$_2$(g); O$_2$(g); S(rhombic-368°K-monoclinic-388°K-l-718°K); S$_2$(718°K-g); Si(s-1685°K-l).

Substance	State	$\Delta H°$ (kilocal mole^{-1}) 298.15°K	$\Delta G°$ (kilocal mole^{-1})						
			298.15°K	500°K	800°K	1100°K	1400°K	1700°K	2000°K
C	g	170.89	169.03	152.55	141.21	129.82	118.47	107.15	95.88
CH$_4$	g	−17.89	−12.14	−7.84	−0.53	7.25	15.20	23.19	31.19
CO	g	−26.42	−32.78	−37.14	−43.61	−49.96	−56.19	−62.32	−68.35
CO$_2$	g	−94.05	−94.26	−94.40	−94.56	−94.66	−94.72	−94.75	−94.75
COS	g	−33.08	−39.59	−43.73	−50.37	−51.10	−51.82	−52.54	−53.24
Fe	g	99.50	88.59	81.22	70.43	60.08	50.23	40.60	31.63
Fe$_{0.947}$O	s	−63.7	−58.4	−55.0	−50.2	−45.2	−40.4	−35.8	−32.5
Fe$_2$O$_3$	s	−196.5	−177.1	−164.1	−145.8	−128.3	−110.8	−93.5	
Fe$_3$O$_4$	s	−267.0	−242.4	−226.1	−204.1	−182.0	−160.4	−139.0	
FeS	s	−24.2	−24.8	−25.0	−27.4	−23.5	−20.0	−17.6	−15.7
FeSiO$_3$	s	−276.	−257.	−244.	−225.	−206.	−186.	−161.	−134.
Fe$_2$SiO$_4$	s	−353.1	−328.5	−312.0	−288.1	−264.0	−240.4	−220.4	−200.2
H	g	52.10	48.59	46.12	42.24	38.20	34.05	29.82	25.54
H$_2$O	g	−57.80	−54.64	−52.36	−49.92	−46.04	−40.66	−36.55	−32.40
H$_2$S	g	−4.82	−7.89	−9.53	−12.10	−8.60	−5.06	−1.52	2.00

	State								
HCN	g	31.20	28.70	27.04	24.63	22.29	19.99	17.71	15.43
Mg	g	35.28	27.02	21.50	13.53	6.25			
MgO	s	4.19	-1.36	-3.02	-10.17	-14.70	-17.90	-16.09	-12.16
$MgSiO_3$	s	-369.89	-349.13	-335.04	-314.24	-293.22	-271.61	-244.05	-214.85
Mg_2SiO_4	s	-520.02	-491.58	-472.29	-443.89	-414.97	-384.75	-342.60	-299.08
N	g	112.96	108.87	106.01	101.56	96.97	92.29	87.56	82.78
NH_3	g	-11.04	-3.97	1.11	9.29	17.78	26.38	35.02	43.66
O	g	59.56	55.40	52.48	47.96	43.32	38.61	33.86	29.08
S	g	65.65	55.98	49.63	39.56	35.29	30.96	26.60	22.20
S_2	g	30.84	19.14	11.81					
SO_2	g	-70.75	-71.74	-71.92	-72.57	-67.33	-62.10	-56.90	-51.73
SO_3	g	-94.47	-88.51	-78.40	-78.06	-66.31	-54.64		
Si	g	106.00	95.38	88.18	77.56	67.05	56.66	46.46	38.37
SiO	g	-24.20	-30.62	-34.90	-41.01	-46.92	-52.67	-58.18	-61.54
SiO_2	s	-217.50	-204.53	-195.73	-182.83	-170.30	-157.93	-145.58	-131.32

Heats of transition $\Delta H_T{}^\circ$ in kcal mole^{-1} (< 0.1 omitted); $(f) =$ (fusion), $(v) =$ (vaporization):

Fe: 1184°K: 0.2; 1665°K: 0.3; 1809°K: 3.6; Fe$_{0.947}$O: 1650°K(f): 7.5;

Fe$_2$O$_3$: 950°K$(\alpha \rightarrow \beta)$: 0.2; Fe$_2SiO_4$: 1490°K$(f)$: 22.0;

H$_2$O: 363°K(v): 9.7;

Mg: 922°K(f): 2.1; 1378°K(v): 30.5; MgSiO$_3$: 1798°K(f): 14.7; Mg$_2$SiO$_4$: 2158°K(f): 20.6;

S: 388°K(f): 0.4; 718°K(v): 2.3;

Si: 1685°K(f): 12.1; 3440°K(v): 91.0; SiO$_2$: 848°K$(\alpha \rightarrow \beta)$: 0.3; 1883°K$(f)$: 2.0.

Based on Garrels & Christ [466, pp. 403–429], JANAF [563], and Kelley [564, pp. 93–96; 565, pp. 14–17].

433

assumed unvarying. The simplest quantity calculable from Table 9.7 is the *vapor pressure* of an element. The vapor pressure is the pressure $P(T)$ at which the condensed phase is in equilibrium with its vapor. The appropriate equation for an element X is then

$$X(s) \rightleftharpoons X(g) \tag{9.3.12}$$

The insensitivity of the free energy ΔG of a solid substance to changes in pressure means that its effective pressure, or fugacity, in reaction (9.3.12) is unity, and hence that by (8.2.10) the vapor pressure equals the equilibrium constant K. For example, the vapor pressure of iron Fe at 1100°K is, applying (8.2.11) to $\Delta G_T°$ from Table 9.7, 8×10^{-13} atmospheres.

If in a primordial gaseous nebula the partial pressure of an element rises above its vapor pressure, then, assuming no chemical reactions, the element will condense. Since such a nebula would have been almost entirely hydrogen H_2, the ratio of the partial pressure $P(X)$ of any other element (in the form of a monatomic gas) to the total pressure P_T will be approximately twice the ratio of its atomic abundance $A(X)$ to that of hydrogen

$$P(X) \approx \frac{2A(X)}{A(H)} P_T \tag{9.3.13}$$

Figure 9.7 is a summary of vapor pressure as a function of temperature for several elements.

Differences of elemental abundances from "cosmic" thus might be used in conjunction with Figure 9.7 to deduce pressures and temperatures of condensation of planets and meteorite parent bodies. However, the actual vapor pressures in the solar nebula may be displaced orders-of-magnitude by alloy formation; diffusion in grains; and the formation of compounds.

To take compound formation into account while still assuming thermodynamic equilibrium, it is necessary first to specify the abundances of the elements, and second to select from Table 9.7 the substances likely to form. For example, with solar or cosmic abundances a likely set would be $C(s)$, CH_4, CO, CO_2, COS, $Fe(s)$, FeS, Fe_2SiO_4, H_2, H_2O, H_2S, Mg_2SiO_4, N_2, NH_3, O_2, $S(s)$, $S_2(g)$, SO_2, and SO_3 (see Problem 9.8). On these twenty quantities are imposed eight relations by the total elemental abundances plus twelve relations by the free energies of formation or equilibrium constants of reactions forming the compounds.

An example is given by the subsystem comprising elements C, O, H and compounds CO, CO_2, CH_4, H_2, and H_2O, for which it is assumed that the significant reactions are:

$$CO_2 + H_2 \rightleftharpoons CO + H_2O$$
$$CO_2 + 4H_2 \rightleftharpoons CH_4 + 2H_2O \tag{9.3.14}$$

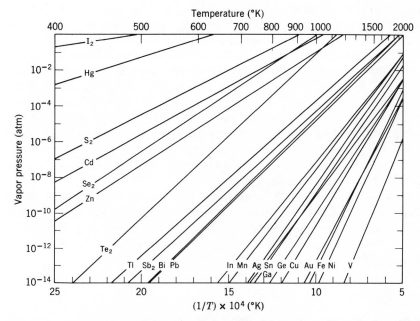

Figure 9.7: Vapor pressures of elements as a function of temperature. From Larimer [485].

The three abundance relations:

$$\sum C = [CO_2] + [CO] + [CH_4]$$
$$\sum O = 2[CO_2] + [CO] + [H_2O] \qquad (9.3.15)$$
$$\sum H = 2[H_2] + 2[H_2O] + 4[CH_4]$$

plus the two equilibrium functions:

$$K_1 = \frac{[CO][H_2O]}{[CO_2][H_2]}$$
$$\qquad (9.3.16)$$
$$K_2 = \frac{[CH_4][H_2O]^2}{[CO_2][H_2]^4}$$

constitute five relations for the five quantities [CO], [CO$_2$], [CH$_4$], [H$_2$], and [H$_2$O]. Since two of the relations are nonlinear the solution must be approximated by series expansion or iteration [379].

An alternative technique more manageable for the larger system is to distribute the eight elements into the twenty substances so as to minimize the total free energy, subject to the abundance and reaction balance restraints. Shimazu [360] carried out this calculation for temperatures 300°K, 1000°K, and 2000°K; pressures 10^{-2}, 1, and 10^2 atm; and hydrogen abundances $\log_{10} \Sigma H$ (normalized to 6.00 for $\log_{10} \Sigma Si$) of 10.5, 8.0, 7.477, 7.00, 6.00, and 5.00. The main conclusions were:

1. Transition from reduced state to oxidized state (i.e., from CH_4, NH_3, H_2S to CO_2, CO, SO_2, etc.) occurs at about $[H_2O]/[H_2] \approx 1$, regardless of temperature or pressure.

2. As the temperature increases, the reduction-oxidation transition requires higher elemental abundance of hydrogen, ΣH, because of the increasing instability of hydrogen compounds.

3. As the temperature increases, CO becomes more stable relative to CO_2, so that the $[CO_2]/[CO]$ ratio decreases.

4. At 300°K, Fe_2SiO_4 is more stable than Fe at both low and high H abundances, but not in between; the range of Fe stability decreases with increasing pressure; at 1000°K, Fe_2SiO_4 is more stable than Fe only for $\log_{10} \Sigma H \leq 6.00$; at 2000°K, Fe is more stable than Fe_2SiO_4 at all hydrogen abundances.

5. FeS is stable only at low temperatures at intermediate H abundances corresponding to Fe_2SiO_4 instability.

Any theory of origin of the terrestrial planets attempts to permit reactions between these compounds to go as far as possible to equilibrium.

Two-Stage Theory

The principal respect in which various theories of the origin of the earth differ is whether there existed any protoplanets (or heating and turbulence in the nebula) as an intervening stage between the initial cold nebula and the final formation of the planets.

A two-stage theory is advocated by Urey [405–408]. Considerable temperatures (and, for some processes, pressures) in a planetary environment are needed to drive off the inert gases while retaining some of the chemically active volatiles; to account for the fractionation processes that produced iron, stony-iron, and achondritic meteorites; and to account for diamonds in meteorites. The means to attain these conditions proposed by Urey are lunar-sized protoplanets (based to some extent on a previous model of Kuiper [229]). These protoplanets are hypothesized to have condensed in a dense solar nebula, and to have been surrounded by great accumulations of gas.

The pressure at the interior of a gas sphere is calculated from the equation of hydrostatic equilibrium (2.1.47); Poisson's equation; and an equation of state of the form:

$$P = \kappa \rho^\gamma \qquad (9.3.17)$$

where κ and γ are constants, called the polytropic gas equation. For ideal gases, the parameter γ is the ratio of specific heats. The temperature is obtained using the ideal gas law, equation (8.2.4). The integration of the equations for realistic values of γ is necessarily numerical, but was carried out and tabulated long ago by Emden. For a given mass of gas, the temperature and pressure at the center depends on the radius. The results of the numerical integration for an Emden hydrogen gas sphere ($\gamma = \frac{5}{3}$) give for the central temperature T_0 and pressure P_0 of a mass M and radius R:

$$T_0 \approx 0.94 \times 10^{-15} \frac{M}{R} \tag{9.3.18}$$

$$P_0 \approx 0.5 \times 10^{-9} \frac{M^2}{R^4} \tag{9.3.19}$$

for cgs units and °K. If the mass of the solar nebula was $1.0 M_{\odot}$, then a lunar-sized body presumably would have associated with it about 1000 times as much mass in gas, 7.5×10^{28} gm. To attain temperatures high enough to volatilize silicates and melt iron—say 2000°K—the radius of the mass would have to contract to about 300,000 km, by (9.3.18). The degree of densification over the solar nebula average would have to be about 10^4, but the gas sphere would still have been much easier to break up than any solid body. However, to attain sufficient pressures for static formation of diamonds, compression in a dense lunar-sized body is still required.

Numerous lunar-sized protoplanets also were favored by Urey to account for the low density of the moon and to make the moon's capture by the earth a not too improbable event. They also help explain the various indications of distinct parent bodies evidenced by meteorites.

The Urey cosmogonical model is thus: (1) a cold ($\ll$300°K) nebula; (2) accumulation of protoplanets at temperatures on the order of 300°K; (3) development of high temperatures ($\sim$2200°K) upon the contraction of protoplanets, with consequent reduction of iron and volatilization of some silicates; (4) collision and breakup of the protoplanets, with loss of most of the gas and varying loss of silicates due to radiation pressure and a strong solar wind; and (5) accumulation of the present planets at temperatures on the order of 270°K.

Single-Stage Theory

A single-stage theory would, of course, be more satisfying esthetically. Ringwood [336–338] has attempted to construct such a theory. In Ringwood's theory, much of the hydrogen is lost prior to the condensation of the planets, so that the reduction of iron and other metals is largely done by carbon instead. Evidence of this process in meteorites is the occurrence of minerals such as troilite (FeS), cohenite (Fe_3C), schreibersite (Fe_3P), and oldhamite (CaS). Ringwood's nebula is rather sparse, so that the small parent bodies of meteorites must have an electromagentic or short-lived radioactive source of heat. In the case of the larger planets, such as the earth, there will be appreciable gravitational heat. When the initial material accreted it was quite cold, so that the volatiles were retained. Material falling in the later part of the accretion added much more gravitational energy and hence generated more heat, resulting in the evaporation of considerable material forming a dense, opaque atmosphere which further accelerated the heating process. This heating reduced the outer material, so there resulted the unstable situation of a hot dense exterior and a cooler light interior. Eventually there was a catastrophic overturn in which the reduced metal, principally iron, fell into the center. Conservation of angular momentum with this infalling of denser material resulted in an increased rotation rate and instability, throwing off volatilized silicates. These silicates combined with other infalling material to form the moon, thus accounting for its lower density. At the same time the dense atmosphere was blown off.

Ringwood emphasizes that the earth is manifestly in disequilibrium chemically. As discussed in Section 2.5, the density of the core is inconsistent with pure iron, but is compatible with an admixture of about 15–20 percent silicon. Such metallic silicon coexistent with oxidized iron in the mantle, despite several $100°K$ difference in reduction temperature, indicates disequilibrium and thus catastrophic formation of the core. In this situation it should not be surprising that some small portions of certain volatiles—e.g., Hg, Cd, Zn—have been retained, and that the terrestrial deficiencies of other metals are not precisely ordered according to volatility (Si, Na, Mg, Ca, Al, decreasingly).

Origin of the Moon

The origin of the moon is still an unsolved problem. As discussed in Section 4.5, there is a time-scale difficulty; extrapolation backward of the orbit with the present phase lag brings the moon back into the earth less than 1.7 Æ ago. Theories of lunar origin are customarily sorted into four categories: binary system; capture; fission; and coagulation. The separate formation of the earth and moon at the same time as a binary system is, of course, implausible because of their considerable density difference; furthermore, to keep two bodies of such different mass from either falling together or falling completely apart requires tricky conditions on the addition of orbital angular momentum in the accretion process. However, the other three categories are still the object of serious consideration.

The capture of the moon is desirable for chemical reasons, as discussed in connection with Urey's theory of planetary origin. Two mechanisms of capture have been proposed. In the theory of Gerstenkorn [133] the moon approaches the earth in a retrograde orbit. Tidal interactions cause the orbital inclination to change so that it becomes direct, and the moon moves outward. Conservation of angular momentum requires an initial rotation period of the earth just barely above stability, 2.6 hours, and the dissipation of enough energy in the earth to melt much of it. In the theory of Singer [371], the moon is captured from a direct hyperbolic orbit, such that the perigee comes within the radius of a synchronous orbit. The reduction of the eccentricity of such an orbit requires a particular dependence of the dissipation factor Q on frequency, however. The interaction with solar perturbations is also important. See Lyttleton [251] for a discussion of conditions affecting capture.

Modern theories of the fission origin of the moon couple it with the formation of the core producing instability, as in the Ringwood theory [337]. Other recent theories are those of Wise [445], who assumed a fluid earth which elongated in a pear-shaped Poincaré figure far enough to push the moon to where the orbital velocity was less than synchronous; and Cameron [64], who assumed shedding at the equator of fragments that later collected. Cameron also associated the origin of the moon with the loss of the earth's atmosphere, in order to carry away that part of the angular momentum required for instability which is in excess of that now in the earth-moon system. Fission theories are difficult to reconcile with the impossibility of getting an inclination of the orbit to the equator less than 10° (Section 4.5), as well as requiring an initial angular-momentum density considerably in excess of that indicated by Figure 5.2.

The coagulation, or many moon, theory of Ruskol [351] and MacDonald [254] alleviates the time-scale difficulty of the tidal-friction calculations, since the rates of orbital evolution of the several small moons will be much less than the rate of the single moon. We are then left with the problem as to which of these several small moons originated by fission, as proposed by Ringwood [338], and which by capture, just as in the case of the single moon. The fact that integration back in time of the moon's orbit obtains an appreciable inclination regardless of dissipation mechanism [142] requires that at least part of the moon be captured.

Entirely aside from the question of fission of the moon, analyses of core formation which take into account the energetics of the problem, plus the strong temperature dependence of viscosity, conclude that it was an unstable process which, once started, carried itself rapidly to conclusion [32, 400]. In this respect it differs from the processes of fractionation of the crust and outgassing of the oceans and atmosphere, which are all believed to have evolved gradually.

Origin of Variations between Planets

The differences in uniform pressure density of the planets given in Table 9.5 are most simply explained as different degrees of reduction, plus possibly loss of silicates, consequent on different degrees of heating. An iron-silicon mixture which has a density of 3.72 gm/cm³ when completely oxidized will increase in density of 3.94 gm/cm³ with complete reduction of the iron (about 850°C), and to 4.16 gm/cm³ with 40 percent reduction of the silica (requiring about 1500°C). This range of density covers Mars, Venus, and the earth, and suggests that reduction is positively correlated with the size of the planet—as would be expected if the source of heat was largely gravitational contraction. The anomalously high density of Mercury, however, is explicable only as a consequence of the active early sun volatilizing most of its silicates and blowing them away with Mercury's atmosphere.

As mentioned previously, Venus has an atmosphere much different from the earth's: almost entirely CO_2; surface temperature 700°K; surface pressure 60–100 atm. Cameron [64] suggested that, unlike the earth, Venus retained some of its primeval atmosphere because it was too small to develop an instability and eject its atmosphere and a moon. However, this theory fails to explain why Mars, farther from the sun, failed to retain any perceptible atmosphere. A more plausible explanation was given by Suess [379], who calculated equilibrium concentrations of H_2, CH_4, CO, CO_2, and H_2O as a function of total H (Equations 9.3.14–16), and showed that for a C/O ratio comparable to solar (1.0: see Table 9.2) and sufficiently low temperatures, a surface of low-volatility carbon compounds could form. With loss of hydrogen due to subsequent heating, the atmosphere would be dominated by CO_2.

Evolution since Origin

The concordance of many meteorite ages and the comparison of terrestrial and meteorite lead and uranium ratios (Sections 1.3, 8.4) indicate that the major events of solar-system formation were concluded about 4.5 Æ ago, and that subsequent interaction between parts of the solar system has been confined to tidal friction and asteroid and comet collisions. There also are some planetary evolution problems dependent on the sun itself, however.

After the sun settles down on the main sequence, it gradually heats up so that the luminosity is about 30 percent higher after 5.0 Æ [358]. Assuming constant albedo and greenhouse effect, the resulting change in temperature at the earth is an increase of about 20°C. A temperature 20 deg lower early in the earth's history creates considerable difficulty in accounting for the extensive erosion more than 3.5 Æ ago evidenced by the oldest rocks, since the earth would have been largely frozen [99]. Some primordial atmosphere or very early stage of extra outgassing seems necessary to put enough CO_2 in the atmosphere to create a sufficient greenhouse effect. The C/H ratio could be somewhat less than on Venus, so that eventually nearly all the primordial CO_2 is fixed in the crust. As demonstrated by Rubey [348], for the most of geologic history the CO_2/H_2O ratio in the oceans and atmosphere has remained relatively constant, indicating replenishment of the CO_2 by outgassing.

Another aspect in which continued solar activity may have had an evolutionary effect is in transmission of angular momentum through the solar wind. Estimates of the mean solar-wind density and velocity yield a torque of about 7×10^{30} gm cm^{-2} sec^{-2}, which suggests that the rotation rate of the sun could have been reduced by about 50 percent in 5.0 Æ [42].

Summary

In summary, it appears highly probable that the terrestrial planets originated by condensation from a cold cloud of dust and gas with an average chemical composition between solar and type I carbonaceous chondritic. This cloud, the solar nebula, was shed by the unstable contracting sun, and then moved outward because it was magnetically coupled to the rotating sun. The opacity of the nebula must have been considerable to permit the temperature to drop sufficiently to facilitate condensation of solid bodies. The relationship between the sweeping away of the excess gas, and possibly dust, and the stages of planet formation is unsure. Certainly there was ample energy wrapped up in the outer parts of the sun by the hydromagnetic-momentum transfer process, and there is evidence from observations of *T Tauri* stars that part of this energy was expended in energetic particle outbursts. Whether the sun was also the source of heat to accomplish reduction and volatilization of the material in the planets and meteorites is dubious; the various disequilibria suggest that the reductions took place in condensed environments, where the heat may have been supplied by gravitational contraction of the planet or short-lived Al^{26} radioactivity or the pressure of accumulation gas.

The great question is the extent to which these condensed environments either have been destroyed or have evolved into a present environment. As more of the pertinent facts are taken into account, it becomes more difficult not to complicate the answers with ad hoc mechanisms. Certainly there are a number of phenomena which suggest significantly different environments, some of them not only at different distances from the sun, but also necessarily at different stages anywhere from 10 to 10^8 years apart: the different densities of the earth and the moon; the loss of volatiles of the earth with respect to chondritic meteorites; the differing iron contents of meteorite classes; the groupings in reduction of chondrites; the groupings in trace-element content and isotope ratios of meteorites; the formation and inclusion of chondrules; the juxtaposition of gas-rich and gas-deficient matter in some meteorites; the varying Xe^{129} excesses relative to the earth; the greatly different CO_2/H_2O ratios in the earth and Venus atmospheres; the uniquely high moon/earth mass ratio; etc.

This account, like any that attempts to be comprehensive, is unavoidably superficial. The narrowing down of the possible explanations (i.e., mainly number, size, and composition of protoplanets; size and composition of protoatmospheres; etc.) will depend not only on new data, but also on the more detailed solution of some physical problems, such as:

1. How does material condense and accrete from a dust cloud in the solar nebula: what are the relative influences of temperature, gas pressure, turbulence, gravitational instability, electromagnetic effects? To what extent are comets pertinent to this problem?

2. What are the conditions of the hydromagnetic transfer of angular momentum in the nebula: the allowable ionization levels and the manner in which they are maintained; what is the time scale, and its relation to the time scale of solar contraction; the extent to which the field can be "wound up" in the sun before it breaks down; the necessary gas pressure to resist breakdown of the field in the nebula; the extent to which dust can be carried along with the gas; the influence of the magnetic field on condensation; etc.?

3. What happens when two objects collide at high-energy levels: the effects of irregularities in allowing small solid pieces to be broken off; the cushioning effect of a large protoatmosphere; the extent of melting and vaporization in complete fragmentation; the extent of gas loss; etc.?

4. How can gas escape by mechanisms other than diffusion or evaporation: the extent to which an explosive blowing off is required; the possibility of making the mechanism selective other than by condensation? Do these mechanisms explain the loss of primordial atmosphere by the earth and the loss of hydrogen by the outer parts of the solar system?

5. What environments will significantly change the C/H ratio: nonequilibrium effects, as well as temperature, pressure, gravity, and the amounts of oxygen, nitrogen, and silicates present?

It must be that in time
The real will from its crude compoundings come, ...

Wallace Stevens
Notes Toward a Supreme Fiction

PROBLEMS

9.1. Given the following observational data for Mars:

Rotation period:	$24^h\ 27^m\ 23^s$
Grav. const. × mass:	4.29×10^{19} cm³/sec²
Equatorial radius:	3375 km
Polar radius:	3350 km
Oblateness J_2:	0.001972

How much does the flattening obtained from the oblateness (J_2) differ from that obtained from the apparent equatorial and polar radii? If this difference is due to an isostatically supported crust with a zero minimum thickness and a crust-mantle density difference $\Delta\rho = 0.6$ gm/cm³, what must be the maximum thickness of the crust?

Assuming that the dynamical flattening of Mars is that of fluid equilibrium, derive the moment of inertia of Mars.

9.2. Given a large number of particles of mass m_i, derive the relationship (known as the virial theorem):

$$\frac{1}{2\sum_i m_i} \frac{d^2}{dt^2}\left(\sum_{ij} m_i m_j r_{ij}{}^2\right) = 2T + V$$

where r_{ij} is the distance between the ith and jth particles, T is the total kinetic energy of the system, and V is the total potential energy. What is a necessary condition for stability of the system, i.e., that it not fly apart? What effect would the existence of a magnetic field or of internal heat energy in the system have on this condition?

9.3. Derive the Roche density:

$$\rho \approx \frac{6}{\pi}\frac{M_\odot}{R^3}$$

i.e., the minimum density sufficient for material to hold itself together by mutual gravitational attraction at a distance R from a sun of mass $M_\odot$.

9.4. Using the information from Section 4.5 that extrapolation backward of the moon's orbit with the present dissipation factor $1/Q$ brings the moon back into the earth 1.6 Æ ago, deduce how many smaller moons of equal mass brought together 1.0 Æ ago to form the present moon are required in order that *their* orbits extrapolated backward at the same $1/Q$ do not fall back into the earth less than 5.0 Æ ago.

9.5. Given a planet in a circular orbit about the sun and considering that it will overtake particles in the sector B on the diagram and be overtaken by particles in the sector A, derive the sense of rotation about its own axis which will be acquired by the planet, neglecting eccentricity of particle orbits.

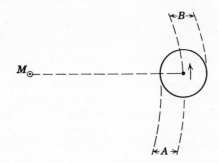

9.6. In which part of the solid earth—crust, mantle, or core—is each of the following elements most likely to have its high proportionate abundance: O, Na, Mg, Al, Si, S, Ar, K, Ca, Fe, Ni, Th, U? State the reasons for each answer (either in the form of a brief reason for each element, or a general discussion).

9.7. Write the reaction equations similar to (9.3.8, 9, 14) involving some of the other compounds in Table 9.7. What will be the equilibrium constants for these reactions? How will they change with increase in temperature?

9.8. Discuss the justification for the selection of 20 substances for the thermodynamical calculations based on the data in Table 9.7. Why were FeO, MgO, SiO_2, and $MgSiO_3$ not included?

REFERENCES

Texts on the solar atmosphere are *Aller* [6] and *Zirin* [454]. More elementary is *Brandt & Hodge* [43]. The best background for the spectroscopy as well as other parts of Section 9.1 is probably a good text on modern physics, such as *Leighton* [241] or *Eisberg* [461]. The most important paper in recent years on abundance determinations is *Goldberg et al.* [138]. More recent work is reviewed by *Aller* [7] and discussed in a symposium volume edited by *Hubenet* [186]. Ultraviolet observations are reviewed by *Pottasch* [322]. Recent papers pertaining to planetary atmospheres are by *Connes et al.* [517, 518] and *Dayhoff et al.* [520]. The atmospheres of Venus and Mars are the subject of a recent volume edited by *Brandt & McElroy* [548]. Jupiter's atmosphere is analysed by *Greenspan & Owen* [556]. The gamma-ray observations of the moon are described by *Vinogradov et al.* [421], and the alpha-scattering experiment by *Turkevich et al.* [508, 583]. The principal compilation of abundances is by *Suess & Urey* [382]. Other compilations and discussions are by *Aller* [5] and *Cameron* [62]. The fundamental paper on nucleosynthesis is *Burbidge et al.* [59], supplemented by *Fowler et al.* [126], *Wagoner et al.* [424], and *Bernas et al.* [540]. Recent reviews and modifications are by *Fowler* [124, 125], *Burnett & Fowler* [60], *Tayler* [389, 545] and *Wagoner* [423]. A recent general review of solar system abundances is by *Urey* [509].

Papers on the interiors of the terrestrial planets used in Section 9.2 are *Jeffreys* [197], *MacDonald* [253], *Kovach & Anderson* [223], and *Anderson & Kovach* [16].

General reviews on planetary interiors are by *De Marcus* [91] and *Wildt* [440]. Recent papers are by *Fricker et al.* [465] and *Kozlovskaya* [567]. The major planets are analyzed by *Kieffer* [480] and *Peebles* [578].

The classic on the dynamics of stellar formation is *Jeans* [196]. A comprehensive exposition of more recent developments is given by *Mestel* [277], and effects of the magnetic field on collapse of clouds are discussed by *Parker* [492]. The classic on the constitution of stars is *Eddington* [107]. The modern fundamental treatise on stellar structure is by *Schwarzschild* [358], supplemented by *Hayashi et al.* [167]. Recent collections on stellar problems are edited by *Aller & McLaughlin* [8] and *Stein & Cameron* [374]. A general description of the T Tauri stars is given by *Herbig* [524, 558]. The principal modern theories on the formation of the solar system are those of *Hoyle* [184, 560] and of *Cameron* [63, 550]. The magnetohydrodynamic aspects are also treated by *Schatzman* [544]. General discussions on solar-system origin and related problems are given in *Jastrow & Cameron* [195], *Whipple* [437], *Cameron* [65], and *McMahon* [272]. Questions of stellar and planetary rotation are discussed by *Artem'ev & Radzievski* [19], *Huang* [185], and *Brown* [54]. The formation of the major planets has been discussed in greatest detail recently by *De Marcus* [91] and *Öpik* [300].

The principal modern theories on the formation of the terrestrial planets are those of *Urey* [405–408] and *Ringwood* [336–338]. Some important chemical problems are investigated by *Latimer* [237], *Suess* [379, 381], *Larimer* [485], *Lord* [571], and *Shimazu* [360]. Chemical considerations are also discussed in the volume edited by *Brancazio & Cameron* [41], as well as in many of the references to Chapter 8. Theories pertaining particularly to the origin of the moon are given by *Gerstenkorn* [133], *Wise* [445], *Cameron* [64], *MacDonald* [254], *Ruskol* [351], *Lyttleton* [251], and *Singer* [371]. The origin of the core is considered in detail by *Birch* [32] and *Tozer* [400]. The problems of escape of gases is investigated by *Öpik* [301]; the heating of planets by resistive losses of induced electric currents by *Sonett & Colburn* [581]; the solar-wind torque by *Brandt* [42]; and the geological effect of the cool early sun by *Donn et al.* [99].

Bibliography

1. Alfvén, H. & C. G. Fälthammar, *Cosmical Electrodynamics*, Clarendon Press, Oxford, 228 pp., 1963.
2. Ahrens, L., *Distribution of the Elements in Our Planet*, McGraw-Hill, New York, 110 pp., 1965.
3. Alder, B. J., Is the mantle soluble in the core? *J. Geophys. Res.*, **71**, 4973–4979, 1966.
4. Allen, C. W., *Astrophysical Quantities*, 2nd ed., Athlone Press, London, 291 pp., 1963.
5. Aller, L. H., *The Abundance of the Elements*, Interscience, New York, 283 pp., 1961.
6. Aller, L. H., *Astrophysics 1. The Atmospheres of the Sun and Stars*, 2nd ed., Ronald Press, New York, 650 pp., 1963.
7. Aller, L. H., The abundance of elements in the solar atmosphere, *Advan. Astron. & Astrophys.*, **4**, 1–25, 1965.
8. Aller, L. H., & D. B. McLaughlin, Eds., *Stellar Structure*, Univ. Chicago Press, 648 pp., 1965.
9. Alterman, Z., H. Jarosch, & C. L. Pekeris, Oscillations of the Earth, *Proc. Roy. Soc.*, A, **252**, 80–95, 1959.
10. Al'tshuler, L. V., Use of shock waves in high-pressure physics, *Sov. Phys. Uspekhi*, **8**, 52–91, 1965.
11. Anders, E., Meteorite ages, in B. M. Middlehurst & G. P. Kuiper, Eds., *Solar System* **4**, *The Moon, Meteorites and Comets*, Univ. Chicago Press, 402–495, 1963.
12. Anders, E., Origin, age, and composition of meteorites, *Sp. Sci. Rev.*, **3**, 583–714, 1964.
13. Anders, E., & M. E. Lipshutz, Critique of paper by N. L. Carter and G. C. Kennedy, "Origin of diamonds in the Canyon Diablo and Novo Urei meteorites", *J. Geophys. Res.*, **71**, 643–661, 1966.
14. Anderson, D. L., Recent evidence concerning the structure and composition of the earth's mantle, *Phys. Chem. Earth*, **6**, 1–131, 1965.
15. Anderson, D. L. & C. B. Archambeau, The anelasticity of the earth, *J. Geophys. Res.*, **69**, 2071–2084, 1964.
16. Anderson, D. L., & R. L. Kovach, The internal structure of the moon and the terrestrial planets, in H. Brown, G. J. Stanley, D. O. Muhleman, & G. Münch, Eds., *Proc. Caltech-JPL Lunar & Plan. Conf., Sept. 13–18, 1965*, 84–91, 1966.
17. Anderson, J. D., Determination of the masses of the moon and Venus and the astronomical unit from radio tracking data of the Mariner II Spacecraft, *JPL Tech. Rep.*, **32-816**, 298 pp., 1967.
18. Arnold, J. R., The origin of meteorites as small bodies, I:, in H. Craig, S. L.

Miller, & G. J. Wasserburg, Eds., *Isotopic and Cosmic Chemistry*, North-Holland Publishing Co., Amsterdam, 347–364, 1964; II & III, *Astrophys. J.*, **131**, 1536–1556, 1965.

19. Artem'ev, A. V. & V. V. Radzievskii, The origin of the axial rotation of planets, *Sov. Astron. AJ*, **9**, 96–99, 1965.

20. Ash, M. E., I. I. Shapiro, & W. B. Smith, Astronomical constants and planetary ephemerides deduced from radar and optical observations, *Astron. J.*, **72**, 338–350, 1967.

21. Baldwin, R. B., *The Measure of the Moon*, Univ. Chicago Press, 488 pp., 1963.

22. Baldwin, R. B., The crater diameter-depth relationship from Ranger VII photographs, *Astron. J.*, **70**, 545–547, 1965.

23. Baker, G., Tektites, *Mem. Natl. Museum Victoria*, **23**, 313 pp., 1959.

24. Barrett, A. H., Passive radio observations of Mercury, Venus, Mars, Saturn, and Uranus, *J. Res. N.B.S. Radio Science*, **69D**, 1565–1573, 1965.

25. Beard, D. B., Absence of craters on the far side of the moon, *Nature*, **184**, 1631, 1959.

26. Beckmann, P., & A. Spizzichino, *The Scattering of Electromagnetic Waves from Rough Surfaces*, Pergamon Press-Macmillan, New York, 503 pp., 1963.

27. Belousov, V. V., *Basic Problems in Geotectonics*, McGraw-Hill, New York, 816 pp., 1962.

28. Belousov, V. V. & M. V. Gzovsky, Experimental tectonics, in L. H. Ahrens, F. Press, S. K. Runcorn, & H. C. Urey, Eds., *Physics and Chemistry of the Earth*, **6**, Pergamon Press, Oxford, 409–498, 1965.

29. Belton, M. J. S., Dynamics of interplanetary dust, *Science*, **151**, 35–44, 1966.

30. Binder, A. B., Mariner IV: Analysis of preliminary photographs, *Science*, **152**, 1053–1055, 1966.

31. Birch, F., Elasticity and constitution of the earth's interior, *J. Geophys. Res.*, **57**, 277–286, 1952.

32. Birch, F., Energetics of core formation, *J. Geophys. Res.*, **70**, 6217–6221, 1965.

33. Bjork, R. L., Analysis of the formation of Meteor Crater, Arizona: a preliminary report, *J. Geophys. Res.*, **66**, 3379–3387, 1961.

34. Bjork, R. L., N. B. Brooks, & R. Papetti, A numerical technique for the solution of multi-dimensional hydrodynamic problems, *Rand Corp. Res. Mem.*, **RM-2628-PR**, Santa Monica, Calif., 59 pp., 1963.

35. Blackett, P. M. S., E. Bullard, & S. K. Runcorn, Eds., A Symposium on Continental Drift, *Phil. Trans. Roy. Soc. A.*, **258**, 323 pp., 1965.

36. Blanco, V. M., & S. W. McCuskey, *Basic Physics of the Solar System*, Addison-Wesley, Reading, Mass., 307 pp., 1961.

37. Bowen, N. L., *The Evolution of the Igneous Rocks*, Princeton Univ. Press, 1928; republ. by Dover, New York, 334 pp., 1956.

38. Boyd, F. R., Geological aspects of high pressure research, *Science*, **145**, 13–20, 1964.

39. Bradley, R. S., *High Pressure Physics and Chemistry*, 2 vols., Academic Press, New York, 805 pp., 1963.

40. Brady, J. L., Effect of the planetary system on the nearly-parabolic comets, *Astron. J.*, **70**, 279–282, 1965.

41. Brancazio, P. J., & A. G. W. Cameron, Eds., *The Origin and Evolution of Atmospheres and Oceans*, Wiley, New York, 314 pp., 1964.

42. Brandt, J. C., Consequences of the torque exerted on the sun by the solar wind, *Astrophys. J.*, **144**, 1221-1222, 1966.

43. Brandt, J. C., & P. W. Hodge, *Solar System Astrophysics*, McGraw-Hill, New York, 457 pp., 1964.

44. Bridgman, P. W., *The Physics of High Pressures*, Bell, London, 445 pp., 1949.

45. Brouwer, D., Secular variations of the orbital elements of minor planets, *Astron J.*, **56**, 9-32, 1951.

46. Brouwer, D., The problem of the Kirkwood gaps in the asteroid belt, *Astron J.*, **68**, 152-159, 1963.

47. Brouwer, D., & G. M. Clemence, *Methods of Celestial Mechanics*, Academic Press, New York, 598 pp., 1961.

48. Brouwer, D., & G. M. Clemence, Orbits and masses of planets and satellites, in G. P. Kuiper & B. M. Middlehurst, Eds., *The Solar System*, **3**, *Planets and Satellites*, Univ. Chicago Press, 31–94, 1961.

49. Brouwer, D., & G. I. Hori, The motion of the moon in space, in Z. Kopal, Ed., *Physics and Astronomy of the Moon*, Academic Press, New York, 1–26, 1962.

50. Brouwer, D., & A. J. van Woerkom, The secular variations of the orbital elements of the principal planets, *Astron. Papers, Am. Ephem. & Naut. Alm.*, **13**, 85–107, 1950.

51. Brown, E. W., *An Introductory Treatise on the Lunar Theory*, Cambridge Univ. Press, London, 1896; republ. by Dover, New York, 292 pp., 1960.

52. Brown, E. W., Theory of the motion of the moon; containing a new calculation of the expression for the coordinates of the moon in terms of time, *Mem. Roy. Astron. Soc.*, **53**, 39–116, 163–202; **54**, 1–64; **57**, 51–145; **59**, 1–104; 1897–1908.

53. Brown, E. W., & C. Shook, *Planetary Theory*, Cambridge Univ. Press, London, 1933; republ. by Dover, New York, 302 pp., 1967.

54. Brown, H., Planetary systems associated with main-sequence stars, *Science*, **145**, 1177–1181, 1964.

55. Brown, H., G. J. Stanley, D. O. Muhleman, & G. Münch, Eds., *Proceedings of the Caltech-JPL Lunar and Planetary Conference September 13–18, 1965*, Calif. Inst. Tech.-JPL, Pasadena, 307 pp., 1966.

56. Bullard, E. C., C. Freedman, H. Gellman, & J. Nixon, The westward drift of the earth's magnetic field, *Phil. Trans. Roy. Soc. A.*, **243**, 67–82, 1950.

57. Bullard, E. C., & H. Gellman, Homogeneous dynamics and terrestrial magnetism, *Phil. Trans. Roy. Soc. A.*, **247**, 213–278, 1954.

58. Bullen, K. E., *Introduction to the Theory of Seismology*, 3rd ed., Cambridge Univ. Press, London, 381 pp., 1963.

59. Burbidge, E. M., G. R. Burbidge, W. A. Fowler, & F. Hoyle, Synthesis of the elements in the stars, *Rev. Mod. Phys.*, **29**, 548–650, 1957.

60. Burnett, D. S., W. A. Fowler, & F. Hoyle, Nucleosynthesis in the early history of the solar system, *Geochim. Cosmochim. Acta*, **29**, 1209–1241, 1965

61. Cain, J. C., W. E. Daniels, & S. J. Hendricks, An evaluation of the main geomagnetic field, 1940–1962, *J. Geophys. Res.*, **70**, 3647–3674, 1965.

62. Cameron, A. G. W., A revised table of abundance of the elements, *Astrophys. J.*, **129**, 676–699, 1959.

63. Cameron, A. G. W., The formation of the sun and planets, *Icarus*, **1**, 13–69, 1962.

64. Cameron, A. G. W., The origin of the atmospheres of Venus and the earth, *Icarus*, **2**, 249–257, 1963.

65. Cameron, A. G. W., Origin of the solar system, in W. N. Hess, Ed., *Introduction to Space Science*, Gordon & Breach, New York, 553–584, 1965.

66. Carlson, R. H., & G. D. Jones, Distribution of ejecta from cratering explosions in soils, *J. Geophys. Res.*, **70**, 1897–1910, 1965.

67. Carter, N. L., & G. C. Kennedy, Origin of diamonds in the Canyon Diablo and Novo Urei meteorites, *J. Geophys. Res.*, **69**, 2403–2421, 1964.

68. Chandrasekhar, S., *Hydrodynamic and Hydromagnetic Stability*, Clarendon Press, Oxford, 652 pp., 1961.

69. Chao, E. C. T., Shock effects in certain rock-forming minerals, *Science*, **156**, 192–202, 1967.

70. Chapman, D. R., & H. K. Larson, On the lunar origin of tektites, *J. Geophys. Res.*, **68**, 4305–4358, 1963.

71. Chapman, S., & J. Bartels, *Geomagnetism*, Clarendon Press, Oxford, 2 vols., 1049 pp., 1940.

72. Charters, A. C., High-speed impact, *Sci. Am.*, **203**(4), 128–140, 1960.

73. Clark, S. P., Radiative transfer in the earth's mantle, *Trans. Am. Geophys. Un.*, **38**, 931–938, 1957.

74. Clark, S. P. Jr., Ed., *Handbook of Physical Constants*, Geol. Soc. Am. Mem., **97**, 587 pp., 1966.

75. Clark, S. P., Jr., & A. E. Ringwood, Density distribution and constitution of the mantle, *Revs. Geophys.*, **2**, 35–88, 1964.

76. Cohen, C. J., & E. C. Hubbard, Libration of the close approaches of Pluto to Neptune, *Astron. J.*, **70**, 10–14, 1965.

77. Collinson, D. W., K. M. Creer, & S. K. Runcorn, *Methods in Paleomagnetism*, Elsevier, Amsterdam, 609 pp., 1967.

78. Colombo, G., & I. I. Shapiro, The rotation of the planet Mercury, *Astrophys. J.*, **145**, 296–307, 1966.

79. Contopoulos, G., Ed., *The Theory of Orbits in the Solar System and in Stellar Systems*, Academic Press, New York, 380 pp., 1966.

80. Cook, A. H., The contribution of observations of satellites to the determination of the earth's gravitational potential, *Sp. Sci. Revs.*, **2**, 355–437, 1963.

81. Corson, D. R., & P. Lorrain, *Introduction to Electromagnetic Fields and Waves*, Freeman, San Francisco, 552 pp., 1962.

82. Cowling, T. G., *Magnetohydrodynamics*, Interscience, New York, 115 pp., 1957.

83. Cox, A., & R. R. Doell, Long-period variations of the geomagnetic field, *Bull. Seismol. Soc. Am.*, **54**, 2243–2270, 1964.

84. Craig, H., S. Miller, & G. J. Wasserburg, Eds., *Isotopic and Cosmic Chemistry*, North-Holland Publ. Co., Amsterdam, 553 pp., 1964.

85. Dagley, P., R. L. Wilson, J. M. Ade-hall, P. L. Walker, S. E. Haggerty, T. Sigurgeirsson, N. D. Watkins, P. J. Smith, J. Edwards, & R. L. Grasty, Geomagnetic polarity zones for Icelandic lavas, *Nature*, **216**, 25–29, 1967.

86. Danby, J. M. A., *Fundamentals of Celestial Mechanics*, Macmillan, New York, 348 pp., 1962.

87. Daniels, F., & R. A. Alberty, *Physical Chemistry*, 2nd ed., Wiley, New York, 744 pp., 1961.

88. Darwin, G. H., *Tidal Friction and Cosmogony*, **2**, *Scientific Papers*, Cambridge Univ. Press, London, 516 pp., 1908.

89. Deal, W. E., Jr., Dynamic high-pressure techniques, in R. H. Wentorf, Jr., Ed., *Modern Very High Pressure Techniques*, Butterworth, Washington, 200–227, 1962.

90. Deer, W. A., R. A. Howie, & J. Zussman, *An Introduction to the Rock-Forming Minerals*, Wiley, New York, 528 pp., 1966.

91. De Marcus, W. C., Planetary interiors, in S. Flügge, Ed., *Handbuch der Physik*, **52**, Springer-Verlag, Berlin, 419–448, 1959.

92. de Sitter, L. U., Structural geology, *International Series in the Earth Sciences*, 2nd ed., McGraw-Hill, New York, 551 pp., 1964.

93. Dicke, R. H., The secular acceleration of the earth's rotation and cosmology, in B. G. Marsden & A. G. W. Cameron, Eds., *The Earth-Moon System*, Plenum Press, New York, 98–164, 1966.

94. Dietz, R. S., Continent and ocean basin evolution by spreading of the sea floor, *Nature*, **190**, 854–857, 1961.

95. Doell, R. R. & A. Cox, Paleomagnetism of Hawaiian lava flows, *J. Geophys. Res.*, **70**, 3377–3405, 1965.

96. Doell, R. R., G. B. Dalrymple, & A. Cox, Geomagnetic polarity epochs: Sierra Nevada data, 3, *J. Geophys. Res.*, **71**, 531–541, 1966.

97. Dollfus, A., Polarization studies of the planets, in G. P. Kuiper & B. M. Middlehurst, Eds., *The Solar System*, **3**, *Planets and Satellites*, Univ. Chicago Press, 343–399, 1961.

98. Dollfus, A., Visual and photographic studies of planets at the Pic du Midi, in G. P. Kuiper & B. M. Middlehurst, Eds., *The Solar System*, **3**, *Planets and Satellites*, Univ. Chicago Press, 534–571, 1961.

99. Donn, W. L., B. D. Donn, & W. G. Valentine, On the early history of the earth, *Geol. Soc. Am. Bull.*, **76**, 287–306, 1965.

100. Doodson, A. T., Oceanic tides, *Adv. Geophys.*, **5**, 118–153, 1958.

101. Drake, F., Radio measurements of the moon, in W. N. Hess, D. H. Menzel, & J. A. O'Keefe, Eds., *The Nature of the Lunar Surface*, Johns Hopkins Press, Baltimore, 277–284, 1966.

102. Dyce, R. B., G. H. Pettengill, & I. I. Shapiro, Radar determinations of the rotations of Venus and Mercury, *Astron. J.*, **72**, 351–359, 1967.

103. Eckhardt, D. H., Computer solutions of the forced physical librations of the moon, *Astron. J.*, **70**, 466–471, 1965.

104. Eckhardt, D., K. Larner, & T. Madden, Long-period magnetic fluctuations and mantle electrical conductivity estimates, *J. Geophys. Res.*, **68**, 6279–628ℓ, 1963.

105. Eckert, W. J., On the motions of perigee and node and the distribution of mass in the moon, *Astron. J.*, **70**, 787–792, 1965.

106. Eckert, W. J., M. J. Walker, & D. Eckert, Transformations of the lunar coordinates and orbital parameters, *Astron. J.*, **71**, 314–332, 1966.

107. Eddington, A., *The Internal Constitution of the Stars*, Cambridge Univ. Press, 1926; republ. by Dover, New York, 407 pp., 1959.

108. Ehmann, W. D., & J. F. Lovering, The abundance of mercury in meteorites and rocks by neutron activation analysis, *Geochim. Cosmochim. Acta*, **31**, 357–376, 1967.

109. Elsasser, W. M., Hydromagnetism, *Am. J. Phys.*, **23**, 590–609. 1955; **24**, 85–110, 1956.

110. Elsasser, W. M., Hydromagnetic dynamo theory, *Revs. Mod. Phys.*, **28**, 135–163, 1956.

111. Elsasser, W. M., Thermal structure of the upper mantle and convection, in P. M. Hurley, Ed., *Advances in Earth Science*, M. I. T. Press, Cambridge, 461–502, 1966.

112. Engel, A. E. J., Geologic evolution of North America, *Science*, **140**, 143–152, 1963.

113. Evans, J. V., Radar studies of the moon, *J. Res. N. B. S. Radio Science*, **69D**, 1637–1659, 1965.

114. Evans, J. V., & T. Hagfors, Study of radio echoes from the moon at 23 centimeters wavelength, *J. Geophys. Res.*, **71**, 4871–4889, 1966.

115. Evans, J. V., & G. H. Pettengill, The scattering behavior of the moon at wavelengths of 3.6, 68, and 784 centimeters, *J. Geophys. Res.*, **68**, 423–447, 1963.

116. Ewing, J., J. L. Worzel, M. Ewing, & C. Windisch, Age of horizon A and the oldest Atlantic sediments, *Science*, **154**, 1125–1132, 1966.

117. Ewing, M., X. Le Pichon, & J. Ewing, Crustal structure of the mid-ocean ridges, 4. Sediment distribution in the South Atlantic Ocean and the Cenozoic history of the mid-Atlantic ridge, *J. Geophys. Res.*, **71**, 1611–1636, 1966.

118. Fielder, G., *Structure of the Moon's Surface*, Pergamon Press, Oxford, 266 pp., 1961.

119. Finney, J. L., & J. D. Bernal, Random close packing and the heats of fusion of simple liquids, *Nature*, **213**, 1079–1082, 1967.

120. Fisher, D. E., The origin of meteorites: space erosion and cosmic radiation ages, *J. Geophys. Res.*, **71**, 3251–3259, 1966.

121. Fisher, D. E., On the origin of fissiogenic xenon in meteorites, *J. Geophys. Res.*, **72**, 765–769, 1967.

122. Fleischer, R. L., C. W. Naeser, P. B. Price, R. M. Walker, & M. Maurette, Cosmic ray exposure ages of tektites by the fission track technique, *J. Geophys. Res.*, **70**, 1491–1496, 1965.

123. Fleischer, R. L., P. B. Price, R. M. Walker, & M. Maurette, Origins of fossil charged particle tracks in meteorites, *J. Geophys. Res.*, **72**, 331–366, 1967.

124. Fowler, W. A., The origin of the elements, *Proc. Nat. Acad. Sci.*, **52**, 524–548, 1964.

125. Fowler, W. A., *Nuclear Astrophysics*, American Philos. Soc., Philadelphia, 109 pp., 1967.

126. Fowler, W. A., J. L. Greenstein, & F. Hoyle, Nucleosynthesis during the early history of the solar system, *Geophys. J., Roy. Astron. Soc.*, **6**, 148–220, 1962.

127. Garland, G. D., *The Earth's Shape and Gravity*, Pergamon Press, Oxford, 183 pp., 1965.

128. Gast, P. W., Limitations on the composition of the upper mantle, *J. Geophys. Res.*, **65**, 1287–1297, 1960.

129. Gault, D. E., E. D. Heitowit, & H. J. Moore, Some observations of hyper-velocity impacts with porous media, in J. W. Salisbury & P. E. Glass, Eds., *The Lunar Surface Layer: Materials and Characteristics*, Academic Press, New York, 151–178, 1964.

130. Gault, D. E., W. L. Quaide, &. V. E. Oberbeck, Interpreting Ranger photographs from impact cratering studies, in W. N. Hess, D. H. Menzel, & J. A. O'Keefe, Eds., *The Nature of the Lunar Surface*, Johns Hopkins Press, Baltimore, 125–140, 1966.

131. Gault, D. E., E. M. Shoemaker, & H. J. Moore, Spray ejected from the lunar surface by meteoroid impact, *NASA Tech. Note*, **D-1767**, 39 pp., 1963.

132. Geiss, J., & E. D. Goldberg, Eds., *Earth Science and Meteoritics*, North-Holland Publ. Co., Amsterdam, 312 pp., 1963.

133. Gerstenkorn, H., Uber Gezeitenreibung beim Zweikörpenproblem, *Z. Astrophys.*, **26**, 245–274, 1955.

134. Gilvarry, J. J., Lindemann and Grüneisen laws and a melting law at high pressure, *Phys. Rev. Letters*, **16**, 1089–1091, 1966.

135. Girifalco, L. A., *Atomic Migration in Crystals*, Blaisdell, New York, 162 pp., 1964.

136. Glass, B., Microtektites in deep-sea sediments, *Nature*, **214**, 372–374, 1967.

137. Gold, T., The moon's surface, in W. N. Hess, D. H. Menzel, & J. A. O'Keefe, Eds., *The Nature of the Lunar Surface*, Johns Hopkins Press, Baltimore, 107–121, 1966.

138. Goldberg, L., E. A. Muller, & L. H. Aller, The abundances of the elements in the solar atmosphere, *Astrophys. J. Suppl.*, **45**, 1–138, 1960.

139. Goldreich, P., On the eccentricity of satellite orbits in the solar system, *Mo. Not. Roy. Astron. Soc.*, **126**, 257–268, 1963.

140. Goldreich, P., An explanation of the frequent occurrence of commensurable mean motions in the solar system, *Mo. Not. Roy. Astron. Soc.*, **130**, 159–181, 1965.

141. Goldreich, P., Final spin states of planets and satellites, *Astron. J.*, **71**, 1–7, 1966.

142. Goldreich, P., History of the lunar orbit, *Revs. Geophys.*, **4**, 411–439, 1966.

143. Goldreich, P., & S. J. Peale, Spin-orbit coupling in the solar system, *Astron. J.*, **71**, 425–438, 1966.

144. Goldreich, P., & S. J. Peale, Spin-orbit coupling in the solar system II: the resonant rotation of Venus, *Astron. J.*, **72**, 662–668, 1967.

145. Goldreich, P., & S. Soter, Q in the solar system, *Icarus*, **5**, 375–389, 1966.

146. Goldstein, H., *Classical Mechanics*, Addison-Wesley, Reading, Mass., 398 pp., 1950.

147. Gordon, R. B., Diffusion creep in the earth's mantle, *J. Geophys. Res.*, **70**, 2413–2418, 1965.

148. Gordon, R. B., & C. W. Nelson, Anelastic properties of the earth, *Revs. Geophys.* **4**, 457–474, 1966.

149. Greenland, L., Gallium in chondritic meteorites, *J. Geophys. Res.*, **70**, 3813–3817, 1965.

150. Green, D. H., & A. E. Ringwood, An experimental investigation of the gabbro to eclogite transformation and its petrological applications, *Geochim. Cosmochim. Acta*, **31**, 767–833, 1967.

151. Griggs, D. T., & J. Handin, Eds., *Rock Deformation*, Geol. Soc. Am. Mem., **79**, 382 pp., 1960.

152. Gutenberg, B., *Physics of the Earth's Interior*, Academic Press, New York, 240 pp., 1959.

153. Hagfors, T., Backscattering from an undulating surface with applications to radar returns from the moon, *J. Geophys. Res.*, **69**, 3779–3784, 1964.

154. Hagfors, T., R. A. Brockelman, H. H. Danforth, L. B. Hanson, & G. M. Hyde, Tenuous surface layer on the moon: evidence derived from radar observations, *Science*, **150**, 1153–1156, 1965.

155. Hagihara, Y., The stability of the solar system, in G. P. Kuiper & B. M. Middlehurst, Eds., *The Solar System*, **3**, *Planets and Satellites*, Univ. Chicago Press, 95–158, 1961.

156. Hamilton, E. I., *Applied Geochronology*, Academic Press, New York, 267 pp., 1965.

157. Hamilton, W., & W. B. Meyers, Cenozoic tectonics of the western United States, *Revs. Geophys.*, **4**, 509–549, 1966.

158. Hapke, B., A theoretical photometric function for the lunar surface, *J. Geophys. Res.*, **68**, 4545–4570, 1963.

159. Hapke, B., An improved theoretical lunar photometric function, *Astron. J.*, **71**, 333–339, 1966.

160. Hapke, B., Surveyor I and Luna IX pictures and the lunar soil, *Icarus*, **6**, 254–269, 1967.

161. Harris, D. L., Photometry and colorimetry of planets and satellites, in G. P. Kuiper & B. M. Middlehurst, Eds., *The Solar System*, **3**, *Planets and Satellites*, Univ. Chicago Press, 272–342, 1961.

162. Harrison, J. C., An analysis of the lunar tides, *J. Geophys. Res.*, **68**, 4269–4280, 1963.

163. Hartmann, W. K., Secular changes in meteoritic flux through the history of the solar system, *Icarus*, **4**, 207–213, 1965.

164. Hartmann, W. K., Martian cratering, *Icarus*, **5**, 565–576, 1966.

165. Hawkins, G. S., A study of tektites, *J. Geophys. Res.*, **68**, 895–910, 1963.

166. Hawkins, G. S., Interplanetary debris near the earth, *Ann. Rev. Astron. Astrophys.*, **2**, 140–164, 1964.

167. Hayashi, C., R. Hoshi, & D. Sugimoto, Evolution of the stars, *Suppl. Prog. Theoret. Phys.*, **22**, 1–183, 1962.

168. Heacock, R. L., G. P. Kuiper, E. M. Shoemaker, H. C. Urey, & E. A. Whitaker, Ranger VII: Part II. Experimenters' analyses and interpretations, *JPL Tech. Rep.*, **32-700**, 154 pp., 1965.

169. Heacock, R. L., G. P. Kuiper, G. M. Shoemaker, H. C. Urey, & E. A. Whitaker, Ranger VIII and IX: Part II. Experimenters' analyses and interpretations, *JPL Tech. Rep.*, **32-800**, 382 pp. 1966.

170. Heezen, B. C., The deep-sea floor, in S. K. Runcorn, Ed., *Continental Drift*, Academic Press, New York, 235–288, 1962.

171. Heiskanen, W. A., & H. Moritz, *Physical Geodesy*, Freeman, San Francisco, 364 pp., 1967.

172. Herring, C., Diffusional viscosity of a polycrystalline solid, *J. Appl. Phys.*, **21**, 437–445, 1950.

173. Hess, H. H., Mid-oceanic ridges and tectonics of the sea-floor, in W. F. Whittard & R. Bradshaw, Eds., *Submarine Geology and Geophysics*, Butterworth, London, 317–332, 1965.

174. Hess, W. N., Ed., *Introduction to Space Science*, Gordon & Breach, New York, 919 pp., 1965.

175. Hess, W. N., D. H. Menzel, & J. A. O'Keefe, Eds., *The Nature of the Lunar Surface*, Proc. 1965 *IAU-NASA Symposium*, Johns Hopkins Press, Baltimore, 320 pp., 1966.

176. Heymann, D., On the origin of hypersthene chondrites: ages and shock effects of black chondrites, *Icarus*, **6**, 189–221, 1967.

177. Hide, R., The hydrodynamics of the earth's core, *Phys. Chem. Earth*, **1**, 94–137, 1956.

178. Hide, R., Planetary magnetic fields, *Planet. Sp. Sci.*, **14**, 579–586, 1966.

179. Hide, R., The hydromagnetic oscillations of the earth's core and the theory of the geomagnetic secular variation. *Phil. Trans. Roy. Soc. A.*, **259**, 615–647, 1966.

180. Hide, R., & P. H. Roberts, The origin of the main geomagnetic field, *Phys. Chem. Earth*, **4**, 27–98, 1961.

181. Honda, M., & J. R. Arnold, Effects of cosmic rays on meteorites, *Science*, **143**, 203–212, 1964.

182. Hori, G. I., & G. Giacaglia, Secular perturbation of Pluto, unpublished work, Yale University, 1965.

183. Hough, S. S., On the application of harmonic analysis to the dynamical theory of the tides, *Phil. Trans. Roy. Soc. A*, **189**, 201–257, 1897.

184. Hoyle, F., On the origin of the solar nebula, *Quart. J. Roy. Astron. Soc.*, **1**, 28–55, 1960.

185. Huang, S.-S., Rotational behavior of the main-sequence stars and its plausible consequences concerning formation of planetary systems, *Astrophys. J.*, **141**, 985–992, 1965.

186. Hubenet, H., Ed., *Abundance Determinations in Stellar Spectra*, Academic Press, New York, 398 pp., 1966.

187. Hurley, P. M., Ed., *Advances in Earth Science*, M. I. T. Press, Cambridge, 502 pp., 1966.

188. Irving, E., *Paleomagnetism*, Wiley, New York, 399 pp., 1964.

189. Ito, K., & G. C. Kennedy, Melting and phase relations in a natural peridotite to 40 kilobars, *J. Geophys. Res.*, **73**, in press, 1968.
190. Jackson, J. D., *Classical Electrodynamics*, Wiley, New York, 641 pp., 1962.
191. Jacobs, J. A., *The Earth's Core and Geomagnetism*, Macmillan, New York, 137 pp., 1963.
192. Jaffe, L. D., Depth of the lunar dust, *J. Geophys. Res.*, **70**, 6129–6138, 1965.
193. Jaffe, L. D., Lunar surface strength, *Icarus*, **6**, 75–91, 1967.
194. Jaffe, L. D., and 30 others, Report on Surveyor project, *J. Geophys. Res.*, **72**, 771–856, 1967.
195. Jastrow, R., & A. G. W. Cameron, Eds., *Origin of the Solar System*, Academic Press, New York, 176 pp., 1963.
196. Jeans, J., *Astronomy and Cosmogony*, 2nd ed., Cambridge Univ. Press, London, 1929; republ. by Dover, New York, 428 pp., 1961.
197. Jeffreys, H., The density distributions in the inner planets, *Mo. Not. Roy. Astron. Soc. Geophys. Suppl.*, **4**, 62–71, 1937.
198. Jeffreys, H., The secular accelerations of satellites, *Mo. Not. Roy. Astron. Soc.*, **117**, 585–589, 1957.
199. Jeffreys, H., *The Earth*, 4th ed., Cambridge Univ. Press, London, 420 pp., 1959.
200. Joos, G., & I. M. Freeman, *Theoretical Physics*, Blackie, London, 885 pp., 1958.
201. Judd, W. R., Ed., *State of Stress in the Earth's Crust*, American Elsevier Publ. Co., New York, 732 pp., 1964.
202. Kahle, A. B., E. H. Vestine, & R. H. Ball, Estimated surface motions of the earth's core, *J. Geophys. Res.*, **72**, 1095–1108, 1967.
203. Kamb, W. B., Theory of preferred crystal orientation developed by crystallization under stress, *J. Geol.*, **67**, 153–170, 1959.
204. Kaula, W. M., Elastic models of the mantle corresponding to variations in the external gravity field, *J. Geophys. Res.*, **68**, 4967–4978, 1963.
205. Kaula, W. M., Tidal dissipation by solid friction and the resulting orbital evolution, *Revs. Geophys.* **2**, 661–685, 1964.
206. Kaula, W. M., *Theory of Satellite Geodesy*, Blaisdell, Waltham, Mass., 124 pp., 1966.
207. Kaula, W. M., Tests and combination of satellite determinations of the gravity field with gravimetry, *J. Geophys. Res.*, **71**, 5303–5314, 1966.
208. Kaula, W. M., Recent developments in determination of the lunar gravitational field from satellite orbits, *Phil. Trans. Roy. Soc. A*, **262**, 148–155, 1967.
209. Keil, K., &. K. J. Fredricksson, The iron, magnesium and calcium distribution in coexisting olivines and rhombic pyroxenes of chondrites, *J. Geophys. Res.*, **64**, 3487–3515, 1964.
210. Kellerman, K. J., The thermal radio emission from Mercury, Venus, Mars, Saturn, and Uranus, *Icarus*, **5**, 478–490, 1966.
211. Kern, J. W., & E. H. Vestine, Magnetic field of the earth and planets, *Sp. Sci. Rev.*, **2**, 136–171, 1963.
212. King-Hele, D. G., *Theory of Satellite Orbits in an Atmosphere*, Butterworth, London, 165 pp., 1964.

213. Kittel, C., *Introduction to Solid State Physics*, 3rd ed., Wiley, New York, 648 pp., 1966.

214. Knopoff, L., Equations of state of solids at moderately high pressures, in R. S. Bradley, Ed., *High Pressure Physics and Chemistry*, **1**, Academic Press, New York, 227–245, 1963.

215. Knopoff, L., Q, *Revs. Geophys.*, **2**, 625–660, 1964.

216. Knopoff, L., The convection current hypothesis, *Revs. Geophys.*, **2**, 89–122, 1964.

217. Kopal, Z., Ed., *Physics and Astronomy of the Moon*, Academic Press, New York, 538 pp., 1962.

218. Kopal, Z., Topography of the moon, *Sp. Sci. Revs.*, **4**, 737–855, 1965.

219. Kopal, Z., *Photographic Atlas of the Moon*, Academic Press, New York, 277 pp., 1965.

220. Kopal, Z., Luminescence of the moon and solar activity, in W. N. Hess, D. H. Menzel, & J. A. O'Keefe, Eds., *The Nature of the Lunar Surface*, Johns Hopkins Press, Baltimore, 173–184, 1966.

221. Kraut, E. A., *Fundamentals of Mathematical Physics*, McGraw-Hill, New York, 464 pp., 1967.

222. Kraut, E. A., & G. C. Kennedy, New melting law at high pressure, *Phys. Rev.*, **151**, 668–675, 1966.

223. Kovach, R. L., & D. L. Anderson, The interiors of the terrestrial planets, *J. Geophys. Res.*, **70**, 2873–2882, 1965.

224. Koziel, K., Libration of the moon, in Z. Kopal, Ed., *Physics and Astronomy of the Moon*, Academic Press, New York, 27–59, 1962.

225. Koziel, K., Differences in the moon's moments of inertia, *Proc. Roy. Soc. A.*, **296**, 248–253, 1967.

226. Krinov, E. L., *Principles of Meteoritics*, Pergamon Press, New York, 535 pp., 1960.

227. Krinov, E. L., Meteorite craters on the earth's surface, in G. P. Kuiper & B. M. Middlehurst, Eds., *The Solar System*, **4**, *The Moon, Meteorites, and Comets*, Univ. Chicago Press, 183–207, 1963.

228. Krotikov, V. D., & V. S. Troitskii, Radio emission and nature of the moon, *Sov. Phys. Uspekhi*, **6**, 941–871, 1964.

229. Kuiper, G. P., On the evolution of the protoplanets, *Proc. Natl. Acad. Sci.* **37**, 383–393, 1951.

230. Kuiper, G. P., Ed., *Photographic Lunar Atlas*, Univ. Chicago Press, 253 pp., 1960.

231. Kuiper, G. P., Interpretation of the Ranger records, in H. Brown, G. J. Stanley, D. O. Muhleman, & G. Münch, Eds., *Proc. Caltech-JPL Lunar and Planetary Conference, Sept. 13–18, 1965*, 24–29, 1966.

232. Kuiper, G., & B. M. Middlehurst, Eds., *The Solar System*, **3**, *Planets and Satellites*, Univ. Chicago Press, 601 pp., 1961.

233. Kulp, J. L., Geologic time scale, *Science*, **133**, 1105–1114, 1961.

234. Kulp, J. L., Ed., Geochronology of rock systems, *Ann. N.Y. Acad. Sci.*, **91**, 159–594, 1961.

235. Lahiri, B. N., & A. T. Price, Electromagnetic induction in non-uniform conductors, and the determination of the conductivity of the earth from terrestrial magnetic variations. *Phil. Trans. Roy. Soc. A*, **237**, 509–540, 1939.

236. Lamb, H., *Hydrodynamics*, 6th ed., Cambridge Univ. Press, London, 1932; republ. by Dover, New York, 738 pp., 1945.

237. Latimer, W. M., Astrochemical problems in the formation of the earth, *Science*, **112**, 101–104, 1950.

238. Lee, W. H. K., Ed., *Terrestrial Heat Flow, American Geophysical Union Monograph*, **8**, Am. Geophys. Un., Washington, 276 pp., 1965.

239. Lee, W. H. K., *Thermal History of the Earth*, unpublished Ph.D. dissertation, Univ. Calif., Los Angeles, 344 pp., 1967.

240. Lee, W. H. K., & S. Uyeda, Review of heat flow data, in W. H. K. Lee, Ed., *Terrestrial Heat Flow, American Geophysical Union Monograph*, **8**, Am. Geophys. Union, Washington, 87–190, 1965.

241. Leighton, R. B., *Principles of Modern Physics*, McGraw-Hill, New York, 795 pp., 1959.

242. Leighton, R. B., The photographs from Mariner IV, *Sci. Am.*, **214**(4), 54–68, 1966.

243. Leighton, R. B., & B. C. Murray, Behavior of carbon dioxide and other volatiles on Mars, *Science*, **153**, 135–144, 1966.

244. Leighton, R. B., B. C. Murray, R. P. Sharp, J. D. Allen, & R. K. Sloan, Mariner IV photography of Mars: initial results, *Science*, **149**, 627–630, 1965.

245. Levin, B. Yu., The origin of meteorites, *Sov. Phys. Uspekhi*, **8**, 360–378, 1965.

246. Lin, S. C., Cometary impact and the origin of tektites, *J. Geophys. Res.*, **71**, 2427–2437, 1966.

247. Longman, I. M., Computation of Love numbers and load deformation coefficient for a model earth, *Geophys. J. Roy. Astron. Soc.*, **11**, 133–137, 1966.

248. Loomis, A. A., Some geologic problems of Mars, *Bull. Geol. Soc. Am.*, **76**, 1083–1104, 1965.

249. Love, A. E. H., *Some Problems in Geodynamics*, Cambridge Univ. Press, 1911; republ. by Dover, New York, 180 pp., 1967.

250. Lyttleton, R. A., *The Comets and Their Origin*, Cambridge Univ. Press, London, 173 pp., 1953.

251. Lyttleton, R. A., Dynamical capture of the moon by the earth, *Proc. Roy. Soc. London A*, **296**, 285–292, 1967.

252. MacDonald, G. J. F., Thermal history of the earth, *J. Geophys. Res.*, **64**, 1967–2000, 1959.

253. MacDonald, G. J. F., The internal constitutions of the inner planets and the moon, *Sp. Sci. Revs.*, **2**, 473–557, 1963.

254. MacDonald, G. J. F., Tidal friction, *Revs. Geophys.*, **2**, 467–541, 1964.

255. MacDonald, G. J. F., Geophysical deductions from observed heat flow, in W. H. K. Lee, Ed., *Terrestrial Heat Flow, American Geophysical Union Monograph*, **8**, Am. Geophys. Un., 191–210, Washington, 1965.

256. MacDonald, G. J. F., The figure and long-term mechanical properties of the earth, in P. M. Hurley, Ed., *Advances in Earth Science*, M. I. T. Press, Cambridge, 199–245, 1966.

257. MacDonald, J. R., Theory and application of a superposition model of internal friction and creep, *J. Appl. Phys.*, **32**, 2385–2398, 1961.

258. Malkus, W. V. R., Precessional torques as the cause of geomagnetism, *J. Geophys. Res.*, **68**, 2871–2886, 1963.

259. Malkus, W. V. R., Hydromagnetic planetary waves, *J. Fluid Mech.*, **28**, 793–802, 1966.

260. Margenau, H., & G. M. Murphy, *The Mathematics of Physics and Chemistry*, 2nd ed., Van Nostrand, Princeton, 604 pp., 1956.

261. Markowitz, W., N. Stokyo, & E. P. Federov, Longitude and latitude, in H. Odishaw, Ed., *Research in Geophysics*, **2**, 149–162, 1964.

262. Marsden, B. G., & A. G. W. Cameron, Eds., *The Earth-Moon System*, Plenum Press, New York, 288 pp., 1966.

263. Mason, B., *Meteorites*, Wiley, New York, 274 pp., 1962.

264. Mason, B., Organic matter from space, *Sci. Am.*, **208(3)**, 43–49, 1963.

265. Mason, B., *Principles of Geochemistry*, 3rd ed., Wiley, New York, 329 pp., 1966.

266. Mason, B., The enstatite chondrites, *Geochim. Cosmochim. Acta*, **30**, 23–39, 1966.

267. McConnell, R. K., Jr., Isostatic adjustment in a layered earth, *J. Geophys. Res.*, **70**, 5171–5188, 1965.

268. McDonald, K. L., Penetration of the geomagnetic secular field through a mantle with variable conductivity, *J. Geophys. Res.*, **62**, 117–141, 1957.

269. McKenzie, D. P., The viscosity of the lower mantle, *J. Geophys. Res.*, **71**, 3995–4010, 1966.

270. McKenzie, D. P., The geophysical importance of high temperature creep, *Proc. NASA Conference on the Earth's Crust*, Princeton Univ. Press, in press, 1968.

271. McLellan, A. G., A thermodynamical theory of systems under nonhydrostatic stresses, *J. Geophys. Res.*, **71**, 4341–4347, 1966.

272. McMahon, A. J., *Astrophysics and Space Science*, Prentice-Hall, Englewood, N.J., 449 pp., 1965.

273. Merrihue, C., Xenon and krypton in the Bruderheim meteorite, *J. Geophys. Res.*, **71**, 263–313, 1966.

274. Melchoir, P., *The Earth Tides*, Pergamon Press, New York, 458 pp., 1966.

275. Menard, H. W., *Marine Geology of the Pacific*, McGraw-Hill, New York, 271 pp., 1964.

276. Message, P. J., On nearly-commensurable periods in the restricted problem of three bodies, with calculations of the long-period variations in the interior 2:1 case, in G. Contopoulos, Ed., *The Theory of Orbits in the Solar System and in Stellar Systems*, Academic Press, New York, 197–222, 1966.

277. Mestel, L., Problems of star formation, *Quart. J. Roy. Astron. Soc.*, **6**, 161–198, 265–298, 1965.

278. Mestel, L. & L. Spitzer, Jr., Star formation in magnetic dust clouds, *Mo. Not. Roy. Astron. Soc.*, **116**, 503–514, 1956.

279. Middlehurst, B. M., & G. P. Kuiper, Eds., *The Solar System*, **4**, *The Moon, Meteorites, and Comets*, Univ. Chicago Press, 810 pp., 1963.

280. Miller, G., The flux of tidal energy out of the deep oceans, *J. Geophys. Res.*, **71**, 2485–2489, 1966.

281. Moore, W. T., *Physical Chemistry*, 3rd ed., Prentice-Hall, Englewood, N.J., 844 pp., 1962.

282. Moulton, F. R., *An Introduction to Celestial Mechanics*, 2nd ed., Macmillan, New York, 437 pp., 1914.

283. Mueller, R. F., Phase equilibria and the crystallization of chondritic meteorites, *Geochim. Cosmochim. Acta*, **28**, 189–207, 1964.

284. Muhleman, D. O., Planetary characteristics from radar observations, *Sp. Sci. Revs.*, **6**, 341–364, 1966.

285. Munk, W. H., & G. J. F. MacDonald, *The Rotation of the Earth*, Cambridge Univ. Press, London, 323 pp., 1960.

286. Murray, B. C., & J. A. Westphal, Infra-red astronomy, *Sci. Am.*, **213**(2), 20–29, 1965.

287. Murray, B. C., R. L. Wildey, & J. A. Westphal, Venus: a map of its brightness temperature, *Science*, **140**, 391–392, 1963.

288. Nautical Almanac Offices of the United Kingdom and the United States of America, *Explanatory Supplement to the American Ephemeris and Nautical Almanac*, H.M. Stationery Office, London, 503 pp., 1961.

289. Odishaw, H., Ed., *Research in Geophysics*, **2**, *Solid Earth and Interface Phenomena*, M. I. T. Press, Cambridge, 595 pp., 1964.

290. O'Keefe, J. A., Ed., *Tektites*, Univ. Chicago Press, 228 pp., 1963.

291. O'Keefe, J. A., The moon, in W. N. Hess, Ed., *Introduction to Space Science*, Gordon & Breach, New York, 631–667, 1965.

292. O'Keefe, J. A., The origin of tektites, *Sp. Sci. Revs.*, **6**, 174–221, 1966.

293. O'Keefe, J. A., P. D. Lowman, Jr., & W. S. Cameron, Lunar ring dikes from Lunar Orbiter I, *Science*, **155**, 77–79, 1967.

294. Oliver, J., A summary of observed seismic surface wave dispersion, *Bull. Seismol. Soc. Am.*, **52**, 81–86, 1962.

295. Oort, J. H., The structure of the cloud of comets surrounding the solar system, and a hypothesis concerning its origin, *Bull. Astron. Inst. Neth.*, **11**, 91–110, 1950.

296. Oort, J. H., Empirical data on the origin of comets, in B. M. Middlehurst & G. P. Kuiper, Eds., *The Solar System*, **4**, *The Moon, Meteorites, and Comets*, Univ. Chicago Press, 665–673, 1963.

297. Öpik, E., Note on stellar perturbations of nearly parabolic orbits, *Proc. Am. Acad. Arts. Sci.*, **67**, 169–183, 1932.

298. Öpik, E. J., Collision probabilities with the planets and the distribution of interplanetary matter, *Proc. Roy. Irish Acad.*, **54A**, 164–194, 1951.

299. Öpik, E. J., *Physics of Meteor Flight in the Atmosphere*, Interscience, New York, 174 pp., 1958.

300. Öpik, E. J., Jupiter: chemical composition, structure, and origin of a giant planet, *Icarus*, **1**, 200–257, 1962.
301. Öpik, E. J., Selective escape of gases, *Roy. Astron. Soc. Geophys. J.*, **7**, 490–509, 1963.
302. Öpik, E. J., The Martian surface, *Science*, **153**, 255–265, 1966.
303. Öpik, E. J., The stray bodies in the solar system, *Advances in Astronomy and Astrophysics*, **2**, Academic Press, New York, 219–262, 1963; **4**, 30 1–336, 1966.
304. Opdyke, N. D., B. Glass, J. D. Hays, & J. Foster, Paleomagnetic study of Antarctic deep-sea cores, *Science*, **154**, 349–357, 1966.
305. Orowan, E., Convection in a non-Newtonian mantle, continental drift, and mountain building, *Phil. Trans. Roy. Soc. A*, **258**, 284–313, 1965.
306. Palmeira, R. A., & G. F. Peiper, Cosmic rays, in W. N. Hess, Ed., *Introduction to Space Science*, Gordon & Breach, New York, 383–422, 1965.
307. Parker, E. N., Hydromagnetic dynamo models, *Astrophys. J.*, **122**, 293–314, 1955.
308. Parker, E. N., The perturbation of interplanetary dust grains by the solar winds, *Astrophys. J.*, **139**, 951–958, 1964.
309. Paul, W., & D. M. Warschauer, Eds., *Solids under Pressure*, McGraw-Hill, New York, 478 pp., 1963.
310. Peale, S. J., Evidence against a geocentric contribution to the zodiacal light, *J. Geophys. Res.*, **73**, 3025–3033, 1968.
311. Pepin, R. O., & P. Signer, Primordial rare gases in meteorites, *Science*, **149**, 253–265, 1965.
312. Petit, E., Planetary temperature measurements, in G. P. Kuiper & B. M. Middlehurst, Eds., *The Solar System*, **3**, *Planets and Satellites*, Univ. Chicago Press, 400–428, 1961.
313. Pettengill, G. H., A review of radar studies of planetary surfaces, *J. Res. N. B. S. Radio Science*, **69D**, 1617–1623, 1965.
314. Pettengill, G. H., R. B. Dyce, & D. B. Campbell, Radar measurements at 70 cm of Venus and Mercury, *Astron. J.*, **72**, 330–337, 1967.
315. Piddington, J. H., & H. C. Minett, Microwave thermal radiation from the moon, *Australian J. Sci. Res.*, **2**, 63–77, 1949.
316. Pike, R. J., Schroeter's rule and the modification of lunar crater impact morphology, *J. Geophys. Res.*, **72**, 2099–2106, 1967.
317. Pippard, A. B., The *Elements of Classical Thermodynamics*, Cambridge Univ. Press, 165 pp., 1964.
318. Plummer, H. C., *An Introductory Treatise on Dynamical Astronomy*, Cambridge Univ. Press, London, 1918; republ. by Dover, New York, 343 pp., 1960.
319. Pollack, J. B., & C. Sagan, The microwave phase effect of Venus, *Icarus*, **4**, 62–103, 1965.
320. Pollack, J. B., & C. Sagan, Secular changes and dark-area regeneration on Mars, *Icarus*, **6**, 434–439, 1967.
321. Porter, J. G., The statistics of comet orbits, in B. M. Middlehurst & G. P. Kuiper, Eds., *The Solar System*, **4**, *The Moon, Meteorites, and Comets*, Univ. Chicago Press, 550–572, 1963.

322. Pottasch, S. R., On the interpretation of the solar ultraviolet emission line spectrum, *Sp. Sci. Revs.*, **3**, 816–855, 1964.

323. Press, F., Long-period waves and free oscillations of the earth, in H. Odishaw, Ed., *Research in Geophysics*, **2**, M. I. T. Press, Cambridge, 1–26, 1964.

324. Press, F., Seismological information and advances, in P. M. Hurley, Ed., *Advances in Earth Sciences*, M. I. T. Press, Cambridge, 247–286, 1966.

325. Quaide, W. L., D. E. Gault, & R. A. Schmidt, Gravitative effects on lunar impact structures, *Ann. N. Y. Acad. Sci.*, **123**, 563–572, 1965.

326. Rabe, E., Third-order stability of the long-period Trojan librations, *Astron. J.*, **72**, 10–17, 1967.

327. Rayleigh, Lord, On convection currents in a horizontal layer of fluid when the higher temperature is on the underside, *Phil. Mag. Ser. 6*, **32**, 529–546, 1916.

328. Rea, D. G., The atmosphere and surface of Mars—a selective review, in H. Brown, G. J. Stanley, D. O. Muhleman, & G. Münch, Eds., *Proc. Caltech— JPL Lunar and Planetary Conference Sept. 13–18, 1965*, 209–238, 1966.

329. Rea, D. G., N. Hetherington, &. R. Mifflin, The analysis of radar echoes from the moon, *J. Geophys. Res.*, **69**, 5217–5223, 1964.

330. Reed, G. W., Jr., &. S. Jovanovic, Mercury in chondrites, *J. Geophys. Res.*, **72**, 2219–2228, 1967.

331. Reif, F., *Fundamentals of Statistical and Thermal Physics*, McGraw-Hill, New York, 651 pp., 1965.

332. Reynolds, J. H., Xenology, *J. Geophys. Res.*, **68**, 2939–2956, 1963.

333. Rice, M. H., R. G. McQueen, & J. M. Walsh, Compression of solids by strong shock waves, *Solid State Physics*, **6**, Academic Press, New York, 1–63, 1958.

334. Richter, N., *The Nature of Comets*, Methuen, London, 221 pp., 1963.

335. Rikitake, T., *Electromagnetism and the Earth's Interior*, Elsevier, Amsterdam, 308 pp., 1966.

336. Ringwood, A. E., On the chemical evolution and densities of the planets, *Geochim. Cosmochim. Acta*, **15**, 257–283, 1959.

337. Ringwood, A. E., Some aspects of the thermal evolution of the earth, *Geochim. Cosmochim. Acta*, **20**, 241–259, 1960.

338. Ringwood, A. E., Chemical evolution of the terrestrial planets, *Geochim. Cosmochim. Acta*, **30**, 41–104, 1966.

339. Ringwood, A. E., Genesis of chondritic meteorites, *Revs. Geophys.*, **4**, 113–176, 1966.

340. Ringwood, A. E., The chemical composition and origin of the earth; Mineralogy of the mantle, in P. M. Hurley, Ed., *Advances in Earth Science*, M. I. T. Press, Cambridge, 287–399, 1966.

341. Ringwood, A. E., & M. Seabrook, Olivine-spinel equilibria at high pressure in the system Ni_2GeO_4–Mg_2SiO_4, *J. Geophys. Res.*, **67**, 1975–1985, 1962.

342. Roberts, P. H., Convection in a self-gravitating sphere, *Mathematika*, **12**, 128–137, 1965.

343. Roberts, P. H., & S. Scott, On analysis of the secular variation; 1. A hydromagnetic constraint: theory, *J. Geomag. Geoelec.*, **17**, 137–151, 1965.

344. Robertson, H. P., Dynamical effects of radiation in the solar system, *Mo. Not. Roy. Astron. Soc.*, **97**, 423–438, 1937.

345. Rochester, M. G., Geomagnetic westward drift and irregularities in the earth's rotation, *Phil. Trans. Roy. Soc. A*, **252**, 531–555, 1960.

346. Rochester, M. G., & D. E. Smylie, Geomagnetic core-mantle coupling and the Chandler wobble, *Geophys. J. Roy. Astron. Soc.*, **10**, 289–315, 1965.

347. Roy, A. E., &. M. W. Overdon, On the occurrence of commensurable mean motions in the solar system, *Mo. Not. Roy. Astron. Soc.*, **114**, 232–241, 1954; **115**, 296–309, 1955.

348. Rubey, W. W., Geologic history of sea water, *Bull. Geol. Soc. Am.*, **62**, 1111–1173, 1951; republ. in P. J. Brancazio & A. G. W. Cameron, Eds., *The Origin and Evolution of Atmospheres and Oceans*, Wiley, New York, 1–63, 1964.

349. Runcorn, S. K., Ed., *Continental Drift*, Academic Press, New York, 338 pp., 1962.

350. Runcorn, S. K., Changes in the convection pattern in the earth's mantle and continental drift: evidence for a cold origin of the earth, *Phil. Trans. Roy. Soc. A*, **258**, 228–251, 1965.

351. Ruskol, E. L., The origin of the moon, *Sov. Astron. AJ*, **4**, 657–668, 1960.

352. Sagan, C., J. P. Phaneuf, & M. Ihnat, Total reflection spectrophotometry and thermogravimetric analysis of simulated Martian surface materials, *Icarus*, **4**, 43–61, 1965.

353. Sagan, C., & J. B. Pollack, On the nature of the canals of Mars, *Nature*, **212**, 117–121, 1966.

354. Sagan, C., & J. B. Pollack, Elevation differences on Mars, *J. Geophys. Res.*, **73**, 1373–1387, 1968.

355. Sagan, C., J. B. Pollack, & R. M. Goldstein, Radar Doppler spectroscopy of Mars. I. Elevation differences between bright and dark areas, *Astron. J.*, **72**, 20–34, 1967.

356. Salisbury, J. W., & P. E. Glaser, *The Lunar Surface Layer: Materials and Characteristics*, Academic Press, New York, 532 pp., 1964.

357. Schubart, J., Long-period effects in nearly commensurable cases of the restricted three-body problem, *Smithsonian Inst. Astrophys. Obs.*, **149**, 36 pp., 1964.

358. Schwarzschild, M., *Structure and Evolution of the Stars*, Princeton Univ. Press, 296 pp., 1958.

359. Shapiro, I. I., D. A. Lautman, & G. Colombo, The earth's dust belt: fact or fiction? *J. Geophys. Res.*, **71**, 5695–5741, 1966.

360. Shimazu, Y., Thermodynamical aspects of formation processes of the terrestrial planets and meteorites, *Icarus*, **6**, 143–174, 1967.

361. Shoemaker, E. M., Interpretation of lunar craters, in Z. Kopal, Ed., *Physics and Astronomy of the Moon*, Academic Press, New York, 283–359, 1962.

362. Shoemaker, E. M., Impact mechanics at Meteor Crater, Arizona, in B. M. Middlehurst & G. P. Kuiper, Eds., *The Solar System*, **4**, *The Moon, Meteorites, and Comets*, Univ. Chicago Press, 301–336, 1963.

363. Shoemaker, E. M., The geology of the moon, *Sci. Am.*, **211**(6), 38–47, 1964.

364. Shoemaker, E. M., Preliminary analysis of the fine structure of the lunar surface in Mare Cognitum, in W. H. Hess, D. H. Menzel, & J. A. O'Keefe,

Eds., *The Nature of the Lunar Surface*, Johns Hopkins Press, Baltimore, 23–78, 1966.

365. Shoemaker, E., & C. J. Lowery, Airwaves associated with large fireballs and the frequency distribution of energy of large meteoroids, *Meteoritics*, **3**, 123–124, 1967.

366. Shoemaker, E. M., R. I. Hachman, & R. E. Eggleston, Interplanetary correlation of geologic time, *Advan. Astron. Sci.*, **8**, 70–89, 1962.

367. Short, N. M., A comparison of features characteristic of nuclear explosion craters and astroblemes, *Ann. N. Y. Acad. Sci.*, **123**, 573–616, 1965.

368. Short, N. M., Shock processes in geology, *J. Geol. Ed.*, **14**, 149–166, 1966.

369. Shorthill, W., & J. M. Saari, Recent discovery of hot spots on the lunar surface: a brief report of infrared measurements on the eclipsed moon, in W. N. Hess, D. H. Menzel, & J. A. O'Keefe, Eds., *The Nature of the Lunar Surface*, Johns Hopkins Press, Baltimore, 215–228, 1966.

370. Signer, P., & H. E. Suess, Rare gases in the sun, in the atmosphere, and in meteorites, in J. Geiss & E. D. Goldberg, Eds., *Earth Science and Meteoritics*, Wiley, New York, 241–272, 1963.

371. Singer, S. F., The origin and dynamical evolution of the moon, *The Physics of the Moon, Proc. Amer. Astronaut. Soc. Symp.*, Washington, 1967.

372. Sinton, W. M., On the composition of Martian surface materials, *Icarus*, **6**, 222–228, 1967.

373. Smith, P. J., The intensity of the ancient geomagnetic field: a review and analysis, *Geophys. J. Roy. Astron. Soc.*, **12**, 321–362, 1967.

374. Stein, R. J., & A. G. W. Cameron, Eds., *Stellar Evolution*, Plenum Press, New York, 464 pp., 1966.

375. Stewartson, K., The dispersion of a current on the surface of a highly conducting fluid, *Proc. Camb. Phil. Soc.*, **53**, 774–775, 1957.

376. Stewartson, K., On the motion of non-conducting body through a perfectly conducting fluid, *J. Fluid Mech.*, **8**, 82–96, 1960.

377. Stewartson, K., & P. H. Roberts, On the motion of a liquid in a spheroidal cavity of a precessing rigid body, *J. Fluid Mech.*, **17**, 1–20, 1963.

378. Studier, M. H., R. Hayatsu, & E. Anders, Organic compounds in carbonaceous chondrites, *Science*, **149**, 1455–1459, 1965.

379. Suess, H. E., Thermodynamic data on the formation of solid carbon and organic compounds in primitive planetary atmospheres, *J. Geophys. Res.*, **69**, 2029–2034, 1962.

380. Suess, H. E., The Urey-Craig groups of chondrites and their state of oxidation, in H. Craig, S. Miller, & G. J. Wasserburg, Eds., *Isotopic and Cosmic Chemistry*, North-Holland, Amsterdam, 385–400, 1964.

381. Suess, H. E., Chemical evidence bearing on the origin of the solar system, *Ann. Rev. Astron. Astrophys.*, **3**, 217–234, 1965.

382. Suess, H. E., & H. C. Urey, Abundances of the elements, *Revs. Mod. Phys.*, **28**, 53–74, 1956.

383. Sykes, L. R., The seismicity and deep structure of island arcs, *J. Geophys. Res.*, **71**, 2981–3006, 1966.

384. Sykes, L. R., Mechanism of earthquakes and nature of faulting on the mid-oceanic ridges, *J. Geophys. Res.*, **72**, 2131–2153, 1967.

385. Takeuchi, H., *Theory of the Earth's Interior*, Blaisdell, Waltham, Mass., 131 pp., 1966.

386. Takeuchi, H., & H. Kanamori, Equations of state of matter from shock wave experiments, *J. Geophys. Res.*, **71**, 3985–3994, 1966.

387. Talwani, M., X. Le Pichon, & J. R. Heirtzler, East Pacific Rise: the magnetic pattern and the fracture zones, *Science*, **150**, 1109–1115, 1965.

388. Talwani, M., X. Le Pichon, & M. Ewing, Crustal structure of the mid-ocean ridges. 2. Computed model from gravity and seismic refraction data, *J. Geophys. Res.*, **70**, 341–352, 1965.

389. Tayler, R. J., The origin of the elements, *Reps. Prog. Phys.*, **24**, 489–538, 1966.

390. Taylor, G. I., Tidal friction in the Irish Sea, *Phil. Trans. Roy. Soc. A*, **220**, 1–93, 1919.

391. Taylor, H. P., Jr., M. B. Duke, L. T. Silver, & S. Epstein, Oxygen isotope studies of minerals in stony meteorites, *Geochim. Cosmochim. Acta*, **29**, 489–512, 1965.

392. Taylor, H. P., & S. Epstein, Comparison of oxygen isotope analyses of tektites, soils, and impactite glasses, in H. Craig, S. Miller, & G. J. Wasserburg, Eds., *Isotopic and Cosmic Chemistry*, North-Holland, Amsterdam, 181–199, 1964.

393. Taylor, S. R., Trace element abundances and the chondritic earth model, *Geochim. Cosmochim. Acta*, **28**, 1989–1998, 1964.

394. Taylor, S. R., Australites, Henbury impact glass and subgreywacke: a comparison of the abundance of 51 elements, *Geochim. Cosmochim. Acta*, **30**, 1121–1136, 1966.

395. Taylor, S. R., & M. Sachs, Geochemical evidence for the origin of australites, *Geochim. Cosmochim. Acta*, **28**, 235–264, 1964.

396. Ter Haar, D., & A. G. W. Cameron, Historical review of theories of the origin of the solar system, in R. Jastrow & A. G. W. Cameron, Eds., *Origin of the Solar System*, Academic Press, New York, 4–37, 1963.

397. Thompson, T. W., Lunar mapping by coherent-pulse analysis, *J. Res. N. B. S. Radio Science*, **69D**, 1667–1669, 1965.

398. Tilton, G. R., & S. R. Hart, Geochronology, *Science*, **140**, 357–366, 1963.

399. Tozer, D. C., Heat transfer and convection currents, *Phil. Trans. Roy. Soc. A.*, **258**, 252–271, 1965.

400. Tozer, D. C., Thermal history of the earth: 1. The formation of the core, *Roy. Astron. Soc. Geophys. J.*, **9**, 95–112, 1965.

401. Troitskii, V. S., Investigation of the surfaces of the moon and planets by means of thermal radiation, *Proc. Roy. Soc. A*, **296**, 366–395, 1967.

402. Turner, F. J., & J. Verhoogen, *Igneous and Metamorphic Petrology*, 2nd ed., McGraw-Hill, New York, 694 pp., 1960.

403. Turner, G., Extinct iodine 129 and trace elements in chondrites, *J. Geophys. Res.*, **70**, 5433–5445, 1965.

404. Tryor, J. G., The distribution of the directions of perihelia of long-period comets, *Mo. Not. Roy. Astron. Soc.*, **117**, 370–379, 1957.

405. Urey, H. C., *The Planets*, Yale Univ. Press, New Haven, Conn., 245 pp., 1952.
406. Urey, H. C., On the dissipation of gas and volatilized elements from proto-planets, *Astrophys. J. Suppl.*, **1**, 147–173, 1954.
407. Urey, H. C., Boundary conditions for theories of the origin of the solar system, *Phys. Chem. Earth*, **2**, 46–76, 1957.
408. Urey, H. C., The origin and evolution of the solar system, in D. P. Le Galley, Ed., *Space Science*, Wiley, New York, 123–168, 1963.
409. Urey, H. C., A review of atomic abundances in chondrites and the origin of meteorites, *Revs. Geophys.*, **2**, 1–34, 1964.
410. Urey, H. C. Biological material in meteorites: a review, *Science*, **151**, 157–166, 1966.
411. Urey, H. C., Observations on the Ranger VIII and IX pictures, in H. Brown, G. J. Stanley, D. O. Muhleman, & G. Münch, Eds., *Proc. Caltech-JPL Lunar & Plan. Conf., Sept. 13–18, 1965*, 1–23, 1966.
412. Vaucouleurs, G. de, *Physics of the Planet Mars*, Faber & Faber, London, 365 pp., 1954.
413. Vaucouleurs, G. de., Geometric and photometric parameters of the terrestrial planets, *Icarus*, **3**, 187–235, 1964.
414. Van Schmus, W. R., & J. A. Wood, A chemical-petrological classification for the chondritic meteorites, *Geochim. Cosmochim. Acta*, **31**, 747–765, 1967.
415. van Woerkom, A. J. J., On the origin of comets, *Bull. Astron. Inst. Neth.*, **10**, 445–472, 1948.
416. Verhoogen, J., Heat balance of the earth's core, *Geophys. J. Roy. Astron. Soc.*, **4**, 276–281, 1961.
417. Verhoogen, J., Phase changes and convection in the earth's mantle, *Phil. Trans. Roy. Soc., A*, **258**, 276–283, 1965.
418. Vicente, R. O., The theory of nutation and the internal constitution of the earth, in L. H. Ahrens, F. Press, & S. K. Runcorn, Eds., *Physics and Chemistry of the Earth*, **4**, Pergamon Press, Oxford, 251–280, 1961.
419. Vine, F. J., Spreading of the ocean floor: new evidence, *Science*, **154**, 1405–1415, 1966.
420. Vine, F. J., & D. H. Matthews, Magnetic anomalies over oceanic ridges, *Nature*, **199**, 947–949, 1963.
421. Vinogradov, A. P., A. Surkov, & G. M. Chernov, Investigation of intensity and spectral composition of the moon's gamma radiation by the Luna-10 orbiter, *Doklady Acad. Sci. USSR Earth Sciences*, trans. by Amer. Geol. Inst., **170**, 9–11, 1967.
422. Violet, C. E., A generalized empirical analysis of cratering, *J. Geophys. Res.*, **66**, 3461–3470, 1961.
423. Wagoner, R. V., Cosmological element production, *Science*, **155**, 1369–1376, 1967.
424. Wagoner, R. V., W. A. Fowler, & F. Hoyle, On the synthesis of elements at very high temperatures, *Astrophys. J.*, **148**, 3–49, 1967.
425. Wasserburg, G. J., Geochronology, and isotopic data bearing on development of the continental crust, in P. M. Hurley, Ed., *Advances in Earth Science*, M. I. T. Press, Cambridge, 431–439, 1966.

426. Wasserburg, G. J., G. J. F. MacDonald, F. Hoyle, & W. A. Fowler, Relative contributions of uranium, thorium, and potassium to heat production in the earth, *Science*, **143**, 465–467, 1964.

427. Wasson, J. T., Concentrations of Ni, Ga, and Ge in a series of Canyon Diablo and Odessa meteorite specimens, *J. Geophys. Res.*, **72**, 721–730, 1967.

428. Wasson, J. T., The chemical classification of iron meteorites: I: A study of iron meteorites with low concentrations of gallium and germanium, *Geochim. Cosmochim. Acta*, **31**, 161–180, 1967.

429. Weertman, J., Steady-state creep through dislocation climb, *J. Appl. Phys.*, **28**, 362–364, 1957.

430. Weertman, J., & J. R. Weertman, *Elementary Dislocation Theory*, Macmillan, New York, 213 pp., 1964.

431. Wells, J. W., Paleontological evidence of the rate of the earth's rotation, in B. G. Marsden & A. G. W. Cameron, Eds., *The Earth-Moon System*, Plenum Press, New York, 70–81, 1966.

432. Wetherill, G. W., Collisions in the asteroid belt, *J. Geophys. Res.*, **72**, 2429–2444, 1967.

433. Wetherill, G. W. & J. G. Williams, Evaluation of Apollo asteroids as sources of stone meteorites, *J. Geophys. Res.*, **73**, 635–648, 1968.

434. Wetherill, G. W., M. E. Bickford, L. T. Silver, & G. R. Tilton, Geochronology of North America, *Publ. Natl. Acad. Sci.-Natl. Res. Council*, **1276**, 315 pp., 1965.

435. Whipple, F. L., A comet model. I. The acceleration of comet Encke, *Astrophys. J.*, **111**, 375–394, 1950.

436. Whipple, F. L., On the distribution of semimajor axes among comet orbits, *Astron. J.*, **67**, 1–9, 1962.

437. Whipple, F. L., The history of the solar system, *Proc. Nat. Acad. Sci.*, **52**, 565–594, 1964.

438. Whipple, F. L., Evidence for a comet belt beyond Neptune, *Proc. Natl. Acad. Sci.*, **51**, 711–718, 1964.

439. Whipple, F. L., The meteoritic environment of the moon, *Proc. Roy. Soc. A*, **296**, 304–315, 1967.

440. Wildt, R., Planetary interiors, in G. P. Kuiper & B. M. Middlehurst, Eds., *The Solar System*, **3**, *Planets and Satellites*, Univ. Chicago Press, 159–212, 1961.

441. Wilkins, G. A., The system of astronomical constants, *Quart. J. Roy. Astron. Soc.*, **5**, 23–31, 1964; **6**, 70–73, 1965.

442. Wilson, J. T., The development and structure of the crust, in G. P. Kuiper, Ed., *The Solar System*, **2**, *The Earth as a Planet*, Univ. Chicago Press, 138–214, 1954.

443. Wilson, J. T., A new class of faults and their bearing on continental drift, *Nature*, **207**, 343–347, 1965.

444. Wilson, J. T., Transform faults, oceanic ridges, and magnetic anomalies southwest of Vancouver Island, *Science*, **150**, 482–485, 1965.

445. Wise, D. U., An origin of the moon by rotational fission during formation of the earth's core, *J. Geophys. Res.*, **68**, 1547–1554, 1963.

446. Wood, J. A., Physics and chemistry of meteorites, in B. M. Middlehurst &

G. P. Kuiper, Eds., *The Solar System*, **4**, *The Moon, Meteorites, and Comets*, Univ. Chicago Press, 337–401, 1963.

447. Wood, J. A., On the origin of chondrules and chondrites, *Icarus*, **2**, 153–180, 1963.

448. Wood, J. A., Chondrites and chondrules, *Sci. Am.*, **209** (4), 65–82, 1963.

449. Wood, J. A., The cooling rates and parent planets of several iron meteorites, *Icarus*, **3**, 429–459, 1964.

450. Wood, J. A., Chondrites: their metallic minerals, thermal history, and parent planets, *Icarus*, **6**, 1–49, 1967.

451. Woolard, E., Theory of the rotation of the earth around its center of mass, *Astron. Papers, Am. Ephem. Naut. Almanac*, **15**, 3–165, 1953.

452. Younkin, R. L., A search for limonite near-infra-red spectral features on Mars, *Astrophys. J.*, **144**, 809–818, 1966.

453. Ziman, J. M., *Principles of the Theory of Solids*, Cambridge Univ. Press, 360 pp., 1964.

454. Zirin, H., *The Solar Atmosphere*, Blaisdell, Waltham, Mass., 502 pp., 1966.

455. Ahrens, L. H., Observations on the Fe-Si-Mg relationship in chondrites, *Geochim. Cosmochim. Acta*, **29**, 801–806, 1965.

456. Ahrens, T. J., & Y. Syono, Calculated mineral reactions in the earth's mantle, *J. Geophys. Res.*, **72**, 4181–4188, 1967.

457. Akimoto, S., & H. Fujisawa, Olivine-spinel solid state equilibria in the system Mg_2SiO_4-Fe_2SiO_4, *J. Geophys. Res.*, **73**, 1467–1469. 1968.

458. Anderson, D. L., Phase changes in the upper mantle, *Science*, **157**, 1165–1173, 1967.

459. Antoniadi, E. M., *La Planète Mars*, Libr. Sci. Hermann et Cie, Paris, 230 pp., 1930.

460. Craig, H., Petrological and compositional relationships in meteorites, in H. Craig, S. L. Miller, & G. J. Wasserburg, Eds., *Isotopic and Cosmic Chemistry*, North-Holland, Amsterdam, 401–451, 1964.

461. Eisberg, R. M., *Fundamentals of Modern Physics*, Wiley, New York, 729 pp., 1961.

462. Eshleman, V. R., Radar astronomy, *Science*, **158**, 585–597, 1967.

463. Ewing, J., & M. Ewing, Sediment distribution on the mid-ocean ridges with respect to spreading of the sea floor, *Science*, **156**, 1590–1591, 1967.

464. Faul, H., *Ages of Rocks, Planets, and Stars*, McGraw-Hill, New York, 109 pp., 1966.

465. Fricker, P. E., R. T. Reynolds, & A. L. Summers, On the thermal history of the moon, *J. Geophys. Res.*, **72**, 2649–2663, 1967.

466. Garrels, R. M., & C. L. Christ, *Solutions, Minerals, and Equilibria*, Harper & Row, New York, 450 pp., 1965.

467. Gary, B., Mercury's microwave phase effect, *Astrophys. J.*, **149**, L141–145, 1967.

468. Gault, D. E., Cratering rates on the moon, *J. Geophys. Res.*, **73**, in press, 1968.

469. Gibson, R. D., & P. H. Roberts, Some comments on the theory of homogeneous dynamos, in W. R. Hindmarsh, F. J. Lowes, P. H. Roberts, & S. K. Runcorn, Eds., *Magnetism and the Cosmos*, Elsevier, New York, 108–120, 1967.

470. Goldich, S. S., W. R. Muehlberger, E. G. Lidiak, & C. E. Hedge, Geo-chronology of the midcontinent region, United States 1. Scope, methods and principles, *J. Geophys, Res.*, **71**, 5375–5388, 1966.

471. Goldstein, J. I., & J. M. Short, The iron meteorites, their thermal history and parent bodies, *Geochim. Cosmochim. Acta*, **31**, 1733–1770, 1967.

472. Greenland, L., & J. F. Lovering, Minor and trace element abundances in chondritic meteorites, *Geochim. Cosmochim. Acta*, **29**, 821–858, 1965.

473. Hayes, J. M., Organic constituents of meteorites—a review, *Geochim. Cosmochim. Acta*, **31**, 1395–1440, 1967.

474. Herzenberg, A., Geomagnetic dynamos, *Phil. Trans. Roy. Soc. A*, **250**, 543–583, 1958.

475. Hey, M. H., *Catalogue of Meteorites*, 3rd ed., Trustees of the British Museum (Natural History), London, 637 pp., 1966.

476. Hills, E. S., *Elements of Structural Geology*, Wiley, New York, 483 pp., 1963.

477. Hohenberg, C. M., M. N. Munk, & J. H. Reynolds, Spallation and fissiogenic xenon and krypton from stepwise heating of the Pasamonte achondrite; the case for extinct plutonium-244 in meteorites; relative ages of chondrites and achondrites, *J. Geophys. Res.*, **72**, 3139–3177, 1967.

478. Hohenberg, C. M., F. A. Podosek, & J. H. Reynolds, Xenon-iodine dating: sharp isochronism in chondrites, *Science*, **156**, 233–236, 1967.

479. Horn, M. K., & J. A. S. Adams, Computer-derived geochemical balances and element abundances, *Geochim. Cosmochim. Acta*, **30**, 279–297, 1966.

480. Kieffer, H. H., Calculated physical properties of planets in relation to com-position and gravitational layering, *J. Geophys. Res.*, **72**, 3179–3197, 1967.

481. Koziel, K., The constants of the moon's physical libration derived on the basis of four series of heliometric observations from the years 1877 to 1915, *Icarus*, **7**, 1–28, 1967.

482. Krauskopf, K. B., *Introduction to Geochemistry*, McGraw-Hill, New York, 719 pp., 1967.

483. Kuz'min, A. D., The results of radio observations of the planets, in A. Dollfus, Ed., *Moon and Planets*, North-Holland Publ. Co., Amsterdam, 91–102, 1967.

484. Landolt-Börnstein: *Numerical Data and Functional Relationships in Science and Technology*, H. H. Voigt, Ed., New Series, Group VI, **1**, *Astronomy and Astrophysics*, Springer-Verlag, Berlin, 711 pp., 1965.

485. Larimer, J. W., Chemical fractionation in meteorites: I. Condensation of the elements, *Geochim. Cosmochim. Acta*. **31**, 1215–1238, 1967.

486. Malkus, W. V. R., Precession of the earth as the cause of geomagnetism, *Science*, **160**, 259–264, 1968.

487. McConnell, R. K., Jr., L. A. McClaine, D. W. Lee, J. R. Aronson, & R. V. Allen, A model for planetary igneous differentiation, *Revs. Geophys.*, **5**, 121–172, 1967.

488. McIntosh, B. A., The determination of meteor mass distribution from radar echo counts, *Can. J. Phys.*, **44**, 2729–2748, 1966.

489. McQueen, R. G., S. P. Marsh, & J. N. Fritz, Hugoniot equation of state of twelve rocks, *J. Geophys. Res.*, **72**, 4999–5036, 1967.

490. Ney, E. P., N. J. Woolf, & R. J. Collins, Mechanisms for lunar luminescence, *J. Geophys. Res.*, **71**, 1787–1793, 1966.

491. O'Leary, B. T., The opposition effect on Mars, *Astrophys. J.*, **149**, L147–149, 1967.

492. Parker, E. N., The dynamical state of the interstellar gas and field, *Astrophys. J.*, **145**, 811–833, 1966; **149**, 517–552, 1967.

493. Reed, G. W., Jr., & R. O. Allen, Jr., Halogens in chondrites, *Geochim. Cosmochim. Acta*, **30**, 779–800, 1966.

494. Ringwood, A. E., & D. H. Green, An experimental investigation of the gabbro-eclogite transformation and some geophysical implications, *Tectonophysics*, **3**, 383–427, 1966.

495. Ringwood, A. E., & A. Major, Synthesis of Mg_2SiO_4-Fe_2SiO_4 spinel solid solutions, *Earth Plan. Sci. Let.*, **1**, 241–245, 1966.

496. Ringwood, A. E., & A. Major, High-pressure transformations in pyroxenes, *Earth Plan. Sci. Let.*, **1**, 351–357, 1966.

497. Roberts, P. H., *An Introduction to Magnetohydrodynamics*, Elsevier, New York, 274 pp., 1967.

498. Ruskol, E. L., The tidal history and origin of the earth-moon system, *Sov. Astron. AJ*, **10**, 659–665, 1967.

499. Ryan, J. A., Adhesion of silicates in ultrahigh vacuum, *J. Geophys. Res.*, **71**, 4413–4425, 1966.

500. Saari, J. M., &. R. W. Shorthill, Review of lunar infrared observations, *Boeing Sci. Res. Lab. Doc.*, **DI-82-0586**, 43 pp., 1966.

501. Schnetzler, C. C., W. H. Pinson, &. P. M. Hurley, Rubidium-strontium age of the Bosumtwi Crater area, Ghana, compared with the age of the Ivory Coast tektites, *Science*, **151**, 817–819, 1966.

502. Shapiro, I. I., Resonance rotation of Venus, *Science*, **157**, 423–425, 1967.

503. Smith, R. L., Terrestrial calderas, associated pyroclastic deposits, and possible lunar applications, in W. N. Hess, D. H. Menzel, & J. A. O'Keefe, Eds., *The Nature of the Lunar Surface*, Johns Hopkins Press, Baltimore, 241–257, 1966.

504. Sonett, C. P., D. S. Colburn, & R. G. Currie, The intrinsic magnetic field of the moon, *J. Geophys. Res.*, **72**, 5503–5507, 1967.

505. Taylor, S. R., The origin and growth of continents, *Tectonophysics*, **4**, 17–34, 1967.

506. Toksöz, M. N., M. A. Chinnery, & D. L. Anderson, Inhomogeneities in the earth's mantle, *Geophys. J. Roy. Astron. Soc.*, **13**, 31–59, 1967.

507. Turcotte, D. L., & E. R. Oxburgh, Finite amplitude convection cells and continental drift, *J. Fluid Mech.*, **28**, 29–42, 1967.

508. Turkevich, A. L., E. J. Frazgrote, & J. H. Patterson, Chemical analysis of the moon at the Surveyor V landing site, *Science*, **158**, 635–637, 1967.

509. Urey, H. C., The abundance of the elements with special reference to the problem of the iron abundance, *Quart. J. Roy. Astron. Soc.*, **8**, 23–47, 1967.

510. Vogt, P. R., & N. A. Ostenso, Steady state crustal spreading, *Nature*, **215**, 810–817, 1967.

511. Vrebalovich, T., L. D. Jaffe, & 40 others, Surveyor III Mission Report: Part II. Scientific Results, *Jet. Prop. Lab. Tech. Rep.*, **32-1177**, 216 pp., 1967.

512. Wasson, J. T., & J. Kimberlin, The chemical classification of iron meteorites— 2. Irons and pallasites with germanium concentrations between 8 and 100 ppm., *Geochim. Cosmochim. Acta*, **31**, 2065–2093, 1967.

513. Wetherill, G. W., Steady-state calculations bearing on geological implications of a phase-transition Mohorovicic discontinuity, *J. Geophys. Res.*, **66**, 2983–2993, 1961.

514. Whipple, F. L., On maintaining the meteoritic complex, *Smithsonian Astrophys. Obs. Spec. Rep.*, **239**, 1–45, 1967.

515. Wildey, R. L., On the treatment of radiative transfer in the lunar diurnal heat flow, *J. Geophys. Res.*, **72**, 4765–4667, 1967.

516. Clark, B. G., & A. D. Kuz'min, The measurement of the polarization and brightness distribution of Venus at 10.6-cm wavelength, *Astrophys. J.*, **142**, 23–44, 1965.

517. Connes, P., J. Connes, W. S. Benedict, & L. D. Kaplan, Traces of HCl and HF in the atmosphere of Venus, *Astrophys. J.*, **147**, 1230–1237, 1967.

518. Connes, J., P. Connes, & L. D. Kaplan, Mars: new absorption bands in the spectrum, *Science*, **153**, 739–740, 1966.

519. Cox., A., G. B. Dalyrmple, & R. R. Doell, Reversals of the earth's magnetic field, *Sci. Am.*, **216** (2), 44–54, 1967.

520. Dayhoff, M. O., R. V. Eck, E. R. Lippincott, & C. Sagan, Venus: atmospheric evolution, *Science*, **155**, 556–558, 1967.

521. Gary, B., Results of radiometric moon-mapping investigation at 3 millimeters wavelength, *Astrophys. J.*, **147**, 245–254, 1967.

522. Gaskell, T. F., Ed., *The Earth's Mantle*, Academic Press, New York, 509 pp., 1967.

523. Hapke, B., Lunar surface: composition inferred from optical properties, *Science*, **159**, 76–79, 1968.

524. Herbig, G. H., The youngest stars, *Sci. Am.*, **217** (2), 30–36, 1967.

525. Jaffe, L. D., & 42 others, Surveyor V mission report: Part II: science results, *Jet. Prop. Lab. Tech. Rep.*, **32-1246**, 185 pp., 1967.

526. Morrison, D., & C. Sagan, The microwave phase effect of Mercury, *Astrophys. J.*, **150**, 1105–1110, 1967.

527. Murray, B. C., Infrared radiation from the daytime and night time surface of Mercury, *Trans., Am. Geophys. Un.*, **48**, 148–149, 1967.

528. O'Keefe, J. A., & R. F. Scott, Chondritic meteorites and the lunar surface, *Science*, **158**, 1174–1176, 1967.

529. Pfann, W. G., Zone refining, *Sci. Am.*, **217** (6), 62–72, 1967.

530. Pollack, J. B., & C. Sagan, An analysis of Martian photometry and polarimetry, *Smithsonian Inst. Astrophys. Obs. Spec. Rep.*, **258**, 96 pp., 1967.

531. Roberts, P. H., Convection in horizontal layers with internal heat generation, Theory, *J. Fluid Mech.*, **30**, 39–49, 1967.

532. Runcorn, S. K., Ed., *Mantles of the Earth and Terrestrial Planets*, Wiley, New York, 584 pp., 1967.

533. Scott, R. F., The feel of the moon, *Sci. Am.*, **217** (5), 34–43, 1967.
534. TASS, Venus 4: an automatic interplanetary station, Translation, *Trans., Am. Geophys. Un.*, **48**, 931–937, 1967.
535. Tozer, D. C., Towards a theory of thermal convection in the earth's mantle, in T. F. Gaskell, Ed., *The Earth's Mantle*, Academic Press, New York, 325–353, 1967.
536. Urey, H. C., Water on the moon, *Nature*, **216**, 1094–1095, 1967.
537. Van Allen, J. A., S. M. Krimigis, L. A. Frank, & T. P. Armstrong, Venus: an upper limit on intrinsic magnetic dipole moment based on absence of a radiation belt, *Science*, **158**, 1673–1675, 1967.
538. Wahl, W. H., & H. H. Kramer, Neutron-activation analysis, *Sci. Am.*, **216**(4), 68–82, 1967.
539. Wetherill, G. W., Stone meteorites: time of fall and origin, *Science*, **159**, 79–82, 1968.
540. Bernas, R., E. Gradsztajn, H. Reeves, & E. Schatzman, On the nucleosynthesis of lithium, beryllium, and boron, *Ann. Phys.*, **44**, 428–478, 1967.
541. Goldreich, P., & A. Toomre, Some remarks on polar wandering, *J. Geophys. Res.* **73**, in press, 1968.
542. Harris, P. G., A. Reay, & T. G. White, Chemical composition of the upper mantle, *J. Geophys. Res.*, **72**, 6359–6369, 1967.
543. O'Mara, B. J., The solar abundance of light elements, *Astrophys. J. Ltrs.*, in press, 1968.
544. Schatzman, E., A theory of the role of magnetic activity during star formation, *Ann. Astrophys.*, **25**, 18–29, 1962.
545. Tayler, R. J., The helium problem, *Quart. J. Roy. Astron. Soc.*, **8**, 313–333, 1967.
546. Allan, R. R., Evolution of commensurabilities in the solar system, *Plan. Sp. Sci.*, **16**, in press, 1968.
547. Bellomo, E., G. Colombo & I. I. Shapiro, Theory of the axial rotations of Mercury and Venus, in S. K. Runcorn, Ed., *Mantles of the Earth and Terrestrial Planets*, Wiley, New York, 193–211, 1967.
548. Brandt, J. C., & M. B. McElroy, Eds., *The Atmospheres of Venus and Mars*, Gordon & Breach, New York, 1968.
549. Brune, J. N., Seismic moment, seismicity, and rate of slip along major fault zones, *J. Geophys. Res.*, **73**, 777–784, 1968.
550. Cameron, A. G. W., Dissipation of the primordial solar nebula, *Astron. J.*, **73**, S6-S7, 1968.
551. Chapman, C. R., Interpretation of the diameter-frequency relation for lunar craters photographed by Rangers VII, VIII, and IX, *Icarus*, **8**, 1–22, 1968.
552. Colombo, G., F. A. Franklin, & C. M. Munford, On a family of periodic orbits of the restricted three-body problem and the question of the gaps in the asteroid belt and Saturn's rings, *Astron. J.*, **73**, 111–123, 1968.
553. Conti, P. S., The Li/Be ratio in main-sequence stars, *Astrophys. J.*, **151**, 567–576, 1968.
554. Creer, K. M., A synthesis of world-wide paleomagnetic data, in S. K. Runcorn,

Ed., *Mantles of the Earth and Terrestrial Planets*, Wiley, New York, 351–382, 1967.

555. Fish, R. A., G. G. Goles, & E. Anders, The record in the meteorites. III. On the development of meteorites in asteroidal bodies, *Astrophys. J.*, **132**, 243–258, 1960.

556. Greenspan, J. A., & T. Owen, Jupiter's atmosphere: its structure and composition, *Science*, **156**, 1489–1493, 1967.

557. Heirtzeler, J. R., G. O. Dickson, E. M. Herron, W. C. Pitman, III, & X. Le Pichon, Marine magnetic anomalies, geomagnetic field reversals, and motions of the ocean floor and continents, *J. Geophys. Res.*, **73**, 2119–2136, 1968.

558. Herbig, G. H., The properties and problems of T Tauri stars and related objects, *Advan. Astron. & Astrophys.*, **1**, 47–103, 1962.

559. Hertz, H. G., Mass of Vesta, *Science*, **160**, 299–300, 1968.

560. Hoyle, F., & N. C. Wickramasinghe, Condensation of the planets, *Nature*, **217**, 415–418, 1968.

561. Hurley, P. M., F. F. M. de Almeida, G. C. Melcher, U. G. Cordani, J. R. Rand, K. Kawashita, P. Vandoros, W. H. Pinson, Jr., & H. W. Fairbairn, Test of continental drift by comparison of radiometric ages, *Science*, **157**, 495–500, 1967.

562. Jaffe, L. D., & 43 others, Surveyor VI mission report, Part II: Science results, *Jet. Prop. Lab. Tech. Rept.*, **32–1262**, 193 pp., 1968.

563. *JANAF Tables of Thermochemical Data*, The Dow Chemical Co., Midland, Mich., 1960.

564. Kelley, K. K., Contributions to the data on theoretical metallurgy: XIII: High-temperatue heat-content, heat capacity, and entropy data for the elements and inorganic compounds, *U.S. Bur. Mines. Bull.*, **584**, 232 pp., 1960.

565. Kelley, K. K., Heats and free energies of formation of anhydrous silicates, *U.S. Bur. Mines Rep. Inv.*, **5901**, 32 pp., 1962.

566. Kobaschewshi, O., & E. L. Evans, *Metallurgical Thermochemistry*, Pergamon Press, London, 426 pp., 1958.

567. Kozlovskaya, S. V., Models for the internal structure of the earth, Venus, and Mars, *Sov. Astron. AJ*, **10**, 865–876, 1967.

568. Larimer, J. W., & E. Anders, Chemical fractionation in meteorites—II. Abundance patterns and their determination, *Geochim. Cosmochim. Acta*, **31**, 1239–1270, 1967.

569. Le Pichon, X., Sea floor spreading and continental drift, *J. Geophys. Res.*, **73**, 3661–3697, 1968.

570. Lingenfelter, R. E., S. J. Peale, & G. Schubert, Lunar rivers, *Science*, **161**, in press, 1968.

571. Lord, H. C., III, Molecular equilibria and condensation in a solar nebula and cool stellar atmospheres, *Icarus*, **4**, 279–288, 1965.

572. McKenzie, D. P., The influence of the boundary conditions and rotation on convection in the earth's mantle, *J. Geophys. Res.*, **73**, in press, 1968.

573. McKenzie, D. P., & R. L. Parker, The north Pacific: an example of tectonics on a sphere, *Nature*, **216**, 1276–1280, 1967.

574. Morgan, W. J., Rises, trenches, great faults, and crustal blocks, *J. Geophys. Res.*, **73**, 1959–1982, 1968.

575. Mueller, R. F., System Fe-MgO-SiO$_2$-O$_2$ with applications to terrestrial rocks and meteorites, *Geochim. Cosmochim. Acta*, **29**, 967–976, 1965.

576. O'Connell, R. J., & G. J. Wasserburg, Dynamics of the motion of a phase change boundary to changes in pressure, *Revs. Geophys.*, **5**, 329–410, 1967.

577. Parkin, D. W., & D. Tilles, Influx measurements of extraterrestrial material, *Science*, **159**, 936–946, 1968.

578. Peebles, P. J. E., The structure and composition of Jupiter and Saturn, *Astrophys. J.*, **140**, 328–347, 1964.

579. Ross, H. P., A simplified mathematical model for lunar crater erosion, *J. Geophys. Res.*, **73**, 1343–1354, 1968.

580. Shapiro, I. I., Theory of the radar determination of planetary rotations, *Astron. J.*, **72**, 1304–1323, 1967.

581. Sonett, C. P., & D. S. Colburn, The principle of solar wind induced planetary dynamos, *Phys. Ea. & Plan. Int.*, **1**, in press, 1968.

582. Stacey, F. D., Electrical resistivity of the earth's core, *Earth & Plan. Sci. Let.*, **3**, 204–206, 1967.

583. Turkevich, A., Lunar surface chemical composition, *Pres. Am. Geophys. Un. 49th Ann. Mtg.*, Washington, 1968.

584. Van Allen, J. A., L. A. Frank, S. M. Krimigis, & H. K. Hills, Absence of Martian radiation belts and implications thereof, *Science*, **149**, 1228–1233, 1965.

585. Whipple, F. L., Chondrules: suggestion concerning their origin, *Science*, **153**, 54–56, 1966.

586. Wyllie, P. J., Ed., *Ultramafic and Related Rocks*, Wiley, New York, 464 pp., 1967.

AUTHOR INDEX

475

SUBJECT INDEX

483